Eye Movement

Desensitization and

Reprocessing (EMDR)

Scripted Protocols

About the Editor

Marilyn Luber, PhD, is a licensed clinical psychologist in general private practice in Center City, Philadelphia, Pennsylvania. Dr. Luber has a general psychology practice, working with adolescents, adults, and couples, especially addressing the resolution of complex post-traumatic stress disorder (C-PTSD), trauma and related issues, and dissociative disorders. She has worked as a Primary Consultant for the FBI field division in Philadelphia. She was trained in eye movement desensitization and reprocessing (EMDR) in 1992. She consults with individuals and runs consultation groups for EMDR practitioners. She is an EMDR International Association certified practitioner and consultant. She has coordinated trainings in EMDR-related fields in the greater Philadelphia area since 1997. She teaches Facilitator and Supervisory trainings and other EMDR-related subjects both nationally and internationally and was on the EMDR Task Force for Dissociative Disorders. She was on the Founding Board of Directors of the EMDR International Association (EMDRIA) and served as the Chairman of the International Committee until June 1999. In 1997, Dr. Luber was given a Humanitarian Services Award by the EMDR Humanitarian Association, and later, in 2003, she was presented with the EMDR International Association's award "For Outstanding Contribution and Service to EMDRIA." In 2005, she was awarded "The Francine Shapiro Award for Outstanding Contribution and Service to EMDR." In 2001, through EMDR HAP (Humanitarian Assistance Programs), she published *Handbook for EMDR Clients,* which has been translated into eight languages. She has written the "Around the World" and "In the Spotlight" articles for the EMDRIA Newsletter, four times a year since 1997. In 2009, she edited *Eye Movement Desensitization and Reprocessing (EMDR) Scripted Protocols: Basics and Special Situations* (Springer Publishing).

Eye Movement Desensitization and Reprocessing (EMDR) Scripted Protocols

Special Populations

EDITOR Marilyn Luber, PhD

SPRINGER PUBLISHING COMPANY

New York

Portions of this book are reprinted with permission from *Eye Movement Desensitization and Reprocessing (EMDR): Basic Principles, Protocols, and Procedures,* by Dr. Francine Shapiro, The Guilford Press (2001), and *EMDR New Notes on Adaptive Information Processing with Case Formulation Principles, Forms, Scripts and Worksheets,* by Dr. Francine Shapiro, The EMDR Institute (2006).

Springer Publishing Company, LLC
11 West 42nd Street
New York, NY 10036
www.springerpub.com

Acquisitions Editor: Sheri W. Sussman
Project Manager: Julia Rosen
Cover design: Steve Pisano
Composition: Apex CoVantage, LLC

Ebook ISBN: 978-0-8261-2245-2

09 10 11 12 / 5 4 3 2 1

Library of Congress Cataloging-in-Publication Data

Eye movement desensitization and reprocessing (EMDR) scripted protocols : special populations / editor, Marilyn Luber.
    p. ; cm.
  Includes bibliographical references and index.
  ISBN 978-0-8261-2239-1 (alk. paper)
  1. Eye movement desensitization and reprocessing. 2. Eye movement desensitization and reprocessing for children. I. Luber, Marilyn.
    [DNLM: 1. Desensitization, Psychologic—methods. 2. Eye Movements—physiology. 3. Mental Disorders—therapy. 4. Psychotherapy—methods.
WM 425.5.D4 E975 2010]
  RC489.E98E945 2010
  616.89'165—dc22   2009012550

Printed in the United States of America by Bang Printing.

To Francine Shapiro and Robbie Dunton, who are models of
how to create community through limitless heart,
intelligence, vision, and intention

Never doubt that a small group of thoughtful, committed citizens can change the world. Indeed, it is the only thing that ever has.

—Margaret Mead

Contents

PART I

EMDR With Children and Adolescents

PART II

EMDR and Couples

PART III

EMDR, Dissociative Disorders, and Complex Post-Traumatic Stress Disorder

PART IV

EMDR and Clients With Addictive Behaviors

PART V

EMDR and Clients With Pain

PART VI

EMDR and Specific Fears

PART VII

EMDR and Clinician Self-Care

Robbie Adler-Tapia, PhD, is a licensed psychologist who has worked with traumatized children and their families for 23 years. She is certified in EMDR, an EMDRIA Approved Consultant, a Facilitator, an EMDR/HAP (Humanitarian Assistance Program) Trainer and works with the EMDR HAPKIDS Project. Along with her coauthor, Carolyn Settle, Dr. Adler-Tapia is coauthor of the new book *EMDR and the Art of Psychotherapy With Children* and accompanying treatment manual for clinicians (Springer Publishing, 2008).

Lucina Artigas, MA, MT, is a Trainer of Trainers, EMDRIA and EMDR-Ibero-America Approved Consultant. She is cofounder and Executive Director of EMDR-Mexico, AMAMECRISIS, and International Center of Psychotraumatology. In 2000, she received the EMDRIA Creative Innovation Award for the Butterfly Hug, and, in 2007, she received the EMDR-Ibero-America Francine Shapiro Award. She is a trainer for the International Critical Incident Stress Foundation and Green Cross Academy of Traumatology. She is coauthor of the EMDR-Integrative Group Treatment Protocol that has been applied successfully with disaster survivors worldwide. She has presented workshops and has published articles on EMDR, Crisis Intervention and Compassion Fatigue. Since 1997, she has been involved in humanitarian projects in Latin America and Europe.

Don Beere, PhD, ABPP, has Bachelor degrees in Physics and Philosophy, an MA in Experimental Psychology and a doctorate in Clinical Psychology. He is currently in full-time private practice in the Greater Cincinnati, Ohio area, and specializes in the treatment of severe trauma and the dissociative disorders. Dr. Beere is a Certified Therapist and Consultant in EMDR, a Facilitator, and a Specialty Presenter on the dissociative disorders. He was one of the original faculty selected by the International Society for the Study of Trauma and Dissociation (ISST-D) to teach in the Dissociative Disorders Psychotherapy Treatment Program. The chapters in this volume summarize his research and present Beere's theory of the dissociative disorders.

Neal Daniels, PhD, received his MA in Social Psychology from the New School for Social Research and his PhD from Kansas University and Menninger Clinic. In 1981, he left his long service as a Family Therapist with the Philadelphia Child Guidance Clinic to become Director of the newly formed program for PTSD at the Philadelphia VA Hospital where EMDR became an integral part of the treatment program. An article, "Post Traumatic Stress Disorder and Competence to Stand Trial," was published in the *Journal of Psychiatry and Law,* Spring 1984. His research on the EMDR treatment of triggers remains unfinished due to his retirement and final illness.

Michael D'Antonio, PhD, is a licensed psychologist, EMDRIA-certified EMDR Therapist, and Consultant and AAMFT-Approved Supervisor. He is a Senior Clinician at Council for Relationships in Philadelphia, supervising the Council's EMDR continuing education program. Dr. D'Antonio maintains a clinical practice specializing in couples, men's issues, personal empowerment, and transcending relational trauma.

Ad de Jongh, PhD, DDS, is both a Clinical Psychologist and Dentist. He is Professor of Anxiety and Behavior Disorders at the University of Amsterdam. He is an expert in the field of dental phobia, and author of more than 150 scientific articles and book chapters as well as the author of four books on the treatment of anxiety disorders. He is Director of the Centre for Psychotherapy and Psychotrauma in Bilthoven and of the Trauma Treatment Unit of D.O.E.N. in Druten. Ad de Jongh is an approved trainer for the EMDR Europe Association.

Carlijn De Roos, MA, is a clinical psychologist and psychotherapist working with traumatized children, adolescents, and adults as well as with patients suffering from chronic pain. In her present post, she coordinates a specialized Trauma Centre for children and adolescents, which is part of the Mental Health Centre (GGZ) Rivierduinen in Leiden, the Netherlands. She is an EMDR-Europe approved child and adolescent trainer and consultant, president of the Dutch EMDR Association, and a member of the EMDR Europe Child Board.

Mark Dworkin, LCSW, has practiced EMDR since 1991. His experience in treating traumatized populations started in 1975 when he began working for the Bronx VA Medical Center, just as the war in Vietnam was ending. He is a Facilitator; an Approved Consultant and Approved Trainer for the EMDR International Association, and served on its Board of Directors. He is a graduate of the Manhattan Institute for Psychoanalysis, and studied Gestalt Therapy with Laura Perls, PhD. He is published in the *Journal of Psychotherapy Integration* and he taught Consultation Psychiatry on the Faculty of the Mount Sinai School of Medicine. He is currently in full-time private practice in East Meadow, New York, and consults to different professional organizations. He is the author of *EMDR and the Relational Imperative: The Therapeutic Relationship in EMDR Treatment* (2005).

Dagmar Eckers, Dipl.-Psychologin, is a psychotherapist in private practice, who works with children, adolescents, and adults in Berlin, Germany. She uses Behavior Therapy, Hypnotherapy, Family Therapy, and EMDR. She is a Facilitator and an Approved European Child and Adolescent Trainer in EMDR.

Catherine G. Fine, PhD, is a clinical psychologist specializing in trauma, dissociative disorders, anxiety, and depression as well as women's issues. She teaches nationally and internationally focusing on outpatient management of overwhelming traumata, affect management, and structured interventions using formal or informal hypnosis. She has served as President of ISSMPD and ASCH.

Carol Forgash, LCSW, BCD, is the Board President of the EMDR-Humanitarian Assistance Programs and has a clinical and consulting practice in Smithtown, New York. She is a Facilitator, and an EMDRIA Approved Consultant. She is a lecturer and consultant on the treatment of dissociation, complex post-traumatic stress disorders, the complex health issues of sexual abuse survivors, and the integration of EMDR with Ego State therapy and psychodynamic treatment. She has coauthored and edited *Healing the Heart of Trauma and Dissociation With EMDR and Ego State Therapy* (Springer Publishing, 2007), the first book to offer an integrative approach to successfully treating clients with the most severe trauma-related disorders.

Denise Gelinas, PhD, is an EMDRIA Approved Consultant, a Facilitator and is a Specialty Presenter on Dissociation. She conducts her private practice of psycho-therapy and consultation in Northampton, Massachusetts, and is a member of the Associate Professional Staff, Department of Psychiatry, Baystate Medical Center. She is the author of *Integrating EMDR Into Phase-Oriented Treatment for Trauma* (2003) and coauthor as part of the International Society for the Study of Dissocia-tion Task Force on Revision of *Guidelines for Treating Dissociative Identity Disorder in Adults* (2005).

Ana Gomez, LPC, is a psychotherapist in private practice in Phoenix, Arizona. She works with children and families affected by trauma. She has served as a practi-cum supervisor at the Educational Psychology Department at Northern Arizona University. She is the author of *Dark, Bad Day . . . Go Away,* a book for children about trauma and EMDR. She has been a presenter at the EMDRIA conference and she was a preconference guest speaker at the 2008 EMDRIA conference. She is an EMDRIA Training Provider and an Approved Consultant. She is a Facilitator, a spe-cialty presenter on EMDR with children, and an EMDR-HAP trainer-in-training.

Mark Grant, MA, is a psychologist who treats sufferers of pain and stress in Sydney, Australia. He has published several papers including a case study design research article regarding EMDR in the treatment of chronic pain. He has also presented at numerous conferences and workshops around the world. His work has been cited in the *New York Times* ("Living With Pain That Just Won't Go Away"). His self-help CDs have been published in English and Spanish and attracted an award for didactic material from the University Education Distancia (UNED), Madrid, Spain. He maintains a Web site for chronic pain sufferers (www.overcomingpain.com).

Michael Hase, MD, is a Psychiatrist and Psychotherapist, EMDR Senior Trainer and head of the Department of Psychosomatic Medicine and Psychotherapy at the Reha-Centrum Hamburg (former Reha-Zentrum Berliner Tor). His specialties include treat-ment of psychosomatic disorders, addiction, and acute stress disorders.

Arne Hofmann, MD, is a specialist in Psychosomatic and Internal Medicine. He is a Senior Trainer and is a Trainers' Trainer in Europe. He introduced EMDR into the German-speaking countries of Europe after a 1991 residency at the Mental Research Institute in Palo Alto, California, where he learned about EMDR and went on to head the German EMDR Institute. In 1994, he started the first inpatient trauma program in a psychiatric hospital near Frankfurt, Germany, where he assisted in de-veloping aftercare programs subsequent to mass disaster events like the 1998 train catastrophe in Eschede, the 2002 school shooting in Erfurt, and the 2004 Tsunami in Southeast Asia. He is a Founding Board Member of the German-speaking Society of Traumatic Stress Studies (DeGPT) and EMDR-Europe where he currently serves as vice president. He also is a member of a German National Guideline Commission on the treatment of PTSD and Acute Stress Disorder. He has published a number of articles (mostly in German), a book on EMDR, and coedited three other books on trauma and EMDR. He has been teaching at the Universities of Cologne, Witten-Herdecke, and Peking. He lectures internationally and received the Ron Martinez Award from the EMDR International Association in 2005.

Ignacio Jarero, PhD, EdD, MT, is a Trainer of Trainers, EMDRIA and EMDR-Ibero-America cofounder and Approved Consultant. He is cofounder and President of EMDR-Mexico, AMAMECRISIS, and International Center of Psychotraumatology. In 2007, he received the EMDR-Ibero-America Francine Shapiro Award and, in 2008, the Argentinian Society of Psychotrauma (ISTSS Affiliate) awarded him the Psychotrauma Trajectory Award. He is a Trainer for the International Critical Incident Stress Foundation and Green Cross Academy of Traumatology. He is coauthor of the EMDR Integrative Group Treatment Protocol that has been applied successfully with disaster survivors worldwide. He has presented workshops and has published articles on EMDR, Crisis Intervention, and Compassion Fatigue. Since 1997, he has been involved in humanitarian projects in Latin America and Europe.

Jim Knipe, PhD, has been a Licensed Psychologist in private practice in Colorado and uses EMDR in his practice. He has written about how to extend EMDR to clients who present with self-defeating psychological defenses or dissociative symptoms. He is an EMDR-HAP Trainer, an EMDRIA Approved Consultant and Instructor, and was designated a Master Clinician by EMDRIA in 2007. In 2006 and 2007, he was the guest speaker at the EMDRIA Annual Conferences, and in 2008 he was the guest speaker in the EMDR-Europe Annual Conferences and national EMDR conferences. He has been involved with the EMDR Humanitarian Assistance Programs, serving on the Board of Directors and as Research and Training Director. In addition, he is a coauthor of published outcome research documenting the effects of EMDR with survivors of 9/11 and with those traumatized by the 1999 Marmara earthquake in Turkey.

Ulrich Lanius, PhD, is a Clinical Psychologist and Neuropsychologist who specializes in the treatment of traumatic stress. He is a Facilitator and EMDRIA Approved Consultant. He has presented at conferences nationally and internationally. He is in the forefront of integrating recent neuroscience research into the treatment of traumatic stress syndromes and has been instrumental in adapting EMDR for clients with significant dissociative symptoms.

Brurit Laub, MA, is a senior Clinical Psychologist, with over 30 years of experience working in community mental health in Israel. She is also a teacher and supervisor at the Machon Magid School of Psychotherapy at Hebrew University in Jerusalem and at different marriage and family counseling centers. She is an accredited hypnotherapist, and a supervisor in psychotherapy and family therapy. She presents workshops concerning models developed independently and together with colleagues on narrative therapy, script changing therapy, coping with monsters, dialectical cotherapy, trans-generational tools, recent trauma, resource development and work with subpersonalities nationally and internationally. She has published 15 articles on the above topics in international and Israeli journals. In 1998, she became a Facilitator and she is an EMDR-Europe Accredited Consultant. She has been involved with HAP trainings in Turkey and Sri-Lanka. She developed a Resource Connection Envelope (RCE) for the Standard EMDR Protocol and presented it in workshops and for EMDR conferences in Tel-Aviv, London, Vancouver, Denver, Istanbul, and Norway. With Esti Bar-Sade, she developed the Imma EMDR Group Protocol, which is an adaptation of Artigas, Jarero, Alcalá, and López's IGTP. Together with Elan Shapiro, she presented their Recent Traumatic Episode Protocol (R-TEP) at a workshop for the EMDR-Europe Consultants' day at the 2008 EMDR-Europe Annual Conference in London, following the publication of their article in the *Journal of EMDR Practice & Research*. In 1994, she coauthored, with S. Hoffman and S. Gafni, "Co-therapy With Individuals, Families." In 2006, she collaborated again with S. Hoffman on "Innovative Interventions in Psychotherapy." She lives in Rehovot and is in private practice.

Barry K. Litt, MFT, received his Master's degree in family therapy at Hahnemann University in Philadelphia where he studied contextual therapy with its founder,

Ivan Boszormenyi-Nagy. His continuing fascination with contextual therapy's integration of psychodynamic thinking and systems theory was brought to a whole new level when he began using EMDR and studying dissociation in the early 1990s. His professional activities have included in-home family therapy, outpatient substance abuse treatment, consultation and training for Head Start programs and group homes, and investigating misconduct complaints for the New Hampshire Board of Examiners. In addition, Litt has taught MFT students at two graduate schools and given numerous workshops to international audiences on contextual theory, couples therapy, dissociation, and EMDR. He is a regular presenter at ISST-D and EMDRIA annual conferences. He is author of a chapter entitled "The Child as Identified Patient: Integrating Contextual Therapy and EMDR" in F. Shapiro, F. Kaslow, & L. Maxfield (Eds.), *Handbook of EMDR and Family Therapy Processes* (2007). He has also written a chapter entitled "The Marriage of EMDR and Ego State Theory in Couples Therapy: A Contextual Integration" in C. Forgash & M. Copeley (Eds.), *Healing the Heart of Trauma and Dissociation With EMDR and Ego State Therapy* (Springer Publishing, 2008). Litt is an AAMFT Approved Supervisor and an EMDRIA Approved Consultant and is currently in private practice in Concord, New Hampshire.

Marina Lombardo, LCSW, is a licensed psychotherapist and personal coach in private practice in Orlando, Florida. For over 20 years, she has worked with adults and couples in addressing a full range of issues, including marriage and relationships, life transitions, and the emotional aspects of infertility. She writes the column "Emotionally Speaking" for *Conceive Magazine,* and serves on their advisory board. She is the author of the book *I Am More Than My Infertility: 7 Proven Tools for Turning a Life Crisis Into a Personal Breakthrough* (2007). She has presented, in seminars and on radio, on a range of subjects, including general and fertility lifestyle issues, always building on the premise that within life's challenges are opportunities for growth. She has developed an IVF education series for couples, served as a fertility consultant, and facilitated fertility support groups. In addition, she has served on the adjunct faculty staff of Valencia College, in Orlando, Florida, designing and teaching continuing education classes in body-centered psychotherapy. She is a Certified Therapist in EMDR, and is a member of EMDRIA and the Mental Health Professional Group of the American Society of Reproductive Medicine.

Regina Morrow, EdS, LMFT, LMHC, NCC, is an EMDR HAP Trainer, Facilitator, EMDRIA Approved Consultant and Orlando, Florida, EMDRIA Regional Coordinator. She owns a private practice in Windermere, Florida, specializing in marital therapy, trauma, and EMDR consultation. She is a member of EMDRIA, ISTSS, AAMFT, and ACA.

Sandra Paulsen, PhD, has spoken internationally, written, and consulted on the power, benefits, and risks of EMDR and ego state therapy since 1992. She was an invited Master Series Lecturer for EMDRIA in Montreal and invited faculty for the First World Congress of Ego State Therapy in Bad Orb, Germany. She teaches advanced specialty trainings in dissociation and ego state therapy through EMDRIA. She moderates a forum on EMDR at www.behavior.net and cofounded the Bainbridge Institute for Integrative Psychology in Bainbridge Island, Washington. Her illustrated book will be published in early 2009.

Sabitha Pillai-Friedman, PhD, received her degree in Social Work from Graduate School of Social Work and Social Research at Bryn Mawr College. She is a licensed social worker and an AASECT–certified sex therapist. She is also trained in the use of EMDR and has been using the technique in creative ways to enhance her treatment of individuals and couples. She practices individual, couple, and sex therapy at the Institute for Sex Therapy at the Council for Relationships in Philadelphia. She is also the adjunct assistant professor and the director of supervision in the Couple and Family Therapy Program at Thomas Jefferson University in Philadelphia. She has been practicing psychotherapy for over 18 years.

Arnold J. (AJ) Popky, PhD, is a former Marine and has been involved in EMDR from its beginning. He has over 25 years experience in sales and marketing with high-technology Silicon Valley start-ups. He is a Master Practitioner of NLP and is a Senior Facilitator with over 19 years EMDR experience. He is certified in Ericksonian Hypnosis and was on the teaching staff of the Los Gatos Institute of Medical Hypnosis. He specializes in addictions and core traumatic issues and has developed DeTUR: an urge protocol for the treatment of addictions and dysfunctional behaviors. He consults with therapists worldwide and presents at EMDR training sessions and international conferences. He has interned at the Santa Clara County Drug and Alcohol Agency, Catholic Charities, Mental Research Institute, and the Haight-Ashbury Free Drug Clinic. He is a lifetime charter member and Certified Consultant of EMDRIA and has a private practice in Los Angeles, California.

Gene Schwartz, LCSW-C, is a Licensed Clinical Social Worker, practicing in Baltimore, Maryland, since 1971. He spent 30 years working at the Veterans Administration Hospital in Baltimore. Since his retirement, in December 2000, he is in private practice in Towson, Maryland.

Carolyn Settle, **MSW, LCSW,** is a Facilitator, Specialty Presenter, EMDRIA Approved Consultant, as well as an EMDR Humanitarian Assistance Program (HAP) Trainer-in-Training and a regular HAP volunteer. Ms. Settle has presented several times at the EMDR International Association Annual Conferences and at the EMDR Europe Conference on using EMDR with children. She provides advanced training workshops on using the 8 Phases of EMDR with children. Her areas of specialization are in post-traumatic stress disorder, depression, anxiety, phobias, ADHD, and gifted counseling for children, adolescents, and adults. Ms. Settle's experience working in community mental health centers, psychiatric hospitals, and with managed care insurance companies gives her practical knowledge that helps in her private practice in Scottsdale, Arizona. Ms. Settle is coinvestigator on a research study focused on the efficacy of using EMDR with children 2 to 10 years of age. Along with Robbie Adler-Tapia, Ms. Settle is coauthor of the new book *EMDR and the Art of Psychotherapy With Children* and the accompanying treatment manual for clinicians (Springer Publishing, 2008).

Robert Tinker, PhD, PC, a licensed Clinical Psychologist in private practice for more than 30 years, and specializes in EMDR treatment for adults and children. He is senior author of *Through the Eyes of a Child: EMDR With Children* (1999). Dr. Tinker is coauthor of several published EMDR research articles (*Journal of Consulting and Clinical Psychology*, 1995, 1997; *International Journal of Stress Management*, 2001). He has been keynote speaker with EMDR Europe in Paris, 2007 and with EMDRIA in Phoenix, Arizona in 2008, both to standing ovations. With Dr. Wilson, he has trained other therapists in using EMDR with adults and children, most recently in China in October 2008.

Joanne H. Twombly, LICSW, MSW, is in private practice in Waltham, Massachusetts, specializing in complex trauma and dissociative disorders. She also provides consultation in EMDR, hypnosis, and Internal Family Systems (IFS). She has given many workshops and written articles and chapters on diagnosis and treatment of dissociative disorders, the use of EMDR in treating dissociative disorders, EMDR, IFS (with Richard Schwartz), and hypnotic language. She is a Director on the International Society for the Study of Trauma and Dissociation's Executive Council and a Facilitator for the EMDR Humanitarian Assistance Program. She is an EMDRIA Certified Consultant and an American Society of Clinical Hypnosis Certified Consultant.

Sandra Veenstra, MA, is a clinical psychologist, psychotherapist, and child psychologist working in a private practice in Tilburg, the Netherlands. Before that she worked 18 years in a general hospital in which she developed her neuropsychological knowledge. In 2002 she was level I trained in EMDR, in 2003 she completed her level II training for adults, and in 2004 she completed her EMDR training for children. Mrs. Veenstra specializes in working with patients with medical complaints, especially chronic pain and chronic fatigue. She has written several articles about pain and the brain. Besides her private practice, she is visiting lecturer at the University of Tilburg and at the Dutch postgraduate training for health psychologists (RINO). She is also a cognitive behavioral therapist and supervisor.

Sandra A. Wilson, PhD, is Executive Director and founder of the Spencer Curtis Foundation in Colorado Springs, which conducts humanitarian projects and treatment outcome studies of EMDR. She has published research on EMDR in the *Journal of Consulting and Clinical Psychology*, a tier-one peer-reviewed journal (Wilson, Becker, & Tinker, 1995, 1997) and in the *International Journal of Stress Management*. Dr. Wilson has directed EMDR relief programs, including the programs in Oklahoma City after the bombing of the Murrah Building and with ethnic Albanian children after the war in Kosovo. More recently, she has initiated training of all therapists at Pikes Peak MHC in EMDR to treat returning military at Fort Carson, Colorado. She is coauthor with Dr. Tinker of *Through the Eyes of a Child: EMDR With Children* (1999).

Barbara Wizansky, MA, is a senior clinical psychologist, trauma specialist, associated with the Child and Adolescent Outpatient Psychiatric Unit of the Sheba Medical Center, Tel Hashomer, Israel. She is a Facilitator and EMDR Europe Child Trainer. At the present time, she works in private practice, teaches, and supervises both individuals and groups.

Eye Movement Desensitization and Reprocessing (EMDR) Scripted Protocols: Special Populations, a companion volume to *Eye Movement Desensitization and Reprocessing (EMDR) Scripted Protocols: Basics and Special Situations*, will forever be embedded in our memory because of its landmark impact in the field of EMDR as well as the field of psychotherapy (unlike the 1958 song from *Gigi*, "I Remember It Well," performed by Maurice Chevalier and Hermione Gingold, which cautions us about the vicissitudes of memory in highly emotionally charged situations). Yes, this book we will remember very well. Dr. Marilyn Luber's edited book concretizes for novice as well as experienced therapists the intentionality, creativity, and focus of EMDR-trained specialists working to ameliorate the treatment of human suffering, to facilitate the successful processing of overwhelming experiences, and to more rapidly achieve successful outcome. From the beginning of her involvement in the field of EMDR, Dr. Luber has been dedicated first as a student of EMDR, then as a user, and eventually as a facilitator and trainer of facilitators and consultants to the correct utilization of the protocol devised by Dr. Francine Shapiro.

This second volume was made possible not only through Dr. Luber's unending efforts but also from the thoughtful, innovative, and groundbreaking efforts of many clinicians, each working in their separate area of expertise. Each contributor introduced EMDR to their patients and their practice slowly and progressively, monitoring their improvements and cautiously avoiding pitfalls. The one case study became the many case observations, soon to result in clinical investigations with larger sample sizes. We are now positioned to promote and implement evidence-based multisite clinical research.

The EMDR arenas explored in this book presuppose knowledge and mastery over the concepts discussed in Dr. Luber's first book and familiarity with the protocols therein. This second book addresses very specialized groups of patients each with their own separate dilemmas, struggles, and clinical battles; these special patient populations require an adaptation of the Standard EMDR Protocol to accommodate their particular clinical circumstances. The scripted protocols in this second volume are derived from the Standard EMDR Protocol that they often rejoin; however, the scripts also consider the distinct characteristics and predicaments commanded by certain diagnostic categories and patient types.

Part I is devoted to the scripted EMDR protocols used to develop resources for children and adolescents who may have suffered traumatic events in their life. The protocols take into account the particular difficulties of this developmental group and help minimize common difficulties and major hurdles. Part II describes scripted EMDR protocols designed by couples therapists and sex therapists to further the progress of their patients precisely targeting templates of relational interaction, anxiety, or sexual dysfunction.

Part III of the scripted protocols is the closest to my heart and to my soul. These protocols represent the structured scripted efforts of many trauma therapists over a considerable number of years. This journey I know to have been long and painful but ultimately productive. Dr. Luber's introduction to Part III captures effectively the multitude of efforts, starts, fits, and stalls in the field of Complex Posttrauma Stress Disorder (CPSD) and Dissociative Disorders (DD). She effectively elaborates on the journey of EMDR and the Standard EMDR Protocol in these much traumatized populations. She rightly honors the gargantuan efforts of Francine Shapiro in assuring the appropriate usage of EMDR in these easily destabilized patient populations.

Francine Shapiro was committed to ensuring that *only* qualified therapists take EMDR training. Before training onset, they had to be licensed in their respective fields. She went to great effort to secure that the Standard EMDR Protocol was well elaborated, understood, and practiced by the trainees. Patient safety was always at the forefront of Francine Shapiro's mind and very rapidly after realizing the power of EMDR and the vulnerability of the patients, she set up a task force to tackle some of the basic concerns about DD and C-PTSD and she included them in her 1995 book *Eye Movement Desensitization and Reprocessing: Basic Principles, Protocols, and Procedures*. Since then, her efforts have continued in bringing to therapists and patients alike the most thorough understanding and the most successful EMDR interventions in the service of the wounded. Part III is the glorious fruit of those labors.

Parts IV and V of this volume address the concretization of much needed scripts for the EMDR treatment of addictions and pain—two interconnected public health worries. Part VI has us travel into the world of people's adaptation to fears and tackles the usage of scripted protocols to detoxify the impact of specific phobias. Part VII demonstrates the usage of scripted EMDR protocols in clinician care and in the management of secondary PTSD and vicarious traumatization, respectfully healing the healers so that they may continue to alleviate the distress of their fellow men and women.

The meticulous scripting of the EMDR protocols presented in this book is essential. The scripted protocols establish a common platform of communication between therapists and patients, clinicians and researchers, and teachers and students of EMDR. These scripted protocols are the next step in refining our thinking on trauma and trauma cure. The sequellae of tangible and scripted EMDR interventions can be measured and documented on brain scans and fMRIs. These scripted concretized protocols can serve as independent variables in both experimental and quasi-experimental studies; they are foundational for a common language in evidence-based investigations and multisite analyses. Their time has come—we *will* remember them well.

All this is true. For me, personally, however, these protocols mean much more. They are a journey well travelled in terms of thinking, air mileage, and friendships. It was in 1985 that Dr. Luber and I met surrounding a clinical consultation on a Dissociative Identity Disorder patient. Yes, we spoke of the patient, but we came to discover that our paths, although separate, had been quite overlapping—taking us both from educational institutions abroad to practically crossing as we travelled the same streets in Paris during the very same years! All of this was out of our awareness. We decided to be more mindful and very consciously decided to remain in touch and we have—both professionally and personally. In the late 1980s we worked with complex PTSD and DD exploring the various strategies for talk therapy and hypnosis; we also discovered together EMDR.

In the early 1990s another "radical" treatment methodology emerged from California called EMD. There were trainings on the West Coast—actually, only an extended workshop. Having befriended David Fenstermaker, an EMD trainer in California, I somehow convinced him to come to the East Coast to do training for a select group of therapists in Philadelphia—the group was taken from study groups that I participated in and was select in that they did not mind doing a training in my basement. Marilyn Luber was part of that group. Dr. Fenstermaker's presentation was appealing and tweaked the interest of a few of us. He encouraged us to train in California with Dr. Shapiro as well. The trip was planned and only one of us (Dr. Luber) embarked (I ran into some unexpected hindrance that prevented me from going). Dr. Luber and I both plowed on upon Dr. Luber's return, supporting one another in the use of EMD (now R) in our practices. Eventually, as two levels of EMDR training evolved, we, of course, signed up. Ultimately, Dr. Luber continued on to become a facilitator and trainer of facilitators, supervisors, and consultants and to travel to Europe, the Middle East, and other countries to spread the good word and good works of EMDR. She has become a beloved contributor to the field of EMDR and trauma and clearly a tireless collector of EMDR protocol scripts.

Dr. Luber's scripted protocol books are timely and welcomed not only for those clinicians who have "trained in basements" but also for those who have more recently joined the field. They promise to be a resource for research as well as for the next generation of therapists. It would behoove us all to tip our hats and bow to Dr. Luber's involvement, productivity, and contribution through these protocols—but if we did so, we would run the risk of being asked to script it.

One day in 1987, Francine Shapiro took a walk in the park that resulted in a major change. By noticing a naturally occurring phenomenon, Dr. Shapiro was continuing her lifelong journey of "using her mind and body as a laboratory to see what worked" to heal. She had cultivated her "ability to carefully self-monitor" and so, on that day, she attended to her observation that eye movement in a certain manner changed her experience of her disturbing thoughts with great interest (Luber & Shapiro, 2009). Her capacity to self-monitor and then act on that experience would ultimately result in strongly effecting the special populations that are included in this book. Her observation was that when she noticed her eyes moving rapidly, her thoughts changed and her negative affect decreased. Combining this idea, with her understanding of psychology and human behavior, Dr. Shapiro created a treatment that she first called Eye Movement and Desensitization (EMD) and then later expanded it to Eye Movement Desensitization and Reprocessing (EMDR) when she realized that EMDR not only resulted in a relaxation response but also metabolized or reprocessed the trauma. This book is about EMDR and the special populations it serves.

Since that day, EMDR has grown into a therapeutic methodology recognized by associations such as the American Psychological Association (APA, 2004; Chambless et al., 1998) and the International Society for Traumatic Stress (Chemtob, Tolin, van der Kolk, & Pitman, 2000; Foa, Keane, Friedman, & Cohen, 2008). Governmental organizations in many different countries have advocated the use of EMDR in the treatment of trauma such as the United Kingdom Department of Health (2001), Israel (Bleich, Kotler, Kutz, & Shalev, 2002), The Netherlands (Dutch National Steering Committee for Guidelines Mental Health Care, 2003), Northern Ireland (Clinical Resource Efficiency Support Team [CREST], 2003), France (French National Institute for Health and Medical Research [INSERM], 2004), the United States (Department of Veterans Affairs and Department of Defense, 2004; National Institute of Mental Health, 2004–2007), United Kingdom (National Institute for Clinical Excellence, 2005), and Australia (Australian Centre for Posttraumatic Mental Health, 2007). In August 2009, Dr. Francine Shapiro herself was recognized by APA Division 56 with an Award for Outstanding Contributions to Practice in Trauma Psychology. This award recognizes distinguished contributions to psychological practice. It may be given for the development of a highly effective intervention, for contributions to practice theory, or for a sustained body of work in the field of trauma psychology practice. It is clear that the efficacy of EMPR is in the process of being recognized worldwide.

Ongoing research has been gathered on different populations: *abuse* (Maxwell, 2003); *addictions* (Amundsen & Kårstad, 2006; Besson et al., 2006; Cox & Howard, 2007; Hase, Schallmayer, & Sack, 2008; Henry, 1996; Popky, 2005; Shapiro, Vogelmann-Sine, & Sine, 1994; Vogelmann-Sine, Sine, Smyth, & Popky, 1998; Zweben & Yeary, 2006), *anxiety* (Doctor, 1994; Feske & Goldstein, 1997; Goldstein & Feske, 1994; Nadler, 1996; Shapiro, 1994, 1999; Shapiro & Forrest, 1997), *body dysmorphia* (Brown, McGoldrick, & Buchanan, 1997), *children and adolescents*

(Greenwald, 1994, 1998, 1999, 2000, 2002; Hensel, 2006; Maxfield, 2007; Russell & O'Connor, 2002; Shapiro, 1991; Tinker & Wilson, 1999), *dissociative disorders* (Beere, 2009a, 2009b; Fine, 1994; Fine & Berkowitz, 2001; Gelinas, 2003; Lazrove, 1994; Lazrove & Fine, 1996; Marquis & Puk, 1994; Paulsen, 1995; Rouanzoin, 1994; Talan, 2007; Twombly, 2000, 2005), *family, marital, and sexual dysfunction* (Capps, 2006; Errebo & Sommers-Flanagan, 2007; Kaslow, Nurse, & Thompson, 2002; Madrid, Skolek, & Shapiro, 2006; Shapiro, Kaslow, & Maxfield, 2007; Wernik, 1993), *multiply traumatized combat vets* (Carlson, Chemtob, Rusnak, Hedlund, & Muraoka, 1998; Errebo & Sommers-Flanagan, 2007; Lipke, 2000; Russell, 2006, 2008; Russell & Silver, 2007; Russell, Silver, Rogers, & Darnell, 2007; Shapiro, 1995; Silver, Brooks, & Obenchain, 1995; Silver & Rogers, 2002), *pain* (Grant & Threlfo, 2002; Ray & Zbik, 2001; Roos de & Veenstra, 2008; Schneider, Hofmann, Rost, & Shapiro, 2007; Tinker & Wilson, 2005; Wilensky, 2006; Wilson, Tinker, Becker, Hofmann, & Cole, 2000), *performance enhancement* (Crabbe, 1996; Foster & Lendl, 1995, 1996; Graham, 2004), *phantom limb pain* (Roos de et al., 2008; Russell, 2008; Schneider et al., 2007; Tinker & Wilson, 2005), *previously abused child molesters* (Ricci, 2006; Ricci, Clayton, & Shapiro, 2006), *stress* (Wilson, Becker, Tinker, & Logan, 2001), *victims of natural and manmade disasters* (Jarero, Artigas, Mauer, Lopez Cano, & Alcala, 1999; Knipe et al., 2003; Konuk et al., 2006), and so forth. The results referenced here are a small sample of the research that has been done in this area.

In fact, former past president of the EMDR International Association (EMDRIA) and EMDR consultant, Barbara J. Hensley's collection of scholarly articles and other writing about EMDR grew so large that—in conjunction with Northern Kentucky University—she turned it into the Francine Shapiro Library, an electronic library available online at http://library.nku.edu/emdr/emdr_data.php. As stated on the Web site, "The intent of the FSL is twofold: (1) to electronically house documents related to EMDR or AIP and (2) to maintain a comprehensive, accurate, and up-to-date list of citations related to AIP and EMDR." As of July 2009, the Library listed 4472 writings that include material written in 20 different languages (Bosnian, Chinese, Danish, Dutch, English, French, German, Hebrew, Italian, Japanese, Korean, Norwegian, Portuguese, Russian, Serbian, Slovak, Slovenian, Spanish, Swedish, and Turkish). Other sources of information and research about EMDR are listed in Appendix C.

Eye Movement Desensitization and Reprocessing (EMDR) Scripted Protocols: Special Populations—as with *Eye Movement Desensitization and Reprocessing (EMDR) Scripted Protocols: Basics and Special Situations* (Springer Publishing, 2009)—evolved from my own learning process. Routinely, after an interesting workshop, I would script the relevant material that I wanted to incorporate into my practice—essentially my own study guide so that I could remember the different steps of whatever I had learned. Later, as I trained Facilitators, then Supervisors and Consultants nationally and internationally, I grew concerned at the lack of understanding of the basic elements of the 11-Step Standard Procedure (Shapiro, 2001) and the Standard 3-Pronged EMDR Protocol and started including the essentials of the protocols into my Supervisory–Consultant manual. After a conversation and request by my colleague, Arne Hofmann, at the 2006 EMDR International Association Conference in Philadelphia, I operationalized this work further by putting together all of the different elements of the protocols, including the specific language used in the form of a script for each of Dr. Shapiro's six basic protocols: Protocol for a Single Traumatic Event, Protocol for Current Anxiety and Behavior, Protocol for Recent Traumatic Events, Protocol for Phobias, Protocol for Excessive Grief, and Protocol for Illness and Somatic Disorders (Luber, 2009). His request was to have these protocols ready for the first European Trainers' Training in March 2007 so that the Trainers could have a clear script that would ensure a standard and these Trainers—who were from a variety of countries—would literally and figuratively be on the same page. The other concern was that there be a standard to inform researchers of all the elements of Shapiro's six basic protocols.

As a result of my personal interaction with many EMDR-trained clinicians and researchers from all over the world, as I attended conferences, regional meetings, study groups and trainings, and participated in listservs about EMDR, I became fascinated by the wealth of creativity alive in the EMDR community. For many, the Standard EMDR formulations worked well; however, we found that many of us who were using EMDR consistently were applying the protocols to our clients and bumping up against similar difficulties and issues depending on the population with which we were working. We had taken our excitement about EMDR into our offices and were coming up with educated ways of working with the protocol within our areas of expertise. Many began to present and write about these areas of specialty, sparking others to think about these unique situations. After I completed scripts for Dr. Shapiro's protocols, I began to look at the work of my colleagues who were using EMDR with different populations and difficult situations and to revisit the work that I had already scripted. In this way, the concept for two books, *Eye Movement Desensitization and Reprocessing (EMDR) Scripted Protocols: Basics and Special Situations* and *Eye Movement Desensitization and Reprocessing (EMDR) Scripted Protocols: Special Populations*, was born and then evolved.

These books of scripted protocols have no official sanction; however, they are informed by my own years of work. I was trained in 1992 and benefited from the years of teaching I had done from 1994 to 1996 working with EMDR-trained practitioners as a Co-Consultant with Steve Silver, later—1998 to the present—as a Facilitator, Supervisor and Consultant Trainer nationally and internationally, and from 2000 to the present as a Certified Consultant for Consultants and Certified Therapist in EMDR through the EMDR International Association since the certification program's inception. The contributors in this volume represent many years of accumulated practice in EMDR in their specialty areas; most are Facilitators, certified Consultants, and/or Trainers. Some of these protocols are in the process of being researched and the others reflect the observation and innovations of skilled clinicians using EMDR within areas of their expertise.

The goals of *Eye Movement Desensitization and Reprocessing (EMDR) Scripted Protocols: Special Populations* are twofold: to provide a standard that reflects the basic elements of the 11-Step Standard Procedure (Shapiro, 2001); and the Standard 3-Pronged EMDR Protocol (Shapiro, 2001, 2006) as they are applied to different populations such as children and adolescents; couples; clients suffering with complex post-traumatic stress disorder and dissociative disorders; clients with anxiety; clients who demonstrate addictive behaviors; clients who deal with pain; clinicians themselves; and to serve as a basis to encourage research into these various applications for EMDR. I have used this structure as much as possible in the chapters that follow.

Many of the chapters reflect the particular needs of their population through a detailed and specific client history. Chapters that reflect resources are part of the Preparation Phase of the 8 phases of the 11-Step Standard Procedure. Most authors have used the 8 phases as the template around which they have structured their material. Some notable places where authors have departed from this format are those related to the section on complex post-traumatic stress disorders and dissociative disorders; the treatment reflected in these chapters uses the Standard EMDR Protocol where possible and incorporates adaptations that reflect the needs of their clients. The reader will notice that different populations may follow the 3-pronged protocol but in a different order than the standard; these, too, reflect the needs of the population with whom they are working as is explained below. There are a few clinical examples; however, this is not uniform throughout the volume.

Even though a script may give the illusion that it need only be read, in fact, that is not accurate. Although these protocols are scripted to encourage the accurate use of the EMDR methodology, they have not been written down for nontrained clinicians to use or for practitioners operating outside their area of expertise to follow. These protocols are only for EMDR-trained clinicians and for those trained to work in their areas of specialty as they have the skill to tailor these protocols to the unique needs of the particular client with whom they are working.

Clinicians are encouraged to seek training in EMDR from recognized trainers who have demonstrated their knowledge, understanding, and success as an EMDR trainer through documentation by the associations that give accreditation for expertise in EMDR. These associations are listed in Appendix C of this volume. In fact, solid instruction, training, and consultation are essential components in the learning curve of mastering this complex psychotherapy. Shapiro's text, *Eye Movement Desensitization and Reprocessing: Basic Principles, Protocols, and Procedures* (2001), is required reading for a comprehensive understanding of EMDR as a clinical approach.

Eye Movement Desensitization and Reprocessing (EMDR) Scripted Protocols: Special Populations is divided into seven sections to address the variety of special populations served in the EMDR community. For the sake of clarity, pronouns are used for the same sex as the author to refer to the therapist and the pronouns for the opposite sex of the author are used to refer to the client. For example, if the author is female, any reference to the therapist would be as "she" while any reference to the client would be referred to as "he." Part I addresses the special needs of children and adolescents while using EMDR. The section begins with a foundational chapter on a special way of doing bilateral stimulation (BLS) created by Luci Artigas and Ignacio Jarero that has been essential in working with large groups of children originally as survivors of natural disasters and then expanded and used with individual children and also adults. Innovative resource work developed by Ana Gomez using olfactory stimulation is applied to the standard safe place and resource development and installation. Barbara Wizansky and Dagmar Eckers sensitively translate resources that were developed for adults originally into solid and important work with children and adolescents. Ms. Wizansky goes on to use bilateral stimulation in the form of footsteps to support problem solving and Robbie Adler-Tapia and Carolyn Settle help therapists understand the importance of framing EMDR assessment specifically for children.

Work with EMDR and couples presents its own unique issues that are clearly illuminated in Michael D'Antonio's and Barry Litt's work on integrating EMDR into couples work. Sabitha Pillai-Friedman offers us a way to work with sexual dysfunction that highlights the particular issues that are important to address this population while Marina Lombardo and Regina Morrow educate us about infertility and how EMDR can be used effectively with this group.

The section on EMDR, Dissociative Disorders, and Complex Post-Traumatic Stress Disorder is a rich part of the book that addresses the particular issues working with this complicated and challenging population. An interesting trend began to appear while studying the way that various practitioners addressed this complex population; all noted the importance of a more extended preparation phase to ascertain that the clients are able to modulate and contain their affect even in the face of talking about or reexperiencing their trauma before proceeding with EMDR. For most, instead of floating back into the past connected issues of the trauma, clinicians stressed the importance of starting by working with clients in the here and now. Carol Forgash introduces us to a number of concepts to help orient clients through her use of working with ego states, "Home Base," "Workplace or Conference Room," and "Orienting the Ego State System to Present Reality." Jim Knipe includes several important chapters that empower clients and help keep practitioners in the loop concerning clients' ability to stay in the present or not, and teaching clients how to be more aware of what usually had been an involuntary process of dissociating. Joanne Twombly—also understanding the necessity of assisting clients to be present—has a number of chapters teaching a variety of ways to support clients in this critical skill. Arne Hofmann and Don Beere have created several ways to work with resources that particularly target the special needs of this population. Carol Forgash includes a chapter that helps clients manage critical life issues while Joanne Twombly has a chapter that addresses how to target traumatic material with this population.

Arne Hofmann's chapter on the Inverted EMDR Standard Protocol for Unstable Complex Post-Traumatic Stress Disorder is an invaluable work that describes how to know when to begin EMDR processing and what skills must be in place before proceeding. Catherine Fine shows us how to imbricate hypnosis and EMDR while working with dissociative patients. In Ulrich Lanius's work on the Bottom Up-Processing Protocol, he integrates his understanding of the importance of somatic work and how that structures his work with this population. Sandra Paulsen takes us through the steps in an EMDR session that inform her work and some of the choice points that are involved while making decisions in this complicated and nuanced work. Don Beere shows us how a basic hypnotic technique can be integrated into EMDR work and allow for clients to fully process a trauma using the Protocol for Recent Traumatic Events. This section ends with Denise Gelinas's important understanding of how to work with the characteristic types of negative cognitions that get stuck when working with patients suffering with complex trauma.

Part IV addresses a particularly important problem in our societies—dealing with addictive behaviors. Jim Knipe provides us with an innovative contribution as he accesses addictive behavior by addressing dysfunctional positive affect to clear the pain of unrequited love, to deal with codependence or obsession with self-defeating behavior, to assist clients with unwanted avoidance defenses, and the difficult problem of procrastination. When Michael Hase works with substance abuse clients, he uses a particularly interesting way to address addictive memories, while A. J. Popky reveals a way to reduce the urges connected with addictions.

Pain patients are an exacting sector of the population that demand different ways of addressing their issues. Mark Grant, along with Carlijn de Roos and Sandra Veenstra, shows us how to work with pain patients while the chapter by Sandra Wilson and Robert Tinker helps us understand the specific needs of working with phantom pain and EMDR.

In Part VI, dentist and psychologist Ad de Jongh addresses the particular difficulty of working with clients who have specific fear phobias and the unique issues that apply when working with this population.

The last section is a part that is also found in *Eye Movement Desensitization and Reprocessing (EMDR) Scripted Protocols: Basics and Special Situations*, although there are some helpful changes in the introduction to that section. The chapters in this section appear in both books as a way to underline and promote the importance of self-care by clinicians while they work with human suffering. Neal Daniels's way to process traumatic residue after a session is essential and would be helpful for any practitioner. Mark Dworkin's chapter helps clinicians become aware of their own internal reactions to client material and how this can impact both therapists and clients.

Appendices A, B, and C also appear in both volumes. Appendix A includes Worksheets for Past, Present Triggers, and Future Template. In Appendix B, Gene Schwartz introduces an addition to the Desensitization Phase that assists clinicians in being thorough while processing through the traumatic material by addressing unconsolidated sensory triggers. There are many resources in the EMDR community and they are included in Appendix C. References, Further Readings and Presentations include more information about EMDR that will support the practitioner.

Eye Movement Desensitisation and Reprocessing (EMDR): Special Populations is a book designed to support the reader's proficiency in EMDR through the scripted protocols written by the skillful EMDR practitioners represented in this volume and informed by the Standard EMDR Protocol of Francine Shapiro (2001).

References

American Psychiatric Association (APA). (2004). *Practice guideline for the treatment of patients with acute stress disorder and posttraumatic stress disorder.* Arlington, VA: American Psychiatric Association Practice Guidelines.

Amundsen, J. E., & Kårstad, K. (2006). Om bare Jeppe visste—EMDR og rusbehandling (Integrating EMDR and the treatment of substance abuse). *Tidsskrift for Norsk Psykologforening, 43*(5), 469.

Australian Centre for Posttraumatic Mental Health. (2007). *Australian guidelines for the treatment of adults with acute stress disorder and posttraumatic stress disorder.* Melbourne: ACPTMHC.

Beere, D. B. (2009a). The self-system as "mechanism" for the dissociative disorders: An extension of the perceptual theory of dissociation. In P. Dell & J. O'Neil (Eds.), *Dissociation and the dissociative disorders: DSM-V and beyond.* New York: Routledge.

Beere, D. B. (2009b). *The effectiveness of EMDR with the dissociative disorders: A research study leading to the development of an EMDR protocol for DID.* Manuscript in preparation.

Besson, J., Eap, C., Rougemont-Buecking, A., Simon, O., Nikolov, C., & Bonsack, C. (2006). Addictions. *Revue Médicale Suisse, 2*(47), 9–13.

Bleich, A., Kotler, M., Kutz, I., & Shalev, A. (2002). *Guidelines for the assessment and professional intervention with terror victims in the hospital and in the community.* A position paper of the (Israeli) National Council for Mental Health, Jerusalem, Israel.

Brown, K. W., McGoldrick, T., & Buchanan, R. (1997). Body dysmorphic disorder: Seven cases treated with eye movement desensitization and reprocessing. *Behavioural and Cognitive Psychotherapy, 25*, 203–207.

Capps, F. (2006). Combining eye movement desensitization and reprocessing with gestalt techniques in couples counseling. *Family Journal: Counseling and Therapy for Couples and Families, 14*(1), 49.

Carlson, J. G., Chemtob, C. M., Rusnak, K., Hedlund, N. L., & Muraoka, M. Y. (1998). Eye movement desensitization and reprocessing treatment for combat related posttraumatic stress disorder. *Journal of Traumatic Stress, 11*(1), 3–24.

Chambless, D. L., Baker, M. J., Baucom, D. H., Beutler, L. E., Calhoun, K. S., Cris-Christoph, P., et al. (1998). Update on empirically validated therapies, II. *The Clinical Psychologist, 51*, 3–16.

Chemtob, C. M., Tolin, D. F., van der Kolk, B. A., & Pitman, R. K. (2000). Eye movement desensitization and reprocessing. In E. A. Foa, T. M. Keane, & M. J. Friedman (Eds.), *Effective treatments for PTSD: Practice guidelines from the International Society for Traumatic Stress Studies.* New York: Guilford.

Clinical Resource Efficiency Support Team (CREST). (2003). *The management of post traumatic stress disorder in adults.* A publication of the Clinical Resource Efficiency Support Team of the Northern Ireland Department of Health, Social Services and Public Safety, Belfast.

Cox, R. P., & Howard, M. D. (2007). Utilization of EMDR in the treatment of sexual addiction: A case study. *Sexual Addiction & Compulsivity, 14*(1), 1.

Crabbe, B. (1996, November). Can eye-movement therapy improve your riding? *Dressage Today, 28*–33.

Department of Veterans Affairs and Department of Defense. (2004). *VA/DoD clinical practice guideline for the management of post-traumatic stress.* Washington, DC: Veterans Health Administration, Department of Veterans Affairs and Health Affairs, Department of Defense. Office of Quality and Performance publication 10Q-CPG/PTSD-04.

Doctor, R. (1994, March). *Eye movement desensitization and reprocessing: A clinical and research examination with anxiety disorders.* Paper presented at the 14th annual meeting of the Anxiety Disorders Association of America, Santa Monica, CA.

Dutch National Steering Committee for Guidelines Mental Health Care. (2003). *Multidisciplinary guideline anxiety disorders.* Utrecht, Netherlands: Quality Institute Health Care CBO/Trimbos Institute.

Errebo, N., & Sommers-Flanagan, R. (2007). EMDR and emotionally focused couple therapy for war veteran couples. In F. Shapiro, F. Kaslow, & L. Maxfield (Eds.), *Handbook of EMDR and family therapy processes.* New York: Wiley.

Feske, U., & Goldstein, A. (1997). Eye movement desensitization and reprocessing treatment for panic disorder: A controlled outcome and partial dismantling study. *Journal of Consulting and Clinical Psychology, 36*, 1026–1035.

Fine, C. (1994, June). *Eye movement desensitization and reprocessing (EMDR) for dissociative disorders.* Presentation at the Eastern Regional Conference on Abuse and Multiple Personality, Alexandria, VA.

Fine, C., & Berkowitz, A. (2001). The wreathing protocol: The imbrication of hypnosis and EMDR in the treatment of dissociative identity disorder and other dissociative responses. *American Journal of Clinical Hypnosis, 43*, 275–290.

Foa, E. B., Keane, T. M., Friedman, M. J., & Cohen, J. A. (Eds.). (2008). *Effective treatments for PTSD: Practice guidelines from the International Society for Traumatic Stress Studies* (2nd ed.). New York: Guilford.

Foster, S., & Lendl, J. (1995). Eye movement desensitization and reprocessing: Initial applications for enhancing performance in athletes. *Journal of Applied Sport Psychology, 7*(Suppl.), 63.

Foster, S., & Lendl, J. (1996). Eye movement desensitization and reprocessing: Four case studies of a new tool for executive coaching and restoring employee performance after setbacks. *Consulting Psychology Journal, 48*, 155–161.

French National Institute for Health and Medical Research (INSERM). (2004). *Psychotherapy: An evaluation of three approaches.* Paris: Author.

Gelinas, D.J. (2003). Integrating EMDR into phase-oriented treatment for trauma. *Journal of Trauma and Dissociation, 4*, 91–135.

Goldstein, A., & Feske, U. (1994). Eye movement desensitization and reprocessing for panic disorder: A case series. *Journal of Anxiety Disorders, 8*, 351–362.

Grant, M., & Threlfo, C. (2002). EMDR in the treatment of chronic pain. *Journal of Clinical Psychology, 58*, 1505–1520.

Greenwald, R. (1994). Applying eye movement desensitization and reprocessing to the treatment of traumatized children: Five case studies. *Anxiety Disorders Practice Journal, 1*, 83–97.

Greenwald, R. (1998). Eye movement desensitization and reprocessing (EMDR): New hope for children suffering from trauma and loss. *Clinical Child Psychology and Psychiatry, 3*, 279–287.

Greenwald, R. (1999*). Eye movement desensitization and reprocessing (EMDR) in child and adolescent psychotherapy.* Northvale, NJ: Jason Aronson Press.

Greenwald, R. (2000). A trauma-focused individual therapy approach for adolescents with conduct disorder. *International Journal of Offender Therapy and Comparative Criminology, 44*, 146–163.

Greenwald, R. (2002). Motivation-adaptive skills-trauma resolution (MASTR) therapy for adolescents with conduct problems: An open trial. *Journal of Aggression, Maltreatment, and Trauma, 6*, 237–261.

Hase, M., Schallmayer, S., & Sack, M. (2008). EMDR reprocessing of the addiction memory: Pretreatment, posttreatment, and 1-month follow-up. *Journal of EMDR Practice and Research, 2*(3), 170–179.

Henry, S. L. (1996). Pathological gambling: Etiological considerations and treatment efficacy of eye movement desensitization/reprocessing. *Journal of Gambling Studies, 12*, 395–405.

Hensel, T. (2006). Effektivität von EMDR bei psychisch traumatisierten Kindern und Jugendlichen [Effectiveness of EMDR with psychologically traumatized children and adolescents]. *Kindheit und Entwicklung, 15*(2), 107.

Jarero, I., Artigas, L., Mauer, M., Lopez Cano, T., & Alcala, N. (1999, November). *Children's post traumatic stress after natural disasters: Integrative treatment protocols.* Poster presented at the annual meeting of the International Society for Traumatic Stress Studies, Miami, FL.

Kaslow, F. W., Nurse, A. R., & Thompson, P. (2002). EMDR in conjunction with family systems therapy. In F. Shapiro (Ed.), *EMDR as an integrative psychotherapy approach: Experts of diverse orientations explore the paradigm prism* (pp. 289–318). Washington, DC: American Psychological Association.

Knipe, J., Hartung, J., Konuk, E., Colleli, G., Keller, M., & Rogers, S. (2003, September). *EMDR humanitarian assistance programs: Outcome research, models of training, and service delivery in New York, Latin America, Turkey, and Indonesia.* Symposium presented at the annual meeting of the EMDR International Association, Denver, CO.

Konuk, E., Knipe, J., Eke, I., Yuksek, H., Yurtsever, A., & Ostep, S. (2006). The effects of eye movement desensitization and reprocessing (EMDR) therapy on posttraumatic stress disorder in survivors of the 1999 Marmara, Turkey earthquake. *International Journal of Stress Management, 13*(3), 291.

Lazrove, S. (1994, November). *Integration of fragmented dissociated traumatic memories using EMDR.* Paper presented at the 10th annual meeting of the International Society for Traumatic Stress Studies, Chicago, IL.

Lazrove, S., & Fine, C. G. (1996). The use of EMDR in patients with dissociative identity disorder. *Dissociation, 9,* 289–299.

Lipke, H. (2000). *EMDR and psychotherapy integration.* Boca Raton, FL: CRC Press.

Luber, M. (2009). *Eye movement desensitization and reprocessing (EMDR) scripted protocols: Basics and special situations.* New York: Springer Publishing.

Luber, M. & Shapiro, F. (2009). Future directions for EMDR. Interview with Francine Shapiro: *Journal of EMDR Practice and Research.*

Madrid, A., Skolek, S., & Shapiro, F. (2006). Repairing failures in bonding through EMDR. *Clinical Case Studies, 5,* 271–286.

Marquis, J. N., & Puk, G. (1994, November). *Dissociative identity disorder: A common sense and cognitive-behavioral view.* Paper presented at the annual meeting of the Association for Advancement of Behavior Therapy, San Diego, CA.

Maxfield, L. (2007). Integrative treatment of intrafamilial child sexual abuse. In F. Shapiro, F. W. Kaslow, & L. Maxfield (Eds.), *Handbook of EMDR and family therapy processes* (pp. 344–364). Hoboken, NJ: Wiley.

Maxwell, J. P. (2003). The imprint of childhood physical and emotional abuse: A case study on the use of EMDR to address anxiety and lack of self-esteem. *Journal of Family Violence, 18,* 281–293.

Nadler, W. (1996). EMDR: Rapid treatment of panic disorder. *International Journal of Psychiatry, 2,* 1–8.

National Institute for Clinical Excellence (NICE). (2005, March). *Post-traumatic stress (PTSD): The management of PTSD in adults and children and secondary care.* United Kingdom: National Collaborating Centre for Mental Health.

National Institute of Mental Health (NIMH). (2004–2007). *Therapy Advisor.* Retrieved March 21, 2009, from http://www.therapyadvisor.com

Paulsen, S. (1995). Eye movement desensitization and reprocessing: Its use in the dissociative disorders. *Dissociation, 8,* 32–44.

Popky, A. J. (2005). DeTUR, an urge reduction protocol for addictions and dysfunctional behaviors. In R. Shapiro (Ed.), *EMDR solutions: Pathways to healing* (pp. 167–188). New York: W. W. Norton.

Ray, A. L., & Zbik, A. (2001). Cognitive behavioral therapies and beyond. In C. D. Tollison, J. R. Satterthwaite, & J. W. Tollison (Eds.), *Practical pain management* (3rd ed., pp. 189–208). Philadelphia: Lippincott.

Ricci, R. J. (2006). Trauma resolution using eye movement desensitization and reprocessing with an incestuous sex offender: An instrumental case study. *Clinical Case Studies, 5*(3), 248.

Ricci, R. J., Clayton, C. A., & Shapiro, F. (2006). Some effects of EMDR treatment with previously abused child molesters: Theoretical reviews and preliminary findings. *Journal of Forensic Psychiatry and Psychology, 17,* 538–562.

Roos de, C., & Veenstra, A. C. (2008). Het EMDR protocol voor actuele pijn. In E. Ten Broeke, A. de Jongh, & H. Oppenheim (Eds.). *Praktijkboek EMDR: Casusconceptualisatie en specifieke patientengroepen.* Amsterdam: Harcourt.

Roos de, C., & Veenstra, A. C., Jongh de, A., Hollander-Gijsman den, M. E., Wee van der, N. J. A., Zitman, F. G., et al. (2008). *Treatment of chronic phantom limb pain (PLP) with eye movement desensitization and reprocessing (EMDR): Ten cases.* Manuscript submitted for publication.

Rouanzoin, C. (1994, March). *EMDR: Dissociative disorders and MPD.* Paper presented at the 14th annual meeting of the Anxiety Disorders Association of America, Santa Monica, CA.

Russell, A., & O'Connor, M. (2002). Interventions for recovery: The use of EMDR with children in a community-based project. *Association for Child Psychiatry and Psychology, Occasional Paper No. 19,* 43–46.

Russell, M. (2006). Treating combat-related stress disorders: A multiple case study utilizing eye movement desensitization and reprocessing (EMDR) with battlefield casualties from the Iraqi war. *Military Psychology, 18,* 1–18.

Russell, M. (2008). Treating traumatic amputation-related phantom limb pain: A case study utilizing eye movement desensitization and reprocessing (EMDR) within the armed services. *Clinical Case Studies, 7*(2), 136–153.

Russell, M. C., & Silver, S. M. (2007). Training needs for the treatment of combat-related posttraumatic stress disorder. *Traumatology, 13,* 4–10.

Russell, M. C., Silver, S. M., Rogers, S., & Darnell, J. (2007). Responding to an identified need: A joint Department of Defense–Department of Veterans Affairs training program in eye movement desensitization and reprocessing (EMDR) for clinicians providing trauma services. *International Journal of Stress Management, 14,* 61–71.

Schneider, J., Hofmann, A., Rost, C., & Shapiro, F. (2007). EMDR and phantom limb pain: Case study, theoretical implications, and treatment guidelines. *Journal of EMDR Practice and Research, 1,* 31–45.

Shapiro, F. (1991). Eye movement desensitization and reprocessing procedure: From EMD to EMDR: A new treatment model for anxiety and related traumata. *Behavior Therapist, 14*, 122–125.

Shapiro, F. (1994). Eye movement desensitization and reprocessing: A new treatment for anxiety and related trauma. In L. Hyer (Ed.), *Trauma victim: Theoretical and practical suggestions* (pp. 501–521). Muncie, IN: Accelerated Development Publishers.

Shapiro, F. (1995). *Eye movement desensitization and reprocessing: Basic principles, protocols, and procedures.* New York: Guilford Press.

Shapiro, F. (1999). Eye movement desensitization and reprocessing (EMDR) and the anxiety disorders: Clinical and research implications of an integrated psychotherapy treatment. *Journal of Anxiety Disorders, 13*(1–2, Excerpt), 35–67.

Shapiro, F. (2001). *Eye movement desensitization and reprocessing: Basic principles, protocols, and procedures* (2nd ed.). New York: Guilford Press.

Shapiro, F. (2006). *EMDR: New notes on adaptive information processing with case formulation principles, forms, scripts and worksheets.* Watsonville, CA: EMDR Institute.

Shapiro, F., & Forrest, M. (1997). *EMDR the breakthrough therapy for overcoming anxiety, stress and trauma.* New York: Basic Books.

Shapiro, F., Kaslow, F. W., & Maxfield, L. (2007). *Handbook of EMDR and family therapy processes.* Hoboken, NJ: Wiley.

Shapiro, F., Vogelmann-Sine, S., & Sine, L. (1994). Eye movement desensitization and reprocessing: Treating trauma and substance abuse. *Journal of Psychoactive Drugs, 26*, 379–391.

Silver, S. M., Brooks, A., & Obenchain, J. (1995). Eye movement desensitization and reprocessing treatment of Vietnam war veterans with PTSD: Comparative effects with biofeedback and relaxation training. *Journal of Traumatic Stress, 8*, 337–342.

Silver, S. M., & Rogers, S. (2002). *Light in the heart of darkness: EMDR and the treatment of war and terrorism survivors.* New York: W. W. Norton.

Talan, B. S. (2007). Integrating EMDR and imago relationship therapy in treatment of couples. In F. Shapiro, F. W. Kaslow, & L. Maxfield (Eds.), *Handbook of EMDR and family therapy processes* (pp. 187–201). Hoboken, NJ: Wiley.

Tinker, R. H., & Wilson, S. A. (1999). *Through the eyes of a child: EMDR with children.* New York: W. W. Norton.

Tinker, R. H., & Wilson, S. A. (2005). The phantom limb pain protocol. In R. Shapiro (Ed.), *EMDR solutions: Pathways to healing* (pp. 147–159). New York: W. W. Norton.

Twombly, J. (2000). Incorporating EMDR and EMDR adaptations into the treatment of clients with dissociative identity disorder. *Journal of Trauma and Dissociation, 1*, 61–81.

Twombly, J. H. (2005). EMDR for clients with dissociative identity disorder, DDNOS, and ego states. In R. Shapiro (Ed.), *EMDR solutions: Pathways to healing* (pp. 88–120). New York: W. W. Norton.

United Kingdom Department of Health. (2001). *Treatment choice in psychological therapies and counselling evidence based clinical practice guideline.* London.

U.S. Department of Veterans Affairs, Veterans Health Administration & Department of Defense. (2004, January). *VA/DoD clinical practice guideline for the management of post-traumatic stress.* Version 1.0. Washington, DC: Veterans Health Administration and Department of Defense.

Vogelmann-Sine, S., Sine, L. F., Smyth, N. J., & Popky, A. J. (1998). *EMDR chemical dependency treatment manual.* New Hope, PA: EMDR Humanitarian Assistance Programs.

Wernik, U. (1993). The role of the traumatic component in the etiology of sexual dysfunctions and its treatment with eye movement desensitization procedure. *Journal of Sex Education and Therapy, 19*, 212–222.

Wilensky, M. (2006). Eye movement desensitization and reprocessing (EMDR) as a treatment for phantom limb pain. *Journal of Brief Therapy, 5*, 31–44.

Wilson, S. A., Becker, L. A., Tinker, R. H., & Logan, C. R. (2001). Stress management with law enforcement personnel. A controlled outcome study of EMDR versus a traditional stress management program. *International Journal of Stress Management, 8*, 179–200.

Wilson, S. A., Tinker, R., Becker, L. A., Hofmann, A., & Cole, J. W. (2000, September). *EMDR treatment of phantom limb pain with brain imaging (MEG).* Paper presented at the annual meeting of the EMDR International Association, Toronto, Canada.

Young, W. (1994). EMDR treatment of phobic symptoms in multiple personality. *Dissociation, 7*(2), 129–133.

Zweben, J., & Yeary, J. (2006). EMDR in the treatment of addiction. *Journal of Chemical Dependency Treatment, 8*, 115–127.

Acknowledgments

When we are in a community active in the art and science of healing, it is an opportunity to learn and grow. The process of editing this volume and *Eye Movement Desensitization and Reprocessing (EMDR) Scripted Protocols: Basics and Special Situations* has resulted in much more than I would have ever dreamed when I began this journey. As in the words of Sheenagh Pugh's poem "Sometimes" (1990), "Sometimes our best efforts do not go amiss; sometimes we do as we meant to"; the authors of these volumes—my peers—and I have done more than I dared possible. Our collective work has brought to light how much better we are for the work that we are and have been doing. I would like to acknowledge these authors and the growth and depth of understanding I have experienced in the course of absorbing and clarifying their work in an active exchange of ideas with each of them so that I could pass these ideas on in scripted form to other clinicians. To each one of you, I would like to say, "Thank-you." We are all truly able to benefit from their knowledge. I hope in using this book, you will have the same experience.

This book is dedicated to Francine Shapiro and Robbie Dunton. They are two of the most community-oriented people that I have met. They are passionate in their pursuit of teaching EMDR and creating a healing community worldwide. Through watching, listening, and learning from Robbie, I learned how to create community. From Francine, I learned what it takes to germinate an idea, plant it, and watch it grow into an effective healing community. This book is a tribute to the seeding that you, Francine and Robbie, have done since the beginning of the EMDR journey.

I would also like to acknowledge the international community at the International School of Geneva that I joined at the impressionable age of 11 years. Through the day-to-day rubbing elbows and ideas with people from diverse cultures, belief systems, religions, and teaching styles, I learned a great deal about the importance of the boundaries of my own ways and the transformation that occurred by learning early that there are many more ways to think about a problem than my own.

To my colleagues in the greater EMDR community, I would like to acknowledge the many gifts I have received through the experience of knowing each one of you. It is the friendships, small and large kindnesses, and reaching out at times of happiness and sorrows that has made this experience in my life a rich and profound one. I have learned from the lessons of interpersonal conflict, friendship, and leadership and have been truly impacted by the exchange. Most of all, I have been deeply touched by the consistent changes that we have begun to make as we work with clients on their inappropriately stored life experiences to their large "T" traumas. I am awed by the work that our community has done throughout the world in the face of man-made and natural disasters. The world is a more compassionate and healthy place as a result of our EMDR community.

I also recognize the importance of the staff of Springer Publishing, especially Sheri W. Sussman and Deborah Gissinger and Julia Rosen of Apex CoVantage. Thank you for your help and guidance during these two projects. In particular, I would like to thank Sheri for barely blinking when she was presented with much more material than she expected.

Again, without Lew Rossi and his ability to handle any of the major issues that have come about concerning the software and hardware of my computer, this project would never have even approached completion; thank you for all of your hard work. The Internet is also a source of great gratitude as without the benefit of this medium, this book would have taken much longer and possibly resulted in less diversity.

I would like to thank my kind colleagues and recognize them as they took time away from their busy schedules to read over some of the text and/or provide support and guidance: they are Elaine Alvarez, Sheila Bender, Michael Broder, Catherine Fine, Irene Giessl, Richard Goldberg, Barbara Hensley, Jennifer Lendl, Donald Nathanson, Udi Oren, Sandra Paulsen, Zona Scheiner, Elan Shapiro, Howard Wainer, Stuart Wolfe, and Bennet Wolper. To Emmy, my inimitable therapy dog, I would like to acknowledge the trials and tribulations that she has gone through mirroring my intensity and focus while working with these scripts and her ability to always make me smile during the course of the day. Although I have neglected my friends during this time of concentrated and solitary work, I want them to know how much I have appreciated all their support from the wings and airways. I would like to acknowledge and remember my cousin, Steven Waxman, who was friend and counsel until his passing away this year. I would like to thank Shirley Luber always for her support and loving kindness.

PART 1

EMDR With Children and Adolescents

Understanding child development is the foundation upon which to build our clinical skills. It enriches our thinking and helps us understand the types of clinical interventions to choose as we work with our clients—child, adolescent or adult. The chapters in this section can be used not only for working with children and adolescents but with our adult clients as well.

The integration of EMDR and working with this population began as soon as Francine Shapiro taught Robbie Dunton how to do Eye Movement Desensitization (EMD) and later EMDR. Ms. Dunton could not believe the power of EMDR when she worked with the behavioral issues of school-aged children as it helped her uncover the histories of early trauma in her students. By understanding the presenting learning problem, she began to see the connection between the problem and a trauma or issue that precipitated the learning issue. If a child came in with a fraction problem, as this skill was taught in fourth grade, Ms. Dunton would ask, *"What happened in fourth grade?"* Often, there was a trauma that became the target for reprocessing; frequently resulting in the decrease or disappearance of the presenting learning issue (Luber, 2007). Ms. Dunton presented her work on the "Treatment of Learning Disabilities" in Australia in 1992 at the EMDR Symposium at the Fourth World Congress of Behavior Therapy and in 1993 at the Second Annual EMDR Conference in Sunnyvale, California, setting a high bar for all of the child and adolescent therapists who followed her.

In August 1991, the EMDR Institute published Volume 1, Issue 1 of the *Network Newsletter*. The EMDR Institute communicated with those who participated in EMDR Institute trainings through the *Network Newsletter*. The newsletter was filled with information and concerns from Dr. Shapiro, reviews of relevant professional papers and books, information from the EMDR Professional Issues Committee

(EPIC), the *International Update,* and a column by Ron Martinez called "Innovative Uses." It is in here that practitioners such as Liz Mendoza-Weitman (1992), Ricky Greenwald (1993b), and Joan Lovett (1994) broached such issues as depression in a 10-year-old boy whose father abandoned him at age 5, treating a child's nightmares with EMDR, and a case report on treating a toddler with EMDR. It became an excellent way to find out what people were doing in EMDR. In June 1996, the *Network Newsletter* turned into the *EMDRIA Newsletter* when the EMDR International Association was formed.

One of the first articles published about EMDR was in the *Journal of Behavior Therapy and Experimental Psychiatry* (Pellicer, 1993) on EMDR and the treatment of a child's nightmare. Meanwhile, through the EMDR Institute Conferences that began in 1991, child therapists began to present their work. During the second annual EMDR Conference, topics such as working with school behaviors and learning issues (Dunton, 1993), EMDR and a sexually abused child (Sutton, 1993), and children and critical incidents (Greenwald, 1993a) were explored. By the 1994 EMDR Conference, Robert Tinker was presenting on attention deficit/hyperactivity disorder (ADHD; 1994), Michael Abruzzese was addressing the use of Tourette's disorder with EMDR (1994), and Jean Sutton continued to present on traumatized children and EMDR (1994). In 1995, the EMDR Institute hosted a joint conference with the newly formed EMDR International Association in Santa Monica. There were five presentations addressing child and adolescent issues concerning case presentations (Greenwald, 1995), disruptive behaviors (Abruzzese, 1995), fears (Klaff, 1995), darkness phobias (Cocco, 1995), and with toddlers (Lovett, 1995). An all-day workshop for child and adolescent therapists was widely attended and included "Using EMDR to Treat Children" (Tinker, 1995), "Treating Severely Traumatized Children—Assessment and Treatment Strategies for Using EMDR" (York, 1995), and "Using EMDR With Adolescents" (Thompson, 1995). The interest in child and adolescent work with EMDR was clear.

In 1996, the baton was passed formally to the EMDR International Association and this group began to host the EMDR Conference with the mission to uphold the standard of EMDR practice. In this spirit, a meeting to promote the development of EMDR for children and adolescents was called by Ricky Greenwald (Chair) along with his panel members; Michael Abruzzese, Ann Godwin, Joan Lovett, Robert Tinker, and Carol York. Some of their goals included working on research and publications for the efficacy of EMDR for children and adolescents, maintaining an updated literature review, offering support for research projects, promoting EMDR training for mental health professionals in schools, understanding child trauma and EMDR internationally and with the medical community, developing diagnostic and screening tools for EMDR appropriateness, increasing the focus on child EMDR skills in the standard trainings, and establishing standards of training for a specialty with children and adolescents. In the following years, presentations and research on EMDR with children and adolescents increased.

The year 1999 was a banner one for EMDR and the treatment of children and adolescents. Four of the early pioneers working with EMDR in this field turned their knowledge into the following books: *Eye Movement Desensitization and Reprocessing (EMDR) in Child and Adolescent Psychotherapy* (Greenwald, 1999a), *Small Wonders: Healing Childhood Trauma With EMDR* (Lovett, 1999), and *Through the Eyes of a Child: EMDR With Children* (Tinker & Wilson, 1999). Each book added knowledge to the already growing ways to treat children and adolescents with EMDR. In the same year, mirroring the interest of practitioners in this area, the EMDRIA Newsletter had a special edition on "Children, Adolescents, & EMDR: A Closer Look" with articles on "EMDR With Children: The First Ten Years" (Greenwald, 1999b); "Developmental Considerations in Using EMDR With Adolescents" (Geller, 1999); "Slaying the Monsters" (Spindler-Ranta, 1999); "The Butterfly Hug:

Some History and Updates on Its Use With Children" (Boel, 1999); "After Zero: Further Processing with Teens" (Greenwald, 1999e); "Book Reviews: Three EMDR Book About Children and Adolescents" (Dutton, 1999); "Group EMDR Therapy in Young Children" (Forte, 1999); "A Crisis Response Approach for Suicidal Teens" (Greenwald, 1999d), and "Breaking the Cycle of Violence: EMDR Treatment of a Traumatized Violent Teen Girl" (Van Winkle, 1999).

Child and adolescent therapists in Europe trained with Robert Tinker and Sandra Wilson in the late 1990s. Many of these clinicians went on to become accredited Child Trainers. The accredited Child Trainers in Europe—at this writing—are the following: Joanne Morris-Smith (Great Britain), Kamala Müller (Great Britain), Renee Beer (Netherlands), Carlijn de Roos (Netherlands), Barbara Wizansky (Israel), Esti Bar-Sade (Israel), Dagmar Eckers (Germany), Beatrix Musaeus-Schürmann (Germany), Lutz-Ulrich Besser (Germany), Edeltraud Toddy Sochaczewsky (Germany), Thomas Hensel (Germany), Margareta Friberg (Sweden), Reet Oras (Sweden), Lene Jacobson (Denmark), Michel Silvestre (France). Currently, there is a Child Committee in the EMDR European Association that decides on the rules for training child and adolescent therapists in coordination with the Standard Committee of EMDR Europe.

In the United States, the EMDR for Children and Adolescents Special Interest Group continued to flourish. They sponsor conferences annually and work on special projects such as creating a resource packet for EMDR clinicians that contain information on helpful resources for children and EMDR. Marsha Heiman, an EMDR practitioner living in northern New Jersey, helped create a brochure to explain trauma to professionals in other related fields. The brochure (Child and Adolescent Special Interest Group, 2007), "EMDR & Children: A Guide for Parents, Professionals, and Others Who Care About Children" is available for purchase through the EMDR International Association (www.emdria.org). Anyone who is a member of EMDRIA can join this special interest group (SIG) and the Child SIG Clinical Listserv.

The new millennium has brought many more presentations, chapters in books, articles and books concerning this area; in fact, as of June 2009, the Francine Shapiro Library reported 318 abstracts about children. EMDR is being used with children and adolescents for a wide range of issues all over the world. A short sample of work includes *art therapy* (Cohn & Chapman, 2002); *attachment* (Wesselman, 2007); *family* (Klaff, 2002); *grief* (Donovan, 2005); *hospital trauma* (Lovett, 2002); *juvenile sex offenders* (Gates, 2002); *joy* (Morris-Smith, 2003); *learning disabilities* (Bacon, 2001); *man-made and natural disasters* (Artigas, Jarero, Alcala & Lopez, 2009); *phobias* (Nofal, 2008); and *PTSD* (Maxfield et al., 2004).

Clearly, there is a great interest in EMDR and the treatment of children and adolescents. Part I of this book is aimed at the community of child and adolescent specialists, as well as those clinicians who work only with adult populations, who are always looking for new and creative ways to work with their adult clients—especially those with early trauma—both large "T" and small "t" traumas. The first part of this section addresses how to develop resources for children and adolescents. In the first chapter, Lucina Artigas and Ignacio Jarero show us how to use the "Butterfly Hug." This way to help children learn bilateral stimulation in the face of natural disaster was an innovation that was heard around the world. Practitioners have taught their child and adult clients this helpful intervention during man-made catastrophes and natural disasters (see Part VI, Artigas, Jarero, Alcalá, & López, 2009) to help them work through their terrible experiences.

Ana Gomez has been presenting at the EMDRIA Conferences for a number of years and is so inventive that her work is shown as a demonstration during the current EMDR Institute Basic Trainings. Using olfactory stimulation may be more effective in reaching different parts of the brain if the thalamic activity is decreased;

Dr. Gomez has turned this information into an original way of pairing olfactory stimulation with the Resource Development and Installation and Safe Place Protocols for optimal results with her clients.

Barbara Wizansky and Dagmar Eckers have modified adult techniques so that they may be used with children. Ms. Wizansky has taken Brurit Laub's Resource Connection and added her own modification to support children in reinforcing their resources and using them as needed. Dr. Eckers's work with the Absorption Technique for Children is an adaptation of Arne Hofmann's adaptation (chapter 23) of Roy Kiessling's "The Wedging Technique" (Kiessling, 2009) and is used for present challenges and future concerns. Ms. Eckers also has adapted Jim Knipe's "Method of Constant Installation of Present Orientation and Safety" (CIPOS; chapter 18) for children. She incorporates drawing into this method to help the child have a sense of their current security and stability and the establishing of a safe place while using CIPOS.

Barbara Wizansky's Footsteps Through the Maze Protocol (chapter 7) has created a problem-solving tool that uses bilateral stimulation (BLS) to create resources that eventually lead to the introduction of the Standard EMDR Protocol.

Robbie Adler-Tapia and Carolyn Settle, as many clinicians who become serious about EMDR, joined a study group that included other practitioners interested in working with EMDR and children. They began a research study on using EMDR with young children with the goal of helping therapists adhere to the EMDR protocol. The result is a state of the art text, *EMDR and the Art of Psychotherapy With Children* (2008a) and the accompanying manual, *EMDR and the Art of Psychotherapy With Children Treatment Manual* (2008b). This book and manual can be consulted for a more in-depth treatment of work with children. In their chapter on EMDR Assessment and Desensitization Phases with children, they give step-by-step directions on how to move through these phases.

These scripts can be used to help expand your treatment skills and learn important ways to build resources and work with children and adolescents with EMDR. It is important to note here that those clinicians who use these protocols with children and adolescents should have extensive knowledge of how to work with EMDR and with children and adolescents before they begin work with their clients.

The Butterfly Hug

Lucina Artigas and Ignacio Jarero

The Butterfly Hug was originated and developed by Lucina Artigas during her work performed with the survivors of Hurricane Pauline in Acapulco, Mexico, 1997 (Artigas, Jarero, Mauer, López Cano, & Alcalá, 2000; Jarero, Artigas, & Montero, 2008).

For the origination and development of this method, Lucina Artigas was honored in 2000 with the Creative Innovation Award by the EMDR International Association. In Francine Shapiro's 2001 EMDR text, she wrote that "The Butterfly Hug has been successfully used to treat groups of traumatized children in Mexico, Nicaragua and Kosovar refugee camps" (Shapiro, 2001, p. 284). By 2009, The Butterfly Hug had become standard practice for clinicians in the field while working with survivors of man-made and natural catastrophes.

The Butterfly Hug Script

The "Butterfly Hug" provides a way to self-administer dual attention stimulation (DAS) for an individual or for group work.

> Say, *"Would you like to learn an exercise that will help you to feel better?"*

_____

_____

> Say, *"Please watch me and do what I am doing. Cross your arms over your chest, so that with the tip of your fingers from each hand, you can touch the area that is located under the connection between the clavicle and the shoulder. Your eyes can be closed or partially closed looking toward the tip of your nose. Next, you alternate the movement of your hands, like the flapping wings of a butterfly. You breathe slowly and deeply* (abdominal breathing), *while you observe what is going through your mind and body such as thoughts, images, sounds, odors, feelings, and physical sensation without changing, pushing your thoughts away, or judging. You can pretend as though what you are observing are like clouds passing by."*

This exercise can be done for as long as the person(s) wishes to continue. Watch to make sure that the children are following along with you. If not, check to find out what is going on and then return to teaching The Butterfly Hug.

Uses for This Method

To install the Safe Place:

> Say, *"Now, please close your eyes and use your imagination to go to a place where you feel safe or calm. What images, colors, sounds, and so forth do you see in your safe place?"*

_____

_____

When in groups, the Emotional Protection Team moves among the children listening to them as they answer out loud.

The goal here is to make sure that each child has found a Safe/Calm Place they imagined.

The following is optional:

> Say, *"Now, please take out your paper and draw the Safe/Calm Place that you imagined. When you are finished, please do the Butterfly Hug while looking at your drawing."*
> Say, *"You are welcome to take your picture home and you can use it with the Butterfly Hug whenever you need to feel better."*

Make sure to notice the children's responses. There is no talking during this time so that the children are not taken out of their process.

Once the patients or clients (children or adults) have learned the Butterfly Hug, they can be instructed to take this method with them to use between sessions, whether to modulate any disturbing effect that arises, to reground with their Safe Place or simply to help them get to sleep more easily.

> Say, *"Now that you have learned the Butterfly Hug you can use it anytime that you are having disturbing feelings, or you want to go back to your Safe Place. You can also use it to get to sleep more easily. Do you have any questions before we stop for today?"*

_____

_____

There are many uses for the Butterfly Hug such as the following:

- To anchor positive affect, cognitions, and physical sensations associated with images produced by the technique of "guided imagination."
- During the EMDR Standard Protocol, some clinicians have also used it with adults and children to facilitate primary processing of a fundamental traumatic memory or memories. Instead of the clinicians being in charge of the bilateral stimulation, the client is asked to do the Butterfly Hug during the Phases 4, 5, and 6. It is thought that the control obtained by the client over their contralateral stimulation may be an empowering factor that aids their retention of sense of safety while processing traumatic memories.
- During in vivo exposure to process the experience. For example, in the Quiche's region of Guatemala the persons that are witnessing the burial of their relatives use the Butterfly Hug to be self-comforted and to cope with the experience.
- In the EMDR Integrative Group Treatment Protocol (EMDR-IGTP) used to work with children and adults who have survived traumatic events, to process primary traumatic memory or memories including the death of family members. During this process, the children and adults are under the close supervision of mental health professionals who form the Emotional Protection Team. (Jarero et al., 2008).
- Use of the Butterfly Hug in session with the therapist can be a self-soothing experience for many trauma-therapy clients. For instance, the therapist might say, *"Would you like to use the Butterfly Hug while you are telling me what happened?"*
- Some professionals use the Butterfly Hug simultaneously with their client as an aid to prevent secondary traumatization.
- Other professionals have used this method as a substitute for touching clients and they might say, *"Please give yourself a Butterfly Hug for me."*
- Professionals report that they have used the Butterfly Hug with clients with debilitated egos because it produces less abreaction than other bilateral stimulation techniques.
- Teachers in a Guatemalan school for child victims of parental violence tell the children that they can feel Father God's love through the Butterfly Hug.
- During the Pasta de Conchos mine tragedy in Mexico in 2006, a paramedic stabilized and saved the life of a mine engineer who was having a heart attack using the Butterfly Hug.

Using Olfactory Stimulation With Children to Cue the Safe or Happy Place

Ana Gomez

The standard Safe Place Protocol uses a word for cuing and self-cuing (Shapiro, 2001). For many clients, using a cue word to elicit the Safe Place and its positive associations may be effective, however, this author has hypothesized that other forms of cuing may be more effective, depending on the severity of their trauma and patterns of neurobiological responses. For the last 3 years, this author has used olfactory stimulation with more than 30 children and adolescents to cue the Safe Place and resources installed with the Resource Development and Installation (RDI) Protocol (Korn & Leeds, 2002). These children have shown positive responses with increased self-regulation to self-cuing with olfactory stimulation using simple scents and scented lotions. The effectiveness of olfactory cues to assist traumatized children in accessing previously installed resources for self-regulation may be associated with the relationship between trauma and thalamic activity. The thalamus is the sensory gateway to the cortex and the limbic system. This means that all incoming sensory information is routed through the thalamus with the exception of olfactory stimulation (Bergmann, 2008a). Several studies conducted by Ruth Lanius and her colleagues (R. Lanius et al., 2004; R. Lanius, Bluhm, Lanius, & Pain, 2006; R. Lanius, Lanius, Fisher, & Ogden, 2006), suggest that thalamic response patterns may be different depending on the type of trauma. Individuals with simple post-traumatic stress disorder (PTSD) might show an increase in thalamic activity and those with complex PTSD, a decrease in thalamic activity. According to Ulrich Lanius (2006), if thalamic activity decreases as a result of trauma and PTSD, then incoming information will not be efficiently sent to other parts of the brain. Ulrich Lanius has hypothesized that this might be the case in complex PTSD and dissociative individuals. With this information in mind, when using the Safe Place and RDI Protocols, olfactory stimulation may be more effective in reaching different regions of the brain even if thalamic activity is decreased.

For many years, aromatherapy has been used as an adjunctive form of therapy in mental health. Some research studies even suggest that the use of scents and aromas may be effective as a tool for crisis management in adolescents and adults (Fowler, 2006).

Initially, the use of olfactory stimulation with Safe Place and RDI resources was limited to youngsters with symptoms of dissociation and complex PTSD, but, later on, it was extended to young clients with simple PTSD and other trauma-related disorders. These children reported that using scents and lotions for self-cuing facilitated the effective use of resources when they were experiencing negative emotions, resulting in an increased ability for self-regulation. In addition, children, and especially the younger ones, reported that self-cuing with lotions and scents made the use of the Safe Place and other resources very motivating. However, at this point, this is an anecdotal report with objective measures and no controls. The effectiveness of using olfactory stimulation to cue Safe Place and RDI has not been established.

As described in earlier reports (Korn & Leeds, 2002; Shapiro, 2001), if at any point while you are using the Safe Place or RDI resource protocol the child reports negative emotions, reevaluate the resource and assist the child in identifying a different Safe Place or a new resource that has only positive associations. A child who is unable to identify any Safe Place or any positive resources shows you the magnitude of the child's deficits. If this is the case, do a more thorough assessment of the child's support system and environment, since a chaotic environment may be maintaining the child in the alarm state. More work might be necessary with the caregivers and support system to stabilize the environment.

The following is the adapted Safe Place Protocol for children using olfactory stimulation. This protocol can be used with children and adolescents from 4 to 12 years of age. Some young children might not understand the word "safe" so referring to the Safe Place as the Happy Place might be more appropriate. Before using this protocol, assess the presence of allergies or skin conditions that can be worsened by the use of lotions and scents. This applies to the child, the parents, and the clinician as well. Even though this author has yet to have any child report negative associations to the selected scent, any stimulus can potentially become negative. If this is the case, you can encourage the child to choose another lotion or scent at any point during the administration of this protocol.

Safe Place Protocol Script Notes

Before establishing the Safe Place, it is important that you explain to the child and the caregivers what EMDR is and how it works, especially the different forms of bilateral stimulation (BLS). Based on research, Dr. Francine Shapiro has suggested that eye movement might have a stronger effect than other forms of BLS for adults that can tolerate them. On the other hand, it has been suggested that tactile and auditory stimulation seem to create a less concentrated, more diffused and evidently gentler signal to the brain in comparison to eye movement (Bergmann, 2008b). When working with highly dissociative individuals, less activation to the brain during trauma reprocessing might be more appropriate (Bergmann, 2008c; Lanius, 2008). Therefore, using tactile or auditory BLS might be more suitable. It has yet to be established whether one form of BLS is more effective with children, but if we follow adult research, eye movements should be offered first unless the child cannot tolerate them or reports discomfort. However, when working with highly dissociative children using tactile and auditory stimulation might be more appropriate.

In order to make eye movements more appealing for children, this author has created a set of finger puppets that are part of a team called the "EMDR Helpers." This team consists of a group of finger puppets that are introduced to the child when EMDR is explained for the first time so the child can develop a relationship with the helpers. The names of these finger puppets form the acronym EMDR: **E**lizabeth, **M**ario, **D**avid, and **R**obbie are always available to assist the child by providing the BLS. Through clinical observation, it has been noted that children are usually more motivated to do EMDR and use eye movement when they have developed a relationship with a puppet. Every time the clinician needs to provide BLS, it is important to ask the child for the name of the helper puppet.

The following Safe Place Protocol has been adapted from the adult Safe Place Protocol developed by Neal Daniels in his work with veterans at the Veterans Administration Hospital in Philadelphia and formalized in Shapiro (1995). Depending on the child's age and preference, use your clinical judgment to determine the appropriateness of having the caregiver present during the session.

Safe or Happy Place Script

Say, "*I want you to meet my EMDR helpers. They help kids do EMDR.*"

Say the name of each puppet and have the puppets introduce themselves.

Say, "*Hi, my name is Elizabeth. Hi, my name is Mario. Hi, my name is David, and my name is Robbie and we are THE EMDR HELPERS! We help kids move their eyes from side to side, please follow us.*"

Have children follow the puppets with their eyes while you move the finger puppets back and forth. If the child cannot tolerate eye movement, have the puppets tap the child's hands or knees. Demonstrate the other forms of BLS.

Say, "*Okay, how about if I have the puppets tap your hands? Would that be okay to try?*"

_____

_____

If the child can tolerate eye movement say, the following:

Say, "*Good job, now pick your favorite one, which EMDR helper would you like to have today?*"

_____

_____

Say, "*We are going to practice EMDR with good stuff and you are going to move your eyes from side to side* (if the child cannot tolerate eye movement, mention the BLS selected by the child). *Which EMDR helper would you like to have today?*"

_____

_____

Image

Say, "*Can you think of a place where you have been or that is in your imagination, where you feel good, happy, and safe? This is a place where you remember good things happening and where nothing bad has ever happened. What place do you have in mind? What colors, sounds, and smells do you remember in this place?*"

_____

_____

Emotions and Sensations

Say, "*When you think about this place, how do you feel?*"

_____

_____

Say, "*Where do you feel that inside your body?*"

_____

_____

Enhancement (Optional)

Ask the child to draw a picture of the Safe Place.

> Say, *"I would like you to draw a picture of this place that you created in your mind. Think about this place and all the colors, the sounds, the smells, and everything that you see around it that make you feel* _____ (repeat the emotions identified by the child previously). *You can use paper and pencils, crayons, or paint to draw your Safe or Happy Place."*

Or create the Safe or Happy Place using the sandbox.

> Say, *"I would like you to use the sandbox to make this place that you have created in your mind. Think about this place and all the colors, the sounds, the smells, and everything that you see around it that make you feel* _____ (repeat the emotions identified by the child previously). *You can use any figures to create your Safe or Happy Place* (have different sandbox figures the child can choose from to create the safe place)."

_____

_____

Bilateral Stimulation (BLS)

> Say, *"Now I would like you to bring up your Safe or Happy Place and those* _____ (repeat the emotions reported by the child) *feelings that you feel in your body and follow* _____ (say the name of the EMDR helper selected by the child)."

Do 4 to 6 slow passes of BLS.

Say, *"What do you feel now?"*

_____

_____

Repeat several times if the emotions and positive associations to the Safe Place continue to be enhanced.

Say, *"Go with that"* or *"Think of that."*

Do 4 to 6 slow passes of BLS.

If negative feelings and associations occur, assist the child in identifying a different Safe Place.

> Say, *"Okay, it looks like when you think about this place you are getting some mixed-up feelings. How about if we find another place where you don't have any mixed-up feelings and you only feel good, happy, and safe. Can you think of another place?"*

_____

_____

You could also ask the child for a safe or happy place they have had in their dreams.

If the child cannot identify such a place, more intensive stabilization work with the child and caregivers might be necessary.

Cue Scent

Have different lotions, scents, or essential oils available for the child. (Hand lotions and essential oils can be found at any department store.) Allow the child to explore and experiment with different scents and lotions. Have a small container ready and give it to the child.

> Say, *"I would like you to try the lotions and scents that are here so that you can pick one that will help you remember your Safe or Happy Place and the good feelings that you have when you think about this place. It can be any lotion or smell you want. Make sure it is a scent that does not remind you of anything bad or yucky."*

_____

_____

> Say, *"That's a great choice. Here is your own special container to put it in. What would you like to call this lotion?"*

_____

_____

Most children call it the "good feelings lotion" or my "safe place lotion" or my "happy feelings lotion." If the child does not come up with a name you can say the following:

> Say, *"Some children like to call their lotion the 'good feelings lotion' or my 'safe place lotion' or 'my happy feelings lotion.' You can use these names or any other name that you might think of that makes you think about your lotion."*

_____

_____

> Say, *"Now, I would like you to think about your Safe or Happy Place and the _____ (repeat the emotions identified by the child) feelings. Now, smell the _____ (state the name of the lotion the child chose) and continue to hold the container to your nose and follow _____ (state the EMDR helper's name)."*

Do 4 to 6 slow passes of BLS with the finger puppet.

> Say, *"What happened? How do you feel?"*

_____

_____

> Say, *"Great, go with that."*

_____

_____

Repeat several times as long as the experience continues to be enhanced.

> Say, *"You can put the container down now. How do you feel?"*

_____

_____

Self-Cuing

Say, *"Now, I would like you to smell the lotion again and ask your mind to think about your Safe or Happy Place and see what happens."*

_____

_____

Allow the child to stay in their Safe Place for about 60 seconds.

Say, *"How do you feel now?"*

_____

_____

If the child reports positive emotions, then say the following:

Say, *"Okay, just notice or think about those* _____ (repeat the positive emotions reported by the child) *feelings and follow* _____ (state the EMDR helper's name)."

_____

_____

Do 4 to 6 slow BLS with the finger puppet.

Cuing With Disturbance

Say, *"I would like you to think about something from your life that might be happening now that is a bit upsetting for you or that makes you have mixed-up feelings just a little bit. Let me know when you have it."*

_____

_____

When the child has identified the situation, say the following:

Say, *"Now, tell me where you feel the mixed-up or upsetting feelings in your body."*

_____

_____

Say, *"Okay, now I would like to put the* _____ (state the name of the lotion the child chose) *next to your nose or you can put some lotion on your hands and smell the lotion from your hands and see what happens."*

_____

_____

Allow the child to stay in their Safe Place for about 60 seconds.

Say, *"How do you feel now?"*

_____

_____

If the child reports a positive difference then say the following:

Say, *"Okay, just notice or think about those* (repeat the positive emotions reported by the child) _____ *feelings and follow* _____ (the EMDR helper's name).*"*

_____

_____

Do 4 to 6 slow BLS with the finger puppet.

Self-Cuing With Disturbance

Say, *"Now, we are going to do this again but this time you are going to smell the lotion yourself and you are going to take your mind to your Safe or Happy Place by yourself. Ready?"*

_____

_____

Say, *"I would like you to think once again about that thing from your life that is a bit upsetting for you or that makes you have mixed-up feelings just a little bit. Let me know when you are thinking about it."*

_____

_____

Wait until the child tells you he is thinking about it.

Say, *"Now tell me where you feel the mixed-up or upsetting feelings in your body?"*

_____

_____

Say, *"Now, whenever you want, smell and use your* _____ (state the name of the lotion the child chose) *and see what happens."*

_____

_____

Allow enough time for the child to do it.

Say, *"How do you feel now?"*

_____

_____

If the child reports a positive difference then say the following:

Say, *"Okay, just notice or think about those* _____ (repeat the positive emotions reported by the child) *feelings and follow* _____ (the EMDR helper's name).*"*

Do 4 to 6 slow BLS with the finger puppet.

If the child reports negative emotions, check if the negative associations come from the Safe Place or the scent. Check for the appropriateness of the Safe Place. Also check if the child wants to pick a different scent.

Say, *"Do these mixed-up feelings come from the Safe Place or from _____ (state the name of the lotion or scent)?"*

_____

_____

If the scent is changed, go back to the Cue Scent step.

Practice

Say, *"Okay, if you want, you can decorate your container with any of the stickers that you like."*

Let the child decorate the container.

Say, *"You can take your _____ (state the name of the lotion). Whenever you feel down or bad or you have mixed-up feelings, you can use your _____ (state the name of the lotion) so it can help you remember your Safe or Happy Place and get the good feelings back."*

If the parents were not present in the session, invite the parents before the session ends.

Say, *"We can share this with mom and dad (or the caregiver) so they can help you remember to use your _____ (state the name of the lotion) and think about your Safe or Happy Place. Is that okay with you?"*

_____

_____

If the child does not want the parents to know about their Safe Place, gently explore the reason behind it. This could be diagnostic of problematic parent–child dynamics that need to be addressed in therapy.

If the child is in agreement about the parents' involvement, proceed to invite the parents into the session.

Say, *"_____ (name of child) would you like to tell your parents about your Safe or Happy Place and the lotion? Or, would you like me to tell them?"*

_____

_____

If the child wants you to talk to the parents:

Say, *"Today _____ (name of child) did such a great job. We did EMDR with good stuff for the first time. _____ (name of child) created a Safe or Happy Place. When ___ (name of child) thinks about this place, ____(he or she) has really good feelings. _____ (name of child) also picked a special lotion with a very special name ___ (say the name* of the lotion). *When _____ (name of child) smells the lotion, it helps ____ (him or her) remember ____ (his or her) Safe or Happy Place and all the good feelings. So, whenever ____ (name of child) feels down or bad or has mixed-up feelings ___ (name of child) can use ___ (his or her) _____ (state the name of the lotion) so it can help ____ (him or her) remember the Safe or Happy Place and get the good feelings back. So if _____ (name of child) forgets to use the _____ (state the name of the lotion), you can help ____ (him or her) remember by saying: ____ (name of child) I can see that you are having some mixed-up feelings now, let's use your special lotion together. Let's get your special container and put some lotion on your hands and let's think about your Safe or Happy Place so you can get your good feelings back."*

_____

_____

Say to the caregivers, *"You continue to encourage ____ (name of child) to stay in ___ (his or her) Safe or Happy Place until ____ (name of child) calms down or reports having positive feelings."*

Make sure that you have the scent chosen by the child available or ask the child to bring the lotion to every session. You can use the lotion if the child uses the stop signal during reprocessing or at the end of an incomplete session to cue to child to go to the Safe or Happy Place.

Using Olfactory Stimulation With Children to Cue Resource Development and Installation (RDI)

Ana Gomez

According to Korn and Leeds (2002), the main goal of developing and installing resources is to increase the client's capacity for self-regulation by enhancing their ability to access memory networks that contain adaptive and functional information. The RDI Protocol should only be considered based on specific criteria that suggest it is needed for the individual child. The following criteria may indicate the need for extending the Preparation Phase and considering using RDI with children:

- Child was unable to find a safe place or the safe places reported by the child became contaminated with negative associations or emotions.
- Caregivers and, as a result, the child do not have developmentally appropriate capacities for self-soothing.
- Child is in a chaotic and unstable home environment and is experiencing current crisis.
- Child is unable to tolerate emotional distress.
- Child exhibits poor impulse control and is unable to calm down once he becomes agitated.
- Child has developmental deficits due to insecure attachment history.
- Child lives with a caregiver with poor ability for self-regulation that maintains the child in a state of hypervigilance.

Remember that the purpose of doing RDI is to increase the child's ability to change state adaptively and tolerate disturbance so the child can prepare for trauma reprocessing. Traumatized children deserve to be treated with the full EMDR reprocessing protocol so that they can make a complete recovery.

Because of the short attention span in children, this protocol may take two sessions to complete. Often, school-aged children can do the protocol in one session. For younger children, installing one resource might be more appropriate, older children can often use up to three resources effectively. A simplified version with preschoolers may be necessary. The following RDI protocol has been adapted from the adult RDI protocol developed by Deborah Korn and Andrew Leeds (2002).

Using Olfactory Stimulation With Children to Cue Resource Development and Installation (RDI) Protocol Script

Say, *"I want you to meet my EMDR helpers. They help kids do EMDR."*

Say the name of each puppet and have the puppets introduce themselves.

Say, *"Hi, my name is Elizabeth. Hi, my name is Mario. Hi, my name is David, and my name is Robbie and we are THE EMDR HELPERS! We help kids move their eyes from side to side, please follow us."*

Have children follow the puppets with their eyes while you move the finger puppets back and forth. If the child cannot tolerate eye movement, have the puppets tap the child's hands or knees. Demonstrate the other forms of bilateral stimulation (BLS).

Say, *"Okay, how about if I have the puppets tap your hands? Would that be okay to try?"*

_____

_____

If the child can tolerate eye movement, say the following:

Say, *"Good job, now pick your favorite one. Which EMDR helper would you like to have today?"*

_____

_____

Say, *"We are going to practice EMDR with good stuff and you are going to move your eyes from side to side (or mention the BLS selected by the child)."*

_____

_____

Say, *"Which EMDR helper would you like to have today?"*

_____

_____

Step 1. Identify Needed Resource

Say, *"I would like you to think about something that is happening now at home or school that makes you have mixed-up feelings and thoughts or that makes you get in trouble. Tell me when you have it."*

_____

_____

Say, *"What are the good feelings and thoughts that you want to have when that upsetting thing happens?"*

_____

_____

Say, *"Do you want to feel good, strong, happy, safe, or_____ (state the positive feelings or thoughts the child might like to have)?"*

_____

_____

Say, *"What would you like to be able to do so you don't have mixed-up feelings or thoughts and you don't get in trouble?"*

_____

_____

Step 2. Exploring Types of Resources

Mastery

Say, *"Okay, let's think of a time when you felt _____ (repeat the positive feelings or thoughts the child would like to have, e.g., good, safe, etc.). When was that?"*

_____

_____

Or say, *"Think about times when you were able to _____ (repeat appropriate responses or behavior reported by the child in Step 1). What are they?"*

_____

_____

Relational

Say, *"Let's think of the people, animals, superheroes, or friends that help you have those _____ (repeat the positive feelings or thoughts the child would like to have) feelings or thoughts. Who are they?"*

_____

_____

Another way to say this is the following:

Say, *"Let's think about the people, helpers, friends, pets, superheroes that you look up to. Who are the ones that you really look up to?"*

_____

_____

Metaphors or Symbolic Figures

Say, *"Let's think of a story you read or a picture in your mind that helps you feel _____ (repeat the positive feelings or thoughts the child would like to have). What might that be?"*

_____

_____

With younger children and preschoolers it might be more appropriate to use only one resource. If the child identified more than three resources, ask the child for the three favorite resources, for example:

Resource 1: Playing with my dog. Amber makes me feel good.
Resource 2: Thinking about the time I had an A in math.
Resource 3: Imagining my grandmother next to me.

Follow Steps 3 through 5 with each resource.

Say, *"Think of all the good stuff that you told me about. What are the three things that you think help you the most with that problem you have?"*

   Resource 1: _____

   Resource 2: _____

   Resource 3: _____

Step 3. Installing Resources

Resource 1

Emotions and Sensations With Resource 1

Say, *"Now, I would like you to think about _____ (repeat Resource 1) and see how you feel. Where do you feel that feeling inside your body?"*

_____

_____

Checking Resource 1

Draw a scale on a piece of paper to make it more tangible and concrete for the child. For younger children use your hands.

Say, *"When you think about _____ (repeat the challenging or upsetting situation), how much does _____ (repeat Resource 1) help you feel good again on a scale of 1 to 7 where 1 means that it does not help you feel good at all and 7 means that it helps you feel good a lot?"*

   1   2   3   4   5   6   7

Say, *"Using your hands show me how much _____ (repeat Resource 1) helps you feel good."*

_____

_____

Now with your hands show the child as you say the following:

Say, *"This means nothing, this means a little, this means in the middle, and this means a lot. Please show me how you feel with your hands."*

_____

_____

If the child reports that the resource is not helpful, do not proceed to enhancing but move to the next resource. If this is the only resource selected by the child, then go back to Step 1 and assist the child in identifying a different resource.

If the child is having difficulty putting together the challenging situation and the resource because the child is too young or because of their mental age, use a simplified version of the protocol omitting Step 4. Checking the Resource and Step 5. Future Desired Outcome. Once again, for younger children or developmentally delayed children, developing and installing only one resource might be more appropriate.

Enhancing Resource 1

Say, *"Now I would like you to think about* _____ *(repeat Resource 1) and those* _____ *(repeat the feelings reported by the child) feelings that you feel in your body and follow* _____ *(say the name of the EMDR helper selected by the child)."*

_____

_____

Say, *"Go with that."*

_____

_____

Do 4 to 6 slow BLS.

Say, *"How are you feeling now?"*

_____

_____

Repeat several times if the emotions and positive associations to the resource continue to be enhanced. Stop if the child reports negative associations or disturbance arises.

Say, *"Okay, now I would like you to check all the lotions and scents that I have and pick one that helps you remember your* _____ *(repeat Resource 1) and the good feelings that you have when you think about* _____ *(repeat Resource 1). It can be any lotion or smell you want. You can put some in your container."*

_____

_____

Say, *"What would you like to name your special lotion?"*

_____

_____

Most children call it the "good feelings lotion" or my "good stuff lotion" or my "happy feelings lotion." If the child does not come up with a name you can make suggestions like the ones mentioned above.

Say, *"Many children call it the 'good feelings lotion' or my 'good stuff lotion' or my 'happy feelings lotion.' What would you like to call your lotion?"*

_____

_____

Be aware that the child will be putting a different scent for each resource selected in the same container. Make sure the child puts even portions of the lotion according to the number of resources.

Resource 2

Emotions and Sensations With Resource 2

Say, *"Now, I would like you to think about _____ (repeat Resource 2) and see how you feel. Where do you feel that feeling inside your body?"*

_____

_____

Checking Resource 2

Say, *"When you think about _____ (repeat the challenging or upsetting situation), how much does _____ (repeat Resource 2) help you feel good again on a scale of 1 to 7 where 1 means that it does not help you feel good at all and 7 means that it helps you feel good a lot?"*

   1   2   3   4   5   6   7

Say, *"Using your hands show me how much _____ (repeat Resource 2) helps you feel good."*

_____

_____

Now with your hands show the child as you say the following:

Say, *"This means nothing, this means a little, this means in the middle, and this means a lot. Please show me how you feel with your hands."*

_____

_____

If the child reports that the resource is not helpful do not proceed to enhancing but move to the next resource. If this is the only resource selected by the child, then go back to Step 1 and assist the child in identifying a different resource.

Enhancing Resource 2

Say, *"Now I would like you to think about _____ (repeat Resource 2) and those _____ (repeat the feelings reported by the child) feelings that you feel in your body and follow _____ (say the name of the EMDR helper selected by the child)."*

Do 4 to 6 slow BLS.

Say, *"Let's stop. How are you feeling now?"*

_____

_____

Repeat several times if the emotions and positive associations to the resource continue to be enhanced. Stop if the child reports negative associations or disturbance arises.

Say, *"Okay, now I would like you to check all the lotions and scents that I have and pick one that helps you remember your _____ (repeat Resource 2) and the good feelings that you have when you think about _____ (repeat Resource 2). It can be any lotion or smell you want. You can put some in your container."*

_____

_____

Resource 3

Emotions and Sensations With Resource 3

Say, *"Now, I would like you to think about _____ (repeat Resource 3) and see how you feel. Where do you feel that feeling inside your body?"*

_____

_____

Checking Resource 3

Draw a scale on a piece of paper to make it more tangible and concrete for the child. For younger children use your hands.

Say, *"When you think about _____ (repeat the challenging or upsetting situation), how much does _____ (repeat Resource 3) help you feel good again on a scale of 1 to 7, where 1 means that it does not help you feel good at all and 7 means that it helps you feel good a lot?"*

1   2   3   4   5   6   7

Say, *"Using your hands, show me how much _____ (repeat Resource 3) helps you feel good."*

_____

_____

Now with your hands show the child as you say the following:

Say, *"This means nothing, this means a little, this means in the middle, and this means a lot. Please show me how you feel with your hands."*

_____

_____

Enhancing Resource 3

Say, *"Okay, now I would like you to check all the lotions and scents that I have and pick one that helps you remember your _____ (repeat Resource 3) and the good feelings that you have when you think about _____ (repeat Resource 3). It can be any lotion or smell you want. You can put some in your container."*

_____

_____

Cue Scent

Say, *"You have done an amazing job, now you have a lot of good stuff in your container that helps you get those good feelings back when you need them. Right?"*

_____

_____

Say, *"Okay, we are going to mix the lotions, the good stuff, and the good feelings all together. Ready? Go!"*

_____

_____

Have the child mix the lotions.

Say, *"Now, I would like you to think about _____ (repeat Resources 1, 2, and 3) and the _____ (repeat the feelings identified by the child with Resources 1, 2, and 3) _____ feelings. Now, smell the lotion (have the child hold the container next to his nose with the lotion for the duration of the passes of BLS) and follow _____ (state the EMDR helper's name)."*

Do 4 to 6 slow BLS.
Repeat several times.
With younger children it is helpful to repeat out loud each of the resources as the child is doing BLS.

Self-Cuing

Say, *"Now I would like you to smell the lotion and see what happens."*

Allow the child to think about the resources for about 60 seconds.

Say, *"How do you feel now?"*

_____

_____

If the child reports positive emotions then say:

Say, *"Okay, just notice or think about those _____ (repeat the positive emotions reported by the child) feelings and follow _____ (the EMDR helper's name)."*

_____

_____

Do 4 to 6 slow BLS with the EMDR puppets.

Say, *"You have done an amazing job! Congratulations."*

_____

_____

Step 4. Future Desired Outcome

Say, "Okay, *I would like you to imagine* _____ (repeat what the child identified as upsetting in Step 1). *Imagine that this is happening tomorrow or in 2 days but this time you are helping yourself with your lotion and all the good stuff* _____ (repeat Resources 1, 2, and 3). *As you think about this, you can smell the lotion or put some on your hands and smell your hands. Ready?"*

_____

_____

Say, *"Think about this and tell me how you feel now and how much you are able to help yourself by using your lotion and all the good stuff?"*

_____

_____

If the child reports negative emotions or that the resources are not helpful, do not proceed to using BLS. Go back to Step 1 and assist the child in identifying different resources.

If the child reports positive associations and that the resources are helpful then proceed to the BLS.

Say, *"Okay, just notice or think about* _____ (repeat what the child identified as upsetting in Step 1). *Imagine that this is happening tomorrow or in 2 days. Remember that this time you are helping yourself by using your lotion and by thinking about all the good stuff* _____ (repeat Resources 1, 2, and 3). *You can also draw a picture of it if you want. As you think about this or as you look at your picture, you can smell the lotion or put some on your hands and smell your hands. Now follow* _____(the EMDR helper's name)."

Say, *"Now, remember whenever you have that problem that we practiced with today or whenever you start to feel bad or yucky you can smell your lotion so you can help yourself and you can get your good feelings back."*

_____

_____

Step 5: Practice

Say, *"Okay, if you want, you can decorate your container with any of the stickers that you like."*

Let the child decorate the container.

Say, *"You can take your* _____ (state the name of the lotion). *Whenever* _____ (repeat what the child identified as upsetting in Step 1) *happens or whenever you feel down or bad or you have mixed-up feelings, you can use your* _____ (state the name of the lotion) *so it can help you remember* _____ (repeat Resources 1, 2, and 3) *and get all the good feelings back."*

_____

_____

If the parents were not present in the session, invite the parents before the session ends.

If the child wants you to talk to the parents:

Say, *"Today* _____ (name of child) *did such a great job. We did EMDR with good stuff.* _____ (name of child) *came up with good stuff* _____ (he or she) *can use to feel good. When* _____ (name of child) *thinks about* _____ (repeat Resources 1, 2, and 3), _____ (he or she) *has really good feelings.* _____ (name of child) *also picked a special lotion with a very special name* _____ (say the name of the lotion). *When* _____ (name of child) *smells the lotion, it helps* _____ (him or her) *remember all the good stuff and to feel all the good feelings. So, whenever* _____ (name of child) *feels down or bad or has mixed-up feelings* _____ (he or she) *can use the* _____ (state the name of the lotion) *so it can help* _____ (him or her) *remember the good stuff and to get the good feelings back. So, if* _____ (name of child) *forgets to use the* _____ (state the name of the lotion), *you can help him or her remember by saying"*:

*"*_____(name of child), *I can see that you are having some mixed-up feelings now, let's use your special lotion together. Let's get your special container and put some lotion on your hands and let's think about* _____ (repeat Resources 1, 2, and 3) *so you can get your good feelings back."*

Say to the caregivers, *"You continue to encourage* _____ (name of child) *to think about* _____ (repeat Resources 1, 2, and 3) *until* _____ (name of child) *calms down or reports having positive feelings."*

_____

_____

Resource Connection for Children

Barbara Wizansky

The Resource Connection for Children is a search to support children in finding their own unique ways to feel the safety, confidence, and relief of making a solid connection with their therapists in the here and now of the therapeutic session. These are their principle supports as they enter and go through the EMDR processing. The term *Resource Connection*, as well as the idea of a continuation of resources threaded through the EMDR Standard Protocol, was first used by Brurit Laub (2001) in her work with adults.

The procedure is based on three principles:

1. Children do not access memories in as organized a manner as adults.
2. Children live and function in the present much more completely than do adults.
3. Children have a much more immediate and labile reaction to their present emotions compared to adults.

The Resource Connection Protocol Script Notes

Instead of asking the child to remember an event as we do with adults, the therapist's task is to be aware of the child's resources throughout the protocol. The therapist must not only question parents to be aware of this child's strengths but also observe closely the unique experience of the child in the here and now of the playroom. Observing this small segment of the child's life, the therapist watches for the appearance of the positive aspects of his being, such as joy, humor, or competence. The therapist then focuses and installs sensory, emotional, and cognitive aspects of this resource immediately with bilateral stimulation (BLS). These naturally occurring events may arise directly, as the child wins a game or they may arise indirectly, as in a body sensation or a body position. Examples might be the feeling of a cool breeze through the window on a hot day that leads to a feeling of comfort and well being, or the flexing of his muscles as he tells how strong or what a good helper he was when he lifted the living room rug.

The components of the Resource Connection for Children are the following:

- Identifying the resource.
- Emphasizing the sensory, the emotional, and the cognitive aspects of the resource experience.
- Instructing the child to either freeze and focus or exaggerate and focus on the resource.
- Bilateral stimulation to install the resource.

The Resource Connection for Children Script

Phase 1: History Taking

The parents are questioned closely, not only about the child's trauma and problem behaviors but also about his strengths, successes, and what makes him feel good. The therapist should be maximally aware of these resources when she begins to connect with the child. In addition to the questions usually asked about developmental and trauma history in Phase 1, it is important to begin the search for resources.

Say, *"Tell me what you like about your child. What makes _____ (him or her) unique?"*

_____

_____

Say, *"What do you see as ____ (his or her) strengths?"*

_____

_____

Say, *"What successes has ____ (he or she) had?"*

_____

_____

Say, *"What makes ___ (him or her) feel good?"*

_____

_____

Say, *"How do you calm ____ (him or her) when ___ (he or she) is upset?"*

_____

_____

Phase 2: Preparation

Preparation for EMDR is conducted as usual with an emphasis on establishing the therapeutic relationship and the child's feelings of safety. The most direct path, here, is through the child's own competencies and positive feelings about himself. Resource Connections can be elicited through direct positive questions. The resource is named together with the emotion and the body feelings.

Say, *"What do you do best?"*

_____

_____

Say, *"What is most fun for you?"*

_____

_____

Say, *"Whom do you like to be close to?"*

_____

_____

Say, *"Think about doing* _____ (state what the child likes to do) *and being with* _____ (state with whomever he likes to be close to). *How does that make you feel?"*

_____

_____

Say, *"Can you feel that in your body?"*

_____

_____

Say, *"Can you put your hand on the place where you feel it?"*

_____

_____

Say, *"Let's stop and think about that* _____ (state what he likes to do and with whom he likes to be close to) *and the good feeling it gives you in your body.*

So I guess you're a _____ (boy or girl) *who can* _____ (if possible, state the positive material that you have been given in the form of a resource, otherwise, simply repeat what he has described)."*

_____

_____

Use BLS to install the resource.

Say, *"I'm going to tap your knees with my wand* (or other BLS that has been agreed upon) *so that you can remember* _____ (state what he or she likes to do), *the good feeling and how good it feels in your body when you think about* _____ (if possible, state as a resource; otherwise, simply repeat what he likes to do)."*

_____

_____

The therapist can create a Resource Connection (RC) as the child plays or moves about the room. She does this by identifying the action as a resource and naming the feelings, sensations, and positive cognitions that go with it. The difference between the child and adult versions of RC is the element of the "Freeze" game. The therapist watches carefully. When the resource appears (i.e., the child shoots a basket, wins a game, stretches comfortably on the sofa), the therapist says the following:

Say, *"Freeze. You've just* _____ (state what resource the child has demonstrated). *You look like you* _____ (state how the child looks like he is feeling)."*

_____

_____

Say, *"Where do you feel that in your body?"*

_____

_____

Say, *"How do you feel now?"*

_____

_____

Say, *"What do you think of yourself now?"*

_____

_____

Say, *"So you're a ____ (boy or girl) who can _____ (if possible, state as
     a generalized resource, otherwise, state what he or she can do)."*

_____

_____

Install the resource with BLS.

Say, *"Think of ____ (state what he or she has done) and how it feels
     in your body and that you can _____ (state the action as
     a resource, if possible, otherwise, repeat the action) and follow my
     fingers (or whatever BLS you are using)."*

_____

_____

Note that the positive resource is installed either in the form of a description of
what he has done at that moment (i.e., "You can shoot baskets" or as a generalized
resource, "You're a guy who has good control of his hands and legs"). The positive resource is an intrinsic, personal resource, such as a competency or the ability
to have fun. It may, or may not be the positive cognition (PC), depending on the
problem to be processed.

Phase 3: Assessment

The Assessment Phase is carried out as usual. It is much easier for the child to
find both a negative cognition (if he is old enough) and a positive cognition for the
target he has chosen, if a number of resources have been collected and installed
during the Preparation Phase.

Negative Cognition (NC)

Say, *"What words best go with the picture that express your negative
     belief about yourself now?"*

_____

_____

Positive Cognition (PC)

Say, *"When you bring up that picture or incident, what would you like
     to believe about yourself now?"*

_____

_____

Validity of Cognition (VoC)

Say, *"When you think of the incident* (or picture) *how true do those words* ____ (clinician repeats the positive cognition) *feel to you now on a scale of 1 to 7, where 1 feels completely false and 7 feels completely true?"*

1	2	3	4	5	6	7
(completely false)				(completely true)		

Phase 4: Desensitization

Desensitization is carried out as usual with appropriate flexibility to suit the child's developmental age. Identifying resources, during this phase, may unlock stalled processing and strengthen the ability to continue. During the process when the resource is identified and installed, the therapist returns with the child to the initial target to allow the processing to continue.

The resource may appear during desensitization. It is often expressed as a body movement (i.e., the anger of a kicking foot or a hand that moves in a pushing away motion). First identify the action, then intensify the activity, and name the feelings and body sensations. The addition here is the exaggeration of the movement and its identification as a resource. The therapist watches carefully for any unique or expressive body movement. Focus on the movement and say the following:

Say, *"Can you do that again with* _____ (state what the child did)*?"*

_____

_____

Say, *"Can you do that harder? And harder?"*

_____

_____

Say, *"How does it make you feel when you do that?"*

_____

_____

Say, *"What is your hand or foot saying? What is your* _____ (state party of body) *saying?"*

_____

_____

Say, *"Where do you feel it in your body?"*

_____

_____

Say, *"What do you like about that?"*

_____

_____

Say, *"What does that show that you can do?"*

_____

_____

Say, *"What kind of a _____ (boy or girl) are you?"*

_____

_____

Say, *"Think about that while I tap your knees (or whatever BLS you are using, some children like to continue the movement during the installation)."*

_____

_____

Sounds and words may also express resources (i.e., jokes, giggles, yuck). Identify them as resources, intensify the words, and name the feelings and sensations that go with them.

Say, *"I hear that you know how to _____ (state the feeling the child knows how to display) and tell people how you feel _____ (state what child knows how to feel)."*

_____

_____

Say, *"Can you say _____ (state the action that expresses the resource), and _____ (state what he needs to do to exaggerate it)?"*

_____

_____

Say, *"How does that make you feel?"*

_____

_____

Say, *"How does it feel in your body?"*

_____

_____

Say, *"Think of all that while I _____ (state BLS)."*

_____

_____

Phase 5: Installation of the Positive Cognition

The installation of the PC is conducted as usual with the adaptations made for the child and his present developmental stage. Often, the identified resources and the PC match or complement each other (Laub, 2001). These congruencies should be noted.

Say, *"I see that your knowing or being _____ (the identified resource) can help you to know that _____ (state the PC)."*

_____

_____

The child can draw a resource picture and look at it as the PC is installed.

Say, *"Can you draw a picture of yourself* _____ *(state the resource)?"*

_____

_____

Say, *"Look at the picture as you think of* _____ *(state the PC)."*

For older children, say the following:

Say, *"How true does* _____ *(state the PC) feel to you now on a scale of 1 to 7, where 1 feels completely false and 7 feels completely true?"*

1	2	3	4	5	6	7
(completely false)				(completely true)		

For younger children say, *"Go with that."*
Do BLS.

Say, *"What do you notice now?"*

_____

_____

Continue as usual until the PC is maximally strengthened.

Phase 6: Body Scan

The Body Scan is conducted as usual.

Say, *"Close your eyes and keep in mind the original memory and the _____ (repeat the selected PC). Now bring your attention to the different parts of your body, starting with your head and working downward. Any place you find any tension, tightness, or unusual sensation, tell me."*

_____

_____

If any sensation is reported, say the following:

Say, *"Go with that."*

_____

_____

Do BLS.
If a positive or comfortable sensation is reported, do BLS to strengthen the positive feeling.

Say, *"Go with that."*

_____

_____

Do BLS.
If a sensation or discomfort is reported, reprocess until discomfort subsides and then repeat the Body Scan procedures.

Say, *"Go with that."*

Phase 7: Closure

The child may choose a resource to take home with him. Often, the closing minutes are devoted to play where the hunt for resources can continue. During the closing phase, resources from the day's session may be written down or drawn and placed in a special box decorated for that purpose.

Say, *"If you like, you can choose a resource to take home with you. Which one(s) would you like to choose?"*

_____

_____

Say, *"We can write down or draw your resources and place them in your special box."*

_____

_____

Phase 8: Reevaluation

Reevaluation is conducted as usual with the additional emphasis on how and what resources have appeared during the week.

Say, *"What have you noticed over the past week?"*

_____

_____

Say, *"Did you use the resources from your special box during the week?"*

_____

_____

Say, *"How were they helpful to you this week?"*

_____

_____

Say, *"Did you find any new resources this week?"*

_____

_____

CLINICAL CASE EXAMPLES

Case 1

Roie is afraid of being blown up. He is a 9-year-old boy who is terrified of terrorist attacks. His anxiety was intense and had generalized to many facets of his life. He didn't want to go to school by himself or to visit friends. His fear often flung him into dissociative reactions. After the Preparation Phase during which he established his room at home as a safe place, he tried hard to target a picture representing his fear that he might be blown up. He quickly became so anxious that he stopped the conversation to move nervously around the room. He finally began to shoot darts. He was good at it and his involvement in the game allowed him to move away from his fear. The therapist noticed his pride, joy, and excitement when he hit a high number. His facial expression, his glad cry, "Yesh!" (in Hebrew the equivalent of "Great!"), and his open body position. She was looking at Roie's unique resources, such as good coordination, the ability to succeed in age-appropriate games, and an openness to fun. This was certainly a frightened, quivering boy, but one who had within him reserves of competency and joy that could allow him to cope more comfortably with his fears.

Identifying the Resource and Naming the Feelings, Sensations, and Thoughts

When he hit a high number and jumped up and down joyfully, the therapist said, "Freeze!" and asked him to stand still as a statue. The dialogue went as follows:

Therapist:	"Where do you feel the 'Yesh!' in your body?"
Roie:	"In my hands and my feet."
Therapist:	"What feelings do you have?"
Roie:	"Happy!"
Therapist:	"It sounds like you're a boy who can make his hands and feet do what he wants. It sounds like you like to win."
Therapist:	"What do you think of yourself now?"
Roie:	"I'm pretty good at this. I can do stuff. This is fun."

Install the Resource

Therapist:	"Think of all those feelings in your body and the fun and how you're pretty good at making your hands and feet do what they want, and look at my fingers."

The therapist continued watching his game and calling "Freeze!" when he succeeded.

By the time he had hit the 100 mark on the target five times and had undergone five installations of his feelings of competency and pleasure, he was ready to continue with the protocol and process to a positive and appropriate cognition.

Roie:	"Eema (mother) doesn't let me go to dangerous places. I can feel safe."

Case 2

Lidor, age 10, had been attacked viciously by a dog. Since the attack, he had changed from a sturdy, assertive child to a boy who clung to his mother and was afraid to leave the house by himself. The processing was looping around the picture of the "dog's teeth" and "nothing." He was able to continue the processing only after he had connected to feelings of direct anger, power, and competency.

Identifying the Resource and Naming the Feelings, Sensations, and Thoughts

The therapist noticed that one of his feet was moving back and forth against the chair leg. She suggested that he let his foot kick the chair leg as hard as he could, harder and harder.

Therapist: "How does your leg feel when it kicks?"

Lidor: "Strong."

Therapist: "How does your body feel?"

Lidor: "Kind of mad. Now, really mad. I can kick hard. I got a goal in football."

Therapist: "I see that you're a strong boy who knows how to be angry."

Install the Resource

Therapist: "Think of all those things and follow my fingers."

Lidor sat straighter in his chair and continued the processing through his anger at the dog and the stupid kid who let the dog off the leash to a resolution where he could talk about carrying a stick when he went out. Lidor also said the following:

Lidor: "I really like dogs. Most dogs are nice."

His PC was: "I can usually manage dogs."

This procedure is designed to help the child consciously connect to his strengths and resources as an integral part of the EMDR protocol. An emphasis on resources can enable even a very frightened child to begin processing within a single session. Alternatively one can collect the child's resources as they appear through a number of sessions and store them in a special box to take out when needed. As we help the child to have a felt access to his own personal resources, we are helping him deal more effectively with processing trauma within the EMDR setting, and will hopefully use this connection to enable continued development and enjoyment of day-to-day life in spite of whatever difficulties and uncertainties may surround him.

The Absorption Technique for Children

Dagmar Eckers

The Absorption Technique for Children Script Notes

The Absorption Technique for Children is a protocol that was derived from the work of Arne Hofmann (2003) who based his work on an adaptation of "The Wedging Technique" (Kiessling, 2009). The Absorption Technique for Children is a resource technique that supports children in creating resources for present issues and future challenges such as dealing with a difficult teacher or handling a disagreement with a classmate and so forth. This is accomplished by asking the child to imagine 3 strengths or skills that could help them during their problem or issue to reduce their negative feelings. When a child focuses on a specific strength or skill it enables him to create a wedge of safety or control that can assist him when he has to deal with difficult situations in the future. For young children, usually one strength or skill is used for simplicity. In this author's experience, if a child is of school age or an adolescent, eye movements work very well. When a child is 6 years old or younger, or does not like eye movements, tapping on the back of the hands is more helpful.

Basically, the Absorption Technique for Children is used for present challenges and future concerns. This author uses Resource Installation for stressful situations first.

The Absorption Technique for Children Script

Define a present challenge or future concern that the child would like to work on.

> Say, *"What is the present challenge or future worry you would like to work on today?"*

_____

_____

Picture

> Say, *"What picture represents the entire incident?"*

_____

_____

Subjective Units of Disturbance (SUD)

> Say, *"On a scale of 0 to 10, where 0 is no disturbance or neutral and 10 is the highest disturbance you can imagine, how disturbing does it feel now to think of the problem?"*

1	2	3	4	5	6	7	8	9	10
(no disturbance)									(most disturbance)

Skill or Strength

> Say, *"What skills, strengths, or abilities do you think would help you handle this situation in a better way?"*

Resource 1: _____

Resource 2: _____

Resource 3: _____

For younger children, give them 3 or 4 abilities as choices.

> Say, *"Would it be helpful to be brave, relaxed, self-confident, or anything else?"*

_____

_____

First Ability

> Say, *"Can you think of a situation in the last 2 months or before when you were or felt _____ (state the skill, strength, or ability the child chose) a bit already? How would you describe the situation?"*

_____

_____

Image

> Say, *"If you think of the situation what do you get as a picture?"*

_____

_____

For younger children, you can ask them to draw a picture to concretize the experience.

Say, *"Please draw a picture of this good experience."*

_____

_____

Feelings and Sensation

Say, *"That is a really nice picture! What a wonderful experience that must have been! When you think of it now does it feel good? Where in your body do you have a good feeling thinking about it now?"*

_____

_____

Enhance

Say, *"Now, please think of the picture* (or with younger children have them look at the drawing) *and notice the feeling you have in your body. If you want, you can place your hand there. Think of it and follow my fingers with your eyes."*

_____

_____

Or say, *"Think of it and notice if the feeling changes while I tap on your hands."*

_____

_____

Use 5 to 7 slow eye movements or 7 to 10 taps on the back of the hands of the child.

Say, *"How do you feel now?"*

_____

_____

The goal of this exercise is that the child feels better. If he feels no difference, you can repeat the set for a longer period of time. If you started with four sets and the child does not notice any positive change in his body, try six or seven slow eye movements or taps.

If he feels worse, try another situation with the same ability and see if the results are positive. The goal is to find a situation where the child is not ambivalent or connected to negative feelings.

Say, *"Think of another time when you felt _____* (state the skill, ability, or attribute the child is working on).*"*

_____

_____

Say, *"How would you describe the situation?"*

_____

_____

Second Ability

Say, *"Can you think of a situation in the last 2 months or before when you were or felt _____ (state the second skill, strength, or ability the child chose) a bit already? How would you describe the situation?"*

_____

_____

Image

Say, *"If you think of the situation what do you get as a picture?"*

_____

_____

For younger children, you can ask them to draw a picture to concretize the experience.

Say, *"Please draw a picture of this good experience."*

_____

_____

Feelings and Sensation

Say, *"That is a really nice picture! What a wonderful experience that must have been! When you think of it now does it feel good? Where in your body do you have a good feeling thinking about it now?"*

_____

_____

Enhance

Say, *"Now, please think of the picture (or with younger children have them look at the drawing) and notice the feeling you have in your body. If you want, you can place your hand there. Think of it and follow my fingers with your eyes."*

_____

_____

Or say, *"Think of it and notice if the feeling changes while I tap on your hands."*

_____

_____

Use 5 to 7 slow eye movements or 7 to 10 taps on the back of the hands of the child.

Say, *"How do you feel now?"*

_____

_____

The goal of this exercise is that the child feels better. If he feels no difference, you can repeat the set for a longer period of time. If you started with four sets and the child does not notice any positive change in his body, try six or seven slow eye movements or taps.

If he feels worse, try another situation with the same ability and see if the results are positive. The goal is to find a situation where the child is not ambivalent or connected to negative feelings.

Third Ability

Say, *"Can you think of a situation in the last 2 months or before when you were or felt _____ (state the third skill, strength, or ability the child chose) a bit already? How would you describe the situation?"*

_____

_____

Image

Say, *"If you think of the situation what do you get as a picture?"*

_____

_____

For younger children, you can ask them to draw a picture to concretize the experience.

Say, *"Please draw a picture of this good experience."*

_____

_____

Feelings and Sensation

Say, *"That is a really nice picture! What a wonderful experience that must have been! When you think of it now does it feel good? Where in your body do you have a good feeling thinking about it now?"*

_____

_____

Enhance

Say, *"Now, please think of the picture (or with younger children have them look at the drawing) and notice the feeling you have in your body. If you want, you can place your hand there. Think of it and follow my fingers with your eyes."*

_____

_____

Or say, *"Think of it and notice if the feeling changes while I tap on your hands."*

_____

_____

Use 5 to 7 slow eye movements or 7 to 10 taps on the back of the hands of the child.

Say, *"How do you feel now?"*

_____

_____

The goal of this exercise is that the child feels better. If he feels no difference, you can repeat the set for a longer period of time. If you started with four sets and the child does not notice any positive change in his body, try six or seven slow eye movements or taps.

If he feels worse, try another situation with the same ability and see if the results are positive. The goal is to find a situation where the child is not ambivalent or connected to negative feelings

When the child has installed three abilities, ask the child to think about the original problem.

Subjective Units of Disturbance (SUD)

Say, *"On a scale of 0 to 10, where 0 is no disturbance or neutral and 10 is the highest disturbance you can imagine, how disturbing does it feel now?"*

1   2   3   4   5   6   7   8   9   10
(no disturbance)   (most disturbance)

Say, *"You can use this good feeling any time you are dealing with _____ (state what the problem is). Sometimes, it even feels better when you put your hand on the place in your body where you can feel your good feeling."*

_____

_____

If the child is able to work with two or three abilities, it is possible to connect each ability with a resourceful situation from the past and install it with slow bilateral stimulation (BLS).

Getting the Resources Together

Say, *"Think of the three abilities together and where you felt them in your body. Just nod if you are in contact with all three body feelings."*

_____

_____

Only use the successfully installed resources.
If the client nods, stimulate with a short set of BLS.

Say, *"Go with that."*

_____

_____

Check for the Issue

Say, *"As you are feeling your resources, take a look back at the issue that troubles you. How stressful is that to you on a scale of 0 to 10, where 0 is no disturbance or neutral and 10 is the highest disturbance you can imagine, how disturbing does it feel now?"*

0	1	2	3	4	5	6	7	8	9	10
(no stress)										(worst stress)

When the child returns, it is essential to ask how he was able to handle the challenge or future concern (e.g., dealing with a difficult teacher). That means if the child gets along with the teacher only a bit better after the Absorption Technique—but not well—it is possible to use EMDR. Using the Absorption Technique for Children before the EMDR session creates an excellent effect and motivates the child to work on the issue with EMDR after the Absorption Technique is done. Through observation, after the work on this skill, the SUD in Phase 3 is usually much lower than without the support of the Absorption Technique.

In this author's experience, the Absorption Technique, and the Constant Installation of Present Orientation and Safety (CIPOS) Technique (see chapter 6), are excellent ways to encourage children to work with EMDR step-by-step even if they are not prepared to work with the worst issue in the beginning.

The Method of Constant Installation of Present Orientation and Safety (CIPOS) for Children

Dagmar Eckers

The fundamental idea of the Method of Constant Installation of Present Orientation and Safety (CIPOS) is to reinforce a client's current sense of security and stability using bilateral stimulation. Jim Knipe constructed CIPOS (see chapter 18) for adults. For this protocol, CIPOS has been adapted to work with children. Children often have more problems than adults when confronted with traumatic memories; they try to avoid them at all costs.

CIPOS for Children Script Notes

The CIPOS method is helpful in assisting children to overcome their fear of their traumatic memories. With the help of a strong, basic feeling of security and stability, the child focuses on the memory of a traumatic experience for a defined and very controlled period of time. This can be done by imagery—depending on the age of the child—or with the help of pictures the child has drawn. The imagery or picture depends on the preference of the child. Drawing and active movement is helpful when working with younger children and for the older, active child as well.

If the child can tolerate working with the worst moment, it is helpful to start there. If the child is consciously avoiding the traumatic image, he will often react, for instance, by refusing to draw a picture of the worst moment. If this occurs, it is helpful to focus on a less distressing issue such as "a struggle with a friend" instead of "the house burned down." The child will feel more comfortable, confident, and motivated in his ability to do EMDR if he can first work with the less distressing theme than the more traumatic one.

If the child is in danger of slipping into an altered or dissociative state when the traumatic image is viewed, choose a very small issue or a problem in the future concerning his daily life (e.g., a difficult exam at school or confrontation with neighbor's dog). If the child is familiar with CIPOS, he will be more able to decide on what issue he will work on next time. Jim Knipe uses the Back of the Head Scale (chapter 18) to assess the patient's degree of present orientation in the session, however, for children, in this author's experience, this is not necessary as children are much more present than adults, especially when they play and move their bodies. Even children who tend to dissociate their emotions or sensations are really able to work with the CIPOS technique on the condition that they are well informed, have a feeling of control, and a strong, good body feeling in that moment.

The child can be given a description of the CIPOS steps after stabilization is established and before trauma work begins. Then, these steps can be used during the actual trauma work to insure the child keeps an orientation to the safe present. If children are having difficulty with CIPOS, it is a signal that more stabilization is needed and it is necessary to understand what possible issues prevent them from feeling safe enough to work with any small distress.

Alternatives to catching the ball in the CIPOS Protocol for Children could be using the Safe Place to interrupt the process, or drawing a Safe Place and using the picture. If the exercise is still too threatening, the child can use a toy or stuffed animal to answer the questions asked instead of answering directly. Using the alternatives depends on the needs of the child as explained below. The alternative protocols are included toward the end of the chapter.

The Method of Constant Installation of Present Orientation and Safety (CIPOS) for Children Script

Say, *"When you think of _____ (state the problem), what is the worst moment for you now?"*

_____

_____

Let the child paint a picture of the traumatic situation because, with painting, the child focuses on the action of painting instead of being emotionally agitated.

Say, *"Could you draw or paint a picture of what this bad moment is like for you now?"*

_____

_____

Say, *"Okay, now that you have drawn your picture please turn the picture face down."*

_____

_____

With children, it is helpful to not ask for feelings and sensations directly after they have completed their drawing. The idea is to sever the connection with the picture then have them connect with a good feeling in the body such as playing ball. After they have experienced a good feeling, move on to working with the picture.

Say, *"Great, can you catch this ball* (or do some activity that requires the child to react physically and is fun)*?"*

_____

_____

After some ball catching, say the following:

Say, *"How are you now? Do you feel good in your whole body? Where in the body do you have a good feeling?"*

_____

_____

When the child has a good feeling in their body, install the feeling with bilateral stimulation (BLS), either slow short sets of eye movements or tapping.

Say, *"Great, go with that."*

_____

_____

As it gets stronger, say the following:

Say, *"Go with that."*

_____

_____

Say, *"In a moment, I am going to turn your drawing over. How long do you think you can look at it? If you like, we could look at it for a short time. It will be for about the time it takes me to count backward from four to zero. Would you be willing to try this?"*

_____

_____

Say, *"Okay, afterward I will turn it over again. Would you like to tell me to 'Start!' to let me know when I should turn the drawing around?"*

_____

_____

Make sure to count backward audibly in seconds and not any more than 4 seconds. Then, turn the drawing down again at zero, so that the child can no longer see the drawing.

Say, *"Okay, when you are ready let me know by saying 'Start'!"*

_____

_____

Say, *"Four, three, two, one, zero."*

_____

_____

Turn the drawing over.

Say, *"You have done that very well! How was it to look at the picture?"*

_____

_____

It is always helpful to praise the child for his effort. Praise is even more important in work with children than in work with adults.

Say, *"Was it difficult?"*

_____

_____

Say, *"Okay, let's play with the ball to have fun and to have that wonderful feeling in your body again!"*

_____

_____

After some ball catching, say the following:

Say, *"How do you feel?"*

_____

_____

Install the good feeling with one or two slow sets of eye movements or taps.

Say, *"Go with that."*

_____

_____

Say, *"Okay, can you look at the picture a second time while I count from four to zero?"*

_____

_____

Say, *"That is great that you can look at the picture again. Are you ready to tell me when to 'Start'?"*

_____

_____

Say, *"Four, three, two, one, zero. How is it now? Did it feel like the first time or did it change?"*

_____

_____

If the child is willing to do it again, repeat the sequence of ball catching, turning the drawing over, and counting. It is important to close the session with positive body feelings.

Alternatives

There are several alternatives to playing with the ball to help create positive body feelings. You can suggest one of the following:

Installation

Think of the Safe Place before and after looking at the picture and install the positive and safe body feelings connected to the Safe Place.

Say, *"Let's start by creating a Safe Place."*

_____

_____

Note: The Safe Place is best installed *earlier* in treatment before the CIPOS technique is introduced.

Say, *"What would be the best place in the whole world that you can imagine? It could be an imaginary place or a place that already exists. If that place already exists, you could change it in your imagination to be just the way that you want it."*

_____

_____

In this way, the *real* place then has the quality of an imaginary place.

Then say, *"Now that you have described your Safe Place, what else would you add to it to make it just the way that you want it? Some children add colors, or make sure the weather is just the way they like it, while others include wonderful smells, special animals, or even fairies. What would you like to include in your Safe Place?"*

_____

_____

Say, *"Now that you have your Safe Place, what would you like to name it? Some children call it 'my wonderful place,' others call it 'my fairy room,' and some others call it 'my hiding place.' What would you like to call your place so that you know it is your special place?"*

_____

_____

Say, *"Now when you think of _____ (state the child's name for the Safe Place), what does it feel like in your body?"*

_____

_____

Say, *"Please tell me where you feel your good feeling(s)."*

_____

_____

Say, *"If you want, you can place your hand there to feel how good it feels."*

_____

_____

Then say, *"Now think of your Safe Place and feel the nice feeling in your body. Can you get both of them together?"*

_____

_____

Say, *"Great, now follow my fingers and you can use your imagination to continue to make _____ (state the child's name of the Safe Place) exactly like you want it."*

_____

_____

Continue substituting the Safe Place for playing with the ball in the script.

Draw a Picture of the Safe Place

Have the child draw a picture of the Safe Place instead of just thinking of it. In this way he can have a concrete image to look at it while he calms down. Then install the positive body feelings when the child is ready. Use the short time sequence explained previously to look at the bad picture.

Say, *"Please draw a picture of your Safe Place."*

_____

_____

When the child completes the drawing, say the following:

Say, *"Great! When you look at your wonderful drawing does it feel good in your body? Where in your body do you feel that now?"*

_____

_____

Say, *"If you want, you can place your hand there to feel how good it feels."*

_____

_____

Then say, *"Now think of your Safe Place and feel the nice feeling in your body. Can you get both of them together?"*

_____

_____

Say, *"Great, now follow my fingers and go with that."*

_____

_____

Do BLS.

Say, *"What do you notice now?"*

_____

_____

Continue as above, substituting looking at the picture of the Safe Place for playing with the ball in the script.

Use the first CIPOS script above. Instead of using, *"Great, can you catch this ball (or do some activity that requires the child to react physically and is fun)?"* start with the following:

Say, *"Great, can you look at the Safe Place?"*

_____

_____

Then continue with the script.

Toy or Stuffed Animal

Ask the child to bring a toy or stuffed animal so that the toy can look at the picture and we can ask the toy instead of the child what it felt and if the feeling changed the second or third time that it looked at the picture. This is a controlled form of dissociation; by asking the toy pet instead of the child, the child does not have to talk about his negative feelings when looking at the picture. The installation of the Safe Place and the good sensation in the body is done with the child. Instead of saying, *"In a moment, I am going to turn your drawing over. How long do you think you can look at it? If you like, we could look at it for a short time. It will be for about the time it takes me to count backward from four to zero. Would you be willing to try this?"* in the above script for CIPOS:

Say, *"In a moment, I am going to turn your drawing over. Can you have your _____* (state the name of the stuffed animal) *look at the picture?"*
How long do you think _____ (state the name of the stuffed animal) *can look at it? If you like, _____* (state the name of the stuffed animal) *could look at it for a short time. It will be for about the time it takes me to count backward from four to zero. Would _____* (state the name of the stuffed animal) *be willing to try this?"*

_____

_____

Then continue with the CIPOS script substituting the name of the stuffed animal for the child.

For some children, CIPOS is very helpful to minimize their fear of future stress incidents: with CIPOS the child can focus on the next difficult exam at school or a fearful confrontation with the neighbor's dog, for example. If the child can cope with his affect better with the help of CIPOS, he will be eager to work with us in EMDR next time. The CIPOS method can motivate the child to tolerate stressful memories or fear of the future and can be a very helpful bridge between resource work and trauma work.

Footsteps Through the Maze

Barbara Wizansky

The Maze, as a metaphor for a place where problems live and are solved, was developed out of the necessity of working with children who were too anxious, embarrassed, or afraid to experience the uncomfortable feelings around their problem areas. Such children often present as actively oppositional or sullenly silent. It was necessary to find a distancing technique that was both nonthreatening and interesting to gradually establish communication between therapist and child about issues that cause them discomfort.

The main purpose of the maze is to gradually sensitize the child to the possibility of exploring the defended inner space where unpleasant, scary emotions dwell. The maze is a concept with which most children are acquainted. They have experienced both feelings of frustration and competence as they followed the convoluted lines with their pencils in workbooks. Many have raced through them in amusement parks, shrieking at the scariness connected with going in and losing oneself, and the fun at finding the way out. This protocol serves as a distancing game to gradually sensitize the child to the fact that he is capable of going through a process within himself (the space symbolized by the maze) where he may meet uncomfortable feelings but also good ones. He is responsible for finding the path to the exit. Because the footsteps are his, he always has maximum control of the internal process and the experience of dual attention.

The elements of the protocol include the following:

1. *The Maze.* The child draws a maze of his choice. Each maze has an entrance and an exit.
2. *Drawings.* The child creates a drawing of the problem, which he places at the entrance to the maze. At the end of the process, he creates an exit drawing. If he decides to share his experience inside the maze, he may create interim drawings or, alternatively, write or dictate words. Many children, especially those labeled with various oppositional behavioral difficulties, need time before they can share their inner world. Pressing them too soon for associations or cognitions can break communication. The maze allows him to face his discomfort silently with maximum control until he is ready to share.
3. *The Footsteps.* The child taps his knees as he looks at the problem drawing and at the maze. This provides an experience of bilateral stimulation (BLS)

and dual attention. He continues "walking" until he gets to the drawing that he wants to create and place at the exit.

The child may traverse many of these problem mazes silently, from entrance to exit, as he experiences facing the emotional content of his inner space and finding the solutions. Often, the child works only with mazes during a treatment, but, more often, they serve as part of the preparation for processing with the Standard EMDR Protocol in the usual way.

Footsteps Through the Maze Protocol Script

Step 1. The Child Is Asked to Draw His Own Maze—Drawing 1

Say, *"Do you know what a maze is? Have you ever been inside one?"* (Allow the child to tell you about his experience with mazes at amusement parks, etc.)

_____

_____

Say, *"Could you draw me a maze?"*

_____

_____

If the child doesn't want to draw, say the following:

Say, *"If you tell me which way to move the pencil, I'll draw your maze just the way you want it."*

_____

_____

Possible discussion issues that encourage communication are the following:

Say, *"Everyone has their own maze. This one is yours. It is often hard to find the right path out but every maze has an exit. But sometimes it is a worry to be inside, sometimes it makes us mad, and other times you may think that there is a monster inside.*

Sometimes we feel like 'big shots' and are sure that we'll have no trouble getting out. Other times we feel upset when we can't find our way but there is always a way out."

Child and therapist together identify points of entrance and exit.

Say, *"Let's find all the ways that we can enter and all the ways we can exit."*

_____

_____

Step 2. The Maze Is Like a Big Mixed-Up Problem

Say, *"A maze is kind of like a problem. When you have a problem, it's really hard to find the way out. Sometimes you do all the wrong things, go in all the wrong directions—and you're still inside."*

The therapist can point out the paths that lead nowhere with the eraser end of her pencil.

Say, *"Every kid's maze looks different because every kid's problem is different.*

Sometimes kids don't know they are inside a problem maze. They just feel lost and kind of scared. The therapist's job is to help them find the way out. There's always a way out of a maze, even if it's hard to find."

_____

_____

The therapist and the child talk about possible problems that could lead a kid into a maze.

Say, *"What kind of problems could lead a child into a maze?"*

_____

_____

Then think of examples. Start with examples that are removed from the child's own experience.

Say, *"I knew a kid whose friend told him to take some stuff from a drugstore without paying. He felt terrible, but his friend thought it was cool and they started doing it everyday. Before he knew it, that kid was right inside a problem maze. He was scared he'd get caught and go to jail. He wanted to stop but he didn't want his friend to think he was scared. He felt bad that he was lying to his mom but he didn't know how to get out."*

If necessary give one more example also removed from the child's experience.

Then say, *"Can you think of one?"*

_____

_____

Say, *"Great, what is it?"*

_____

_____

If the child has trouble say the following:

Say, *"What about a kid who wets his pants or a kid who everybody picks on?"*

_____

_____

Usually the child gradually cites examples that bring him closer to his own problem.

Step 3. Drawing the Problem—Drawing 2

If the child has described his own problem in step 2, say the following:

Say, *"Maybe we can find the way out of that maze today. Could you draw a picture of that problem or write words to describe it for me?"*

_____

_____

If the child has not yet mentioned his own difficulty the therapist can say the following:

Say, *"I'm going to show you a great way for getting out of problem mazes. If you would like, you could draw what is bothering you right now. You can draw whatever makes you the most _____ (state appropriate affect or emotion)."*

_____

_____

If the child has trouble, use what you know about the child. Pick a minor difficulty and say the following:

Say, *"Some children draw about the fact that one of their parent's made them come to therapy, or that the therapist talks too much, or they draw a bad dream, or not getting a toy that they want. It can be whatever is bothering you right now."*

_____

_____

Problems suggested should be his and not the parents' presenting problem.

Step 4. The Path Through the Maze

Say, *"Let's put this drawing at the entrance to your maze. Now we've gone right inside and we have to find the way out."*

The therapist and child again identify the exit.

Say, *"Where is the exit in your maze?"*

_____

_____

Say, *"I wonder how we can get there. At the exit there's usually a different drawing. I wonder if the problem would feel different if we got there. What do you think?"*

_____

_____

Say, *"Nobody would know how to get to the exit. That's why it's a maze. If we go inside, usually we can let our brain and our footsteps take us to the exit."*

Step 5. Footsteps Through the Maze

Say, *"This is how we do it. Look at your problem drawing at the entrance and then you can drum with your fingers on alternate knees like this. These are the footsteps that will take you on the right path through the maze. Is that ok with you?"*

_____

_____

Say, *"When you get a new drawing or new words in your head, please stop and draw or write."*

_____

_____

Some children will drum on their knees and draw several pictures on their path. Others will draw only one more picture to show that they are coming out of the maze.

Step 6. The Solution—Drawing 3

When the child draws his last picture, say the following:

Say, *"Is this the drawing that you want to put at the exit?"*

_____

_____

Note: It is important to accept whatever exit drawing the child creates. Discussion points:

Say, *"Does the problem feel better here at the exit?"*

_____

_____

Say, *"Are you outside of the maze now?"*

_____

_____

Say, *"What makes it feel better?"*

_____

_____

At this point, the therapist can elicit and install a positive cognition that suits the solution drawing.

Say, *"Now that you have drawn your picture, what words go best with it?"*

_____

_____

Say, *"While you look at your drawing and think of the good words that go with it, you can drum with your fingers on alternate knees like we did before."*

_____

_____

The child has now had an experience of safe introspection. He has learned that he can cope with the fear of experiencing his own scary or embarrassing feelings. He has also learned that when he enters his inner psychological space he may also find resources that help him to feel better.

CLINICAL EXAMPLE

Ron, 8 years old, suffers with Encopresis since his parents' stormy divorce. He was furious with his mother for telling him and refused to talk about his problem. Attempts to externalize the Encopresis or draw it brought silence and a stony face.

Step 1: He was relieved when I moved on to ask him if he had ever been in a maze. He told me about his experience in an amusement park, how his brother was scared inside the maze, but he had been brave and planned different strategies to get them out. We talked about how great it felt to find the exit.

Step 2: I introduced the fact that being in the middle of a maze is kind of like being in the middle of a problem and how interesting it is that every kid draws a different maze. I gave examples of problems far from Ron's experience. We talked about a boy who had trouble learning to read (Ron is an excellent reader). He told me about a boy who was afraid of dogs (Ron loves animals). Ron was now participating fully in the conversation and pointing with his hand to the drawing of the maze as he described the problems. I brought the example of a boy who was being hit by some other children. He told me that no one would dare hit him, but there were kids who said mean things to him.

Step 3: I told him that I would show him an interesting game to play with the maze. Could he draw a picture of anything that bothered him so we could put it at the entrance to the maze? Silently, he drew a stick figure sitting in a class at school with a sad look on his face. The teacher was pointing at him. He wrote in a bubble above her head, "Ron, do you have a problem?"

Step 4: We placed his drawing at the entrance to the maze that he had drawn in step 1 and tried to trace the path through to the exit together. I explained that the exit was the place where the problem would feel different and there would be a different drawing or words.

Step 5: I showed him how to "walk" through the maze by tapping his knees. Ron was relaxed as he tapped thoughtfully, then stopped and wrote, "No, I don't have a problem" and placed the small note along the path that he had chosen. He continued tapping, then stopped and wrote: "Phew. It stinks in here" inside of a bubble. He placed this farther along the path and continued tapping. When he stopped again he drew himself leaving the class and going home. This was the drawing that he placed at the exit to the maze. He told me that his mom would let him stay home. His positive statement was "I don't have to stay there." Since we prefer to turn the negative cognition into a true positive cognition, we say: "If you don't have to stay there, what does that say about you?" We're encouraging a positive statement about his ability to choose, such as "I can decide to go home."

His solution that his mother would let him stay home was neither realistic not would it solve the basic problem, but his experience in my presence of quietly allowing himself to think about the fact that he was dirtying his pants and being teased was a valuable one. Inside of that scary problem maze, he had found not only Ron sitting embarrassed in class smelling badly, but also Ron who had the power to walk away from the embarrassment and even remember the resource that was his mother. Ron's experience inside the maze showed him that he could face thinking about the Encopresis and allowing it to come into our conversation. In subsequent sessions, he successfully processed aspects of his toilet problem and was able to face, with the Standard EMDR Protocol, his anger and fear around events connected to his parents' divorce.

This 5-step protocol quickly establishes communication around a problem and gives the child a safe experience of quiet and introspection that shows him that he can survive facing that internal space where difficult feelings reside. For many children, this is a good first step to help him continue processing significant issues safely with the Standard EMDR Protocol. It is important to note that the solution or exit drawing is not always the one that concretely solves the problem. The child's solution must, however, be accepted, valued, and treated as a jumping off point for a continuation of the treatment.

EMDR Assessment and Desensitization Phases With Children: Step-by-Step Session Directions

Robbie Adler-Tapia and Carolyn Settle

This chapter describes the procedural steps of the Assessment Phase and Desensitization Phase of the EMDR Standard Protocol (Shapiro, 2001) with detailed scripts for steering a child through each phase. Further details can be found in *EMDR and the Art of Psychotherapy With Children* (Adler-Tapia & Settle, 2008a). What is important for the therapist to understand is that eliciting the procedural steps for the Assessment Phase and Desensitization Phase is impacted by the child's level of development, and scripts for the procedural steps need to be adjusted accordingly. Generally, these scripts are what the authors use for children 8 years old and up. For children under 8 years old, the authors will give examples that show how to adjust the language to the developmental abilities of the child.

Assessment Phase Notes

This section starts with Target Identification; this is a continuation of what began during the Client History and Treatment Planning Phase. Therefore, for the purposes of this script, it is assumed that the therapist has already worked on and established the following: understanding of the emotions, the Stop Signal, the Safe/Calm Place or other resources, and the symptoms, issues, and problems that need to be addressed. At this juncture, the therapist is asking the child to choose the target before proceeding with the procedural steps. The therapist should already have some idea of what the child may choose given previous target identification procedures such as Mapping and Graphing (Adler-Tapia & Settle, 2008b) or other procedures for eliciting targets with children. Since EMDR is a symptom-focused treatment, the therapist needs to ask the child to identify the target based on the symptoms or issue the child most wants to address.

Once the target has been selected, the therapist continues with Image, Negative Cognition (NC), Positive Cognition (PC), Validity of Cognition (VoC), Emotion,

Subjective Units of Disturbance (SUDs), and Body Sensation to move on to the Desensitization Phase. Complete as much work as time and circumstances allow, leaving adequate time for closure and debriefing. Scripts for the Assessment and Desensitization Phases without commentary are provided at the end of this chapter.

Review the Previous Session

After bringing the child and parent into the office together, check in to get updates since the last session. Ask both the child and parents the following:

Say, *"Is there anything that has come up since our last session together?"*

_____

_____

Review current symptoms and any changes of previously identified symptoms or new symptoms. Also ask the child and parents if they have any questions since the last session.

Say, *"Do you have any questions since our last session?"*

_____

_____

After checking in with the child and parents, it is the therapist's decision whether or not to continue with the parents in the session. You may choose to ask the parents to stay in the waiting room while working with the child, or keep the parents in the session while working with the child. This decision is based on the therapist's preference for clinical practice or on the child's level of comfort with the therapist.

Review Mechanics and Stop Signal

The session now focuses on the child. The therapist begins by reviewing the mechanics of EMDR that were taught to the child in previous sessions.

Say, *"Remember how we used the _____ (state BLS using)?"*

_____

_____

Say, *"If at any time you feel you want to stop, remember what you told me that you would do _____ (demonstrate the Stop Signal previously identified)."*

_____

_____

Review Safe/Calm Place and Resources

Briefly review the Safe/Calm Place and Resource images established in earlier sessions during the Preparation Phase (the script is included at the end of the chapter).

Say, *"Remember that Safe/Calm Place that we talked about before*
_____ (the therapist names the Safe/Calm Place and offers descriptive cues)*?"*

_____

_____

Say, *"We can use that Safe/Calm Place at the end of our session or any*
time that something bothers you too much, if you need to. I also
want to make sure you remember what you told me about _____
(describe the resource images and associated feelings, qualities, or
capacities if needed).*"*

_____

_____

If the therapist determines that the child does not have adequate resources,
decide whether resource development would be helpful. If so do the following:

Say, *"Do any of these* _____ (state resources) *feel like they could*
really help us right now? Do you think there are any people, pets, or
objects that you would want sitting with you who could help you feel
better when we talk about that thing that happened?"

_____

_____

If the therapist determines that the child has adequate resources, the therapist
continues with the protocol.

Target Identification

The therapist decides, in collaboration with the child and parent, what to target
based on symptom presentation and on the list of traumatic experiences established during the Client History and Treatment Planning Process.

Say, *"We have talked about things that worry or bother you before and*
remember we picked this one from your list (or Map), *so how about*
we start with that one today?"

_____

_____

It is important for therapists to recognize that often children's targets are more
current. It is also notable that what the child identifies as the trauma may not be
what the parent identifies as the trauma. For children, often their targets are more
symptom related or behavior focused. The authors' recommend that when choosing a target to reprocess, the therapist should select the target most associated with
the current active symptoms the child is experiencing. The child may have multiple
traumas, but the trauma that is triggering the worst of the current symptoms for
the child should be targeted first. This can be determined during the history-taking
portion of the first phase of EMDR. We encourage therapists to allow the child to
guide the process and ask the child what target they want to start with in EMDR.
This serves to empower the child and engage the child in treatment.

Say, *"Which one bothers you the most?"* or *"Which one do you want to work on today?"*

_____

_____

Then the therapist should check on any previous contributing experiences.

Say, *"Can you remember a time when you felt like this before?"*

_____

_____

This is still addressing the current target but tracing the channel to the past to see if there is an associated memory. Children frequently stay with the current target, which is fine. Frequently children will say they don't remember another time even if there was one. If they have no previous associated memory, target the current one. When you choose the target connected to the worst of the current active symptoms you may also have a generalized desensitization effect on other traumas. A child may have a previous incident of molestation or physical abuse that may get completely reprocessed by targeting the current trigger or symptom. Thus, a generalization effect can occur with children unexpectedly.

The therapist can use drawing, clay, sand tray, and other techniques to identify targets and elicit the worst part of the memory that is associated with the symptom or trauma. This requires that the therapist have patience and become attuned to the child because the target or worst part of the memory may be expressed in nonverbal ways. As a last resort, if the therapist assesses that the child is completely unable to access the memory networks that are believed to be associated with the current symptoms or behaviors, the therapist can request that the parent provide suggested targets along with possible negative and positive cognitions. Once the therapist has determined that an appropriate target has been identified, the therapist can simply ask the child if the session can proceed with that target.

Identifying the Picture and Image

Once the target has been chosen, the next step is to identify the picture or image that represents the worst part of the target. The goal is to help the child express the worst part of the image based on the target. The child can express the image verbally or through art, sand tray, play therapy, or other techniques that are described in detail in other publications. Next, the therapist proceeds with eliciting the negative and positive cognition for reprocessing with EMDR.

Most Disturbing

Say, *"What's the worst or yuckiest part of the incident?"*

_____

_____

Say, *"Can you draw me a picture?"*

_____

_____

Or say, *"Can you show me in the sand tray?"*

_____

_____

Or say, *"Can you show me with the Play-Doh?"*

_____

_____

If the child identifies a picture or image, sound, smell, or body sensation, have the child draw a picture of it or depict an image of it in the sand tray.

If No Picture

Say, *"When you think about that thing, what happens now?"*

_____

_____

Eliciting Negative and Positive Cognitions

The authors have changed the language for eliciting negative and positive cognitions to respond to the developmental needs of the child and to keep the spirit of what the cognitions represent.

Say, *"What's the bad thought and what's the good thought?"*

_____

_____

Even little children can grasp that concept.

The following are tips for eliciting negative and positive cognitions for children. Even though these tips may imply that the therapist eliminate some of the criteria for negative and positive cognitions, the intention is to keep the spirit of the NC and PC in keeping with Adaptive Information Processing theory based on the developmental mastery of the individual child. To be more successful eliciting positive and negative cognitions with children, keep the following in mind.

Attributes of NCs and PCs for Children

1. *Trauma Specific:* Children are more likely to use trauma specific NCs such as "I was scared of the dog" versus "The dog can't get me anymore."
2. *Affectively-laden Resonance:* What parent(s) identify as traumatic is not necessarily what the child identifies. It is important that the NC resonates for the child. When it resonates, the child may tell you in a variety of ways: such as the child can make eye contact, say it, change his body language, change his play, or otherwise indicate.
3. *Self-referencing:* Depending on the child's development the child may not always use "I" statements.
4. *Spontaneous:* NC and PC may first surface in pictures and play.
5. *Emotion as Cognition:* NC and PC may be single emotional words like sad versus glad. If the child has verbalized an emotion, it can be used as the cognition; this is because—developmentally—the ability to verbalize a feeling indicates the child has moved beyond just experiencing the feeling into a cognitive process of verbalizing the feeling.

6. *Protective:* Children may express a negative cognition in the third person in order to protect themselves from the full impact of the cognition.
7. *Telegraphic Speech:* Younger children tend to use telegraphic speech such as "David hurt" and a positive cognition of "David feel better."
8. *Concrete:* Children may provide very concrete NC and PC, like "Jeff bad" versus "Jeff good." These concrete cognitions are oftentimes related to the child's current level of cognitive development and language acquisition level.
9. *Fantasy:* Children may utilize fantasy to express their thoughts about themselves. For instance, 6-year-old Mollie may say, "I'm a witch" versus "I'm a princess." The child's current media exposure can contribute to the child's expressions related to what he thinks about himself.

Tips for Eliciting Negative and Positive Cognitions for Children

1. *Stay with it:* Younger children may originally not be able to come up with an "I" statement. The child may speak in the third person, such as, "David hurt" with a PC of "David feel better," but may come to it eventually if the therapist discusses the statements with the child.
2. *Current Stressors:* Assist the child by eliciting NCs and PCs utilizing knowledge of the child's present stressors. For instance, Katie has to go to the doctor, the therapist might say "Doctor scary" and then suggest that "Doctor fix Katie's owie."
3. *Positive First:* Sometimes you can work backward by getting the positive thought first, then exploring what the negative thought might be.
4. *Symbolic-Using Other Modalities:* Children who struggle with verbalizing NCs and PCs can find greater capacity to express themselves through drawings, sand tray, or other expressive techniques. For instance, asking the child to create his worst world in one area of the sand tray while creating his best world on the other side may lead to identifying cognitions.

Ultimately, it is important to take the time to elicit negative and positive cognitions from children in order to be most effective with EMDR. As with adults, the negative and positive cognitions should resonate for the child. Children will oftentimes make eye contact, give verbal feedback, or change direction in their play behavior when the NC or PC fits. A list of possible negative and positive cognitions for children is included below. When the most appropriate NC and PC are identified for the child, the next phases of EMDR tend to be more valuable.

Negative Cognition (NC)

Say, *"When you think about that thing or picture, what words go with that?"*

_____

_____

Or, you can say the following, especially with younger children who may again need education:

Say, *"What's the bad thought that goes with that?"*

_____

_____

Or, say the following:

Say, *"What's the bad thought about you now?"*

_____

_____

Positive Cognition (PC)

Say, *"When you think about that thing or picture what words would you rather say to yourself instead?"*

_____

_____

Or say, *"What's the good thought that you want to tell yourself instead?"*

_____

_____

Therapists can choose to organize NCs and PCs into categories of safety, responsibility, and choice; however, oftentimes children's cognitions are so concrete that it is difficult to determine the specific category in which the NC or PC falls.

The "Kids' List of Cognitions" can be laminated and used for children who can read. Notice the authors have included cognitions that children frequently state, as well as concrete examples of what children might say.

Kid's List of Cognitions

Bad Thoughts (NC)	*Good Thoughts (PC)*
I'm bad	I'm good
I'm in a fog	I'm in clear place/I'm in sunshine
I'm going to blow	I'm calm
I'm going to explode	I'm calm
I'm hot	I'm cool (as a cucumber)
I don't belong	I do belong
I am stupid	I'm smart
I am dumb	I'm smart
I'm sick	I'm all better
I can't do it	I can do it
I'm hurt	I'm better
I don't understand	I do understand
I can't get help	I can get help
I messed up	I did the best I could
I don't know nothing	I do know
I'm dying	I'm alive
I'm hungry	I'm satisfied
I'm not lovable	I'm lovable
I'm fat	I'm just right
I'm lost	I found my way
I almost drowned and I got very scared and that made me hold my breath.	I tell myself, you should be glad you could hold your breath that long.
I couldn't come out from under the water.	I'm glad I can swim.
I didn't get to go the hospital with dad.	I get to go to the hospital with dad.
I'm not comfortable	I am comfortable
I am uncomfortable in my skin	I fit in my skin

BASIC COMMON COGNITIONS

I'm not safe	I'm safe now
I can't protect myself	I can protect myself
I don't have control	I do have control
I can't trust	I can trust

Measuring the Validity of Cognition (VoC)

When measuring the VoC, children often need simple instructions and a way to concretize the measurement. Given the child's development and the therapist's attunement to the child, the therapist can use different techniques to measure the VoC. Examples include: drawings, games, toys, or the VoC bridge (Adler-Tapia & Settle, 2008a).

> Say, *"When you say those words _____ (repeat PC) how true do those words feel to you right now on a scale of 1 to 7, where 1 feels completely false and 7 feels completely true?"*

> 1   2   3   4   5   6   7
> (completely false)   (completely true)

You can use the distance between your hands to demonstrate the validity of the cognition.

> Say, *"Is it this big* (show hands close together) *or this big* (move hands far apart)*?"*

_____

_____

Or, you can use drawings as in the following:

> Say, *"Let's draw a picture of seven faces. The face on the far right is a happy face that the good thought feels very true. The face on the left is sad and shows that the good thought doesn't feel very true."*

_____

_____

Or for the VoC bridge say the following:

> Say, *"Here's a picture of a bridge with seven steps. The seventh step on the right is the good thought. Let's draw a picture or write down the good thought and put it near this seventh step. We can now show how close or far away the good thought feels by placing a marker (or magnet) on the step that shows us how true the good thought feels."*

_____

_____

Use the measure that is developmentally appropriate for the child. Once the validity of the cognition has been measured, the therapist proceeds with having the children identify the emotion associated with the disturbing incident.

Identifying Emotions and Feelings

Since the therapist has taught the child feeling identification and skills related to emotional literacy during the Preparation Phase, the therapist asks the child to identify a feeling associated with the incident.

Say, *"When you bring up that picture* (or incident) *and words* _____ (negative cognition), *what do you feel now?"*

_____

_____

If the child needs further explanation, the therapist can use a feelings chart or some other type of educational tool used to help children identify emotion. Explore the emotion(s) that the child feels in the present.

Measuring the Subjective Units of Disturbance (SUDs)

Similar to the VoC, children may need a concrete manner to measure the SUDs. Examples can include: distance between hands, drawings, collages, pictures of animals (from small to large), anything with a concrete size that illustrates measurement, and so forth.

Say, *"From 0 to 10, where 0 doesn't bother you at all to 10 where it bothers you a lot, how much does that thing bother you right now?"*

0	1	2	3	4	5	6	7	8	9	10
(no disturbance)								(highest disturbance)		

The therapist can use distance between hands or other type of measure to which the child relates.

Say, *"Is it this big* (show hands close together) *or this big* (move hands far apart)*?"*

_____

_____

Or you can make a collage or drawing that depicts increments from 0 to 10 such as an elephant that represents a SUDs of 10, and a tiny ant that represents a SUDs of 0.

Say, *"How much does that bother you now? Does it bother you as big as an elephant? Or as small as an ant? Or, is it somewhere between?"*

_____

_____

Identifying the Location of Body Sensations

The therapist should refer to any resources that teach about body location and sensation. The therapist can use old metaphors that connect emotion and body sensations such as "I have a broken heart," which represents sadness; "This is a pain in the neck," which represents an annoyance; "I have butterflies in my stomach," which represents nervousness; or "I feel weak in the knees," which describes fearfulness. These metaphors can be taught during the Preparation Phase. It is often helpful for the therapist to actively demonstrate how to scan the body for the location of any body sensations.

Say, *"Where do you feel it in your body?"*

_____

_____

If the child is not initially able to answer, the therapist reminds the child of earlier training about body location and sensation and teaches the child mindfulness of body sensations by pointing to body parts as the therapist says the following:

Say, *"Sometimes people feel it in their head, or their tummy, or their feet. Where do you feel it in your body?"*

_____

_____

Desensitization Phase Notes

The goal of the Desensitization Phase is to reprocess the maladaptively stored memory and bring the incident to adaptive resolution. This is the phase that can be very short especially with children or can take a long time depending on the complexity of the associative chaining associated with the current symptom presentation.

Challenges in the Desensitization Phase include the following:

- To stay out of the way of the client's reprocessing, while also knowing when the client is stuck or looping and a cognitive interweave is indicated.
- To tolerate intense affect.
- To assist the client with a tolerable speed of reprocessing that does not overwhelm and shut down the client.
- To know the techniques for under accessing when the client is reporting that nothing is happening.
- To change types of bilateral stimulation (BLS) more often to keep the child engaged.
- To include more activity in working with children as they reprocess the memory through play therapy, art therapy, drawing, or other expressive psychotherapeutic tools.
- To be patient and diligent in attunement to the unique reprocessing of the individual child in order to bring the disturbance to a SUDs of 0 in order to proceed to the Installation Phase of EMDR.
- To follow the child's lead is the most important course of action during this phase.

The ultimate goal of the Desensitization Phase is to reach a SUD of 0 related to the original target, no matter how many maladaptively stored events the child presents during the session.

Explaining Desensitization to the Child

Say, *"What we're going to do is the _____ (BLS) on that thing _____* (state the target) *and I'm going to do it for awhile and then I'm going to stop and tell you to blank it out and take a breath and then we'll talk a little about it. Sometimes things will change and sometimes they won't. There is no right or wrong answer. What you think or feel is exactly what I want to know and you can tell me anything."*

Beginning Desensitization

Say, *"I'd like you to bring up that picture _____ (label and describe* using client's word), *the words _____ (repeat the negative cognition in client's words), and the_____ (state the type of feeling), and notice where you are feeling it in your body and _____ (state* whatever BLS previously identified)."

_____

_____

Begin the BLS.

At least once or twice during each set of BLS, or when there is an apparent change, therapist may comment to child, "That's it. Good. That's it." With children, the type of BLS may need to be changed often in order to assist the child in sustaining attention.

Strong Emotion During Reprocessing

If the child appears to be too upset to continue reprocessing, it is helpful to reassure and to remind the child of the metaphor identified, such as watching the scenery go by, with the child prior to processing.

Say, *"It's normal for you to feel more as we start to work on this. Re-member we said it's like _____ (state the metaphor used, such as being in a car and watching things go by outside the car window) so just notice it. It's old stuff."*

_____

_____

Only use this if needed or if the child is upset.

Between Sets of Bilateral Stimulation (BLS)

After a set of BLS, say the following:

Say, *"Take a deep breath."*

_____

_____

It is often helpful if the therapist takes an exaggerated breath to model for the child, as the therapist makes the statements to the child.

Say any of these, *"What did you get now?" "Tell me what you got?" "What did you notice?" "What's happening now?" "Can you draw me a picture of what you got?" "Can you show me in the sand tray?"*

_____

_____

If the child needs coaching, say any of the following:

Say, *"What are you thinking, feeling?" "How does your body feel?" "What pictures are you seeing in your head?"*

_____

_____

After the child recounts his or her experience, say the following:

Say, *"Go with that."*

_____

_____

Do another set of BLS. Do not repeat the child's words or statements. As an optional phrasing you can say the following:

Say, *"Just notice that."*

_____

_____

Children may need to draw or express their experience in play, the sand tray, or drawing during the process, however, the therapist does not need to understand at this point what is happening; this is for the child. What matters is that the child is expressing their thoughts or feelings between each set of BLS and they are expressing it in their own way, either verbally, by drawing, or in a sand tray. The therapist needs to simply observe, stay attuned to the child, and keep the child engaged in the process as much as possible.

Continued Reprocessing

Again say, *"What do you get now?"*

_____

_____

If new negative material presents itself, continue down that channel with further sets of BLS.

Continue with sets of BLS until the child's report indicates the end of a memory channel. At that point, the child may appear significantly calmer. No new disturbing material is emerging. Then return to the target and say the following:

Say, *"When you think about that thing we first talked about today, what happens now?"*

_____

_____

Remember children may not show affect and may often process very quickly. So there may be no more disturbing material for the child to access or describe about the target memory. After children recount their experience(s) (children may verbalize, draw, or otherwise demonstrate through play therapy what they have experienced), add a set of BLS.

Say, *"Go with that."*

_____

_____

Positive Associations During Reprocessing

If positive material is reported, add one or two sets of BLS to increase the strength of the positive associations before returning to target. If you believe the child is at the end of a channel, for example, the material reported is neutral or positive then the therapist should say the following:

Say, *"When you go back to that first thing we talked about today _____ (therapist references the picture, sand tray, or whatever was used by the child to identify the original target), what do you get now?"*

_____

_____

Whatever the child reports, add a set of BLS.

Say, *"Go with that."*

_____

_____

Checking the Subjective Units of Disturbance (SUD)

If no change occurs, check the SUD.

> Say, *"When you think about that thing, from 0 to 10 where 0 doesn't bother you at all and 10 where it bothers you a lot, how much does that thing bother you right now?"*

> 0   1   2   3   4   5   6   7   8   9   10
> (no disturbance)   (highest disturbance)

The therapist can use one of the alternate ways of checking the SUDs described in the Assessment Phase.

If the SUD is greater than 0, continue with further sets of BLS time permitting.

> Say, *"Go with that."*

_____

_____

If the SUD is 0, do another set of BLS to verify that no new material opens up.

> Say, *"Go with that."*

_____

_____

Then proceed to the installation of the PC.

Note: Only proceed to the Installation Phase after you have returned to target, added a set of BLS, no new material has emerged, and the SUD is 0.

> Say, *"Now please go back to the target and go with that."*

_____

_____

Complete as much work as time and circumstances allow, leaving adequate time for closure and debriefing.

Complete and Incomplete Desensitization Phase

If the session is a complete session, move to the Installation Phase.

If the session is incomplete (SUD is not at 0), remind the client of the Safe/Calm Place or Container Exercise (scripts are at the end of the chapter) and other relaxation techniques to prepare children for ending the session.

It is important to teach children skills for between sessions. The therapist instructs the parents to remind the children to practice the Safe/Calm Place or Container Exercise.

> Say, *"Remember our _____* (state self-soothing technique such as Safe/Calm Place or Container). *Let's try practicing them now and then you can practice them every day until our next session."*

_____

_____

Assessment Phase Script

Review the Previous Session

Say, *"Is there anything that has come up since our last session together?"*

_____

_____

Say, *"Do you have any questions since our last session?"*

_____

_____

Review Mechanics and Stop Signal

Say, *"Remember how we used the _____ (state the BLS used)?"*

_____

_____

Say, *"If at any time you feel you want to stop, remember what you told me that you would do _____ (demonstrate Stop Signal previously identified)."*

_____

_____

Review Safe/Calm Place and Resources

Say, *"Remember that Safe/Calm Place that we talked about before _____ (therapist names the Safe/Calm Place and offers descriptive cues)?"*

_____

_____

Say, *"We can use that Safe/Calm Place when we are talking about what you remember, if you need to. I also want to make sure you remember what you told me about _____ (describe resource images and associated feelings, qualities, or capacities if needed).*
Do any of these _____ (state resources) feel like they could really help us right now? Do you think there are any people, pets, or objects that you would want sitting with you who could help you feel better when we talk about that thing that happened?"

_____

_____

Target Identification

Say, *"We have talked about things that worry or bother you before and remember we picked this one from your list, so how about we start with that one today?"*

_____

_____

Say, *"Which one bothers you the most?"* or *"Which one do you want to work on today?"*

_____

_____

The therapist should check on any previous contributing experiences.

Say, *"Can you remember a time when you felt like this before?"*

_____

_____

Identifying the Picture and Image

Most Disturbing

Say, *"What's the worst or yuckiest part of the incident?"*

_____

_____

Say, *"Can you draw me a picture?"*

_____

_____

Or say, *"Can you show me in the sand tray?"*

_____

_____

Or say, *"Can you show me with the Play-Doh?"*

_____

_____

If the child identifies a picture or image, sound, smell, body sensation, you can have the child draw a picture of it or depict an image of it in a sand tray.

If No Picture

Say, *"When you think about that thing, what happens now?"*

_____

_____

Eliciting Negative and Positive Cognitions

Say, *"What's the bad thought and what's the good thought?"*

_____

_____

Negative Cognition (NC)

Say, *"When you think about that thing or picture, what words go with that?"*

_____

_____

With younger children who may again need education, you can say the following:

Say, *"What's the bad thought that goes with that?"*

_____

_____

Or say, *"What's the bad thought about you now?"*

_____

_____

Positive Cognition (PC)

Say, *"When you think about that thing or picture, what words would you rather say to yourself instead?"*

_____

_____

Or you can say, *"What's the good thought that you want to tell yourself instead?"*

_____

_____

Measuring the Validity of Cognition (VoC)

Say, *"When you say those words _____ (repeat PC) how true do those words feel to you right now on a scale of 1 to 7, where 1 feels completely false and 7 feels completely true?"*

1	2	3	4	5	6	7
(completely false)				(completely true)		

You can use the distance between your hands to demonstrate the validity of the cognition.

Say, *"Is it this big (show hands close together) or this big (move hands far apart)?"*

_____

_____

Or say, *"Let's draw a picture of seven faces. The face on the far right is a happy face that the good thought feels very true. The face on the left is sad and shows that the good thought doesn't feel very true."*

_____

_____

Or for the VoC bridge, say the following:

Say, *"Here's a picture of a bridge with seven steps. The seventh step on the right is the good thought. Let's draw a picture or write down the good thought and put it near this seventh step. We can now show how close or far away the good thought feels by placing a marker (or magnet) on the step that shows us how true the good thought feels."*

_____

_____

Identifying Emotions and Feelings

Say, *"When you bring up that picture (or incident) and words _____ (negative cognition), what do you feel now?"*

_____

_____

Measuring the Subjective Units of Disturbance (SUDs)

Say, *"From 0 to 10, where 0 doesn't bother you at all to 10 where it bothers you a lot, how much does that thing bother you right now?"*

0   1   2   3   4   5   6   7   8   9   10
(no disturbance)   (highest disturbance)

Say, *"Is it this big (show hands close together) or this big (move hands far apart)?"*

_____

_____

Or say, *"How much does that bother you now? Does it bother you as big as an elephant? Or as small as an ant? Or is it somewhere between?"*

_____

_____

Identifying the Location of Body Sensations

Say, *"There are old sayings that are kind of true about how we feel things in our body, like 'I have a broken heart,' which means the person's sad and they feel it in their heart. Or 'This is a pain in the neck,' people say that sometimes when things are bothering them and they feel it in their neck. Or 'I have butterflies in my tummy,' which means people are feeling nervous and they feel it in their stomach. Or sometimes people will say 'I feel weak in the knees' when they are afraid and they feel it in their knees. Where do you feel it in your body?"*

_____

_____

Say, *"Sometimes people feel it in their head, their tummy, or their feet. Where do you feel it in your body?"*

_____

_____

Desensitization Phase Script

Explaining Desensitization to the Child

Say, *"What we're going to do is the _____ (BLS) on that thing _____ (state the target) and I'm going to do it for awhile and then I'm going to stop and tell you to blank it out and take a breath and then we'll talk a little about it. Sometimes things will change and sometimes they won't. There is no right or wrong answer. What you think or feel is exactly what I want to know and you can tell me anything."*

Beginning Desensitization

Say, *"I'd like you to bring up that picture _____ (label and describe using child's words), the words _____ (repeat the negative cognition in child's words), and the _____ (state the type of feeling), and notice where you are feeling it in your body and _____ (state BLS previously identified)."*

_____

_____

At least once or twice during each set of BLS, or when there is an apparent change, the therapist may comment to child, "That's it. Good. That's it."

Strong Emotion During Reprocessing

Say, *"It's normal for you to feel more as we start to work on this. Remember we said it's like _____ (state the metaphor used) so just notice it. It's old stuff."*

_____

_____

Only use this if needed or if the child is upset.

Between Sets of Bilateral Stimulation (BLS)

Say, *"Take a deep breath."*
Say any of these, *"What did you get now? "Tell me what you got?" "What did you notice?" "What's happening now?" "Can you draw me a picture of what you got?" "Can you show me in the sand tray?"*

_____

_____

Or if the child needs coaching, say the following:

Say, *"What are you thinking, feeling, how does your body feel or what pictures are you seeing in your head?"*

_____

_____

After the child recounts his or her experience, say the following:

Say, *"Go with that"* and do another set of BLS.

_____

_____

As an optional phrasing you can say, "Just notice that."

Continued Reprocessing

Say, *"What do you get now?"*

_____

_____

If new negative material presents itself, continue down that channel with further sets of BLS.

Say, *"Go with that."*

_____

_____

Continue with sets of BLS until the child's report indicates the child is at the end of a memory channel. No new disturbing material is emerging.
Then return to the target and say the following:

Say, *"When you think about that thing we first talked about today, what happens now?"*

_____

_____

Positive Associations During Reprocessing

If you believe the child is at the end of a channel, for example, the material reported is neutral or positive then the therapist says the following:

Say, *"When you go back to that first thing we talked about today _____ (state what was used to identify the original target such as the picture, sand tray, etc.), what do you get now?"*

_____

_____

Whatever the child reports, add a set of BLS.

Say, *"Go with that."*

_____

_____

Checking the Subjective Units of Disturbance (SUD)

Say, *"When you think about that thing, from 0 to 10 where 0 doesn't bother you at all to 10 where it bothers you a lot, how much does that thing bother you right now?"*

   0   1   2   3   4   5   6   7   8   9   10
(no disturbance)   (highest disturbance)

Or say, *"On our animal scale here, how much does it bother you? Does it bother you as big as an elephant? Or as small as an ant? Or is it somewhere between?"*

_____

_____

Complete and Incomplete Desensitization Phase

If it is a complete session, move to the Installation Phase.
If the session is incomplete (SUD is not at 0), say the following:

Say, *"Remember our* _____ (state the self-soothing resource used such as the Safe/Calm Place or Container). *Let's try practicing them now and then you can practice them every day until our next session."*

_____

_____

Safe/Calm Place Script

Say, *"Okay, so I want to do something that's called the Safe/Calm Place. We can use the Safe/Calm Place at the end of sessions or between sessions. I want you to learn how to use the Safe/Calm Place so we're going to practice it."*

_____

_____

Picture or Image

Say, *"Can you think about a real place, or imaginary place that makes you feel safe, calm, relaxed, or happy? What place makes you feel this way the most? Do you have a picture of it?"*

_____

_____

If appropriate, let the child draw a picture or image of the safe, comfortable, or relaxed place.

Say, *"If you like, go ahead and draw a picture of your safe, calm, relaxed, or happy place."*

_____

_____

Emotions and Sensations

Say, *"Think about that safe, comfortable, or relaxed place. What feeling do you have?"*

_____

_____

If the child does not respond, provide examples of feelings in order to educate child.

Say, *"Do you feel relaxed, comfortable, safe, happy, or excited? Where do you feel that _____ (state the type of feeling) in your body?"*

_____

_____

If the child appears confused, provide examples.

Say, *"Well, some children feel it in their heads, some people feel it in their tummy, some feel it in their heart. Where do you feel it? Can you touch it?"*

_____

_____

Enhancement

Say, *"Think about that _____ (state the name), and that _____ (state the feeling), and where you feel it in your body and let's _____ (state the BLS) for a few seconds."*

_____

_____

Do BLS for several seconds.

Say, *"Tell me what happened now?"*

_____

_____

If the child feels better, do several more sets of BLS.

Say, *"Go with that."*

_____

_____

If the child's positive emotions do not intensify, the therapist can try alternative BLS until the child reports improvement.

Cue Word(s)

Say, *"If we could pick one word that would help to remind me how you feel right now, what word would that be? Okay, so when I say _____, what do you notice?"*

_____

_____

Add set of BLS.

Self-Cuing

Say, *"Now I want you to say the word ____ (state the cue word) and when you say it notice what you're feeling."*

_____

_____

Cuing With Disturbance

Say, *"Now let's practice with your word. I want you to think about one tiny little thing that bothers you just a little bit and notice where you feel that in your body."*

_____

_____

Do not use BLS at this time.

Self-Cuing With Disturbance

The therapist then asks the client to bring up a disturbing thought once again and to practice the Safe/Calm Place exercise, this time without the therapist's assistance, to its relaxing conclusion.

> Say, *"Think about that thing that bothers you and remind yourself to think of that word that reminds you of your Safe/Calm Place and see if you can relax all by yourself."*

_____

_____

Homework

Encourage client to practice Safe/Calm Place and word for cuing Safe/Calm Place.

> Say, *"I'd like you to practice your Safe/Calm Place by yourself at home once or twice this week."*

Containers for Children Script

Containers are used to assist children to close incomplete sessions and as another resource for affect management especially between sessions. Containers can also be used to store new skills a child has learned for use in the future when they encounter situations that have previously been problematic. Using containers too early can provide the child with a technique to avoid reprocessing. It is important to teach the child that containers are temporary but eventually the goal is to empty the container.

Say, *"Sometimes we have thoughts or feelings that get in our way at school or at home. Do you ever have thoughts or feeling like that?"*

_____

_____

Say, *"Well, I want you to know that if we need to, we can put those thoughts or feelings in a container like a box or something really strong so that they can't get out. What do you think we could use to hold those thoughts or feelings?"*

_____

_____

Children may need to be taught examples.

Say, *"I want you to be able to put all of those thoughts or feelings, or what we worked on today in that container. Sometimes we need different containers for different thoughts or feelings. Sometimes, I like to draw pictures of my _____ (state container) and make sure it's strong enough to hold everything that I need it to hold. Would you like to draw a picture with me?"*

_____

_____

After the child identifies a container, say the following:

Say, *"Okay, so we drew a picture _____ (note how child identified container) of it, so now let's imagine that everything we worked on today is put in the container and we lock it or seal it away until we get together again and can take it out to work on it again. When we get together we will work to empty your container so there's always room for new stuff if you need it. If you start thinking about things that bother you that are too hard to handle or it seems to come out before our next session, you can just imagine putting it into the container and giving it to me or making sure that I have it."*

_____

_____

The protocols for the Assessment and Desensitization Phases of EMDR—including language specific for children—have been included to assist therapists to understand that it is possible to elicit all the phases of the EMDR protocol with young children. Please refer to Shapiro's book, *Eye Movement Desensitization and*

Reprocessing (2001), to get in-depth direction for each part of the Standard EMDR Protocol and Adler-Tapia and Settle (2008a) for additional guidance on the treatment of children. After completing basic training in EMDR, implementing EMDR in psychotherapy with children requires experience and training. Adolescents may be more capable of following the adult protocol; however, it is important to use trained and experienced clinical skills especially designed for children in order to process the pieces of the EMDR protocol where a developmental framework appropriate to the individual child is essential for successful treatment.

PART II

EMDR and

Couples

Discussion at conferences about EMDR work with couples did not progress as rapidly as with other populations. In 1995, at the EMDR Conference sponsored by the EMDR Institute and the newly formed EMDR International Association, Bernie Zilbergeld (1995) presented on "Using EMDR in the Treatment of Sexual Problems." The following year at the EMDRIA Conference in Denver, Colorado, there were two presentations addressing issues specific to working with couples. Chad Glang and Craig Penner (1996) joined forces to present on "Integrating EMDR With Marital and Family Systems Therapy" and Nutting's (1996) workshop was on "Working With Couples: The Use of EMDR in Relationship Counseling." From 1997 through 2000, topics such as "EMDR and Sex Therapy" (Levine, 1998); "Shapiro Meets Bowen & Satir: The Uses of EMDR in Couples Therapy" (D'Antonio, 1997); "Trust, Intimacy and Sex: An Integrated Approach" (Litt, 1998); and "Integrating EMDR into Sex and Relationship Therapy" (Zangwill, 2000) were the foci of presentations at the EMDRIA Conferences. At the EMDRIA conferences in the new millennium until 2008, Barry Litt (1998, 2003, 2004, 2005, 2006, 2007a, 2008) and Mark Moses (2004) continued to report on the evolution of their work with couples, for the most part, on an annual basis. Frederick Capps (2005) presented on trust issues within the relationship in his workshop on "Rebuilding Trust: Healing for Couples Using EMDR"; Mark Karpel (2005) introduced his work on EMDR: "Targeting the Repetition Compulsion in Couples Therapy"; and Philip Manfield (2005) showed us about "Effective Targeting With Couples." Constance Scharf, Kathy Berliner, Mimi Meyers, Natalie Schwartberg, and Margot Weinshel (2006) reported on "Enhancing Couples Therapy With EMDR." By 2008, the topic was of great enough interest to invite David Treadway (2008a, 2008b) to give the opening plenary lecture. He presented on "Intimacy and Healing: Utilizing EMDR in Couples Therapy" and later gave an all day workshop on "The Heart of Loving: A New Model of Couples Therapy." The presentations from the EMDRIA conferences are all available on audiotape and DVD (www.emdria.org).

Academic articles continued and Protinsky, Sparks and Lemke's paper "Using Eye Movement Desensitization and Reprocessing to Enhance Treatment of Couples" (2001) was published in the *Journal of Marital and Family Therapy*, and Mark Moses published his "Protocol for EMDR and Conjoint Couples Therapy" in the *EMDRIA Newsletter* (2003). Robin Shapiro (2005) wrote a chapter on "Using EMDR in Couples Therapy" in her helpful volume *EMDR Solutions: Pathways to Healing* showing different ways to address issues with couples within the EMDR context.

In 2007, Shapiro, Kaslow, and Maxfield edited *Handbook of EMDR and Family Therapy Processes* addressing the particular needs of family systems. There are four chapters included in this volume that address the specific needs of couples (instead of working with the whole family) using EMDR: "Enhancing Attachments: Conjoint Couple Therapy" (Moses, 2007); "Integrating EMDR and Imago Relationship Therapy in Treatment of Couples" (Talan, 2007); "EMDR and Emotionally Focused Couple Therapy for War Veteran Couples" (Errebo & Sommers-Flanagan, 2007); and Koedam (2007) adds her concerns about sexual trauma in her chapter on "Sexual Trauma in Dysfunctional Marriages: Integrating Structural Therapy and EMDR." While at the EMDR European Conference in London, England (2008), Isabelle Meignant-Ordoux presented on "EMDR with Systemic Couples Therapy."

Compared to the other topics in EMDR, there is a need for more work on EMDR with couples therapy. The following chapters will add to the wisdom of this area. Michael D'Antonio in chapter 9 gives us a thorough look at the integration of EMDR into couples therapy. He incorporates the knowledge of the Bowenian model with trauma to assist highly reactive couples in becoming more differentiated and more competent in their relationships. Using EMDR as the central focus to work on past traumas that create the emotional reactivity in the couple, Dr. D'Antonio integrates his work with the couple individually and conjointly. Couples work is focused, purposeful, and balances the interpersonal with the intrapersonal.

Barry Litt's chapter also focuses on targeting early relational traumas to help couples work on their current dysfunctional ways of relating. Mr. Litt uses a 5-step protocol to help organize the important principles when he works with couples, giving them the possibility of identifying the maladaptive patterns in their relationship and ways to work through them.

Sabitha Pillai-Friedman's work on treating sexual dysfunction in couples gives EMDR therapists a way to organize their work using the EMDR 3-pronged approach for this population. She again underlines the importance of being schooled in working with sexual dysfunction before using this protocol and knowing how to maintain a professional manner when dealing with this sensitive subject. Dr. Pillai-Friedman encourages her clients to look at their past issues concerning their sexual problem, their present triggers, their future anxieties, and positive experiences to create a new way of responding in the future.

Marina Lombardo pairs her expertise in infertility with Regina Morrow's expertise in EMDR. Together they have created a helpful protocol about working with women who have infertility problems. As in many of these protocols for special populations, women with infertility problems require different information-gathering questions and they supply us with a clear way for taking a history where infertility is the presenting problem. Again, this protocol addresses how the 3-pronged protocol unfolds and the particular types of cognitive interweaves that are helpful with this population. Lombardo's Fertility Questionnaire is included to help clients decide when enough is enough concerning infertility treatment.

These four chapters help us think about different ways to approach couples and the types of problems that are part of working with this population. It is important that those clinicians who use these protocols with couples are experienced in this area before working with EMDR.

Integrating EMDR Into Couples Therapy

Michael D'Antonio

This protocol connects a trauma model of relationships to Bowen's concept of differentiation (D'Antonio, 1997). In addition to those couples where a traumatic episode, prior to or during the relationship, has had a clear impact on the relationship (e.g., history of childhood sexual abuse, infidelity, death of child, etc.), highly reactive couples are those who profit most from integrating EMDR into their couples work. Reactivity in couples typically includes a rapid escalation in negative emotion, accompanied by escalation in overt conflict, withdrawal–pursuit, conflict–avoidance, or dominance–submission. EMDR can play an important role when reactivity in sessions blocks therapist interventions or resists routine interventions; when one or both partners are so reactive as to be abusive, coercive, or destructive; or when one or both partners are emotionally shut down or phobic about emotional engagement.

Treatment Goals

When EMDR is used to treat trauma, therapists generally look for treatment change specific to the trauma and its PTSD-like symptoms. In couples therapy, the desired outcomes are more the generalized effects of EMDR and those we might expect from EMDR performance enhancement. Therapists look for the partners to become better differentiated and relationally more competent so that they become less defensive and reactive; they develop a greater ability to identify their own thoughts, feelings, and desires; they become more assertive without becoming aggressive; they develop greater empathy for themselves and one another; and they are open to greater emotional and physical intimacy.

Couples Assessment Process

Phase 1: History Taking

The assessment process described here grows out of a "tripartite intergenerational-intrapsychic-interactional" framework (D'Antonio, 1994). It is, specifically, trauma focused in order to facilitate the introduction of EMDR into the couples therapy should the therapist consider EMDR useful or necessary.

Because it is important to develop therapeutic momentum and a sense of hopefulness, this material is usually covered in one 60-minute session. If necessary, it can be extended into a second session.

Conjoint Intake Session Script

Say, *"Hello, I am _____. It's good to meet both of you. Before we get to what brought you here, I'd like to ask a few quick questions to get a sense of who you are and the important people in your lives so that I understand better who they are should you mention them during our conversation."*

There follows a brief genogram (Sherman & Friedman, 1986, pp. 82–90) in which parents, siblings, and children from this and prior relationships are identified, deaths, major illnesses, separations, and divorces are also noted. More detailed family of origin information is left to subsequent individual sessions with each partner.

Say, *"_____ (state the name of your client), you called me, so is it okay if I start with you? Are your parents alive?"*

_____

_____

If both parents are alive, for each parent:

Say, *"How old are your parents?"*

_____

_____

Say, *"Are they still married to one another?"*

_____

_____

If they are no longer married:

Say, *"When did they separate? Divorce?"*

_____

_____

Say, *"How old were you at the time?"*

_____

_____

Say, *"Did either parent remarry?"*

_____

_____

If yes, say the following:

Say, *"To whom?"*

_____

_____

Say, *"How old were you at the time?"*

_____

_____

Say, *"Are they still married?"*

_____

_____

If not, say the following:

Say, *"When did they separate and divorce?"*

_____

_____

For each parent, ask the following:

Say, *"Any significant problems with her or his health?"*

_____

_____

If either or both parents are deceased, ask for each deceased parent:

Say, *"How old was* _____ (he or she) *when* _____ (he or she) *died?"*

_____

_____

Say, *"What did* _____ (he or she) *die of?"*

_____

_____

Say, *"Had* _____ (he or she) *been ill?"*

_____

_____

Say, *"For how long?"*

_____

_____

Say, *"Were your parents still married at the time of* _____ (his or her) *death?"*

_____

_____

Say, *"How old were you at the time of your* _____ (mother or father's) *death?"*

_____

_____

Say, *"Did _____ (state the name of your surviving parent) remarry?"*

_____

_____

Say, *"When?"*

_____

_____

Say, *"To whom?"*

_____

_____

Say, *"Are they still married?"*

_____

_____

If not, say, *"When did they separate and divorce?"*

_____

_____

Say, *"Was either of your parents married before their marriage to one another?"*

_____

_____

If yes, say, *"When and how long did that marriage or those marriages last?"*

_____

_____

Say, *"Do you have brothers or sisters, including any half-siblings or any siblings who have passed away?"*

_____

_____

If yes, ask the following:

Say, *"Where are you in the birth order?"*

_____

_____

Say, *"So, let's start with the firstborn down to the last, giving the name and age of each."*

_____

_____

For any sibling who passed away:

Say, *"How old was _____ (he or she) at the time of their death?"*

_____

_____

Say, *"How old were you? How long had _____ (he or she) been ill and what did _____ (he or she) die of?"*

_____

_____

The same series of questions is next asked of the partner. In fact, the entire session is structured so that each partner is both allowed and required to speak for themselves.

Say, *"So now ____ (state the partner's name) tell me about your family."*

_____

_____

Start with "Are your parents alive?" And so forth, as above.
Next, move on to their stated goals for therapy.

Say, *"I would like each one of you to tell me what your goals are for therapy. Who would like to start first?"*

_____

_____

Say, *"Great, what are your goals for this therapy?"*

_____

_____

Say, *"What would you like to see different about how you are as a couple?"*

_____

_____

If the client is vague or amorphous, ask clarifying questions:

Say, *"How will you know when you have achieved _____ (state the goal)?"*

_____

_____

Be sure to let the speaker describe his or her goals uninterrupted. If necessary, say to the partner:

Say, *"Please let _____ (partner's name) describe things from _____ (his or her) point of view without any distractions. I'll want to hear your point of view when _____ (he or she) is finished."*

Say to the partner, *"Okay. Now, what are your goals for these meetings? I want to understand your point of view. So please do not respond to what _____ (state partner's name) just said. In fact, pretend that I did not hear a thing ____ (he or she) just said."*

_____

_____

It may be necessary in the course of this partner's describing their goals to remind him or her of the point just made.

Say, *"You have each described how you'd like things to be different between you. Would you please describe in 'video language' (O'Hanlon & Weiner-Davis, 1989) the most recent example of how you are not the way you would like to be with each other; in other words, the problem which brought you here. Please describe what I would see and hear without your interpretations or comments as if I were actually watching the two of you relating this way. Who would like to go first?"*

_____

_____

Once again, you may need to remind the partner:

Say, *"Please let _____ (state partner's name) describe the whole exchange without comment. I'll want to hear your description in a moment."*

Once again, you may need to remind the partner not to comment, interrupt, or clarify.

Say to the partner, *"Please recall that same incident? How would you describe it in video language?"*

_____

_____

_____

_____

On learning of the couple's description of their problematic interaction along with their goals, it is usually possible for the therapist to identify their dysfunctional interactional pattern in terms of "interacting sensitivities" (Wile, 1981). Typically, they are one of the following: attack–counterattack, dominance–submission, pursuit–withdrawal, withdrawal–withdrawal, or victimizing–demoralization.

Say to one, *"It seems that when you see your partner do _____ (state what one partner does), you do _____ (state what the second partner does)."*

Then to the other say, *"And when you see him or her do ____ (state what the second partner does), you ____ (state what first does). The more ____ (state what second partner does) you do, the more _____ (he or she) does _____ (state what first does)."*

Take Tom and Sally, for example. The presenting problem was Sally's distress over Tom's inaction when his adult children from his earlier marriage were hostile or disrespectful to her and Tom's paralysis dealing with either Sally or his daughters. (This couple was so stuck on this issue that the therapist, uncharacteristically, recommended EMDR immediately following the conjoint intake session, without the usual individual sessions and the conjoint feedback session.). "Tom, when Sally gets emotional and particularly when she gets upset over how your daughters treat her, you withdraw. Sally, whenever Tom withdraws as you are struggling with something, you get upset and angry."

Say to both, "_____ (state what one does) *follows* _____ (state what the other does), *follows* _____ (state what the other does), *follows* _____ (state what one does), *and so on. Either of you can start the sequence and you each probably believe the other has started it.*"

Help each understand the underlying emotions.

Say to one partner, *"When you experience _____ (state the name of the partner) doing _____ (state the behavior), what goes on inside you?"*

_____

_____

Say, *"What do you feel?"*

_____

_____

A body scan may be helpful here.

Say, *"Scan your body from head to foot. Notice what you're feeling. What do you notice? And what are you feeling emotionally?"*

_____

_____

Repeat the parallel set of questions for the partner.

Say, *"Now, _____ (state the name of the other partner), what do you feel?"*

_____

_____

Now move on to a brief history of the relationship, marriage, or commitment.

Say, *"How long have you been together?"*

_____

_____

If you don't know whether or not they are married:

Say, *"Are you married?"*

_____

_____

If yes, say the following:

Say, *"How long have you been married?"*

_____

_____

Say, *"Were either of you married before?"*

_____

_____

If either or both answered yes, ask the appropriate partner(s):

Say, *"How many times?"*

_____

_____

Say, *"How old were you when you married* _____ (name of person that time), *when you separated and divorced?"*

_____

_____

Say, *"Do you have children from that marriage?"*

_____

_____

Say, *"Getting back to the two of you, tell me when and where you met?"*

_____

_____

Say, *"How old were each of you at the time?"*

_____

_____

Say, *"What were your life circumstances at the time in terms of school, career, and other relationships?"*

_____

_____

Say, *"Who made the first move?"*

_____

_____

To that partner say, *"What attracted you to _____ (state the partner's name)?"*

_____

_____

To the other say, *"You're together now. So, you responded. What attracted you to _____ (state the partner's name)?"*

_____

_____

To one partner say, *"How would you describe your courtship?"*

_____

_____

Say, *"How was that for you?"*

_____

_____

To the other say, *"How would you describe your courtship?"*

_____

_____

Say, *"How was that for you?"*

_____

_____

To both, if they are married:

Say, *"When and how did you decide to marry?"*

_____

_____

To one say, *"How did your family take to the idea of the two of you getting married or being together (if they are not married)?"*

_____

_____

To the other say, *"And how did you family feel about the two of you marrying or being together?"*

_____

_____

Other questions may arise regarding families of origin, if the couple is living together and not married or in a gay/lesbian relationship.

Back to the marriage or committed relationship:

Say to one, *"What was the early _____ (marriage or committed relationship) like? Any surprises?"*

_____

_____

To the other say, *"What was it like for you? Were you surprised by anything at that stage in the _____ (marriage or committed relationship)?"*

_____

_____

To one say, *"How did the relationship change over time?"*

_____

_____

To the other say, *"How did it change over time for you?"*

_____

_____

To both:

Say, *"Do you have children? What are their names and ages?"*

_____

_____

Take down the names and ages of any children from this and previous relationships not mentioned earlier.

If they have children together,

Say, *"How did you decide to have children?"*

_____

_____

Say, *"How did your relationship change after the birth of each of your children?"*

_____

_____

Explore their sexual relationship in an open-ended manner:

Say, *"Sex plays different roles in the lives of different couples: it can be a source of comfort, pleasure, or connection; it can be the occasion for guilt, pain, or conflict. What role does sex play in your relationship?"*

_____

_____

Say, *"What is intimacy like between you in other areas such as affection, emotional sharing, or conversations about the things that matter to you?"*

_____

_____

Note: Be sure to elicit a response from both before moving on.

Say, *"How have sex and intimacy changed over time?"*

_____

_____

Say, *"What would you like to see different?"* (As always, be sure to get the response from each person.)

_____

_____

Say to one, *"When did you first notice difficulties in the relationship?"*

_____

_____

Say, *"What did you notice?"*

_____

_____

Say, *"How has that changed over time?"*

_____

_____

Say, *"How do you explain the development of these problems to yourself?"*

_____

_____

Say to the other one, *"When did you first notice difficulties in the relationship?"*

_____

_____

Say, *"What did you notice?"*

_____

_____

Say, *"How has that changed over time?"*

_____

_____

Say, *"How do you explain the development of these problems to yourself?"*

_____

_____

Say, *"Have you sought help for these or any other problems in the past?"*

_____

_____

If yes, say, *"How many times has either or both of you sought help?"*

_____

_____

For each past treatment, say the following:

Say, *"When did this treatment occur?"*

_____

_____

Say, *"Who attended the sessions* (individual or conjoint)*?"*

_____

_____

Say, *"What was the presenting problem?"*

_____

_____

Say, *"Who was the therapist?"*

_____

_____

Say, *"How long did treatment last?"*

_____

_____

Say, *"What were the results?"*

_____

_____

Say, *"Were you satisfied with how the therapy went and with the results?"*

_____

_____

Say, *"If not, why not?"*

_____

_____

Say, *"Was any medication prescribed or recommended?"*

_____

_____

Say, *"With what outcome?"*

_____

_____

Say, *"Is either of you on psychotropic or psychiatric medication now?*

_____

_____

If yes, say the following;

Say, *"What are you taking?"*

_____

_____

Say, *"What dose?"*

_____

_____

Say, *"For how long?"*

_____

_____

Say, *"Who prescribed it and who monitors it?"*

_____

_____

Say, *"We have covered a lot of territory in this hour."*

_____

_____

If the therapist has not yet described the couple's dysfunctional interactional pattern in terms of interacting vulnerabilities, they should do so now as in the following:

Say, *"From what I can tell so far, it seems that _____ (describe the couple's dysfunctional interactional pattern)."*

_____

_____

The therapist outlines the format for the assessment and therapy:

Say, *"Before we stop for the day, I would like to outline how our meetings together will proceed. Today is our first session, next you will each have an individual session to help me get to know you better and to help us understand how you have come to be here. In those individual sessions we will focus on the person in the room without discussion of your partner or your relationship. After that, we will have a joint feedback session in which we will pull together everything we have discussed in order to develop an understanding of the problem and a plan for changing things. The plan will include joint meetings, reading, some homework or exercises, and possibly some highly structured individual sessions if needed."*

Note: These refer to EMDR; this is not mentioned by name at this point.

Say, *"Do you have any questions so far?"*

_____

_____

Say, *"In preparation for our individual sessions, I would like each of you to prepare a written list with 10 of your most negative experiences in your life, 5 experiences before age 18 and 5 experiences after age 18. By this, I mean the experiences that had the highest level of negative emotion attached to them regardless of what the emotion was. It could be anger, shame, guilt, fear, anxiety, hatred, disgust, or any other negative emotion. The experience could be something that happened one time or something that happened repeatedly, it could be something that happened to you or something you witnessed."*

If any sexual issue came up earlier in the session, say the following to both partners:

Say, *"I also would like you to prepare a written list of all uncomfortable sexually related experiences you have had. I mean 'sexually related' in the broadest sense: experiences related to how you feel about your body, how you feel about yourself as a man or woman, how you feel about yourself as a sexual person, as well as any experience of a sexual nature that led you to feel guilty, ashamed, or in any way uncomfortable."*

If issues of intense anger or violence were raised or hinted at earlier in the session,

Say to both, *"Finally, also prepare a list of any triggers for, or experiences of, anger or explosive emotion."*

Say, *"Do either of you have any questions about what I've asked you to do in preparation for your individual session?"*

_____

_____

Explain to them how you may handle any sensitive material, previously undisclosed to the partner that may arise in the individual sessions. My colleague at

Council for Relationships, Michele Southworth, JD, LMFT (personal communication, March, 2005), formulated and articulated the following:

> Say, *"Sometimes in a marriage people have secrets from one another, and some secrets have a tremendous impact on people's relationships. Some don't have such a big impact. In our individual sessions, I would like you to feel free to talk to me about anything that is important in understanding your situation, and sometimes that may include a secret that you haven't told your partner. There are a few things to understand about what happens when you tell me a secret in this situation.*
>
> *The first is that everything you tell me in an individual session is confidential and I can't reveal anything without your permission. I have found that the easiest way to handle this is that we agree ahead of time that I am free to talk with your partner about anything that you've told me except specific things you have asked me not to talk about. If there is a secret, we need to evaluate whether it is the kind of secret that is harmful to your marriage. If it isn't harmful, I don't think there is a problem with my not revealing it.*
>
> *If it is harmful, then we have three choices. One is that you tell your partner about it, either with or without my help. The second is that you may need more time and help to get ready to tell your partner, and as long as we have an understanding that you will disclose it and are working on doing that, I will hold the secret for some reasonable period of time, usually not more than a few sessions, until you are ready to talk about it. If you are not prepared to address the secret at all with your partner, then I am in a position where I can't be your couple's therapist because my job is to make the therapy safe for both people, and I can't do that if I have important information affecting your relationship that one of you doesn't have.*
>
> *If that is the case, I will tell both of you at the second joint meeting that I am not able to be your couple's therapist. Do you have any questions about this issue?"*

_____

_____

To solicit their agreement to continue the process, say the following:

> Say, *"You understand that this is the first session in what will likely be a four-session evaluation process—sometimes we can't cover everything we need to in one session so a second individual session may be needed. Do you understand what I have asked each of you to do in preparation for your individual session?"*

_____

_____

> Say, *"Are you clear about how we will handle any sensitive material either of you may have kept secret?"*

_____

_____

Say, *"Are you ready to continue?"*

_____

_____

If both are prepared to continue, we set up the individual sessions. If not, say the following:

Say, *"Then take some time to think about it and talk it over and let me know your decision. If you need another meeting to discuss any reservations or concerns, please call and we'll set that up."*

_____

_____

End of intake session.

Individual Session Script

The goals for these sessions are to identify the central struggle of each partner's life, locate its origin in the past, and help the client begin to recognize its impact in the present, both in the primary relationship and in other relationships. It is equally important that each partner experience the therapist as an empathic witness to that struggle.

Family of Origin

The interview is guided by a search for relational trauma, experiences contributory to high reactivity: empathic failure; parental absence, unavailability, neglect or failure to protect from overwhelming emotion; frank emotional, physical, or sexual abuse.

Say, *"I am interested in understanding more about what it was like for you to grow up in your family. What memories or experiences stand out as you think about growing up?"*

_____

_____

_____

_____

Go on with questions about one parent, then the other, then any stepparents or parent surrogates.

Say, *"Tell me about your father. What was he like when you were growing up? What was he like as a person?"*

_____

_____

Don't let the client give you his parent's curriculum vitae (CV); ask for clarification of any generalities or stereotypes. For example, when a client gives the answer "Your typical state trooper," or "Your typical first generation," say, "What does a typical _____ do? How does ____(he or she) act?"

Next say, *"Please describe five different characteristics of your father as you were growing up?"*

_____

_____

_____

_____

If the client gives you characteristics that seem similar, say the following:

Say, *"*_____ *and* _____ (state the similar characteristics used) *are pretty much the same thing. Please describe him in terms of his different or distinct qualities."*

_____

_____

Say, *"What was he like as a parent?"*

_____

_____

_____

_____

Say, *"How did your relationship with him change over time?"*

_____

_____

If there was a major illness, cut-off or death, say the following:

Say, *"How did things change for you after _____ (state the incident)?"*

_____

_____

Say, *"How was that for you?"*

_____

_____

Listening for issues that might have led to the client feeling sorry for his father, say the following:

Say, *"What stories did he tell about growing up?"*

_____

_____

_____

_____

Say, *"Were there early deaths in his family? Serious illnesses? Substance Problems? Cut-offs?"*

_____

_____

_____

_____

Say, *"What was his role in the family he came from, the 'star,' the 'peacemaker,' the 'outsider,' for example?"*

_____

_____

Finally say, *"When you think of your father, what is the strongest emotion you feel?"*

_____

_____

If the response is a positive emotion, ask the following:

Say, *"And what is the strongest negative emotion you feel when you think about him?"*

_____

_____

Repeat the same interview for the other parent.

Say, *"Tell me about your mother."*

_____

_____

_____

_____

Repeat the interview for any stepparent or parent surrogate.

Say, *"Tell me about your _____."*

_____

_____

_____

_____

Ask about the parent's relationship.

Say, *"How were your parents with one another?"*

_____

_____

Say, *"Did they seem well matched?"*

_____

_____

If not, say, *"How did they seem mismatched?"*

_____

_____

Say, *"How did that affect you? Were your sympathies more with one parent than the other?"*

_____

_____

If either parent had a committed relationship subsequent to the client's parents' marriage, ask the same questions.

Say, *"How were _____* (e.g., your mother and stepfather) *with each other and so forth?"*

_____

_____

For any life-changing event (e.g., death, divorce, etc.) that occurred in the family during the client's formative years (if the event has not yet been addressed) ask about the following:

Say, *"How did things change in the family after _____* (e.g., your mother became ill)*?"*

_____

_____

Say, *"How was that for you?"*

_____

_____

Review relationships with sibling. For each of the siblings, ask the following:

Say, *"Tell me about your sibling(s)."*

_____

_____

_____

_____

As appropriate to the circumstance, ask:

Say, *"Let's start with the oldest. _____* (state the sibling's name) *is _____ years ___* (older or younger) *than you? What was ___* (he or she) *like when you were growing up?"*

_____

_____

Say, *"What was your relationship like growing up?"*

_____

_____

Say, *"What is it like now?"*

_____

_____

Repeat questions for each sibling.

Review of Prior Marriages or Committed Relationships

If the client was previously married, ask the following:

Say, *"Tell me about your first marriage. What was your _____ (husband or wife's) name?"*

_____

_____

Say, *"How old was each of you when you met?*

_____

_____

Say, *"What were your life circumstances at the time in terms of school, career, other relationships?"*

_____

_____

Say, *"What attracted you to _____ (state name of ex-partner)?"*

_____

_____

Say, *"What five different characteristics would you use to describe _____ (state name of ex-partner)?"*

_____

_____

_____

_____

Say, *"How would you describe his or her family?"*

_____

_____

Say, *"What were the struggles in the marriage?"*

_____

_____

Say, *"How did the marriage end?"*

_____

_____

Say, *"What was that like for you?"*

_____

_____

Repeat the same set of questions, for any other prior marriage.
Then ask about prior significant relationships.

Say, *"Tell me about any significant relationships prior to the current relationship. How many would you say there were?"*

_____

_____

Say, *"What were the names of the other person or people with whom you had a significant relationship(s)?"*

_____

_____

_____

_____

For each significant relationship, repeat the set of questions above, substituting *relationship* for *marriage*.

Review List of the 10 Most Negative Experiences

Say, *"Let's look over the 10 most negative experiences that I asked you to write. I know some of them will have come up in our earlier conversation. Just give them to me as headlines and I'll ask questions if I need to know more. I'm sure we could spend a whole session discussing some of them, but, as with significant issues we have already talked about, I want to capture the scope of your life and your relationships at this stage of the process."*

_____

_____

_____

_____

_____

_____

_____

_____

_____

_____

Review of Negative Sexually Related Experiences (If Requested at the First Session)

Say, *"I asked you to identify any negative sexually related experiences you may have had. What did you identify?"*

_____

_____

_____

_____

_____

_____

Review of Anger Triggers or Experiences (If Requested)

Say, *"Are there particular anger experiences that you have had that stick out for you?"*

_____

_____

_____

_____

With the partner who has expressed disproportionate or explosive anger, say the following:

Say, *"What are the triggers for your anger?"*

_____

_____

Suggest Reading on Relevant Topics

Do this as appropriate. Check out the following Web site for helpful suggestions: http://www.councilforrelationships.org/articles/useful-books_1-10-05.htm or suggest your own.

After you checked to see if the client is a reader,

Say, *"I'm also going to recommend some reading for you to do over the next few weeks. Don't rush through and don't think of any of these readings as a checklist. Think of them as illustrating how the past is connected with the present and how emotions are connected with behavior. I would suggest _____ (suggest appropriate readings)."*

Explain and Secure Individual Commitment to Preparation for Conjoint Feedback Session

Say, *"We've talked about a lot today and as I said earlier, we could have spent a whole session on some of the issues our conversation raised. For the next session, I would like you to think about how growing up with the experiences you've had has impacted you as an adult, specifically your relationships and, most specifically, your relationship with _____ (state partner's name)."*

Say, *"Do you have any questions before we stop for today?"*

_____

_____

Conjoint Feedback Session Script

The goals of this session are for the therapist and clients, first, to construct a case formulation that integrates the behavior each learned in order to survive childhood (intergenerational) and their trauma-based reactive emotional states (intrapsychic) with the dysfunctional interactional pattern that brought them to treatment. The second goal is to develop an overarching metaphor for this formulation that can organize the therapy concretely around interacting sensitivities, complementary attachment styles, mutual retraumatization, or some other interlocking interactional pattern.

Explore the Couple's Interaction Since the Intake Session

Use solution-focused interventions to reinforce any positive changes or interactions (O'Hanlon & Weiner-Davis, 1989). The whole session can be spent on this if there is sufficient material, and the feedback session can be postponed to the next meeting. Save any problems they report for incorporation into the case formulation (below).

> Say, *"How have you been with each other since our joint meeting* _____
> (state however long ago it was)*?"*

_____

_____

_____

_____

Then ask the partner, their view of how things have been.

> Say, *"And what's your view of how you've been with each other?"*

_____

_____

_____

_____

After each has given what is usually a global assessment, go back and ask them, in turn, to be more specific.

> Say, *"Can you describe in video language* _____ (repeat the explanation given in the first session, if necessary) *how you were more*
> _____ (whatever the first observation the client made)*?"*

_____

_____

_____

_____

Repeat this question for each significant observation the client made (e.g., "We were more relaxed around each other," "We communicated better," "We had more conflict," etc.).

After you have gotten a more detailed description of significant between session interaction from the first partner, repeat the process with the other.

Say, *"How about you* _____ (state the other partner's name), *how would you describe in video language* _____ (repeat the explanation given in the first session, if necessary) *how you were more* _____ (whatever the first observation the client made)?"

_____

_____

_____

_____

If both partners reported positive changes in their interaction, ask for each change either reported:

Say, *"How was that different from how you have typically interacted with each other?"*

_____

_____

For this and the subsequent questions, be sure to elicit a response from both partners.

Say, *"How did you do that?"*

_____

_____

Say, *"How did it feel to be that way with each other?"*

_____

_____

If both partners report negative interaction during the between session period, clarify how that behavior relates to the dysfunctional interactional pattern that was identified in the first session.

Say, *"How does the interaction you just described fit in with the pattern we identified in the first session?"*

_____

_____

Say, *"Let's see how that pattern connects with what we talked about in each of the individual sessions."*

_____

_____

Say, *"*_____ (state partner you are working with), *how did growing up in your family under the circumstances you did have an impact on you as an adult?"*

_____

_____

_____

_____

If the client has trouble articulating connections, mention what you would identify as a pattern of traumatic experiences and ask the client:

Say, _"How do you remember feeling at those times?"_

_____

_____

Say, _"Children typically protect the image of their parents at their own expense. We feel implicated somehow in what goes wrong around us. For example, 'If I were smarter, more athletic, more popular, or more whatever, dad would have shown more interest in me.' Or 'Mom's life seemed so empty and I just couldn't do anything to make her feel better.' What do you think you carried away from your experiences as a part of yourself?"_

_____

_____

If the client has a hard time connecting with the impact of the past experience, help by suggesting how his or her past and present connect in your mind as their therapist. With Sally, for example: "Your mother favored your brother, this was critical for you to the point of your thinking she hated you. Your father was a nice man, seemed to love you but was extremely passive and stood by idly while your mother criticized and ridiculed you. How do you think that has affected you? Now, whenever Tom's children disrespect you, you go into a rage because he hasn't come to your rescue."

These early response patterns are multidetermined and repetitive. So, help the client identify the whole fabric. Typically both parents have the same impact on the child even though the content of the interaction is different with the two parents. For example, an alcoholic father and dispirited mother both leave their child feeling anxious, inadequate, either dismissively or anxiously attached, and disposed to pair up with someone with the opposite attachment style (D'Antonio, 1994).

Co-Construct the Case Formulation

When each partner has explored how he or she was impacted by his or her family of origin, then help both see how their childhood adaptations play out in their current dysfunctional interaction and help them identify the emotions at play at those times. Help them see how their patterns and vulnerabilities interact, and how what each does to manage anxiety or rescue threatened self-esteem is the very behavior the other finds most anxiety provoking or threatening.

Say, _"We see how each of you has adapted to the circumstances you grew up in. We see also how the two parts fit together. What each of you does to deal with _____ (state how it is dealt with, for example, insecurity or anxiety) is the very thing that leads the other to feel _____ (state how the other ends up feeling)."_

Then describe the pattern as you see it. To stay with the simplified example above, you could say the following: "Tom, you dealt with the emotional chaos in your family by shutting down and becoming invisible. So, any show of emotion on

Sally's part overwhelms you. You become passive and withdrawn and leave Sally feeling alone and abandoned. The more distressed she gets, the more passive you become."

"You, Sally, dealt with your mother's criticism and rejection, and your father's passivity by always being on your best behavior and extending yourself to others to win them over. At any sign of disapproval, criticism or lack of support, you feel hurt, disappointed, and angry. You go into a rage at Tom because he does not stand up for you. The pattern is circular and either one of you can set it off."

Say, *"You,* _____ (state the name of one partner) *dealt with* _____ (talk about the pattern) *while you* _____ (state the name of the other partner) *dealt with* _____ (state this partner's pattern). *The pattern is circular and either one of you can set it off."*

_____

_____

Note: When a dysfunctional interactional pattern occurs in the session, body scans or somatic experiencing may be helpful at clarifying their emotional significance.

Say, *"Let's stop for a moment and notice what you are feeling in your body. As you do a body scan right now, what do you notice?"*

_____

_____

Treatment Plan

Outline standard procedures typically used in conjoint couples therapy and what will be expected of them. Solicit their commitment to treatment.

Say, *"You identified your goals in our first session."* Review the goals they identified.

_____

_____

Say, *"As you can now see, your* (dysfunctional) *interactional pattern, based on the adaptations you made growing up, is at the heart of what keeps you from relating in the ways you would like. So, your overarching goal is to change this pattern by recognizing what triggers it for each of you and by dealing differently with the emotional states that lead you to play out your part of that interaction. To do this, we will meet together and process how you relate to one another. At times, I will propose exercises either in the session or at home. I encourage you to keep up your reading. I may also recommend some 'highly structured individual sessions'* (referring to EMDR without mentioning by name or explaining it now) *at some point in the course of therapy. Are you prepared to continue?"*

_____

_____

If yes, set the next appointment.

If no, say, *"What are the considerations for each of you regarding continuing?"*

_____

_____

Explore their concerns and if they are not ready to proceed say the following:

Say, *"Well, take some time to think about it and get back to me. If you feel you want to come in to discuss it further, give me a call and we'll set a time. In the meantime, take care."*

_____

_____

EMDR

Phase 2: Preparation

Because a quick move to EMDR may be too discordant with the expectations of most clients who come for couples therapy, do not introduce it until or unless the following are of issue:

1. *Strong negative affect.* There is an immediate need to reduce volatility or strong negative affect because couples work does not feel emotionally safe for one or both partners or is so disrupted by their extreme reactive interactions. (This was the case with Tom and Sally.)
2. *No hope.* One partner is demoralized and does not see hope or value in working on the relationship (this partner is probably depressed). With a trauma history, EMDR often has a powerful effect on depression. Evaluation for medication treatment for depression might be postponed until the client has had at least four sessions of EMDR, unless the client is dysfunctional or suicidal.
3. *Well-defined blocking issue.* There is a well-defined issue clearly blocking forward movement; for example, an affair whose images haunt the partner.
4. *No change.* Conjoint sessions do not seem to be moving: the couple's reactivity is not declining.
5. *Interventions fail to hold.* Therapeutic interventions seem appropriate, clients respond in the sessions but the interventions don't seem to hold.

Integrating Couples Therapy and EMDR Script

It is most important that EMDR be seen as a natural progression in the therapy. Thus, the introduction of EMDR must be grounded in the treatment goals: the trauma-based assessment, the case formulation, and overarching treatment metaphor developed in the conjoint feedback session and reinforced in subsequent treatment sessions.

Where volatility makes initiating or continuing conjoint unsafe or unproductive,

Say, *"This* (dysfunctional) *interactional pattern of yours* _____ (describe it in the terms you have developed with them) *is so destructive* (or so deeply entrenched) *to the two of you and your relationship that we need to do something to drain the reservoir of negative emotion that feeds it."*

Here refer back to the emotions identified earlier that drive the interaction for each of them and their origin in family and other early experiences.

Say, *"When you get caught up in that interaction, you are, in effect, having flashbacks to those earlier experiences, not in the sense that you are replaying a video of those times but in the sense that you are reliving the emotions. Think of when* _____ (remind them of the key relationally traumatic events you have identified). *In general, the faster and the higher your negative emotions rise, the less they have to do with the present moment and the more with past negative events. You get caught up in those feelings so quickly and deeply that is very difficult to interrupt the pattern you've developed, even with using ordinary talk-therapy methods. There is a therapeutic process that can drain away the negative emotions that have attached themselves to you from the negative past experiences and that feed this pattern. It is called EMDR."*

Continue in the following manner:

Say, *"There are many ways to describe EMDR. In its simplest terms, EMDR does three things. First, it helps people relax. Second, it acts as a psychological vacuum cleaner, which drains away the negative emotion from past negative experiences, like those you have had. And third, it can be used to enhance positive experiences so that as you make changes in the positive direction as individuals and as a couple, these changes can be reinforced and made more permanent. EMDR can affect the way we feel about past, present, or future events, and can remove the negativity from past events and enhance our positive feelings about positive experiences. We will start with past negative experiences and work our way forward. I have found that when we start with positive events or more recent negative ones, earlier traumas can get triggered. While doing EMDR that way will still be effective, it may make it unnecessarily unsettling for the client.*
I will explain this all over again when you come in for EMDR but this is what I propose we do. Each of you will come in alone for these highly structured sessions. I will ask you to recall an event from the past that I have selected from all the things we have talked about. I'll ask you to see yourself there with whoever was significant in that event, to see it, hear it, and remember how you felt then. Next, I'll

ask you a series of questions about what you are experiencing in the present moment. Finally, I'll turn on those earphones you'll be wearing and you'll hear alternating beeps or tones (or other BLS). *There is nothing special about the tones* (or other BLS) *other than that they alternate, in effect, switching the right and left sides of your brain on and off in rapid alternation. We believe this switching on and off of alternating sides of the brain is the active ingredient in EMDR's effectiveness. Painful memories seem to be lodged in the right side of the brain. The bilateral stimulation seems, then, to provide an integrative function, bringing both the brain's left hemisphere—the more logical, verbal, chronologically ordered side—and right hemisphere— the more impressionistic, emotional, spatially oriented side—to bear on a negative experience. This reprocessing changes our experience of the event, removing any negative emotions that have attached themselves to us from the event.*

As you listen to the tones (or other BLS), *the most important thing for you is simply to let happen whatever happens. It really doesn't matter what happens, just go with whatever you are experiencing. About 90% to 95% of the time, when you start with a negative event, you feel negative at the beginning and the negativity drains away as you listen to the tones* (or other BLS). *About 5% to 10% of the time, you feel more negative as you listen to the tones* (or other BLS). *This does not mean there is anything wrong with you, the process, or me. It simply means that your psyche is gathering up all the negative energy around that event before it let's go of it. The negative feelings will crest and then come down. Any questions?"*

_____

_____

Therapeutic balance is also important. It is a truism in couples therapy that individuals partner with others of the same level of differentiation, reactivity, or relational trauma, even though their differing attachment styles may make one partner look healthier than the other. So, it is best to balance the therapy by doing EMDR with both partners, serially or in tandem, but separately. It is also critical to therapeutic balance that a strict prohibition on discussion of the partner or the relationship be maintained in the EMDR sessions. If EMDR must be done serially, it is probably best, for tactical and therapeutic reasons, to begin with the more overtly reactive partner (i.e., the angrier, the more labile, etc.). But, even if the therapist starts EMDR with one partner, both partners' commitment to EMDR as a part of the couple's treatment must be secured in advance.

After you have explained EMDR, say the following:

Say, *"I would like each of you to contract for three EMDR sessions in a row, no more than a week apart. While three sessions probably will not be all that is required, they are usually enough to determine whether the EMDR is having the desired effect in both your eyes and mine. After the three sessions, we will meet jointly again to assess the impact of the EMDR sessions and plan the next step that will likely be some combination individual EMDR sessions and joint meetings. Are you ready to make a commitment to do this?"*

_____

_____

Say, *"I've put together some materials on EMDR. Reading them is not a requirement for success with EMDR. They are simply to help you understand the process. If you're interested, I can e-mail them to each of you. Would you like that?"*

_____

_____

The e-mail packet contains several short pieces prepared by the author in addition to an article (Edmond, Sloan, & McCarty, 2004) illustrating the differential effect of EMDR and eclectic treatment of sexual abuse survivors. Finally, context is important.

Say, *"EMDR is a highly structured process. In those sessions, we need all of the time to do EMDR. We will not have any extended conversations or talk about the relationship. We'll save those conversations for here when we meet again in no more than 3 weeks from now. EMDR is an integral part of the couples therapy. Joint couples sessions will continue less often but at least every 4th week while EMDR sessions are taking place. In the joint sessions, it is important for us to identify and reinforce any changes in you individually and as a couple. Would that be okay with you both?"*

_____

_____

Working With the EMDR Script

The EMDR sessions must be focused, efficient, and maintain the couple's therapeutic balance. Basically, four variants of EMDR are used in these sessions.

Phase 3: Assessment

The usual client preparation is done. The therapist selects targets from the relationship and other traumas that came to light in each partner's original assessment interview and the lists of negative experiences prepared. They are ordered chronologically from earliest to most recent. In addition to trauma targets, triggers for anger and other reactive behavior are also targeted. Trigger targets are reprocessed after significant trauma targets have been. Because the therapist may reprocess only enough material to gain and keep momentum in the couples work, not all negative material may be reprocessed. The therapist may need to select targets that seem most central to the core issue for the individual and the couple. Reprocessing is carried out in the standard way. The first EMDR session begins with the therapist reviewing the explanation of EMDR given earlier. Each session ends with the client being asked to notice any change between that session and the next.

Incident

Say, *"The memory that we will start with today is _____ (select the next incident to be targeted)."*

_____

_____

Say, *"What happens when you think of the incident?"*

_____

_____

Or say, *"When you think of the incident what do you get?"*

_____

_____

Picture

Say, *"What picture represents the entire incident?"*

_____

_____

If there are many choices or if the client becomes confused, the clinician assists by asking:

Say, *"What picture represents the most traumatic part of the incident?"*

_____

_____

When a picture is unavailable, the clinician merely invites the client to:

Say, *"Think of the incident."*

_____

_____

Negative Cognition (NC)

Say, *"What words best go with the picture that express your negative belief about yourself now?"*

_____

_____

Positive Cognition (PC)

Say, *"When you bring up that picture or incident, what would you like to believe about yourself now?"*

_____

_____

Validity of Cognition (VoC)

Say, *"When you think of the incident* (or picture) *how true do those words* _____ (clinician repeats the positive cognition) *feel to you now on a scale of 1 to 7, where 1 feels completely false and 7 feels completely true?"*

1	2	3	4	5	6	7
(completely false)				(completely true)		

Sometimes, it is necessary to explain further.

Say, *"Remember, sometimes we know something with our head, but it feels differently in our gut. In this case, what is the gut-level feeling of the truth of* _____ (clinician state the positive cognition), *from 1 being completely false to 7 being completely true?"*

1	2	3	4	5	6	7
(completely false)				(completely true)		

Emotions

Say, *"When you bring up the picture* (or incident) *and those words* _____ (clinician states the negative cognition), *what emotion do you feel now?"*

_____

_____

Subjective Units of Disturbance (SUD)

Say, *"On a scale of 0 to 10, where 0 is no disturbance or neutral and 10 is the highest disturbance you can imagine, how disturbing does it feel now?"*

0	1	2	3	4	5	6	7	8	9	10
(no disturbance)							(highest disturbance)			

Location of Body Sensation

Say, *"Where do you feel it* (the disturbance) *in your body?"*

_____

_____

Phase 4: Desensitization

Use the standard way of working with the Desensitization Phase.

Phase 5: Installation

Say, *"How does _____* (repeat the PC) *sound?"*

_____

_____

Say, *"Do the words _____* (repeat the PC) *still fit, or is there another positive statement that feels better?"*

_____

_____

If the client accepts the original positive cognition, the clinician should ask for a VoC rating to see if it has improved:

Say, *"As you think of the incident, how do the words feel from 1 being completely false to 7 being completely true?"*

1	2	3	4	5	6	7
(completely false)				(completely true)		

Say, *"Think of the event and hold it together with the words _____* (repeat the PC).*"*

_____

_____

Do a long set of BLS to see if there is more processing to be done.

Phase 6: Body Scan

Say, *"Close your eyes and keep in mind the original memory and the positive cognition. Then bring your attention to the different parts of your body, starting with your head and working downward. Any place you find any tension, tightness, or unusual sensation, tell me."*

_____

_____

Phase 7: Closure

Say, *"Things may come up or they may not. If they do, great! Write it down, and it can be a target for next time. If you get any new memo-*

*ries, dreams, or situations that disturb you, just take a good snap-
shot. It isn't necessary to give a lot of detail. Just put down enough
to remind you so we can target it next time. The same thing goes for
any positive dreams or situations. If negative feelings do come up,
try not to make them significant. Remember, it's still just the old
stuff. Just write it down for next time. Then use the tape or the Safe
Place Exercise to let as much of the disturbance go as possible. Even
if nothing comes up, make sure to use the tape everyday and give me
a call if you need to."*

As an alternative, say, *"Between now and the next session, I want you
to notice anything different about yourself, particularly your reactions to people, events, and situations. That will be the first thing
I ask you at the beginning of the next session."*

At the beginning of the next session, say the following:

Say, *"What have you noticed different about yourself this week?"*

_____

_____

Any change in the direction of treatment goals is noted and may be briefly
reinforced using solution-focused methods (O'Hanlon & Weiner-Davis, 1989) or
resource installations techniques.

Positive Reinforcement Using Resource Installation

Report of change in the positive direction can be reinforced using a simplified variant of resource installation (Leeds, 2006). This is done on one or more of the reported changes quickly at the beginning of a session to allow maximum time for the EMDR Standard Protocol reprocessing.

> Say, *"Think about and visualize the positive experience you were just telling me about. Do you have it? Great! What do you see?"*

> _____

> _____

> Say, *"Good, see the look on your faces, hear the tone in your voices, and remember how you felt at the time. When you do that what is the strongest emotion you feel right now?"*

> _____

> _____

> Say, *"Feel that emotion in your body. What do you feel physically right now?"*

> _____

> _____

Note: If either the current emotion or body sensation is negative, do not proceed.

If both the current emotion and the body sensation are positive or neutral, say the following:

> Say, *"What positive statement do you want to make about yourself when you see yourself there* _____ (behaving in the new or positive way) *and feel the way you feel now physically and emotionally?"*

> _____

> _____

> Say, *"Okay, see yourself there* _____ (behaving in the new or positive way), *say that* _____ (state the PC) *to yourself, feel what you feel physically, and emotionally and let happen whatever happens."*

> _____

> _____

Initially use a short set of 5 to 10 passes. The number of passes can be lengthened in subsequent sessions as the client is able to stay positive with longer sets. After this, move on to another resource installation or to the EMDR Standard Protocol for trauma or trigger targets.

Behavior Rehearsal Using Future Templates

The Future Template (Shapiro, 1995) is used, in this context, as a form of behavioral rehearsal to help the partners adopt or integrate new behaviors relevant to the treatment goals (e.g., being more assertive, learning to say no, initiating some previously anxiety-provoking sexual behavior, etc.). It is typically used after a significant amount of reprocessing has taken place. Because the therapist does not know if visualizing the desired new behavior will evoke positive or negative affect, this form of Future Template uses a variation of the assessment employed in the EMDR Standard Protocol, postponing the articulation of a positive or negative cognition until after the client's emotion and body sensations have been identified. Thus, the rehearsed behavior will constitute either a resource to be installed or target to be reprocessed depending on the emotion and body sensation attached to it. As a result, the therapist will either create a positive resource or know that there is more reprocessing to do and will set up the target and use the Standard EMDR Protocol.

Future Template Protocol Script

Say, *"Let's start with your visualizing _____ (state your desired* new behavior) *with your partner in whatever setting that feels good to you. Do you have it?"*

_____

_____

Say, *"Okay, see yourself there in the scene* (which illustrates the desired new behavior) *with your partner. See the look on your faces, hear the tone in your voices, and imagine how you will both feel when you are actually relating that way."*

Say, *"Okay, when you do that, what is the strongest emotion you feel right now?"*

_____

_____

Say, *"Feel that emotion in your body. What do you feel physically right now?"*

_____

_____

Future Template With Positive Installation

If both the current emotion and the body sensation are positive or neutral, you are installing a resource and then say the following:

Say, *"When you see yourself there with your partner _____ (name the* desired new behavior) *and you feel the way you do right now physically and emotionally, what positive statement do you want to make about yourself?"*

_____

_____

Say, *"Okay, see yourself in the scene with your partner and feel what you feel right now physically and emotionally and say that _____ (the PC) to yourself and let happen whatever happens."*

Initially use a set of 5 to 10 passes. If the client's positive feelings increase, you may stop here or do another short set of 5 to 10 passes. The number of passes can be lengthened as you do more reprocessing and the client is able to stay positive.

If, on the other hand, the client's state becomes negative, either in terms of emotion or body sensations, have the client visualize the desired new behavior with his or her partner again and follow the Future Template with Standard Protocol below.

Future Template With the EMDR Standard Protocol

If either the current emotion or the body sensation is negative in the future template, say the following:

Say, *"What is the worst thing you can say about yourself when you see yourself in the scene with your partner and you feel physically and emotionally the way you do now?"*

_____

_____

Say, *"Okay, see yourself there behaving _____ (in the desired new way), say that _____ (state the NC) to yourself, feel what you feel physically and emotionally and let happen whatever happens."*

_____

_____

Continue with the EMDR Standard Protocol through the Installation Phase.

Fast Forward Protocol Script

The Fast Forward is an expansion of the Future Template. It consists of an extended visualization or mental videotape of some behavioral or interactional sequence, designed to elicit any disturbing elements in the sequence and help reduce the disturbance in the process. The disturbing elements in the sequence are then targeted using the Standard EMDR Protocol for reprocessing. Fast Forward is routinely used with anxiety and phobias. It is used with couples only after significant trauma and trigger reprocessing with the EMDR Standard Protocol has occurred. It is useful in deactivating charged interactions (e.g., discussion of certain topics, aspects of sexual intimacy, etc.) by uncovering what aspect of the interaction is most loaded for the individual.

First get the client into a calm, relaxed state. This occurs naturally at the end of a positive installation or the installation phase of the EMDR Standard Protocol. So, the Fast Forward can be tacked right on. Alternately, it can also easily be achieved by reinstalling some successfully installed resource or the Installation Phase of a previously reprocessed target.

Once the client is calm and relaxed, say the following:

Say, *"Imagine you have a videotape of _____ (state the sequence) from _____ (designate a beginning point) to _____ (state the end point).*

When I start the tones (or whatever the form of bilateral stimulation is used), *I want you to start your videotape and go through it at a quick but comfortable pace. Anytime you come to a scene in the video where you feel upset or otherwise lose the sense of well being you now feel, stop, focus on that scene until you feel comfortable and relaxed again. Then continue with your videotape. If you don't have to stop, that's fine. If you stop once or more than once, that's fine. Just let me know when you get to the end point."*

_____

_____

Use BLS. When client indicates that the end point was reached, say the following:

Say, *"How many times did you stop?"*

_____

_____

The client can almost invariably give a precise number.

Say, *"What were they?"*

_____

_____

Use the EMDR Standard Protocol to reprocess these scenes one by one.

Therapeutic Format

After each partner has undergone the initial three sessions of EMDR, the format for the therapy becomes quite variable. Ideally, the couple should be seen conjointly every 2 to 4 weeks and both partners should have EMDR sessions in the intervening weeks. Logistics and finances may make this difficult. For some couples, a 3-week cycle with an EMDR session for one partner, followed by one for the other, followed by a conjoint session works well. The therapist will have to determine the therapeutic modality that best meets the couple's immediate needs at any time and which modality moves the treatment along more effectively. This author stresses again the importance of keeping the EMDR sessions focused, both for reasons of practicality and therapeutic balance.

The potential of EMDR to center people in their own lives without making them self-centered; to reduce thoughts, feelings, and sensations of personal diminishment; to render people less defensive and reactive; and to help them become more vulnerable and compassionate is a major contribution to couples therapy. It helps couples move beyond the patterns of the past to deal more effectively with one another in the here and now.

Effective use of EMDR in couples therapy seems to require both expertise in the use of EMDR and sensitivity to the context and demands of couples work. It places special demands on the therapist to orchestrate a coherent therapeutic experience for clients out of disparate elements: a radically individual treatment (after all, EMDR goes on inside the individual's head), and an interpersonal treatment whose desired outcome is interactive. The concepts of reactivity and relational trauma can provide theoretical coherence on which therapists can base this therapeutic experience.

10

From Relational Problems to Psychological Solutions: EMDR in Couples Therapy

Barry Litt

The EMDR method represents a significant advance in psychotherapy. While most of the empirical research on EMDR demonstrates its efficacy as a treatment for post-traumatic stress disorder (PTSD), many clinicians realize its benefits in treating small "t" traumas, including relational traumas. Dysfunctional patterns of relating in the family of origin can imprint themselves on the relational template of adults, only to be reenacted in the contemporary couples relationship. Because EMDR can be effective at transforming these earlier relational traumas, adults can become less reactive, enjoy greater distress tolerance, and have a more resilient ego boundary. Thus, EMDR is an invaluable tool in couples therapy.

One of the clinical challenges to incorporating EMDR into couples work is cultivating a therapeutic contract for this individually based intervention. It is common for clients to come to therapy with the expectation that it is the *other* partner who needs to change. Clients naturally blame their partners for their own dysregulated affect, acting-out behavior, or damaged sense of self. Alternatively, some couples may blame the *relationship itself* for problems, as if the relationship were its own anthropomorphic agent capable of acting upon the partners who are haplessly minding their own business. Such couples may complain of "communication problems" that are the fault of no one in particular—a diffusion of responsibility that belies the fact that they communicate their blame, contempt, and helplessness with alacrity. Thus, it could be said that partners in couples therapy often seek a relational solution to a psychological problem (Litt, 2007a, 2007b).

Challenging a partner to face his or her own motivation and behavior and inviting a contract for change is certainly more art than science. Nonetheless, a 5-step protocol is proposed that can guide therapists to develop an EMDR treatment plan within the context of couples therapy. This protocol can and should be applied to both partners in most cases, but of necessity, the therapist must choose one partner to begin with.

139

The 5 steps are laid out briefly below, followed by detailed descriptions.

Step 1. Identify the pathogenic transaction.
Step 2. Identify the negative cognition, affect, and sensation.
Step 3. Contextualize the transactional experience.
Step 4. Negotiate surrender of the acting-out behavior.
Step 5. Contract for EMDR therapy to address the original trauma.

The 5-Step Protocol for Couples Therapy Script

Step 1: Identify the Pathological Transaction

This step involves observing repetitive or stereotyped patterns of relating in the couple that are suggestive of reenactments of childhood relational configurations (Litt, 2007a, 2007b). Reliance on blame, externalizing, personalizing, and projective identification are processes that have deep roots and are particularly resistant to psychoeducation or cognitive solutions (Litt, 2007a, 2007b). For example, when one partner reliably experiences conflict as a referendum on his or her self-worth, the issue is personalized, the transaction is hijacked, and resolution is unlikely. At this juncture, the therapist describes the sequence of actions that characterize the pattern. The therapist then asks permission to explore the pattern with the couple.

A sample of the therapist's intervention with a couple might go like this:

Say: *"Let me slow you two down for a minute so I can share what I have been noticing.* _____ (name of partner A), *when* _____ (name of partner B) *was talking about* _____ (state the issue at hand), *I noticed that you seemed* _____ (state affect such as angry, sad, frustrated, etc.) *and reacted by* _____ (state the defensive reaction, such as took it as a personal attack, reacted with criticism or blame, just gave up)."

_____

_____

Issue: _____

Affect: _____

Defensive Reaction: _____

The skill here is to focus on the client's reactivity and to not get caught up in why the reaction is justified or turn to the other partner for an explanation or apology.

Say, *"It seems like you became* _____ (state the affect that occurred) *and the issue got sidetracked. Did either of you see that too?"*

_____

_____

Say, *"Can we take some time now to explore that pattern?"*

_____

_____

_____

_____

Say, *"How often does that happen?"*

_____

_____

Say, *"Does the original issue ever get resolved?"*

_____

_____

This same inquiry can be made of the other partner to establish how each triggers a reaction in the other.

Say, *"On the other hand, you* (looking at the other partner) *reacted by _____* (state how partner reacted). *Can we take some time now to explore that pattern?"*

_____

_____

_____

_____

Say, *"How often does that happen?"*

_____

_____

Say, *"Does the original issue ever get resolved according to how you experience it?"*

_____

_____

Step 2: Elicit the Negative Cognition, Affect, and Sensation

This step resembles the Assessment Phase of Shapiro's (2001) the 11-Step Standard Procedure for EMDR. The therapist must choose one of the partners to work up this assessment. The choice may be the partner who is most activated in pathological transaction, the partner who is most available to his or her subjective experience, or the partner who is most likely to blame the other partner. After choosing one partner, the therapist asks permission to explore the affect, sensation, and negative cognitions that were just activated in situ.

Incident or Issue

In this protocol, instead of using a picture, as in the Standard EMDR Protocol, this author emphasizes the incident in situ as the stimulus.

Following up with the couple above, the therapist may proceed as follows:

Say, *"_____* (name of partner A), *you said that you felt _____* (state affect) *when _____* (state name of partner B) *spoke. I would like to understand that better. Can I explore that with you now?"*

_____

_____

Say, *"Would you be willing to do an exercise that will help me get a better grasp of what happens to you?"*

_____

_____

Negative Cognition (NC)

Say, *"Thinking some more about what just happened with _____ (name of partner), what belief about yourself best fits how you feel about yourself now?"*

_____

_____

Positive Cognition (PC)

Say, *"What would you like to believe about yourself, now?"*

_____

_____

Validity of Cognition (VoC)

Say, *"When you think of what just happened, how true do those words _____ (clinician repeats the positive cognition) feel to you now on a scale of 1 to 7, where 1 feels completely false and 7 feels completely true?"*

1   2   3   4   5   6   7
(completely false)   (completely true)

Emotions

Say, *"When you bring about what just happened and those _____ (clinician states the negative cognition), what emotion do you feel now?"*

_____

_____

Subjective Units of Disturbance (SUD)

Say, *"On a scale of 0 to 10, where 0 is no disturbance or neutral and 10 is the highest disturbance you can imagine, how disturbing does it feel now?"*

0   1   2   3   4   5   6   7   8   9   10
(no disturbance)   (highest disturbance)

Location of Body Sensation

Say, *"Where do you feel it (the disturbance) in your body?"*

_____

_____

Step 3: Contextualize the Subjective Experience

This step is intended to identify the original relational context from which the present activation stems. This may be a specific Touchstone Event (Shapiro, 2001) or an ongoing relational configuration in the family of origin that recurred countless times (e.g., an anxious mother, a critical father). This step is critical in helping clients recognize that their relational attitudes, perceptions, and subsequent relational actions are anchored in dysfunctional patterns of the past, and are being reenacted in the present. This awareness is often the springboard for relinquishing blame and accepting responsibility for change.

The method used here is the Affect Bridge, or Float-Back Technique described by Shapiro (2001), in which the client is invited to trace the earliest memory of the current gestalt of negative cognition, affect, sensation. In the present example, the intervention might go as follows:

Say, "_____ (state name of partner A), *as you experience these feelings and sensations, and the thought* _____ (state negative cognition), *I'd like you to close your eyes and think back to one of the earliest memories you have of feeling this way.*"

_____

_____

_____

_____

After the client comes up with one or more memories, the therapist continues.

Say, *"So what type of situations brought about this experience for you?"*

_____

_____

_____

_____

Say, *"With whom did you have a similar experience as the one you had just now?"*

_____

_____

Say, *"What did you do to manage that experience?"*

_____

_____

_____

_____

Say, *"Does any of that seem to fit what happens nowadays with* _____ (state name of partner B)*?"*

_____

_____

Note: Behavioral reactions to defensive activation may change from one relational context to another. For example, adults may be more free to act out hostility to a partner than to a parent, even if the internal activation is the same in each case.

Step 4: Negotiate Surrender of the Acting-Out Behavior

This step builds off the insight derived from the previous step. With an increasing understanding that early relational configurations of the family of origin are playing out in the present, clients become ever more ready to concede that their relational attitudes are archaic and that their current reactions are perpetuating the problem. The therapist gains leverage to negotiate with each partner to change maladaptive, behavioral reactions in favor of options that promote a more responsible, constructive dialogue.

Following up with this couple, the therapist might do the following:

Say, "_____ (state name of partner A), *now that you see how your reaction is defensive, and not only puts* _____ (state name of partner B) *in a parent-like role, but derails the dialogue, would you be willing to do something different at these junctures?"*

_____

_____

Say, *"You may not be able to stop 'feeling' defensive for a while, but perhaps you can at least make it a policy not to react the same old way and instead make it your commitment to hear what* _____ (state name of partner B) *has to say."*

_____

_____

Or, if partner B were the subject of the intervention:

Say, "_____ (state the name of partner B), *now that you recognize that* _____ (state the name of partner A) *gets* _____ (state the appropriate affect), *do you notice how you get* _____ (state the appropriate affect) *in turn?"*

_____

_____

Repeat steps 2 and 3.

Say, *"When this happens at home, do you think it would be possible to recognize that you are getting* _____ (state the appropriate affect) *and take a break?"*

_____

_____

Say, *"Then, it is important that instead of* _____ (state the defensive reaction), *you approach* _____ (name of partner A) *again when both of you are calmer so you can resolve the issue."*

_____

_____

Say, *"Your partner may not always respond favorably, particularly at first, but if you don't persist then this pattern will continue.*

> *Are you willing to persist in good communication even if your partner is defensive?"*

_____

_____

Say, *"Perhaps you could communicate by e-mail or a note. Or try again after a short break, but whatever you do, it is vital that neither of you lose your voice in this relationship."*

_____

_____

Step 5: Contract for EMDR Intervention

In practice, this step may be seamless with the previous step. Therapists can readily empathize with a client's dysfunctional reaction, particularly if the reaction is explored and contextualized. Figuratively walking in the client's shoes, the therapist should be able to genuinely say, "Sure, now I can see how you feel that way and do what you do."

However, the temptation may be to rescue (and collude with) the client by expecting the other partner to change such that the first partner does not get triggered to begin with. This is a limited and one-sided strategy, however, and only serves to reinforce the couple's pathological dependency (Litt, 2007a, 2007b). An empathic response to the reactive client is leverage to hold that person to a higher standard of interpersonal behavior and integrity. Parents who ask their children, "If all your friends stole a bike, would you?" are wisely applying the same principle. The message is that mature, responsible responding is not conditioned upon another's behavior.

> Say, *"Given what you've told me about your earlier experiences, I can understand better what happens to you when _____ (partner B) does _____ (the triggering behavior). And I can appreciate how it makes sense or seems justified to do _____ (the defensive reaction). But I think that when we step back, we can see that your reaction was formed when you were young and emotionally wounded and that it makes the problems worse. What would it be like if, say, 6 months from now, the same situation didn't make you feel bad at all? If instead of feeling _____ (name the affect and negative cognition), you felt okay and saw that your partner was in distress and needed you?"*

_____

_____

Only when a client has taken ownership of a problem (e.g., reactivity, avoidance) does it make sense to offer a remedy. At this juncture, the therapist recommends EMDR as a treatment that can mitigate the client's emotional reactivity and open the door to mindfulness and caring responses in its place. Consider the following therapist's suggestion:

> Say, *"We've discussed how each of you, in your own way, becomes triggered by your partner, who, in turn, becomes triggered by you. There's no good guy or bad guy, and there's no chicken or egg. Each of you can start the cycle, but neither of you yet knows how to end it.*

The bad news is that emotional reactions are reflexes and cannot be undone with a simple act of will or insight. The good news is that we do have a method to reduce your reactivity to the point that you can stay calm and focused, and the cycle either won't get started, or if it does, each of you will have the skill and courage to change it. That method is to use EMDR. Would you be willing to discuss incorporating EMDR into the therapy?"

_____

_____

These steps can and should be used with each partner, as appropriate, during the course of therapy. In this way, each partner in turn is invited to examine how his or her own activation and subsequent defensive reaction is derailing constructive, caring dialogue. It is not important that the therapist afford equal talk time or otherwise balance the session temporally, even if the methodology described here takes the whole session with one partner, or one partner remains the focus of intervention for consecutive sessions. More important is the therapist's commitment to sequentially empathize, then hold each partner accountable to a standard of adult responsibility characterized by compassion and mutuality. Thus, the therapeutic stance of multidirected partiality (Boszormenyi-Nagy & Krasner, 1986) becomes the safeguard of trust and fairness in the therapy room, as opposed to rote formulas based on superficial criteria.

The Benefits of Conjoint EMDR Therapy

With one or both partners contracting to treatment with EMDR, the therapy must now be structured to accommodate the parallel treatment plan(s) of individual (EMDR) plus couples-focused therapy. While the EMDR piece of the therapy can be referred out, there are enormous benefits to working with both partners individually and together. In addition to the obvious advantages of greater information gathering and having no therapy team to split, there is leverage in having the couple accountable to a single therapist (it is harder for clients to conceal or minimize bad behavior), and integrity in having one therapist who is accountable to the clients both individually and collectively (the therapist can be held accountable by the couple or by partner B for interventions with partner A).

EMDR conducted conjointly also has distinct benefits. Partners can provide emotional support to each other for this difficult work; partners gain insight into and develop compassion for each other's deeper issues and suffering; and partners can share in the relief when projected attitudes are resolved and then taken back. Conjoint EMDR is conducted exactly like individual EMDR sessions except that one partner—the witnessing partner—is seated unobtrusively and remains silent while the other—the working partner—receives EMDR (Litt, 2007a, 2007b).

Say, *"We've discussed so far how there are some issues that you two have not been able to resolve, but also how each of you has specific vulnerabilities to being triggered by the other, so that issues cannot get resolved. Therapy can help you in a couple of ways. We can use the sessions to work through specific issues, and we can use EMDR to make each of you more resilient."*

_____

_____

This would be a good place to ask for questions or comments.

Say, *"Do you have any questions or comments?"*

_____

_____

Contraindications for Conjoint EMDR Therapy

Conjoint EMDR is contraindicated if any of the following obstacles prove insurmountable:

1. The working partner is unable to freely emote in the presence of the witnessing partner.
2. The working partner is not ready to disclose personal history or other issues to the witnessing partner.
3. The witnessing partner is likely to use the working partner's revelations in retaliation.
4. The observing partner is unlikely to tolerate the working partner's intense affect or disclosures.
5. The witnessing partner is unable or unwilling to let the working partner have all the therapist's attention (e.g., interrupts the processing with comments or questions; Litt, 2007b, p. 283).

Conjoint EMDR sessions may be contraindicated for one partner, but not for the other. Ultimately, the decision of who goes first and who attends which sessions are best a collaborative effort, once clients are informed of the risks and benefits of conjoint EMDR. Additionally, it is in keeping with the goals set out here that each partner take personal responsibility for his or her own treatment plan, including when to meet for couples work and when to do an EMDR session.

Then say, *"If one or both of you decide to do EMDR, you can meet with me alone to do this or meet with your partner present. The advantage of doing it together is that your partner can be here to support and learn about you. However, if it is not a good idea, one or both of you can each do your EMDR work separately (review the contraindications below). What are your thoughts about this?"*

_____

_____

Say, *"How we structure this is negotiable, but I want each of you to take personal responsibility for the agenda for each session. If you, (name Partner A), want to do EMDR at your next visit, then negotiate that with your partner and let me know at the start of the session. On the other hand, if you (name Partner B), want to talk as a couple to discuss a particular issue, then work that out with your partner and let me know that that is your agenda."*

_____

_____

In practice, this is easier said than done and most couples will rely heavily on the therapist—particularly in the beginning of treatment—for guidance as to how to structure the therapy for optimal benefit.

EMDR is a powerful intervention that can decrease defensive reactivity and thereby enable partners to implement mature, caring options in negotiating their conflicts. By boosting affect tolerance, EMDR enables partners to be emotionally available to one another more consistently, as each is less likely to become activated by the other's intense affect. The challenge in incorporating EMDR in couples therapy has to do with the common expectation clients have that they themselves are not in need of change. The protocol described here is an experiential, dialogic method that engages clients naturalistically in observing their own reactivity and inviting the opportunity for change and growth.

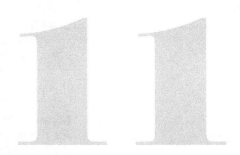

EMDR Protocol for Treating Sexual Dysfunction

Sabitha Pillai-Friedman

Sexual Dysfunction Protocol Script Notes

Sex therapists use different techniques to treat sexual dysfunction successfully. Often, however, they encounter clients who are able to understand rationally why they are suffering from a particular sexual dysfunction, and who are unable to overcome the visceral reactions that compromise their sexual functioning.

This chapter demonstrates a sex therapist's utilization of EMDR—within the context of the 3-pronged approach to target issues related to sexual dysfunction. The EMDR can be used successfully to desensitize reactions related to negative sexual experiences; to facilitate reprocessing of these memories; to target triggers, stimuli, and situations in present functioning; to address anticipatory fears; and to install positive sexual functioning in the future. The first part of this protocol addresses both large "T" Trauma and small "t" trauma events that occurred in the past and relate to an individual's sexuality that can affect their sexual functioning in present time. For instance, a girl who is caught and reprimanded for masturbating may experience an overwhelming sense of shame well into her adult life. This internalized shame, which could be assessed as a small "t," may affect her sexual functioning later in adulthood. Although, the adult client may be able to develop insight into the impact of the trauma on her sexual adjustment, she may not be able to overcome the involuntary responses of her body, such as being inorgasmic, having low sexual desire, and so forth. EMDR can be used to desensitize that involuntary response and help her reprocess the negative cognition related to her childhood trauma. Once the negative cognition is reprocessed then the positive cognition may be installed. In these cases, the therapist focuses on traumatic sexual events during the Assessment Phase. The therapist can begin by asking the client to list 10 or more traumatic sexual events.

Guidelines for Working With Clients While Processing Issues of Sexual Dysfunction

Clients undergoing EMDR treatment for sexual dysfunction may often feel anxious and vulnerable during their sessions. This may be because the act of processing certain sexual events may trigger physical arousal that may lead to feelings of embarrassment and anxiety. It is important for the practitioner to establish a comfortable and safe relationship with the client before beginning EMDR treatment. There are certain guidelines that an EMDR practitioner needs to follow during the use of this protocol. Since the physical proximity of the practitioner may activate arousal or anxiety, it is important to use a longer cord for the EMDR headphones and maintain some physical distance from the clients during EMDR sessions. It is also useful for the practitioner to maintain a uniformly professional and neutral voice during the session. It may also help to prepare clients by letting them know that he or she may experience some arousal during the EMDR session and that it is normal.

Sexual dysfunction is a very vast area of study. Each sexual dysfunction has its own diagnostic criteria, assessment, and treatment. It is very important for clinicians to gain enough training and supervision in sex therapy before using this protocol. Clinicians need to feel comfortable with their own sexuality in order to address sexual problems in clients. Clinicians who have not addressed their own inhibitions, guilt or shame about their sexuality may cause harm to clients and to themselves. This protocol works best within the context of ongoing couple therapy and sex therapy.

Sexual Dysfunction Protocol Script

Phase 1: Client History

Past Memories

Say, *"Please list about 10 events that you have experienced concerning your sexual history. These may be events that were confusing, shameful, overwhelming, physically or emotionally painful, and those sexual experiences that were positive, including situations where you felt positive sexual energy such as appreciative glances from potential sex partners, and so forth."*

_____

_____

_____

_____

_____

_____

Say, *"Let's start from when you were born to age 12? What are the negative sexual incidents that you remember?"*

_____

_____

_____

_____

_____

_____

Say, *"Now what are the positive sexual incidents that you remember?"*

_____

_____

_____

_____

_____

_____

Say, *"How about your teenage years ages 13 to 18? What are the negative sexual incidents that you remember?"*

_____

_____

_____

_____

_____

Say, *"What are the positive sexual incidents that you remember?"*

_____

_____

_____

_____

_____

_____

Say, *"What about from age 19 years on?"*

_____

_____

_____

_____

_____

_____

Say, *"What are the negative sexual incidents that you remember?"*

_____

_____

_____

_____

_____

_____

Say, *"What are the positive sexual incidents that you remember?"*

_____

_____

_____

_____

_____

_____

From this point it is helpful to create a comprehensive plan with your client to be clear about the goals in treatment. Based on the presenting problem, have the client float back to the earliest memory identified by questioning. This will be informed by the above history taking, however, doing this type of questioning may also elicit other memories that the client had not thought about before your questioning. The next step is to choose the first memory to work on. Usually, if it is appropriate, encourage the patient to choose the earliest memory that relates to the dysfunction or sexual problem and create a targeting sequence plan that consists of all the connections or incidents that the client remembers. The first target is the earliest memory unless there is a clinical reason to begin elsewhere. By creating the targeting sequence, the therapist and the client have a treatment plan or a map to follow concerning the presenting problem. Also, present triggers and future templates are part of the treatment plan that can be added to, along the way, as needed.

Say, *"Think of _____ (state the issue that you are working on). Are there earlier times in your life when you had an experience that reminds you of this situation?"*

_____

_____

_____

_____

Or use the Float-Back (all the Float-Back Techniques have been adapted from the Affect Bridge of Watkins & Watkins, 1997) to elicit connections with any relevant sensory data that is prominent for the client such as earlier thoughts or beliefs, sensations, affect, smells, tastes, sounds, and so forth. The idea here is to use the most relevant Float-Back Technique for your patient. It is *not* necessary to use all of them for the targeting sequence. It is important for the clinician to choose judiciously. If it is the earlier thoughts or beliefs about the self that the client is aware of concerning the incident, have him or her use the Float-Back:

Say, *"Think of _____ (state the issue that you are working on). Now notice what thoughts or negative beliefs you have connected with this issue and just let your mind float back to an earlier time in your life when you had those thoughts or negative beliefs about yourself, allow those thoughts to flow into your consciousness easily, just let your mind float back and tell me the earliest scene that comes to mind."*

Pause

Say, *"What comes to mind?"*

_____

_____

_____

_____

Or use the Float-Back to elicit connections to earlier sensations,

Say, *"Think of _____ (state the issue that you are working on). Now notice what sensations you are feeling and just let your mind float back to an earlier time in your life when you had those sensations, allow those thoughts to flow into your consciousness easily, just let your mind float back and tell me the earliest scene that comes to mind."*

Pause

Say, *"What comes to mind?"*

_____

_____

_____

_____

Or use the Affect Scan to elicit connections with earlier affect.

Say, *"Think of _____* (state the issue that you are working on). *Now notice what emotions you are feeling and just let your mind float back to an earlier time in your life when you had those feelings, allow those thoughts to flow into your consciousness easily, just let your mind float back and tell me the earliest scene that comes to mind."*

Pause

Say, *"What comes to mind?"*

_____

_____

_____

_____

If there is other sensory data (i.e., smell, taste, balance, etc.), you can use the Float-Back question to elicit relevant connections.
Ask for any other memories related to these sensory experiences:

Say, *"Are there any other memories that you can connect to the thoughts, emotions, feelings, and sensations associated with this material that we can note to include in our targeting sequence? It is also possible that others will come to mind and we can always add them in."*

_____

_____

_____

_____

Say, *"From what we have discussed, here is the targeting sequence that I have based on the work that we have done so far. (Therapist goes through the targeting sequence.) Do you think that we need to add any others that we have from the earlier history taking that might not yet be included in this sequence?"*

_____

_____

_____

_____

Phase 2: Preparation

During this phase it is important for the clinician to explain what EMDR is and how it works. It is also necessary to tell the client what they can realistically hope to accomplish with EMDR treatment. The clinician may also need to address secondary gain issues. What does the client have to lose if the sexual dysfunction is resolved?

The clinician can introduce the idea of a Safe Place and work with the client to create a relaxation strategy that can be used at the end of an unfinished session and when the client's trauma becomes activated between sessions.

During this phase it is also important to prepare clients for the possibility that they may become sexually aroused during the EMDR sessions. Clients need to know it is quite normal and that there is no need to feel guilty as result of that. Processing sexual trauma may also affect their sexual relationship with their partner between sessions. They experience an increase or decrease in desire or experience flashbacks during sex. These reactions are normal and will get resolved as progress is made through continued EMDR sessions.

Phase 3: Assessment

Choose the first incident to work with from the targeting sequence.

Incident

Say, "*The memory of the actual traumatic sexual event we will start with today from your target sequence is _____* (state the memory you have agreed to work on from your treatment plan)*.*"

_____

_____

Picture

Say, "*What picture represents the entire incident?*"

_____

_____

Negative Cognition (NC)

Say, "*What words best go with the picture that express your negative belief about yourself now?*"

_____

_____

Positive Cognition (PC)

Say, "*When you bring up that picture or incident, what would you like to believe about yourself now?*"

_____

_____

Validity of Cognition (VoC)

Say, "*When you think of the incident* (or picture) *how true do those words _____* (clinician repeats the positive cognition) *feel to you now on a scale of 1 to 7, where 1 feels completely false and 7 feels completely true?*"

1   2   3   4   5   6   7
(completely false)   (completely true)

Emotions

Say, *"When you bring up the picture* (or incident) *and those words _____* (clinician states the negative cognition), *what emotion do you feel now?"*

_____

_____

Subjective Units of Disturbance (SUD)

Say, *"On a scale of 0 to 10, where 0 is no disturbance or neutral and 10 is the highest disturbance you can imagine, how disturbing does it feel now?"*

0	1	2	3	4	5	6	7	8	9	10

(no disturbance)   (highest disturbance)

Location of Body Sensation

Say, *"Where do you feel it* (the disturbance) *in your body?"*

_____

_____

Phase 4: Desensitization

Use the Standard EMDR Protocol.
To begin, say the following:

Say, *"Now remember it is your own brain that is doing the healing and you are the one in control. I will ask you to mentally focus on the target and to follow my fingers* (or any other BLS you are using). *Just let whatever happens, happen, and we will talk at the end of the set. Just tell me what comes up, and don't discard anything as unimportant. Any new information that comes to mind is connected in some way. If you want to stop, just raise your hand."*

Then say, *"Bring up the picture and the words _____* (clinician repeats the NC) *and notice where you feel it in your body. Now follow my fingers with your eyes* (or other BLS)."*

This protocol is to be repeated until the SUD reaches 0. Then the positive cognition is installed. Each traumatic event associated with the sexual problem that is not reprocessed during the normal course of the first target needs to be processed using the above protocol until the SUD reaches an ecological 1 or 0 and the positive cognition is installed.

Phase 5: Installation

Say, *"How does _____* (repeat the PC) *sound?"*

_____

_____

Say, *"Do the words _____ (repeat the PC) still fit or is there another positive statement that feels better?"*

_____

_____

If the client accepts the original positive cognition, the clinician should ask for a VoC rating to see if it has improved:

Say, *"As you think of the incident, how do the words feel to you now on a scale of 1 to 7, where 1 feels completely false and 7 feels completely true?"*

   1   2   3   4   5   6   7
(completely false)   (completely true)

Say, *"Think of the event, and hold it together with the words _____ (repeat the PC)."*

_____

_____

Do a long set of BLS to see if there is more processing to be done.

Phase 6: Body Scan

Say, *"Close your eyes and keep in mind the original memory and the positive cognition. Then bring your attention to the different parts of your body, starting with your head and working downward. Any place you find any tension, tightness, or unusual sensation, tell me."*

_____

_____

Phase 7: Closure

Say, *"Things may come up or they may not. If they do, great, write it down and it can be a target for next time. If you get any new memories, dreams, or situations that disturb you, just take a good snapshot. It isn't necessary to give a lot of detail. Just put down enough to remind you so we can target it next time. The same thing goes for any positive dreams or situations. If negative feelings do come up, try not to make them significant. Remember, it's still just the old stuff. Just write it down for next time. Then use the tape or the Safe Place exercise to let as much of the disturbance go as possible. Even if nothing comes up, make sure to use the tape every day and give me a call if you need to."*

Phase 8: Reevaluation

It is important to pay attention to the following questions when the client returns after doing EMDR work (Shapiro, 2006, pp. 54–59):

1. Reevaluate what has come up in the client's life since the last session.
2. Reevaluate the target worked on in the previous session. Has the individual target been resolved? Whether the previous processing session was complete or incomplete:

Say, *"When you think of whatever is left of the problem that we worked on last time, how disturbing is it now on a scale of 0 to 10, where 0 is no disturbance or neutral and 10 is the highest disturbance you can imagine, how disturbing does it feel now?"*

_____

_____

0   1   2   3   4   5   6   7   8   9   10
(no disturbance)   (highest disturbance)

Say, *"Have you noticed any other material associated with the original memory since the last session?"*

_____

_____

_____

_____

Say, *"Have all the necessary targets been reprocessed so that you can feel at peace with the past? Let's check on the current triggers."*

_____

_____

Present Triggers

Say, *"What are the situations, events, or stimuli that trigger your trauma _____ (state the trauma). Let's process these situations, events, or stimuli triggers one by one."*

_____

_____

Situations, Events, or Stimuli Trigger List

T1:

_____

_____

T2:

_____

_____

T3:

_____

_____

T4

_____

_____

Target or Memory

Say, *"What situation, event, or stimulus that triggers you would you like to use as a target today?"*

_____

_____

Picture

Say, *"What picture represents the* _____ (state the situation, event, or stimulus) *that triggers you?"*

_____

_____

If there are many choices or if the client becomes confused, the clinician assists by asking the following:

Say, *"What picture represents the most traumatic part of the* _____ (state the situation, event, or stimulus) *that triggers you?"*

_____

_____

When a picture is unavailable, the clinician merely invites the client to do the following:

Say, *"Think of the* _____ (state the situation, event or stimulus) *that triggers you."*

_____

_____

Negative Cognition (NC)

Say, *"What words best go with the picture that express your negative belief about yourself now?"*

_____

_____

Positive Cognition (PC)

Say, *"When you bring up that picture or the* _____ (state the situation, event, or stimulus) *that triggers you, what would you like to believe about yourself now?"*

_____

_____

Validity of Cognition (VoC)

Say, *"When you think of the* _____ (state the situation, event, stimulus, or picture) *that triggers you, how true do those words* _____ (clinician repeats the positive cognition) *feel to you now on a scale of 1 to 7, where 1 feels completely false and 7 feels completely true?"*

1	2	3	4	5	6	7
(completely false)				(completely true)		

Sometimes it is necessary to explain further:

Say, *"Remember, sometimes we know something with our head, but it feels differently in our gut. In this case, what is the gut-level feeling of the truth of* _____ (clinician state the positive cognition), *from 1 being completely false to 7 being completely true?"*

1	2	3	4	5	6	7
(completely false)				(completely true)		

Emotions

Say, *"When you bring up the picture* _____ (state the situation, event, or stimulus) *that triggers you and those words* _____ (clinician states the negative cognition), *what emotion do you feel now?"*

_____

_____

Subjective Units of Disturbance (SUD)

Say, *"On a scale of 0 to 10, where 0 is no disturbance or neutral and 10 is the highest disturbance you can imagine, how disturbing does it feel now?"*

0	1	2	3	4	5	6	7	8	9	10
(no disturbance)							(highest disturbance)			

Location of Body Sensation

Say, *"Where do you feel it* (the disturbance) *in your body?"*

_____

_____

Work with each trigger until each one is fully processed.

Future Templates for Anticipatory Anxiety and Optimal Functioning

Current Sexual Difficulties Due to Anticipatory Anxiety

The next part of the protocol for sexual dysfunction is to be used to address current on-going sexual difficulties due to anticipatory anxiety. For instance, a man who suffers from premature ejaculation may have developed so much anxiety due to his past failures that the anticipatory anxiety may predispose him to continued failure. Similarly, a woman who may have suffered from sexual pain may continue to experience pain even after the physiological pain has been successfully treated medically. She may experience phantom pain and experience anticipatory anxiety that may compromise her sexual function. This cycle of defeat can be broken with EMDR.

> Say, *"Describe what happens when you anticipate working with the _____ (state the issue that the client has been working on). Sometimes, people find it helpful to think of it as a movie. Please explain what happens in minute detail what happens before, during, and after you experience the sexual difficulty. Also, it is important to include the responses of your partner as well. For instance, _____ (state what actually happens or give an example) your partner sighs and turns away with disappointment or your partner gets up and leaves the room with an expression of irritation."*

_____

_____

_____

_____

_____

_____

Incident

> Say, *"Let's work with the part of the movie that causes you the most anxiety. We can use that as a target for EMDR work. What part causes you the most anxiety?"*

_____

_____

Picture

> Say, *"What picture represents the entire incident?"*

_____

_____

Negative Cognition (NC)

> Say, *"What words best go with the picture that express your negative belief about yourself now?"*

_____

_____

Positive Cognition (PC)

> Say, *"When you bring up that picture or incident of what causes you the most anxiety, what would you like to believe about yourself now?"*

_____

_____

Validity of Cognition (VoC)

Say, *"When you think of what causes you the most anxiety* (or picture) *how true do those words* _____ (clinician repeats the positive cognition) *feel to you now on a scale of 1 to 7, where 1 feels completely false and 7 feels completely true?"*

1   2   3   4   5   6   7
(completely false)   (completely true)

Emotions

Say, *"When you bring up the picture* (or incident) *and those words* _____ (clinician states the negative cognition), *what emotion do you feel now?"*

_____

_____

Subjective Units of Disturbance (SUD)

Say, *"On a scale of 0 to 10, where 0 is no disturbance or neutral and 10 is the highest disturbance you can imagine, how disturbing does it feel now?"*

0   1   2   3   4   5   6   7   8   9   10
(no disturbance)   (highest disturbance)

Location of Body Sensation

Say, *"Where do you feel it* (the disturbance) *in your body?"*

_____

_____

Continue to work with the full assessment for each issue that is of concern from above.

Positive Future Template

Now that the past sexual trauma and triggers have been processed and current anticipatory anxiety has been treated through EMDR, positive sexual memories or sexual fantasies can be installed to ensure optimal sexual functioning in the patient's future sexual interactions. Positive sexual memories or sexual fantasies can be used to kindle positive sexual energy and desire, create positive anticipation about sexual activity, and avoid cognitive distraction that could interfere with sexual activity. If the client describes more than one positive sexual experience, more than one can be installed. In fact, the more positive sexual experiences the client recalls, the better it is for the client. (The installation of inner resource described below is inspired by the resource work of Popky, 2005.)

Say, *"Now bring to mind a positive sexual experience. It can be an actual sexual experience you have had on your own or with a partner. It can also be a feeling you experienced when you felt positive about your sexuality. For instance, you walked into a party and received admiring glances or compliments from a potential sex partner. You can also bring to mind your favorite sexual fantasy that you use during masturbation or partnered sex."*

_____

_____

_____

_____

Say, *"What image represents the best part of your positive sexual experience?"*

_____

_____

Say, *"When you bring the positive sexual image to mind, what would you like to believe about yourself now?"*

_____

_____

Say, *"When you bring up that image of the positive sexual experience or fantasy and words that go with the image, what emotion(s) do you feel now?"*

_____

_____

Say, *"Step into the image of the positive sexual experience or fantasy. Notice and experience the positive feelings, breathe in these feelings, move around in them, experience being successful. Notice what you see, feel, smell, and taste. Notice what it is like to feel the sexual energy and to function successfully. As you notice and experience those positive sexual feelings, touch your knuckle in this positive state until your positive state is most desirable. Increase pressure slightly to the same place on your knuckle as your positive feelings peak."*

_____

_____

Say, *"Go with that."* (Do BLS)

What do you notice?"

_____

_____

Continue with the following:

Say, *"As you listen to the positive words or sounds that you are saying to yourself and the positive words that others would be saying, adjust the auditory components: the volume, the tone, the tempo, the balance, and so forth, and as the positive experience peaks touch your anchor."*

_____

_____

Say, *"Go with that."* (Do BLS)

Say, *"What do you notice?"*

_____

_____

Test the positive state by having the client touch their knuckle and notice the results. The client should report a positive experience. It is important for the client to have a strong, positive, sensory-based experience of having successfully achieved their goal anchored into their physiology. If this is not the case, repeat it with another memory or work to deepen the current memory.

Say, *"Now touch your knuckle. What do you feel?"*

_____

_____

Say, *"Go with that."* (Do BLS)

Say, *"What do you notice?"*

_____

_____

The 3-Pronged Protocol detailed above addresses sexual trauma in the past, present, and future. Most often, clients report feeling decreased reactivity and increased feelings of confidence after processing the past sexual traumas. The current triggers offer clients a chance to process on-going reactivity to everyday triggers that compromise sexual functioning. At this point, the client has reached a point of neutrality when all negative responses to past and present events have been processed. The client is now ready to address the anticipatory anxiety and create a template for optimal functioning in the future. At the end of this EMDR protocol, clients usually report marked decrease in reactivity related to their sexuality. Most clients also report a gradual change from negative anticipation of sexual events to positive anticipation. The EMDR treatment enables clients to participate in couple therapy and sex therapy with greater success.

Acknowledgments

I am grateful to Dr. Michael D'Antonio for providing me with proper guidelines to develop this protocol. His EMDR supervision group served as a sounding board for my evolving thoughts about the use of EMDR for the treatment of sexual dysfunction. I would like to thank my colleagues who were a part of the supervision group. I would also like to thank Dr. Marilyn Luber for her incisive comments that enabled me to make some necessary edits. It is with great humility that I offer my gratitude to my clients who have trusted me over the years and enabled me to use this protocol during different stages of its evolution.

12

Infertility Protocol With EMDR

Marina Lombardo and Regina Morrow

Protocols for Standard History Taking

Phase 1: History Taking

The following sets of questionnaires are helpful in working with fertility treatment.

Note: As this is a lengthy history, it is recommended that a large "T" representing a big trauma, or a small "t" representing a minor trauma be placed in the margin to assist in alerting the clinician.

General Fertility Issues

1. Say, *"What makes you seek treatment now?"*

_____

_____

_____

_____

2. Say, *"What is your goal in coming in for treatment?"*

_____

_____

3. Say, *"When your issues with fertility began what was happening in your life?"*

_____

_____

_____

_____

167

4. Say, *"Do you have any children?"*

_____

_____

If yes, say, *"Did this happen naturally or as a result of treatment?"*

_____

_____

5. Say, *"Do you have a history of miscarriages—either chemical, prenatal, or any stillbirths?"*

_____

_____

_____

_____

_____

If yes, say, *"When did this happen?"*

_____

_____

Say, *"What was the extent of the pregnancy term?"*

_____

_____

Say, *"Please tell me the specific details of each episode."*

_____

_____

_____

_____

_____

_____

6. Say, *"Are you currently under a physician's care? If so, with whom and how long?"*

_____

_____

7. Say, *"Are you currently in the midst of a treatment cycle?"*

_____

_____

8. Say, *"Are you currently taking any hormones or fertility drugs? If so, which ones?"*

_____

_____

_____

_____

9. Say, _"Have you had any reactions to this medication?"_

_____

_____

10. Say, _"Are you currently seeking any alternative care as well? If so, with what and with whom?"_

_____

_____

11. Say, _"Do you have a present diagnosis for a fertility issue?"_

_____

_____

12. Say, _Please tell me your history with physicians—either traditional or alternative and with whom you have sought care."_

_____

_____

_____

_____

_____

_____

13. Say, _"Please tell me the history of any past treatments or procedures that you have had and the results of these efforts."_

_____

_____

_____

_____

_____

14. Say, _"What physical and emotional reactions did you have to this process, as well as negative or positive outcomes?"_

_____

_____

_____

_____

_____

15. Say, *"Please tell me the history of your fertility medication and the reactions that you have had to these drugs."*

_____

_____

_____

_____

_____

_____

16. Say, *"How do you feel about the medical care you are receiving now?"*

_____

_____

17. Say, *"Do you feel supported by the physician or health care providers or are you upset in some way?"*

_____

_____

Assessment of Marital Relationship and Other Support Systems

Concerning Infertility

1. Say, *"Has your husband been involved in the treatment process* (attending doctor visits; giving injections, etc.)*?"*

_____

_____

2. Say, *"Do you feel supported by your husband or do you feel like you are disappointing him?"*

_____

_____

3. Say, *"Do you feel pressured by your husband, or anyone else, to pursue treatment?"*

_____

_____

4. Say, *"Is he willing to be a part of counseling as well?"*

_____

_____

5. Say, *"What is his vision for a family?"*

_____

_____

6. Say, *"Have you discussed the boundaries of your fertility treatment? How much will you spend? How long will you continue?"*

_____

_____

7. Say, *"How do you make these decisions?"*

_____

_____

8. Say, *"Does one person have more power in decision making?"*

_____

_____

9. Say, *"Is there any conflict in this regard?"*

_____

_____

_____

_____

10. Say, *"Do you as a couple make regular appointments to 'check in' with one another emotionally, debrief each other on the status of fertility treatment, new information, and reassess fertility treatment plans?"*

_____

_____

11. Say, *"Has infertility treatment become the center of your world as a couple, or do you regularly engage in other activities as well?"*

_____

_____

12. Say, *"How has infertility impacted your sex life?"*

_____

_____

13. Say, *"Has sexual intimacy become exclusively linked with procreation and fertility treatment?"*

_____

_____

14. Say, *"Has there been any adverse physical, mental, or emotional reactions to prior or present fertility treatment?"*

_____

_____

15. Say, *"How have you dealt with this?"*

_____

_____

16. Say, *"What has been your husband's reaction?"*

_____

_____

17. Say, *"How has your body image or relationship with your body been affected?"*

_____

_____

_____

_____

In assessing this last question, the following can be helpful.

18. Say, *"What emotion(s) do you feel when you think about your body?"*

_____

_____

19. Say, *"Do you believe that your body is doing the best it can or do you feel betrayed by your body because you are struggling in this way?"*

_____

_____

20. Say, *"When you think about the organs in your reproductive system, what is the picture or mental image that comes up for you?"*

_____

_____

21. Say, *"Have you as a couple isolated because of this issue, or do you have the support of others? Who are they: friends, family, infertility support community?"*

_____

_____

_____

_____

22. Say, *"Have you as a couple decided together with whom to share infertility information and how much to share?"*

_____

_____

23. Say, *"How has extended family responded? Is there anyone in particular that is supportive or anyone who disapproves?"*

_____

_____

_____

_____

24. Say, *"Are there any religious barriers to pursuing treatment?"*

_____

_____

25. Say, *"Is this a source of conflict in the relationship?"*

_____

_____

26. Say, *"What support systems have you accessed? What forms have these taken: community support groups, online support, close friends, family?"*

_____

_____

_____

_____

27. Say, *"Have these been helpful?"*

_____

_____

Reproductive History

1. Say, *"Please tell me about any early life experiences that may be impacting reproductive issues now?"*

_____

_____

_____

_____

2. Say, *"What prior losses have you had including any deaths* (family, friends, pets), *relocations of residences or schools, or events with shame-based themes?"*

_____

_____

_____

_____

_____

3. Say, *"What are your parents' reproductive history?"*

_____

_____

_____

_____

4. Say, *"Tell me about your siblings. How many do you have? Where are you in the birth order and how are your relationship(s) with your sibling(s)?"*

_____

_____

_____

_____

5. Say, *"What is or will be the family legacy of infertility?"*

_____

_____

The following questions are of particular importance to your history taking relative to reproductive issues.

Conception

6. Say, *"Do you have any fears or concerns about pregnancy or delivery?"*

_____

_____

_____

_____

7. Say, *"Do you remember any stories about your mother's conception or pregnancy experience with you or your siblings?"*

_____

_____

8. Say, *"Have you ever had an abortion?"*

_____

_____

If yes, say the following:

9. Say, *"What were the circumstances that led up to and followed this experience, including experiences within the facility and with any educational material provided?"*

_____

_____

10. Say, *"Have you ever been on birth control? What type and for how long?"*

_____

_____

11. Say, *"Did you have any negative experiences?"*

_____

_____

12. Say, *"Was it effective or not?"*

_____

_____

Menstruation

13. Say, *"How old were you when you got your period?"*

_____

_____

14. Say, *"What was that experience like?"*

_____

_____

_____

_____

15. Say, *"Did you know what to expect?"*

_____

_____

16. Say, *"How did your family react, especially mom and dad?"*

_____

_____

17. Say, *"Were you proud or ashamed?"*

_____

_____

Parenting

18. Say, *"Please give me three words to describe your mother."*

_____

_____

19. Say, *"Please give me three words to describe your father."*

_____

_____

20. Say, *"Please tell me the best and worst memory of each."*

_____

_____

_____

_____

_____

_____

21. Say, *"Please give me three words to describe their marriage."*

_____

_____

22. Say, *"Please give me three words to describe them as parents."*

_____

_____

23. Say, *"Do you aspire to be like them as a parent? Why or why not?"*

_____

_____

Siblings

24. Say, *"Which sibling were you closest to growing up?"*

_____

_____

25. Say, *"With whom did you have the most difficult relationship?"*

_____

_____

If client is an only child, say the following:

26. Say, *"What were the pluses and minuses of the relationship?"*

_____

_____

27. Say, *"Do your siblings have children?"*

_____

_____

28. Say, *"Do they live close by?"*

_____

_____

29. Say, *"Are you close to them?"*

_____

_____

30. Say, *"Did you hope that you would have children around the same time?"*

_____

_____

The Whole Person Fertility Program Fill-in-the-Blank Questionnaire (Paulsen-Payne, 1997; adaptation by Marina Lombardo)

The idea is to help the therapist help the client to crystallize information related to her own history and fertility.

1. The biggest message I learned from my family is _____.
2. In my family, we kept _____ a secret.
3. I learned from an early age that women _____.
4. I learned from an early age that men _____.
5. I think I have trouble conceiving or holding onto a pregnancy because _____ happened in my family.
6. Because of _____, everyone in my family got hurt.
7. _____ was the biggest positive influence in my family.
8. _____ changed the course of my life.
9. What hurt me the most in my family was _____.
10. What hurt my mom the most in her family was _____.
11. I'm grateful that my family had _____ or I wouldn't be the person I am today.
12. The person I identify the most with is _____.
13. The pattern(s) that appears to tie into my reproductive difficulty is _____.

Not only can this questionnaire provide important ties to early life experiences, and clues to assist in determining negative cognitions, it can also provide some possibilities for resource installation.

History Related to EMDR Interventions

Resources

Say, *"Since we have been talking about all that has happened in your life, let's note the positive beliefs, past successes, and positive life experiences. Please add any that we have not yet touched on."*

_____

_____

_____

_____

_____

_____

_____

_____

_____

Since many infertility clients are in a state of high emotional distress prior to the beginning of processing, front-loading resources during the Preparation Phase can be helpful. Also, clients may require containment and self-soothing skills before they are able to complete the history.

A basic framework is followed, including assisting the client in "developing an image of the desired resource; expanding the vividness of the image; accessing and expanding the positive feelings, emotions, body sensations, and positive beliefs about oneself associated with the resources; then enhancing and deepening the client's positive experience with BLS" (Kiessling, 2005). The bilateral stimulation (BLS) is kept short (4 to 6 passes) and is continued until the client's positive experience is no longer strengthening. The client is also encouraged to develop a cue word to assist in accessing a particular resource.

If the client is anticipating a challenging situation (undergoing a medical procedure; dealing with a difficult family member), she rehearses with the installed resource during session to help her deal with this circumstance in an optimum way. In addition, the client is encouraged to practice accessing this resource on a regular basis between sessions. Resources are reevaluated at the beginning of each session to determine their use and effectiveness. Additional resources are installed on an as-needed basis.

Determining Targets

Infertility clients often carry within them a strong sense of blame and misplaced personal responsibility. The two primary negative cognitions that appear most often are: "There's something wrong with me," and "I must have done something wrong." As a result, it is helpful to begin by asking a client what she believes about herself as a result of her infertility struggles. If there is more than one belief, responsibility is usually primary, then safety, and then control.

Say, *"Please tell me what you are believing about yourself as a result of this struggle you are having concerning getting pregnant and issues of infertility?"*

_____

_____

_____

_____

Once the negative cognition is identified in terms of the current situation, the Float-Back Technique facilitates the emergence of the Touchstone Event.

Say, *"As you think of this belief that you have about yourself now, please allow yourself to float back to the earliest time you had this belief about yourself. What would that be?"*

_____

_____

_____

_____

Say, *"Are there any other times that stand out for you concerning this belief about _____ (state the belief)?"*

_____

_____

_____

_____

A time line is then constructed, highlighting the most disturbing incidents. The following page represents a construction of a Time Line. Each Time Line corresponds to only one theme: responsibility, trust or control. The related events in the client's life are listed in chronological order, the earliest first, with the age on the top of the line, and cue words that relate to each corresponding incident under the age.

Time Line

Client name: DOB:

Theme: (circle one)

Responsibility/Trust/Control

Negative cognitions:

Age

Incident

Current triggers:

Future templates:

Current triggers are logged on the time line on an ongoing basis, and are usually noted at the time of "check in" at the beginning of each session. Future templates remain relevant to the particular theme: responsibility, safety, or control. If a particular incident has more than one theme, say responsibility and control, two time lines are used, one for each theme. The age is then marked with an asterisk, and the incident is logged onto both time line sheets. Issues relevant to responsibility are processed first, followed by safety issues, and finally control issues. Often, issues of safety and control resolve themselves once the theme of responsibility is addressed and processed. Incidents are processed in chronological order, with the earliest first. An exception to this protocol occurs if the client is in high distress because of current fertility issues. If there is a specific recent event that is causing this high disturbance, this can be processed first. If the general theme of infertility is causing the disturbance,

Say, *"When you think about your struggle with infertility, what is it that you believe about yourself?"*

_____

_____

And then say, *"And if there were a particular incident that represents that struggle, what would it be?"*

_____

_____

A target is constructed and the incident is processed to completion. Usually a return to the Standard EMDR Protocol targeting in chronological order can resume at this point.

Current Triggers

Say, *"Let's think about these beliefs about yourself that you have been talking about. Let's start with _____ (state the belief). What reminds you of it or what situations, events, or stimuli triggers you in your day-to-day life now?"*

_____

_____

_____

_____

Check for triggers for each belief that you have talked about. For fertility clients, this often appears in the form of ongoing treatment, dealing with friends and extended family, relationship with spouse, including intimacy and body image issues.

Phase 2: Preparation

Basic Information About the EMDR Process

Client Education

It is important that the client have general information about the Adaptive Information Processing (AIP) Model in order to ensure optimum participation in treatment. The following script can provide the client with a basic understanding of the model.

The Adaptive Information Processing Model

Say, *"You present today with symptoms of _____ (relate client symptoms). From what we know about how the brain works, your current symptoms have their roots in originating events that happened in your past. At the time that these events first occurred, the information from these experiences was stored improperly in your brain. These events may have been traumatic, or they have may have been no big deal on the surface, but your brain interpreted them in a way that had a negative impact. This information from these events—the negative thoughts, emotions, body sensation, and beliefs about yourself—didn't go onto the long-term storage of your brain the way memories usually do. Instead, the information is frozen, almost as if it's on its own island, away from your brain's neural network, just waiting to be triggered.*

So if you experience something that is similar to the originating event, whether you are aware of it or not, you suddenly get triggered, which means the past wakes up the present. When this happens, you get flooded with the same emotions, body sensation, and negative thoughts and beliefs you had about yourself that you had at the time of the original event. A good way to think about this is to imagine putting a drop of red food coloring into a glass of water. Suddenly, the water becomes red, or in this case, the past becomes the present. This is a problem because even if positive life experiences occur after the original event, the brain can't get to it and use it in a way that cancels the original, negative information out.

In EMDR, you can go back and rework these old memories when those experiences were improperly stored. Like a train, EMDR processing actually lays tracks to build a bridge from the island of old, frozen information to your brain's neural networks, allowing you to release and heal what no longer serves you, and keeps what is useful. The bilateral stimulation in EMDR happens in sets—a certain number of passes back and forth—and just like a train stops at each station, every time you complete a set the negative information gets off and the useful information gets on. When processing is complete, your symptoms dissipate because you are no longer being triggered. Most important, you are able to see things as they really are now and not as a reenactment of your past. This makes it possible for you to assimilate new, positive life experiences, and move in the direction of your goals."

_____

_____

Basic Information About EMDR

Inform the client about what to expect relative to the process and effects of EMDR. Client education as to what can occur during processing is critical to a successful therapeutic partnership. The following script can be used to provide the client with a basic understanding of what can happen during processing.

Say, *"EMDR is a process where old memories are reworked so that they are no longer disturbing and can be stored properly in the neural network. The process through which this occurs is called, 'bilateral stimulation,' where literally both sides of the brain are accessed. A good way to think about this is to compare it to rapid eye movement during sleep; when the brain is dreaming, the eyes move rapidly back and forth so that the brain can process and release emotions accumulated during the course of the day. The way this is done during EMDR is through either tracking a light bar back and forth, listening to alternating tones in headphones, or by holding on to tappers that vibrate alternately in each hand. We can try each method and see which one works best for you.*

Your earliest memories will be processed first. (The exception is when a recent events protocol is followed.) A good way to think about why this works is to imagine that a big weed is growing in your garden. If you want to get rid of it, you can cut off the leaves, or even cut it down by the base, but what will happen if you do that? The weed will grow back. The best way to get rid of the weed is to pull it out by the roots so it can't grow back. Your early life experiences are the roots of your present symptoms and processing these memories first is most effective. Now remember, these disturbing old memories are stored in what we call 'state memory.' This means they are frozen in time, with the sights, sounds, tastes, touches, smells, thoughts, beliefs, and emotions all rolled up together. So as we reprocess these old memories, it's not unusual to reexperience this stored material as it comes to the surface: mental images, body sensations, emotions, or thoughts. That is all normal and it indicates that good work is being done. Now during processing, it's important to remember to have dual attention. That means that you have both an awareness of what you're working on from the past, as well as the awareness that you are sitting in my office in the present. Knowing this helps you to let whatever happens happen. Your job is to just go for a ride on the train and let your brain do the work.

Now remember when I explained EMDR and talked about the train going from station to station? Well, sometimes the way from one station to the next is unpredictable. The train can go into a tunnel up a mountain, or around a bend. This means that you can have some unexpected or big emotions come to the surface. That's fine. All you have to do is continue to ride the train and let it happen. Now big emotions can be thought of as waves, meaning that no matter how big they get, they crest and level out. If you have big emotions, I want to encourage you to ride the waves as best you can by letting the bilateral stimulation continue until the emotion subsides. If, however, it feels like too much for you and you want to stop, you can give me stop sign (teach client stop signal at this point) *and then you can go to your calm place, which we will install in a moment.*

Since EMDR helps the brain create new networks, processing will continue between sessions. I will give you a log sheet before you leave, and your job is to make a note of anything that comes up—thoughts, emotions, body sensations, or anything that triggers you in a positive or negative way. This way we'll be able to tell if the processing is working and it will also let us know if there are new targets to process. If anything is disturbing, you can go to your safe place, or use any self-soothing techniques, which we'll also talk about. And of course, you can call me anytime."

_____

_____

At this point, ask if there are any questions. Then introduce the client to the light bar, headphones, or tappers by installing the calm place, and then testing it with a memory of a minor annoyance in the recent past and in the near future. Also discuss self-soothing strategies with the client, and make a note of these on the TICES Log (trigger, image, cognition, emotion, sensation) sheet the client will take home.

> Say, *"Are there any questions? I would like to introduce you to the many different ways to do bilateral stimulation* (BLS). *You can choose the one that works best for you."*

_____

_____

Special Considerations

Then, based on client needs, *risk considerations* may include: poor self-care and nutrition, side effects of hormone or drug therapy consistent with fertility treatment, marital strain, or weakness in support system. Suggestions on managing these risks follow.

Stress Reduction Techniques

Use the resource installation here, including calm place and guided imagery, particularly if the client is in the midst of treatment.

> Say, *"When you think of the issues and problems that you face, what resources would you need to help you through them?"*

_____

_____

Skill Building

Based on this assessment, life skill deficits are identified, and appropriate skill building is facilitated. These can include skills relative to communication, assertiveness, boundary setting, and decision making. Educating the client on personal ways to nurture spirituality can also be helpful in dealing with issues around grief.

> Say, *"What other skills do you think would be helpful in handling _____* (state whatever issues are confronting the client)*?"*

_____

_____

Support

> Say, *"Is there any pressing need or action that you want to take now before we begin EMDR?"*

_____

_____

If so, say the following:

Say, *"What should we do to help provide you with the support you need? We can create resources, work on self-advocacy and communications skills, help you set boundaries with relatives, and help you with stress reduction techniques. All of these can be used to deal with friends, family, medical personnel, or the challenges of treatment."*

_____

_____

If the client is in need of fertility resources for education, patient advocacy, or social support, there are various professional organizations available. These include the American Society for Reproductive Medicine (www.asrm.org), and Resolve (www.resolve.org), both of which provide support and information through public education and advocacy. Clients are also encouraged to make their own well-being a priority, and discover choices and set boundaries that reflect this awareness. The clients are educated that the skills that they gain from navigating this issue will serve them in meeting all of life's challenges more successfully (Lombardo & Parker, 2007).

Self-Care

Assess the client's relationship with her body and construct an action plan that can allow for support and healing including cognitive strategies. Clients who struggle with infertility often feel betrayed by their bodies and this can manifest in poor self-care. Taking this opportunity to begin to transform the client's relationship with her body is helpful.

Say, *"It's very common with fertility issues to feel like your body is letting you down. Is this true for you?"*

_____

_____

If client answers "yes," ask the following:

Say, *"So what do you believe about your body?"*

_____

_____

_____

_____

And then say, *"How have you been treating your body as a result?"*

_____

_____

Depending on client's answers, client is educated on the necessity of developing a nurturing relationship with her body and on ways to see her body as an ally on this journey. Particular attention is given to the need to maintain a healthy lifestyle consistent with the goal of conception and developing positive cognitions that foster better choices.

Relationship With Spouse

Assess quality of marital relationship and explore ways to bring balance and increased communication into the relationship if necessary. Assess whether the spouse is in need of EMDR treatment. If the couple's relationship is strained, plans will be made to include couple's counseling, or individual counseling for the husband, including EMDR if necessary, as a part of treatment. Again, based on client needs, particular strategies are incorporated. Based on the couple's needs, particular strategies are incorporated. These may include skill building relative to communication, decision making, and boundary setting, particularly with friends and family.

Say, *"Infertility is often the first crisis a couple has to deal with. Would you say this is true for you?"*

_____

_____

If the answer is "no," ask the following:

Say, *"What other crises have happened since you have been together and how have you as a couple coped with these other issues?"*

_____

_____

_____

_____

Say, *"Do you see the impact of those struggles on the relationship?"*

_____

_____

If the answer is "yes," ask the following:

Say, *"Would you say that you and your husband have grown closer or further apart as a result of this challenge?"*

_____

_____

If the answer is "closer," ask the following:

Say, *"What is it about your husband and your relationship that has forged a closer bond?"*

_____

_____

If the answer is "further apart," say the following:

Say, *"This is common for many couples. There are the physical and mental stressors of treatment, financial concerns, and of course the impact this can have on communication and physical intimacy. How would you say this has affected the two of you?"* (Lombardo & Parker, 2007).

_____

_____

_____

_____

Approaching the issue in this way normalizes a wide variety of responses, and allows you to assess where there are specific concerns and needs. For example, to enhance ongoing communication about fertility issues, couples learn the "20 Minute Rule" (Lombardo, 2005), where time is set aside for each person to talk for 10 minutes each. If there is conflict or confusion about whether it's time to take a break, put an end to treatment or consider alternatives. A questionnaire such as "Deciding When Enough Is Enough" (Lombardo, 2005) is administered and discussed. (See questionnaire at the end of this chapter.) The goal is to support the individual and the couple's relationship in growing stronger as a result of this crisis.

Community Support

Community resource information about support systems is available, either in the local area or online. Education about how this emotional support is linked to increased well-being and even improved chances of successful treatment. Encourage the client to access the support of other women dealing with infertility struggles through organizations like Resolve and online support.

Say, *"Many women who are undergoing fertility challenges find a great deal of comfort from other women who are experiencing similar struggles. Infertility support groups provide a forum for women, and often their spouses, to come together and share practical information and emotional support. Resolve* (www.resolve.org) *often sponsors local infertility support groups, as do some local hospitals and fertility clinics. Support groups are also available online."*

Grief

Depending on the answers to these questions, support and education is provided. In all situations, the client learns that infertility is in fact a life crisis. In addition, they are educated about the grief inherent in the diagnosis, as well as the cycle of ongoing grief (hope to disappointment) that occurs every month she is unsuccessful in becoming pregnant and that occurs if there is a procedural failure.

Say, *"Infertility and grief go hand in hand. To begin with there is grief in the very diagnosis of infertility. Something that was supposed to occur naturally and be just between you and your husband has been lost and feelings of anger, bitterness, and sadness are common. Also, every month you wait and hope that this will be the month when you conceive. When this doesn't happen, and your hope turns to disappointment, there is grief again. Riding this roller-coaster of emotions can be exhausting and you may find yourself bouncing between*

these highs and lows. That's why it's important to give yourself time
to recover and find an outlet for these emotions. Let's talk about
ways you can do that."

_____

_____

Suggestions may include writing in a journal, creative outlets, or group support.

Phase 3: Assessment

Constructing the Target

In working with fertility clients, it is most helpful to begin with the Touchstone Event under the theme of responsibility. The only exception to this is if the client has suffered a reproductive trauma that is blocking processing of the Touchstone Event. In this case, this worst event is processed first until it is no longer blocking and then processing continues with the Touchstone Event.

Set up the target experience by gathering an image, negative cognition, desired positive cognition, VoC, emotion, SUD, and physical sensation (Shapiro, 2001)

Say, *"Today we have decided to reprocess _____ (select the next incident to be targeted)."*

_____

_____

Say, *"What happens when you think of the incident?"*

_____

_____

Or say, *"When you think of the incident what do you get?"*

_____

_____

Picture

Say, *"What picture represents the entire incident?"*

_____

_____

If there are many choices or if the client becomes confused, the clinician assists by asking the following:

Say, *"What picture represents the most traumatic part of the incident?"*

_____

_____

Negative Cognition (NC)

Say, *"What words best go with the picture that express your negative belief about yourself now?"*

_____

_____

Positive Cognition (PC)

Say, *"When you bring up that picture or incident, what would you like to believe about yourself now?"*

_____

_____

Validity of Cognition (VoC)

Say, *"When you think of the incident* (or picture) *how true do those words _____* (clinician repeats the positive cognition) *feel to you now on a scale of 1 to 7, where 1 feels completely false and 7 feels completely true?"*

1	2	3	4	5	6	7
(completely false)				(completely true)		

Emotions

Say, *"When you bring up the picture* (or incident) *and those words _____* (clinician states the negative cognition), *what emotion do you feel now?"*

_____

_____

Subjective Units of Disturbance (SUD)

Say, *"On a scale of 0 to 10, where 0 is no disturbance or neutral and 10 is the highest disturbance you can imagine, how disturbing does it feel now?"*

0	1	2	3	4	5	6	7	8	9	10
(no disturbance)								(highest disturbance)		

Location of Body Sensation

Say, *"Where do you feel it* (the disturbance) *in your body?"*

_____

_____

Phase 4: Desensitization

Using the Standard EMDR Protocol, the initial target or node is accessed as it is currently stored and the memory network is fully processed allowing for spontaneous emergence of TICES. It is helpful to note and track new targets, including progressions and blocking beliefs (Morrow, 2008). If information becomes blocked, cognitive interweaves are judiciously used.

Cognitive Interweaves

Common cognitive interweaves with this population can include the following.

Responsibility

In response to a belief that it is the client's fault that she has fertility issues:

> Say, *"Would you blame another woman for her fertility issues?"*

> _____

> _____

> After the client responds, do BLS.

> Say, *"Would you blame someone with heart disease, or cancer, or Alzheimer's?"*

> _____

> _____

After the client responds, do BLS.

In response to a client who believes that she waited too long to start trying for a family or made a lifestyle choice early on that she feels could be to blame, say the following:

> Say, *"At the time that you made that decision, were you going with the best information you had at the time?"*

> _____

> _____

> After the client responds, do BLS.

> Or say, *"At the time that you made that decision, did you have any way of knowing that this would impact your fertility?"*

> _____

> _____

After the client responds, do BLS.

Personal Mentors or Models of Unconditional Love

In response to a client dealing with feelings of anger, shame, and betrayal directed at herself or if a client has a relationship with someone she sees as unconditionally loving, this can be accessed to help the client:

> Say, *"So if you could sit with* _____ (state person in life that is unconditionally loving) *right now and share with her how you feel about yourself, what do you think she would say?"*

> _____

> _____

After the client responds, do BLS.

Let's Pretend

To help a client accept the possibility of change and growth, for instance, if a client is upset at the way she was treated by a family member or health care provider:

Say, *"If you could say something now, what would it be?"*

_____

_____

After the client responds, do BLS.

Phase 5: Installation

When the SUDs is reduced to a 0, the positive cognition is checked for accuracy and then installed.

Say, *"How does _____ (repeat the PC) sound?"*

_____

_____

Say, *"Do the words _____ (repeat the PC) still fit or is there another positive statement that feels better?"*

_____

_____

If the client accepts the original positive cognition, the clinician should ask for a VoC rating to see if it has improved:

Say, *"As you think of the incident, how do the words feel from 1 being completely false to 7 being completely true?"*

1   2   3   4   5   6   7
(completely false)   (completely true)

Say, *"Think of the event and hold it together with the words _____ (repeat the PC)."*

_____

_____

Do a long set of BLS to see if there is more processing to be done.

Phase 6: Body Scan

After the positive cognition is completely installed, the client is asked to scan her body for any residual tension in the form of body sensation. It is possible to clear these residual disturbances by concentrating on and processing any residual, physical sensations with successive sets until they are clear (Shapiro, 2001).

Say, *"Close your eyes and keep in mind the original memory and the positive cognition. Then bring your attention to the different parts of your body starting with your head and working downward. Any place you find any tension, tightness, or unusual sensation, tell me."*

_____

_____

Additional Negative Cognitions

It is possible that one incident could have more than one negative cognition; it is important to reprocess all of them. These can emerge during assessment, or during the course of processing, when a client evidences negative cognitive beliefs in more than one area. For example, after an unsuccessful procedure, one client not only believed "I am worthless" (personal responsibility), but related during processing, "I cannot trust anyone"(anger at her physician). The negative cognition concerning trust is the secondary cognition. Therefore, it is important that after processing is complete under the negative cognition of responsibility, the incident is reassessed relative to trust, and if SUDs greater than 0 emerges, the incident is processed again before moving to the next target.

Phase 7: Closure

If the client is not complete, a self-soothing or containment exercise is performed depending on the client needs (light stream, spiral technique, etc.). The client is reminded that processing continues after the session, and a log is given to the client to keep track of any positive or negative triggers or experiences (for example, the client's reaction to a pregnant coworker). The client is also reminded to implement self-soothing techniques between sessions, and to call the office if necessary.

Say, *"Things may come up or they may not. If they do, great, write it down and it can be a target for next time. If you get any new memories, dreams, or situations that disturb you, just take a good snapshot. It isn't necessary to give a lot of detail. Just put down enough to remind you so we can target it next time. The same thing goes for any positive dreams or situations. If negative feelings do come up, try not to make them significant. Remember, it's still just the old stuff. Just write it down for next time. Then use the tape or the Safe Place exercise to let as much of the disturbance go as possible. Even if nothing comes up, make sure to use the tape every day and give me a call if you need to."*

Note: These triggers are logged on the targeting sequence sheet (see "Triggers" on Time Line sheet) consistent with the theme of the negative cognition, to be checked at a later point.

Phase 8: Reassessment

Reassessment helps to evaluate treatment effects and monitor how these changes are occurring in the client's world. Future templates can facilitate this by allowing the client to try on and project a desired emotional or behavioral response in a certain situation. Specifically, future templates may be used to strengthen relationships or set boundaries with family members, communicate with health care providers, or improve self-image or lifestyle choices. Future templates need to be consistent with the client's goals and consider where she is on her fertility journey. For example, a future template may be a rehearsal on how to respond at a family reunion when everyone is asking, "When are you having a baby?" If the client has chosen to pursue a foreign adoption, the future template may be dealing with people's reactions, especially if the child looks dissimilar. If the client has chosen to live child free, a future template may be dealing with people who may view her choice as selfish. If the client is successful in becoming pregnant, a future template may be the preparation of setting healthy limits with a child who could easily be seen as a treasure and overindulged.

Future templates, however, are *not* used to project specific outcomes in terms of treatment. In fact, with infertility clients, it is often important to separate the desire to conceive from the way that infertility challenged that choice. As grief resolves, and a client is able to regain a healthy self-image, she can often make the distinction between parenthood and pregnancy and even consider the choice to live child free. For example, a client had difficulty setting boundaries with her extended family. After processing related issues, she felt ready to consider her own needs in relationship with others. In this particular example, the client installs a future template of saying "No" to attending a family member's baby shower. She used the positive cognition "I deserve to make myself a priority," and was able to imagine talking to her family member calmly and with clarity, handling the situation (adapted from *EMDR: New Notes on Adaptive Information Processing,* Shapiro, 2006).

1. Say, *"I would like you to imagine yourself coping effectively with* _____ (state the goal) *in the future. With the positive belief* _____ (state the positive belief) *and your new sense of* _____ (state the quality, i.e., strength, clarity, confidence, calm), *imagine stepping into this scene. Notice what you see and how you are handling the situation. Notice what you are thinking, feeling, and experiencing in your body."*

   _____

   _____

2. Say, *"Are there any blocks, anxieties, or fears that arise as you think about this future scene?"*

   _____

   _____

If yes, say the following:

3. Say, *"Then focus on these blocks and follow my fingers* (or any other BLS). *"*

   _____

   _____

If the blocks do not resolve quickly, evaluate if the client needs any new information, resources, or skills to be able to comfortably visualize the future coping scene. Introduce needed information or skills.

   Say, *"What would you need to feel confident in handling the situation?"*

   _____

   _____

Or say, *"What is missing from your handling of this situation?"*

_____

_____

4. If the block still does not resolve and the client is unable to visualize the future scene with confidence and clarity, use direct questions, the Affect Scan, or the Float-Back Technique to identify old targets related to blocks, anxieties, or fears. Use the Standard EMDR Protocol to address these targets before proceeding with the template. (See Worksheets in Appendix A.)

5. If there are no apparent blocks and the client is able to visualize the future scene with confidence and clarity as in the following:

    Say, *"Please focus on the image, the positive belief, and the sensations associated with this future scene and follow my fingers (or any other BLS)."*

_____

_____

6. Process and reinforce the positive associations with BLS. Do several sets until the future template is sufficiently strengthened.

    Say, *"Go with that."*

_____

_____

    Then say, *"Close your eyes and keep in mind the experience that you will have in the future. Then bring your attention to the different parts of your body starting with your head and working downward. Any place you find any tension, tightness, or unusual sensation, tell me."*

_____

_____

If any sensation is reported, do BLS.

If it is a positive or comfortable sensation, do BLS to strengthen the positive feelings.

If a sensation of discomfort is reported, reprocess until the discomfort subsides. Check the VoC.

Say, *"When you think of the incident* (or picture) *how true do those words* _____ (clinician repeats the positive cognition) *feel to you now on a scale of 1 to 7, where 1 feels completely false and 7 feels completely true?"*

1   2   3   4   5   6   7
(completely false)   (completely true)

Next, ask the client to move from imagining this one scene or snapshot to imagining a movie about coping in the future, with a beginning, middle, and end. Encourage the client to imagine coping effectively in the face of specific challenges, triggers, or snafus. Make some suggestions in order to help inoculate him for future problems.

Say, *"This time, I'd like you to close your eyes and play a movie, imagining yourself setting boundaries effectively with your relatives in the future. With the new positive belief of, 'I deserve to make myself a priority,' and with your new sense of confidence, imagine stepping into the future. Imagine yourself coping with ANY challenges that come your way. Make sure the movie has a beginning, a middle, and an end. Notice what you're seeing, thinking, feeling, and experiencing in your body. Let me know if you hit any blocks. If you do, just open your eyes and let me know. If you don't hit any blocks, let me know when you have viewed the whole movie."*

_____

_____

If the client hits blocks, address as above (BLS, interweaves, new skills, information, resources, direct questions, Affect Scan, or Float-Back).

If the client is able to play the movie from start to finish with a sense of confidence and satisfaction, ask the client to play the movie one more time from beginning to end and introduce BLS. In a sense, you are installing this movie as a future template.

Say, *"Play the movie one more time from beginning to end."*

_____

_____

Do BLS. You are installing the movie as a future template (Shapiro, 2006).

Fertility Questionnaire: Deciding When Enough Is Enough

How will you know when it's time to take a break or put an end to treatment and consider alternatives? This quiz can help provide answers.

1. Do you often find yourself mentally and emotionally tired?

2. Are you losing hope about the outcome of your medical treatment? Do you assume failure to guard against disappointment?

3. Does it seem as if your whole world is about infertility and that little else matters?

4. Do you find yourself irritable and resentful on the days when you have a doctor's appointment? Are you resisting following medical instructions?

5. Imagine that your doctor has just informed you that a new groundbreaking treatment has been discovered. Do you wish you didn't know?

6. Are you feeling resentful that you have had to give up other things to pursue treatment?

7. Is there more tension, arguing, or just isolated silence between you and your spouse? Has your relationship lost its energy and joy?

8. Are your money reserves getting dangerously low and putting you at financial risk?

9. Do you find yourself feeling desperate, pursuing treatment against medical recommendation, or willing to pursue pregnancy at any price?

10. Is the idea of being a parent becoming more important to you than being pregnant?

11. Does an end to the demands of treatment and a "return to normal" sound like a relief?

12. Do you look in the mirror and find it hard to remember who you were before, or hard to recognize who you've become?

If you find that you've answered "yes" to a majority of these questions, it may be time for you to consider ending treatment and reassessing your goals. Even if you've only answered "yes" to a few of the questions, you should see these responses as red flags signaling the need to take stock of where you are and strongly consider taking a break from treatment.

PART III

EMDR, Dissociative Disorders, and Complex Post-Traumatic Stress Disorder

Warning: Even though a script may give the illusion that it need only be read, in fact, that is not accurate. Due to the complex nature of this work, the material in this section ethically should only be used by professionals who have an expertise in working with clients with dissociative disorders or complex post-traumatic stress disorder (C-PTSD). There is a vast amount of literature, advanced training, and opportunities for consultation (see www.isst-d.org) that therapists can pursue to educate themselves in this important area. Also, due to the hypnotic phenomena that are often part of the presentation of clients with a dissociative disorder or complex post-traumatic stress disorder, training and competence in beginning and advanced hypnosis is fundamental to working with this population. As with the field of dissociative disorders, there is literature, advanced training, and consultation possibilities in hypnosis (www.asch.net). Francine Shapiro includes the "EMDR Dissociative Disorders Task Force Recommended Guidelines: A General Guide to EMDR's Use in the Dissociative Disorders" (1995, pp. 365-369; 2001, pp. 441–445) in the first and second editions of her EMDR text, which is essential reading for any EMDR practitioner working in this area.

Early in the history of EMDR, there was an interest in working with clients suffering with complex post-traumatic stress disorder and dissociative disorders (then called multiple personality disorders). As a result of the powerful responses some clients had to the EMDR process, clinicians were apprehensive about disturbing their equilibrium too soon without enough safeguards. For the most part, these clients were those with early multiple traumas that occur in the disorders mentioned above.

In addition, there was concern for the safety of the clinicians, attending the basic EMDR trainings with these diagnoses, who might be triggered during the practica as a result of their own early trauma, known or as yet undetected. The Participant's Agreement was one of the EMDR Institute's ways of highlighting the power of this methodology to attendees and gaining their acknowledgment that they understood the risks involved in participating in the practica if they, themselves, had a trauma history; the intention was for participants to take appropriate precautions to support their particular needs.

In 1991, Gerald Puk began the first Level II Specialty Training called "Applications of EMDR in Treating Dissociative Disorders" (1991a) and then went on to present "Eye Movement Desensitization and Reprocessing: Treatment of a More Complex Case, Borderline Personality Disorder" (1991b) at the annual meeting of the Association for the Advancement of Behavior Therapy. Dr. Puk also wrote a paper that year called "Treating Traumatic Memories: A Case Report on the Eye Movement Desensitization Procedure" (1991c) for the *Journal of Behavior Therapy and Experimental Psychiatry* where he reported on working with two successful cases with EMDR; one of the clients was treated for traumatic memories of child sexual abuse.

David Fenstermaker (1991a) began writing about his observations and work in the *EMDR Network Newsletter* with this population. He reported on an informal study he pursued weaving EMDR and hypnosis with 18 of his patients diagnosed with multiple personality disorder. He worked on 371 different memories with these 18 patients and noted that two-thirds passed the 1-year anniversary mark without reliving any portion of the trauma and 98% passed that mark without reexperiencing any portion of an EMDR abreacted memory. Dr. Fenstermaker's work integrating the use of hypnosis and EMDR was the harbinger of the work to come in this field with EMDR.

EMDR practitioners began to present more frequently and more urgently on this topic. Shapiro, Solomon, Kaufman, and Fenstermaker presented at the International Society for Traumatic Stress Studies on "Origins and Update: Origins of EMDR With Critical Incidents: Preliminary Research and Results: Clinical Use of EMDR With Dissociative Patients" (1991). Around the same time that year, Dean, Fenstermaker, and Anderson went to the International Society for the Study of Multiple Personality Disorder (later to change names to the International Society for the Study of Trauma and Dissociation) Fall Conference and talked about the "Clinical Use of Eye Movement Desensitization/Reprocessing (EMD/R) in Recall and Reprocessing of Traumatic Material in MPD Patients" (1991a), and "PTSD Treatments Grow in Evidence and Effectiveness" (1991b). Dr. Fenstermaker also presented that year at the California Psychological Association on "An Innovative Abreactive Process for Dissociative Disorders: Eye Movement Desensitization and Reprocessing (EMDR)" (1991b). All of these practitioners advocated for accurately diagnosing clients with these types of early trauma so that an effective and safe treatment plan would be in place before working with EMDR.

By 1992, Walter Young from the National Center for the Treatment of Dissociative Disorders in Denver, Colorado, called for an open discussion of the treatment of this population in the *Network Newsletter*. Landry Wildwind (1992) worked with early childhood abuse survivors to address perpetrator introjects and the fear of abandonment. Essentially, she helped her clients to differentiate from the perpetrator(s), to hold the positive memories that clients are afraid to lose about their perpetrators in a safe place, and to tolerate negative affect connected with these issues.

By 1993, the EMDR Institute sent out "1993 Update and Cautions" (unpublished) to the approximately 4,000 clinicians that they had trained, concerning dissociative disorders. Walter Young and Catherine Fine—as spokespersons of the newly formed Dissociative Disorders Task Force—contributed to and reviewed this preliminary material. They called for the following when working with this population: appropriate screening; training in dissociative disorders as a specialty before attempting EMDR; attending Level II to learn the training material such as cognitive interweaves and alternative abreactive strategies; reevaluating prior MPD protocols, especially concerning time distortion and hypnotic restraints; using the full EMDR protocol including the negative cognition (NC), positive cognition (PC), and Body Scan where possible; retargeting memories to check that all sensory data has been reprocessed; making sure to use clinical cross-checks to ascertain that the material is actually integrated versus dissociated; and addressing NCs such as fears of integration or fusion, loss of identity or death when clients are stabilized.

Several articles appeared in the *Network Newsletter* in the winter of 1993. Eirin Gould (1993) made a case for the use of the subjective units of disturbance (SUD) and validity of cognition (VoC) to map the memory network, despite the known complexity of the memories associated with early trauma. Curtis Rouanzoin (1993) addressed the common observation of practitioners that their clients often dissociated somewhat rapidly after beginning EMDR. He detected that clients often seemed to look at consistent areas in their visual field when reprocessing or talking about their trauma and he suggested using a spatial map, a method that suggests the clinician use bilateral stimulation (BLS) in that field while processing the trauma. He reported that he had excellent results with this modification.

Presenters at the 2nd Annual EMDR Conference that year spoke on subjects such as "Multiple Personality Disorder" (Fenstermaker, 1993); "Incest Trauma Survivors" (Gould & Belton, 1993); and "Dissociative Disorders" (Young, Puk, & Rouanzoin, 1993); while Sandra Paulsen chaired a symposium at the 1993 International Society for the Study of Multiple Personality Disorder with Silke Vogelmann-Sine, Steven Lazrove, and Walter Young (Paulsen et al. 1993) as the discussant on "EMDR: Its Role in the Treatment of Dissociative Disorders." Dr. Paulsen also presented on "Ego State Disorders (Dissociative, but not MPD)" (1993) and introduced the use of the dissociative table and EMDR.

In 1993, experts in the field such as Catherine Fine, past president of the International Society for the Study of Multiple Personality and Dissociation, and David Calof, speaker and author of "Multiple Personality and Dissociation: Understanding Incest Abuse and MPD" (1993), took the training for EMDR and began to incorporate EMDR into their work with this difficult population. They presented at the EMDR Conference on "EMDR and Structured Therapy for MPD" (Fine, 1993b) and "Managing Self Harm" (Calof, 1993). John Marquis and Gerald Puk presented on "Dissociative Identity Disorder: A Common Sense and Cognitive-Behavioral View" (1994). It was at this time that Deborah Korn (1995, 1996, 1997, 2001, 2002, 2003, 2006, 2008a, 2008b, 2009; Korn, Rozelle & Weir, 2005a; Korn, Weir, & Rozelle, 2005b) began her important work in this field through presentations and later research and articles on complex post-traumatic stress disorder. At the 2nd and 3rd annual EMDR conference, Deborah Korn presented with Eirin Gould, Scott Nelson and Margot Silk Forrest on "Sexual Abuse" (Gould et al., 1993, 1994).

In 1993, it was becoming clear that there was a higher prevalence of undiagnosed dissociative disorders in our clinical populations than originally thought. There was a concern that the premature use of EMDR would come at a high cost to the patient, therapist, and therapeutic alliance; in fact, there were reported cases of alters or ego states revealing themselves during the course of EMDR reprocessing. Interested in addressing this issue as soon as it began to arise—a standard response in the EMDR community—Francine Shapiro called an EMDR Dissociative Disorders Task Force together consisting of Catherine Fine, Marilyn Luber, Sandra Paulsen, Gerald Puk, Curt Rouanzoin, and Walter Young. They created "A General Guide to the Use of EMDR in the Dissociative Disorders." It was published informally by the EMDR Institute (EMDR Dissociation Task Force, 1994) and then was included in both of Dr. Shapiro's texts (1995, 2001) and is part of the EMDR Institute's Basic Training Manuals. This document was constructed to offer "general guidelines to the application of EMDR with the dissociative disorders, with paramount concern for clinical safety, however, it was not intended to supersede expert clinical judgment or training in dissociative disorders or hypnosis" (Shapiro, 2001, pp. 441–445). The important issues to address were the following: screening for dissociative disorders; clarifying the diagnosis; assessing factors important to therapist and patient safety; incorporating EMDR into the treatment plan; preparing for EMDR to minimize possible pitfalls; and suggesting how to use or not use EMDR in the early, middle, and final treatment phases. This document also referenced where to find societies, journals, conferences, workshops, consultation, and suggested reading that addressed issues concerning dissociative disorders and treatment.

The EMDR Institute and EMDR International Joint Conference of 1995 in Santa Monica, California, saw an evening symposium and town meeting by David Calof, Wendy Maltz, Francine Shapiro, and Walter Young (1995), "What Can We Learn From the 'False/Delayed Memory, Controversy?'" while Walter Young, Gerald Puk, and Curtis Rouanzoin (1993) presented on "Current Trends Using EMDR in Dissociative Disorders." There was an all day workshop that highlighted some of the issues involved when working with EMDR and sexual abuse and included topics such as "Healing the Sexual Problems Caused by Sexual Abuse" (Maltz, 1995), "Integrative and Strategic Utilization of EMDR in Treating Survivors of Sexual Abuse" (Korn, 1995), and "Using Dream Work and EMDR With Survivors of Sexual Abuse" (Zahorsky, 1995). Other presentations included "Self-Soothing and the Multiple Trauma Survivor" (Forrest, 1995), and "The Use of Imaginal and Cognitive Interweaves With Sexual Abuse Survivors" (Parnell, 1995). Jim Knipe published his work in the *EMDR Network Newsletter* on "Targeting Defensive Avoidance and Dissociated Numbing" (1995) that highlighted his way of addressing dysfunctional positive affect (see chapters 33–36) that often occur with this population and set the foundation for the important work that he has evolved for working with dissociative clients (1998, 1999, 2002, 2006, 2007, 2008). In this same year, Sandra Paulsen's article "Eye Movement Desensitization and Reprocessing: Its Cautious Use in the Dissociative Disorders" appeared in *Dissociation* (1995).

The 1996 EMDRIA conference included a presentation on ego state therapy, clinical hypnosis, and EMDR (Wade & Wade, 1996). In 1997, new themes, such as forensic issues; survivors of clergy sexual abuse (Farrell, 1997); and issues of shame, dissociation, and transference (Leeds & Korn, 1997) began to be explored. Andrew Leeds (1998) went on to write a chapter on the subject of shame, dissociation, and transference in Philip Manfield's book, *Extending EMDR: A Casebook of Innovative Applications*, incorporating the important information on shame (Nathanson, 1992; Tomkins, 1963) central to the understanding of this population. His chapter was part of a whole section in Dr. Manfield's book devoted to treating adults with histories of chronic childhood trauma or abuse (Knipe, 1998; Lovett, 1998; Manfield, 1998; Vogelmann-Sine, 1998).

In 1999, Laura Parnell (1999) came out with the first book on the treatment of complex post-traumatic stress disorder and EMDR called *EMDR in the Treatment of Adults Abused as Children*. This book was based on her 8 years of working with this population and EMDR; it included illustrative case studies and techniques to address impasses and strategies to handle different problems relevant to this population.

By the end of the 20th century and the new millennium, there was a consistent group of speakers who concentrated in presenting on the pertinent issues specific to ego state therapy with EMDR. They have been contributing to conferences and writing over the past 8 years; Uri Bergmann (2000, 2002, 2003, 2004, 2006, 2007, 2008a, 2008b, 2008c); Carol Forgash (2000, 2002, 2003, 2004, 2005, 2006, 2007; Forgash & Knipe, 2001); Barry Litt (2003, 2004, 2006, 2007a, 2007b, 2008); Litt, Forgash, & Twombly, 2002), Sandra Paulsen (2000, 2001, 2003, 2004a, 2004b, 2006, 2007, 2008b); and Shirley Jean Schmidt (1998, 1999, 2000). Carol Forgash and Margaret Copeley (2008) recently edited *Healing the Heart of Trauma and Dissociation With EMDR and Ego State Therapy*; an important contribution that highlights the different issues of this critical field.

Andrew Leeds continued his work on resource development and early traumatized clients on his own (1998, 2006) and with Deborah Korn (Leeds & Korn, 1997, 1998, 2002), while Ulrich Lanius (2001, 2004a, 2004b, 2005, 2006, 2008) pursued his interests in neurobiology and C-PTSD (as did Uri Bergmann cited above). Joanne Twombly introduced her perspective on using EMDR in the treatment of clients with dissociative disorders. She emphasized the importance of adapting each stage of treatment to address the needs of this particular population teaching clients how to intervene in their "multiple reality disorder" (Kluft, 1993b) to decrease the negative transference and to provide a positive and protective experience that supports adaptive trauma processing (2000a, 2000b, 2001a, 2001b, 2001c, 2004, 2005).

Don Beere, who had been writing about issues concerning dissociation since 1995 (1995, 1996a, 1996b), began to write about EMDR, hypnosis, and trauma (Beere, Simon & Welch, 2001; Welch & Beere, 2002) and presented his work at an all day preconference workshop at the EMDRIA annual conference on "The Dissociative Disorders: Update, Current Research, and Applications of EMDR" (Beere, 2003). His unique approach to stabilization emphasized interventions to strengthen present-time and present-place "locatedness" and used practical interventions to slowly build clients' capacity to manage increasing amounts of distress. His approach derives from his own research and his perceptual theory of dissociation (Beere, n.p., 2009a, 2009b).

Denise Gelinas (2003) wrote her important paper describing the integrating of EMDR into phase-oriented treatment for trauma and published it in the *Journal of Trauma and Dissociation*. She began teaching about how to treat clients with C-PTSD at the EMDR International conferences (2006, 2007, 2008). Meanwhile, Sandra Paulsen began collaborating with John Watkins on working with ego state therapy and EMDR, giving a number of presentations (Paulsen & Watkins, 2003a, 2003b, 2003c, 2005; Watkins & Paulsen, 2003).

Bessel Van der Kolk, Deborah Korn, Jeffrey Weir, and Deborah Rozelle (2004) presented their research on "Looking Beyond the Data: Clinical Lessons Learned From an EMDR Treatment Outcome Study." Korn, Rozelle, and Weir (2005a, 2005b) presented their findings at the EMDR European Association Conference in Brussels on "Bringing EMDR Research Into Practice" and "Beyond the Data: Clinical Lessons Learned From a Four-Year Treatment Outcome Study Comparing EMDR to Prozac." These presentations and articles were based on a 4 year, randomized controlled study comparing EMDR to Prozac. They learned that EMDR was effective in reducing depressive symptomatology in clients with a lifetime of trauma in a relatively short period of time—8 weeks. They found that this population was far more able than previously thought to move quickly into trauma work. To assess client readiness for EMDR they looked for the following criteria: clients can use their resources to address their *fear of fear* and they are able to stop processing and return to an adaptive internal equilibrium with no internal or external catastrophes. If these two criteria were present they were candidates to begin processing with EMDR. The *take home* messages they gleaned from their work were the following:

- Scan and work with activated memories or *follow the heat*;
- Adhere to the protocol as it is the key to success;
- Target adult traumatic material as it is possible to process *pieces* of work without opening up all childhood memories;
- Go forward even when the client is highly aroused and symptomatic—the picture of distress is the reason to begin EMDR;
- Manage your own countertransference and trust the protocol;
- Progress can be made rapidly despite the diagnosis, trauma history, or treatment response;
- Collaborate with colleagues as self-evaluation increases fidelity, skill level and treatment success. (Korn, Rozelle, & Weir, 2005b)

In the German-speaking countries, there has been and continues to be a great interest in treating C-PTSD and DID with EMDR. Arne Hofmann (1999, 2004a, 2004b, 2004c, 2005, 2006), who had been working in this area from the time that he was trained in EMDR in the early 1990s, encouraged his colleagues to pursue study in this area. He has made many presentations on this topic and also inspired research. Tapping into the work of experts already in the field such as Luise Reddemann and Ulrich Sacchsse, Dr. Hofmann inspired other colleagues also (Matthess, 2007; Onofri & Hummel, 2003; Rost, 2005, 2008; Sack & Matthess, 2005).

This substantial—yet not exhaustive—history and report on the trends of interest in the field of EMDR with clients diagnosed with C-PTSD and DD is illustrative of the amount of interest and concentration there has been in this field. It reflects the complexity and the urgency of working with clients who present with these issues. The chapters in this section of the book focus on a wide range of issues that confront the practitioner when working with this population. As in any group, there is a diversity of opinion and different ways of going about the work. By reading through the diverse perspectives that these authors bring to their treatment of their C-PTSD and DD patients, clinicians are able to obtain a sense of the issues confronting them as they incorporate an EMDR approach into their work. It is essential that clinicians choosing to treat these interesting and challenging clients already know the basics of this complex work before introducing EMDR.

As you read through this section, there are several essential principles that guide the work of the authors:

- *Adaptive responses to abnormal situations.* Clients' responses are adaptive given the traumatic events and behaviors to which they were exposed.
- *Respect.* Respect for the myriad ways clients have handled trauma is essential.
- *Safety.* The need for internal and external safety is essential for clients.
- *Hypnosis.* Hypnosis training and the understanding of hypnotic phenomena are essential to successful work.
- *Resources.* The ability to have at least some positive resource is important in assisting clients in their lives and in their trauma work.
- *Adaptive inner focus.* Clients learn how to focus internally without dissociating and accessing trauma material.
- *Negative affect tolerance.* Clients need to be capable of managing and tolerating their affect before incorporating the Desensitization Phase of EMDR into treatment.
- *Boundaries.* Learning how to discern a sense of self as separate from others is fundamental in this work.

- *Orientation.* Clients can maintain one foot in the past and one foot in the present.
- *Positive affect tolerance.* Often, positive affect is poorly tolerated; however, it is essential for clients to progress.

The first chapters in this section address how to begin working with clients who are disconnected or dissociated from the experience of their behaviors, affects, sensations, and knowledge about themselves and their environments. Carol Forgash in her chapters on "Stabilization Phase of Trauma Treatment: Introducing and Accessing the Ego State System" (chapter 13), "Home Base" (chapter 14), "Workplace or Conference Room" (chapter 15), and "Orienting the Ego State System to Present Reality" (chapter 16) gives clinicians a way to teach clients the following skills: building the confidence of clients in acknowledging and addressing their own internal experience, creating safe spaces from which to dialogue and ultimately address all types of experience, learning how to stay in present time, and understanding the difference between the past and the present that is often so confusing for this population.

In chapter 17, the "Back of the Head Scale (BHS)," Jim Knipe creates a simple, helpful way for clients to gauge where they are along the continuum of being in the present to withdrawing or dissociating into the past. By teaching clients this technique, Dr. Knipe has created a respectful way for clients and therapists to be more aware. He links the BHS with "The Method of Constant Installation of Present Orientation and Safety (CIPOS)" (chapter 18) as a way to help clients learn how to come back into the present when dissociating or beginning to dissociate or disconnect.

Joanne Twombly's work focuses on helping clients set up or create a safe enough space. She continues this work by the skillful idea of using bilateral stimulation to install the safe feeling of being in the security of the therapist's office and the sheltering presence of the therapist. Her exercise in teaching clients to orient themselves by measuring their height is eye opening to some clients as it further reinforces that the past is different from the present.

Arne Hofmann's resource work "The Absorption Technique" (chapter 23) has modified the "Wedging Technique" (Kiessling, 2009) and addresses the need for clients to learn how to focus on the positive resources they have and how to use them in difficult situations. While Don Beere's "Modified Resource Development and Installation (RDI) Procedures With Dissociative Clients" (chapter 24) has changed the RDI protocol (Shapiro, 2001) to take into consideration the needs of clients who dissociate by introducing them in a slow and careful way to what EMDR is and how bilateral stimulation will be used. Instead of asking for positive experiences, Dr. Beere uses the positive experiences that naturally occur in the session and then—having already introduced BLS—installs the experience, with the client's permission as they go. Carol Forgash instructs clients how to use their naturally occurring avoidance in a constructive manner to take care of the daily visits to what might be unpleasant environments, as in going to the doctor's or dentist's office, interviews, exams, and so forth. By helping clients sort out the needs of their ego states and then using rehearsal as a way to learn what to expect, she assists them in practicing how to handle the situations.

The next group of chapters in this section addresses either titrated processing leading to using the Standard EMDR Protocol or a more full way of processing. All of these protocols use hypnotic phenomena and techniques to augment the efficacy of their work. *It is essential that practitioners using these protocols have an expertise in hypnosis, working with clients with dissociative disorders and EMDR.* In Joanne Twombly's "Initial Targeting of Traumatic Material: Steps" (chapter 26), she takes some time to introduce, in the Preparation Phase, how to work with a team of parts so that not all parts need to work with the material if it is not indicated. She uses the "Picture in Picture (PIP)" imagery to assist with the trauma work and to support clients being in control of the process. She helps choose a target and ensure the safety of all parts—whether they will be part of the process or not and moves into a titrated process that supports the self-efficacy of her clients and makes sure that, at the end of the processing no matter where they are in the process, clients and parts are safe.

"The Inverted EMDR Standard Protocol for Unstable Complex Post-Traumatic Stress Disorder" (chapter 27) is Arne Hofmann's answer to helping clients with C-PTSD build resources and support their ability to stay in present time by coming back from past trauma into the present without dissociating. He begins in the future by using "The Absorption Technique" (see chapter 23) to support the client's attaining a calm, daily life. As that is accomplished, it is possible to move into working with present day targets and secondary trauma targets by using "The Method Of Constant Installation of Present Orientation and Safety (CIPOS)" (see chapter 18). As these elements are mastered, it is then possible to move into the past traumatic material. Here he has created four criteria or tests as a way to know when clients are ready to do their trauma work. When this is completed, he looks at where the traumatic material comes from, usually targeting secondary traumas first, until clients demonstrate the ability to move into the more difficult material. During the work in the past, he uses resources, CIPOS, and the Standard EMDR Protocol.

Catherine Fine pioneered the work on fractionated abreactions (Fine, 1993a). Here, she uses her expertise to inform her treatment as she weaves EMDR and hypnosis together to work with her clients on their traumatic material. In "The Wreathing Protocol" (chapter 28), her goal is to protect her clients from decompensating while working on this difficult material and help them achieve a congruence along the BASK dimensions of behavior, affect, sensation and knowledge. The BASK model structures Dr. Fine's work and helps her decide how to proceed concerning the processing of the issue at hand. In this way, clients gain a sense of self-efficacy, control, and safety.

The "Bottom-Up Processing Protocol" (chapter 29) by Ulrich Lanius again supports the importance of helping clients stay within their window of tolerance. Dr. Lanius focuses on the sensory element of the trauma to inform how he helps clients to process through their material. By concentrating on this aspect of the experience, he assists clients to slow down the process, fractionate the experience, and support feeling emotion, as well as reduce dissociative responses.

In chapter 30, Sandra Paulsen steps us through her "ACT-AS-IF and ARCHITECTS Approaches to EMDR Treatment of Dissociative Identity Disorders (DID)." Dr. Paulsen takes us through assessment, containment and stabilization, trauma accessing, abreactive association, skills building, integration and future template, and follow up (ACT-AS-IF) and shows how her stages intersect with the EMDR procedures. She emphasizes the types of questions needed for this population and then moves into working with how to teach clients to contain traumatic memories. She models how to handle skillfully the different ego states with the important respect that is necessary and fundamental to a true therapeutic alliance. ARCHITECTS refers to the phase of ACT-AS-IF when EMDR is used. The steps include: access, refine the target, consent, hypnosis/imagery, titrate, EMDR/BLS, closure, technology tranquility and stabilize, synthesize, soothe. In this chapter, she steps us through her method of working and integrating her ego state work with hypnosis, imagery, and EMDR, giving us various suggestions of interventions when problems arise and providing for the integration, future templates, and follow up that are standard in this type of trauma work.

In Don Beere's chapter on "An EMDR Protocol for Dissociative Identity Disorder (DID)" (chapter 31), he demonstrates how through a thorough preparation for EMDR and establishing the hypnotic tool, *Screen,* he creates a context in which he is able to follow the EMDR Recent Event Protocol to assist his clients in working through their trauma. Although aspects of the traumatic memory are not remembered, he has found that his use of hypnosis and EMDR provides a solid matrix to support clients in processing the full trauma without titration. To use this protocol, he makes the following assumptions; the positive cognition is "It is over"; the negative cognition approximates, "It is not over. It is still happening"; and, that the subjective units of disturbance (SUDs) is a 10 (his rationale is that if something is not remembered, it means that it is too horrible to bear in consciousness). In this research-based protocol (Beere, 2009a, 2009b, n.p.), Dr. Beere has found that using the screen technique and working with the structure of the EMDR Recent Event Protocol allows for clients to process their trauma as long as needed to work through the material.

Chapter 32 in this section is one that all of us who work with this population encounter: what happens when negative cognitions get stuck? Denise Gelinas offers us an elegantly executed way out of this dilemma through a particular sequence of Socratic Cognitive Interweaves. The questions in the sequence are needed when the client is looping concerning the issues of responsibility and entitlement. As clients understand the responsibility of their adults for their caretaking, they will often become confused, which indicates it is time to move on to the second cluster concerning issues of disentangling the old relational pattern and accepting the idea that they can contain different feelings for others and themselves at the same time. The chapter concludes with a helpful example of how Dr. Gelinas implements this work.

The material in this section gives a variety of perspectives on the treatment of C-PTSD and DD. *Each author has stressed the importance of using the script as a model, yet not as a rote way to address all clients with these intricate issues. Because of the complex nature of these disorders, it is incumbent upon practitioners to use all of their clinical skills to tailor the treatment and the treatment plan to the client sitting in front of them; these scripts are a means to augment skills already established through the integration of EMDR into therapists' case conceptualization.*

13

Stabilization Phase of Trauma Treatment: Introducing and Accessing the Ego State System

Carol Forgash

Introducing and Accessing the Ego State System Script Notes

The purpose of the protocols in the chapters by this author is to help clinicians learn stabilization interventions for use in the Preparation Phase of EMDR treatment. Using these interventions will aid clients in developing readiness for processing trauma, learning how to manage symptoms of dissociation, dealing with affect regulation, and developing the necessary internal cohesion and resources to utilize the EMDR trauma-processing phase. In EMDR-AIP terms, as new traumatic experiences are stored as memories in the dysfunctional memory network, the expanding network reinforces the previous experiences. Therefore, a client with a multiple trauma history may have many networks of dysfunctionally stored material. They are easily triggered and overwhelmed when put in a position of prematurely having to deal with trauma processing.

Clinical Implications

Earlier negative experiences stored dysfunctionally increase vulnerability to anxiety disorders, depression, and other diagnoses. When assessing a client with a complex trauma history, clinicians need to view current symptoms of PTSD or depression as reflections of the earlier traumas. It is important to evaluate the entire clinical picture to assess vulnerability to triggers, dissociation, and strong emotion. It is well documented that early and ongoing trauma, coupled with more attachment difficulties results in a need for increased preparation prior to trauma work, to avoid destabilization or treatment failure. The strategies dealing with dissociative symptoms, ego state work, and internal stability outlined in the following chapters will help clinicians develop an individualized treatment plan to successfully guide the client through the EMDR phases of treatment.

Introducing and Accessing the Ego State System

Clients with dissociative symptoms often describe hearing voices or inner conversations; these often are the voices of internal parts or ego states. Many clients state that this feels chaotic and may often match the style of communication used in their family of origin. Clients often take these inner conversations as evidence of craziness, defectiveness, and so forth. There is now research showing that difficult, chaotic, disorganized attachment in the childhood home is causative in the development of dissociation (Gold, 2000; Liotti, 2006; Lyons, Dutra, Schuder, & Bianchi, 2006). It is important to give the client clear explanations about the trauma(s), dissociation, and the ego state system. They will require ongoing support and information since they will have periodic doubts about the existence of parts, and about the reality of their traumatic history (Watkins & Watkins, 1997).

Introducing Ego States and Dissociation Script

A helpful introduction to ego states and dissociation is the following:

> Say, *"One way to think about dissociated ego states is to consider that they are neural networks in the brain holding images, cognitions, emotions, and physical sensations. Not only do these neural networks hold negative experiences and dissociated ego states, they hold healthy experiences and ego states as well and that are well functioning, strong, and resourceful."*

Often, the information about ego states needs to be repeated diplomatically again and again as the client slowly begins to understand the nature of his own system of coping. It is important to match the type of language that is used to the client.

> Say, *"All your ego states exist within the adult client's body, heart, or brain. They do not have separate bodies and they do not exist independently in the present, although they may feel that they are separate from you. No ego states live in their childhood home, or with their parents they had in childhood. In fact, even though this may be hard to believe, the childhood trauma has ended."*

Expect resistance and emotional reactions from the client and ego states.

> Say, *"In the first phase of therapy, I will help you get to know and understand the ego state system. Over time, you will learn to manage the dissociative symptoms. You will learn about your resourceful, healthy parts through learning resources and other ego strengthening exercises. You will improve present functioning and together we'll prepare so that you will feel comfortable and solid enough to begin trauma processing."*

Use vocabulary that fits your client's language to describe parts.

> Say, *"These parts can be referred to in many ways. We can use the phrase 'states of mind,' 'fragments,' 'internal objects,' 'internal family system,' 'part selves,' or 'inner children.' Do you have a preference?"*

_____

_____

> Say, *"These parts can be thought of as symbols, metaphors, or even images that live in your mind, heart, or brain."*

You may use a formal or informal introduction of ego state concepts depending on your reading of the client's preferred way of learning.

Accessing the Ego State System

What will best facilitate your client's introduction to the ego state system? If you used a genogram during history taking, mapping the system can be called a genogram of the internal system or family. Or, it is possible to show a client how the terms "parts and ego states" have entered our vocabulary by showing them ego state cartoons?

Say, *"You know ZIGGY the cartoon character? Well, in one cartoon his face is covered with spots and he says, 'I found my inner child and he gave me chicken pox.' Or, the one where a therapist walks into the room where the patient is lying down and he says 'How's everybody?'"*

You can also encourage them to draw or list their ego states.

Say, *"It is very helpful for us to have a map for ourselves of the ego state system. In this way, we can begin to have a better understanding of what is going on inside of you and a way to make sure that we are respectful of all parts of you. Some people like to make a list while others may find it helpful to draw the ego states. What is your preference? Here is another way to think about it. If the internal system or parts could come into this office now, who might you see?"*

_____

_____

Clients' attitudes toward their ego state system vary. You need to know if they have any empathy toward the system.

Say, *"What are the parts like?"* (Notice if there are critics or perfectionists.)

_____

_____

If the client says one is nasty or threatening, ask the following:

Say, *"I've learned from working with many people that the angry, harsh parts were once protective, probably back in childhood. They may not realize that you are now an adult."*

_____

_____

Learn about the client's ability to empathize with the parts.

Say, *"I see that right now, you are _____ (list appropriate emotion such as anger, fear, shame, distress) with these ego states and the way they act (or treat you). Over time, as you learn more about the ego states and work with them, you will probably start to feel differently. When there are disagreements or conflicts, we'll work with the system and teach them how to problem solve and work together. You know how to do this. You are a _____ (state whatever is appropriate such as parent, team member, etc.)."*

You—as a therapist—become an ally to both the ego state system and client. You help clients to learn from your behavior with the parts, and how to treat their ego states in an empathic manner. In this way, they can learn how to be empathic toward themselves and their ego states. Now that you and the client have begun to know who is part of the ego state system, it is possible to get to know the system better by asking questions and learning more about it. Ask the different ego states the following questions:

Say, *"How old were you when that part had to take on that critical function?"*

_____

_____

Say, *"What was going on in your life at that time?"*

_____

_____

Say, *"What was good about having that part function in that way?"*

_____

_____

Say, *"How are you doing now?"*

_____

_____

Say, *"Is there anything else that you think that we need to know about this ego state?"*

_____

_____

Note: Make sure that over time you are able to ask each part questions so that they feel recognized and appreciated for their contribution. Always leave time to debrief the client about what has happened in the session.

Say, *"What do you think about what you have learned?"*

_____

_____

Say, *"What have your ego states learned today?"*

_____

_____

Say, *"How are you feeling now?"*

_____

_____

Say, *"Before we stop for the day, let's do one of our self-soothing exercises. If it is okay, would it be possible to include any of the parts present to do the exercise as well?"*

_____

_____

Say, *"You can use the Safe Place, Lightstream, breathing, or progressive relaxation exercises we have practiced. Why don't you ask any of*

*the parts that are present to participate as well? Which self-soothing
exercise would you like to do today?"*

_____

_____

Say, *"You can close your eyes and think about _____ (state whichever
one they selected)."*

_____

_____

Say, *"How are you feeling now?"*

_____

_____

Say, *"Let's make sure that you and _____ (state the name of the
adult client, the host, or whatever terminology you use) are present
and oriented before you leave."*

_____

_____

For example say, *"Can you hear the clock?"*

_____

_____

Say, *"Can you describe the pillow you are holding?"*

_____

_____

Say, *"Can you feel your body against the couch?"*

_____

_____

Say, *"Can you throw a pillow back and forth with me?"*

_____

_____

Say, *"Great, I am glad that you are back in present time with me. Is
there anything else that you need before we stop for today?"*

_____

_____

If no, you are ready to close.
If yes, check in with all parts to find out what else is needed to end the
session.

Say, *"Let's check in with all parts before we stop for today and find out what else is needed to end the session. Is there anything else that is needed?"*

_____

_____

Stabilization Phase of Trauma Treatment

These are the protocols developed to use during the Stabilization Phase of trauma treatment:

Protocol 1: Home Base
Protocol 2: Workplace or Conference Room
Protocol 3: Orienting the Ego State System to Present Reality (OPR)
Protocol 4: Constructive Avoidance of Present Day Situations: Techniques
    for Managing Critical Life Issues

There are a series of readiness activities that assist in helping dissociative clients access and work with ego states or parts of the self. The readiness activities are sequential steps that help clients and their ego state systems build safe and stable internal structures, become acquainted with each other, establish boundaries, develop healthier attachment styles, and learn protocols to manage symptoms in present life (see chapters 14 through 32 in this section).

14

Home Base

Carol Forgash

There are a series of readiness activities that assist in helping dissociative clients access and work with ego states or parts of the self. The readiness activities are sequential steps that help clients and their ego state systems build safe and stable internal structures, become acquainted, establish boundaries, develop healthier attachment styles and learn techniques to manage symptoms in present life.

Home Base (HB) Notes

It is important to help dissociative clients create a safe area for the ego state system to live, play, and interact. The Home Base (HB) can be a stable place for the internal ego state system. It may be visualized by the client as a metaphorical or a space that the client creates in his mind such as a comfortable scene in nature, a house in the country, the beach, a log cabin, a room in the client's house, and so forth. It is generally a different place from the adult client's place for relaxing. Initially, the home base metaphor may be very sketchy, unclear, and difficult for the client to use. Also, the parts may not be interested in hearing about this exercise. For a client who grew up in a chaotic, violent, or abusive family environment, this idea may be an impossible thought at first. Why should they have to take care of this "system"? They may be angry at this complex, conflicted, and dissociated system, and therefore not want to give them a home, or think it is a foolish idea. It is important to note that negative responses may predict early negative relational and traumatic experiences. Also, it is very important to use language carefully because some clients have found that there is no place that has been safe for them, even an internal space! Therefore, it is helpful to use other words like "comfort" or "relaxation" place instead of "safe."

It is important to respect the client's fears, concerns, and for the therapist to not give up! Look for opportune moments to bring it up. The home base imagery may be installed or strengthened with bilateral stimulation (BLS) if they are comfortable with it. If the client or parts system is uncomfortable with the use of BLS, present the steps of the exercise without it. The client should be familiar with some "parts" prior to introducing Home Base.

Home Base Script

Introducing Home Base

Image

Say some version of the following: *"I'd like you to think about some place you have been or imagine being that feels like a place where you can be comfortable or relaxed. The idea is to create a place that will be an internal home base for your 'parts.' Your Home Base can be a comfortable place where they may live. This is a place that you are choosing to create for your parts inside you. It can be a scene in nature, a house in the country, the beach, a log cabin, a room in the your home, or a tent by a mountain stream. It's a private place where the parts can get to know each other."*

_____

_____

Say, *"Tell the parts about this idea. They may choose to listen or not. We need consensus from them to do this work. Are they okay with this idea?"*

_____

_____

If there is strong opposition, have the client ask what the problem is and try to resolve it.

If there is no consensus, postpone the exercise until it's worked out.

If there is consensus continue with the following:

Say, *"Whatever place works for you is fine."*

Pause

Say, *"What do you see?"*

_____

_____

Emotions and Sensations

Say, *"As you think of Home Base, which has whatever the parts may need in it, notice what you see, hear, and feel right now."*

_____

_____

Pause

Say, *"What do you notice? The 'parts' may be noticing with you."*

_____

_____

Enhancement

Say, *"Focus on your Home Base, its sights, sounds, smells, and body sensations. Tell me more about what you* (and the parts) *are noticing."*

_____

_____

Reinforce

Say, *"Now concentrate on whatever you notice and follow my fingers* (or whatever BLS you use).*"*

_____

_____

Use 4 to 6 sets.

Say, *"How do you feel now?"*

_____

_____

If positive say the following:

Say, *"Focus on that* (repeat BLS). *What do you notice now?"*

_____

_____

Invitation to the Parts

Say, *"Show the parts the Home Base and invite them to look around, and, if they are ready, pick a room or place that they like. Remind them that this is their home now. Perhaps you will be willing to visit with them."*

_____

_____

Practice

Say, *"I'd like you to practice visiting Home Base, just to say hello, or good night to the parts between now and our next session. Keep track of how things go and we'll talk about it next time we meet."*

_____

_____

Workplace or Conference Room

Carol Forgash

Clients who have experienced severe trauma often feel that there is a lack of safety in their lives. Therefore, it is helpful to have an uncontaminated place where it is possible for the client to meet and get acquainted with the ego states and a place where they can meet with each other and work together. Before this, they may know of each other's existence and roles directly or indirectly. Although all parts do not have to come to the Workplace, it is important for them to know that they are all invited and that they may only sense these ego states or parts and not see them. The use of the Workplace for stabilization activities promotes awareness of the ego states or parts and also develops coconsciousness between the parts.

The setting up and utilization of the Workplace is a process and may take time as the client adjusts to the concept and tries it out. Client and ego states' reactions to these ideas that support communication and connection range across the affective spectrum from surprise to relief, feelings of normalcy, disapproval, disgust, revulsion, somatic reactions, or all of the above.

The Development of the Workplace Script

To introduce the client to the concept of a Workplace say the following:

> Say, *"I want to tell you about the idea of a Workplace. Developing a Workplace is a way for you to have an internal place where it is possible for you to meet and get acquainted with the other ego states* (or internal parts). *Although all parts do not have to come to the Workplace, it is important to extend an invitation to all parts of the mind to come if they choose to do so. The Workplace can be an office or a conference room, even the therapist's office or any place that the ego states can be accessed and joint work can take place. What are your thoughts about this?"*

_____

_____

Many types of workplaces or conference rooms are suggested in the literature, for example Fraser's (1991, 2003) "Dissociative Table Technique," in which the client sits at an oval table and invites ego states to sit in the empty chairs around the table. You and the client's parts system can use the Workplace to encourage discussion and dialogue, practice problem solving and conflict resolution and sharing information. It is important to talk with the client about the possible anticipated problems: the taboo against speaking up or out, the need to remain invisible, and so forth.

> Say, *"As we've previously talked about, some parts may want to be invisible, especially at first, others may be perceived by you as ghosts and shadows, others may just be sensed, while others may have a shape but no voice. This is to be expected and respected, and states are never forced to appear. It is not a failure if parts are not seen or heard; it is just a matter of developing readiness and trust.*
>
> *You may want to include a Workplace or conference room in your Home Base. You and your ego state system can equip this room with microphones, speakers, a TV, or movie screens to facilitate communication. Invite the parts to think about this idea of a Workplace with you. Together you will come up with what works. What do you all think that you will need?"*

_____

_____

Also ask for consensus about this idea.

Say, *"Are you all in agreement with what is needed?"*

_____

_____

If yes, continue. If no, say the following:

> Say, *"What would you need to agree on concerning what is needed for the Workplace?"*

_____

_____

> Say, *"If you would like to, look around the Home Base and see what room or space would make a good place to get together. What do you see or experience?"*

_____

_____

> Say, *"If you could see the parts of the self, your internal family, and so forth, who would be around the table and or in the Workplace now?"*

_____

_____

> Say, *"Remember if you can't see any part today, that's okay, let's continue anyway."*

_____

_____

Say, *"What do the parts think about working in this space? Do they think it's comfortable? Does it need anything?"*

_____

_____

Say, *"Thank the parts for coming to the Workplace today. You can use this Workplace for many different activities together. Next session we can start planning how to use the Workplace. Of course, during the week, if anything comes up, you may want to meet together in the Workplace. Let me know in our next session how that worked out."*

_____

_____

After the exercise is completed:

Say, *"What did you think of this exercise?"*

_____

_____

Say, *"What did you notice?"*

_____

_____

Say, *"How are you feeling now?"*

_____

_____

Say, *"It might be helpful for you to go back to your Safe Place, Home Base, or other place or state that allows you to feel good during the time between sessions so that you can practice going there and having the good feelings. Would that be something you would be interested in doing?"*

_____

_____

16

Orienting the Ego State System to Present Reality (OPR)

Carol Forgash

Orientation to Present Reality Script Notes

The purpose of the OPR exercise is to help clients with a dissociative disorder, or help dissociative symptoms work with their ego state system to begin to experience present time and place. This generally enhances feelings of reality and security for the system as well as their sense of appropriate caring and protection by the adult client. Often, one or more ego states of the system are dissociated and not oriented to present time, place, age; or status of the client, and so forth. Clients may notice thoughts and feelings that pull them away from the present that may indicate the presence of these disoriented parts. To begin this process clients must have a beginning understanding of their ego state system. If they do, then they are ready to begin the OPR protocol.

Note: If your client comes into your office and looks around as if he has not been there before, or if his body language and facial expressions change during the session sufficiently to indicate the client is not present, it is important to educate the client about dissociating and its relationship to trauma and ego states or parts. This may take a number of sessions and it may be helpful to review "Introducing and Accessing the Ego State System" (see chapter 13).

The OPR Protocol is done in three steps. This work may take several sessions, and the amount of time will differ with each client. It is important to do only as much as the client can tolerate and remind the client that they and the ego state system always can say, "Stop!" when necessary. The rate at which information can be disseminated will vary with the client, the system, and the stage of treatment.

Orienting to Present Reality (OPR) Script

Step 1. Getting to Know the Ego State(s)

Dissociative clients frequently come into the office and look around as if they have not been there before. When this occurs, say the following:

> Say, *"I am noticing that you are looking around my office as if it seems different or you have not ever been here before. What are you noticing?"*

_____

_____

Notice how the client does looks around, to get an idea of the age of the ego state that may be present.

> Say, *"Who is here today?"*

_____

_____

> Say, *"Ask the ego state* (ES) *if they know who you are."*

_____

_____

If the client says that the part is a she or he, use that pronoun. Otherwise, use the pronoun "they" as a way to be generic and include all. Or if there is a name given, use that name.

> Say, *"Could you ask _____ (state the name or age, e.g., 'the 3-year-old' of the ego state) if ____ (state he, she, or it) recognizes or knows me and is aware of what brings ___ (state him, her or it) to my office now?"*

_____

_____

> If not, say, *"Please say who I am, what I do, and any other information that would be helpful for the part to know."*

_____

_____

> Say, *"What does _____ (state the ego state) think about this?"*

_____

_____

> Say, *"Could you tell your ego state or _____ (state the name of the ego state) what the current year is?"*

_____

_____

In addition say, *"Throughout this exercise, if you need some help from me, I am glad to give it."*

_____

_____

Say, *"Could you tell your ego state or _____ (state the name of the ego state) what season of the year that we are in?"*

_____

_____

Say, *"How about if we discuss some of the important information about you that would be helpful for all parts to know?"*

_____

_____

Say, *"Could you tell your ego state or _____ (state the name of the ego state) how old you are?"*

_____

_____

Say, *"Could you tell your ego state or _____ (state the name of the ego state) what is your gender?"*

_____

_____

Say, *"Could you tell your ego state or _____ (state the name of the ego state) what roles you play in your life* (parent, student, etc.)*?"*

_____

_____

Say, *"Could you tell your ego state or _____ (state the name of the ego state) where you work and what is your job?"*

_____

_____

Step 2. Using the Workplace

After asking this basic information about the ego state(s), if it is possible, you can ask the ego states to come together in the already created spaces such as the Workplace (see chapter 15).

Say, *"Can you ask the parts to go to their Workplace or conference room where they can create an imaginary screen? There, if they would like, they can view images that help ground them in present time and place such as the therapist's office, the adult client in present time, or whatever else would be helpful for them."*

_____

_____

Remind the client of the following:

Say, *"It is important for both of us* (therapist and client) *to realize that ego states may have varying beliefs about time and space, past and present, about you, and the therapist, and so forth."*

_____

_____

Say, *"Would you be willing to create a video or movie that shows your home, job, present life, family, and other life events?"*

_____

_____

If yes, say the following:

Say, *"Great! Would you like to do that now?"*

_____

_____

Or, if the session is closing down:

Say, *"We'll do it next week."*

_____

_____

Otherwise, say the following:

Say, *"Here's an idea that may work for you. Imagine that you have a special remote control. When you pick it up, you can see that it has many dials on it. The first dial is for off and on, the next is for color, after that, one for black and white, then to create a larger or smaller picture, the next is for changing sound from louder or softer and another dial for moderating feelings from high to low. Is that something that makes sense to you?"* (Forgash & Copeley, 2007; Krakauer, 2001)

_____

_____

Say, *"Let's practice using the remote control. How about turning the picture on and off."*

_____

_____

Pause

Say, *"How did that go?"*

_____

_____

Say, *"What if you put a picture of a _____ (state any benign object such as a tree, a fruit, a pet) up on the screen and practice using all of the dials? How is that for you?"*

_____

_____

Say, *"What do you notice?"*

_____

_____

Use bilateral stimulation (BLS) as appropriate for reinforcement to install the skills.

Say, *"What if you tried it with another picture and this time, if it is okay with you, I will use _____ (state BLS you have decided to use together)."*

_____

_____

Say, *"Now, if you would, please turn on the picture, you can invite all of your parts who would like to see this. They don't have to be visible, but they can come to the Workplace and watch. Could you show your ego state system or _____ (the name or age of the specific ego states) the people and pets with whom you live?"*

_____

_____

Say, *"Okay, go ahead and make that movie now. What do you notice?"*

_____

_____

Say, *"If it feels uncomfortable in any way you can move the screen further away for safety or you can slow the movie to a rate that will feel comfortable enough to you. You can also make the sound louder or softer, or even turn the feelings up and down. Is it okay for you now?"*

_____

_____

Step 3. Comparison Between the Present and the Past

Say, *"Sometimes it is helpful to show this movie of your current life but, also, to use a split screen. The reason for the split screen is so, at the same time, you can show, for instance, next to your current home, the home in which you grew up. Or, next to a picture of you now you can compare it with one of you as a child. Would it be okay to try this?"*

_____

_____

If yes, say the following:

Say, *"What would you like to view on the split screen?"*

_____

_____

Say, *"Go ahead."*

_____

_____

Then say, *"What do you get?"*

_____

_____

Always debrief and find out what happened toward the end of the session.

Say, *"You can ask the part(s) what was learned today."*

_____

_____

Or say, *"What was the best thing you learned? What have they learned and what have you learned today?"*

_____

_____

Say, *"We will learn many things together this way. Do you have any thoughts or questions about what we have been doing?"*

_____

_____

This work sets the stage, over time, for an acceptance of reality and changed conditions in the present life of the client. In future sessions, there will be opportunities to disseminate further information as new parts appear, or the system requests or needs additional information using this technique. As the parts can tolerate additional information, they may need to learn that perpetrators are dead (if this is correct) or that the client is an adult who lives independently. This information can be very surprising or even shocking to parts. You need to make sure that the OPR work is titrated as needed. Since the goal is for this material to be tolerated by the system, it is helpful to remind your client about the stop sign frequently.

Say, *"I just want to remind you that any time we use this exercise, or do any work with the parts, you can always say 'Stop,' or put up your hand and we will stop and find out what is needed."*

Generally, OPR will need to be repeated many times during treatment, since parts may appear who need orientation or reorientation during any phase in the therapy. This includes times during EMDR trauma processing when a disoriented part(s) may appear. It is possible to use OPR when these dissociated parts are triggered by processing and need help or information. When the part(s) appear(s), stop the processing and help the client orient that part(s). If this part is not involved in the processing work, have the client bring them to Home Base. Then, if possible return to processing or close down the session.

Say, *"You are looking confused* (or as if you are dissociating). *Is another part here who needs our help?"*

_____

_____

Say, *"Do they know what we are working on? If so, let's find out if they need some information or just to take a break. Please go ahead and ask."*

_____

_____

Say, *"Do they know who you are? If not let them know, and also why you are talking with me. Please tell them anything they need to know."*

_____

_____

Or say, *"If they are not sure why they are here, let's take a break from this target, and you can talk quietly to them and bring them to your Home Base and perhaps introduce them to another part who can stay with them. If they are upset, you just talk with them for a while and we can go back to this work at our next session. Would it be okay to do that now?"*

_____

_____

Note: When the traumatized ego state(s) become(s) oriented to the present, the fixed quality of the state-specific memory or neural network that holds the traumatic material may be altered. The part may be more amenable to learn stabilization skills and may have a different perspective on the trauma(s).

Back of the Head Scale (BHS)

Jim Knipe

Back of the Head Scale Script Notes

It appears that sets of bilateral stimulation (BLS; alternating eye movements, tones or hand taps) have the potential to *invite* unfinished traumatic experience into awareness. This can be a problem for many clients who are dissociative, or who are on the verge of being overwhelmed by a traumatic memory. If disturbing memory material is extremely intense or has been deeply dissociated, the emergence of that material during therapy can potentially overwhelm the client's sense of being safe in the present. The memory can feel more real than the real situation the patient is in, and the experience can be one of nontherapeutic retraumatization.

Given these considerations, it is important, for both the therapist and the client to know when the client is drifting into *derealization*, that is, the client is losing a felt sense of the reality and safety of the present situation. For clients who are potentially dissociative, the degree of orientation to the present situation can be assessed through the use of the BHS. This procedure allows both therapist and client to be able to closely monitor and maintain the *dual attention* aspect of successful trauma processing; the simultaneous co-consciousness of the safe present and the traumatic past. This procedure is introduced to the client during the Preparation Phase, before any desensitization of trauma is begun.

The Back of the Head Scale (BHS) Script

Say, *"Think of a line that goes all the way from here* (hold up two index fingers about 15 inches in front of the person's face) *running right from my fingers, to the back of your head.*

Let this point on the line (move your fingers to indicate the point 15 inches in front of the person's face) *mean that you are completely aware of being present here with me in this room, you can easily listen to what I am saying, and you are not at all distracted by any other thoughts. You are completely present.*

Let the other point on the line at the back of your head (in order to not be intrusive into the space of the client, the therapist points to the back of his own head) *mean that you are so distracted by disturbing thoughts, feelings, or memory pictures that you feel like you are somewhere else. Your eyes may be open but your thoughts and your awareness are completely focused on another time, place, or experience. At this very moment, show with your finger where you are on this line."*

The therapist should check to make sure the client understands this idea. Most clients who have dissociative experiences will quickly recognize this procedure as a way of measuring and expressing a familiar aspect of their mental life. The assumption is that the more the person points toward the *most present* end point of the line, the safer it is to do trauma work with BLS. Clients seem to be able to easily assess the full range of dissociated experiences, either pointing to a place in front of the face, to a place parallel with the eyes, to the temple, or to an area further back in the head, according to what they are experiencing. As a rough rule of thumb, it is assumed that it is necessary for the person to point to a position at least three inches in front of the face in order for trauma-focused work to proceed, although this may vary from client to client. The use of the BHS throughout a therapy session can be very useful in insuring that the client is staying *present* while reprocessing disturbing memories.

18

The Method of Constant Installation of Present Orientation and Safety (CIPOS)

Jim Knipe

Constant Installation of Present Orientation and Safety Script Notes

The CIPOS method can be used to extend the healing power of EMDR to many clients who are potentially vulnerable to dissociative abreaction because of a dissociative personality structure, or because of the client's intense fear of their own memory material. With CIPOS, the client is first helped to experience a full orientation to the present safety of the therapist's office (as assessed and verified through the Back of the Head Scale [BHS] procedure), and then is assisted very briefly to access the disturbing material in a highly controlled and predictable way. Through alternating between safety and carefully titrated exposure to trauma, back and forth, the client can learn, often very quickly, the valuable skill of emerging from a traumatized ego state back to a safe orientation to the present. Bilateral stimulation (BLS) is used to constantly strengthen or *install* in the client's awareness a clear subjective sense of *being present* in the immediate *real life* situation (i.e., the therapy office). This method is described to clients during the Preparation Phase, prior to the Desensitization work, and then may be used during the actual desensitization of a particular highly disturbing traumatic memory. By constantly strengthening the person's present orientation through BLS and carefully controlling the amount of exposure to the trauma memory, the individual is more easily able to maintain dual attention. Through the use of the CIPOS procedure, processing of the memory can proceed more safely, that is, with much less danger of unproductive, dissociated *reliving* of the traumatic event.

With the CIPOS procedure, BLS is paired initially only with images and statements that express present orientation and safety. At the start of the procedure, when the client is most vulnerable to being overwhelmed by disturbance, BLS is not paired with information directly related to the traumatic disturbance. After the procedure continues successfully, usually within a single session, the client will be increasingly able to simultaneously be aware of both present safety and trauma, and, at that point, the usual pairing of BLS with trauma-related information can be safely initiated.

The Method of Constant Installation of Present Orientation and Safety (CIPOS)

The CIPOS steps are as follows:

Permission

Step 1. Obtain full permission from the client to work on the highly disturbing memory in a gradual and safe way, with ample time in the therapy session to complete the work regardless of whatever unexpected traumatic material may emerge during processing. With clients who have dissociated ego states, it is necessary to also ask for and obtain permission from any other parts that are involved in this memory. It is fine if some parts of the system do not wish to participate, but there should be a commitment from the whole system to allow processing of the memory. Since the way to ask the system for permission can be quite variable—with the words for one not necessarily appropriate for another—the following is only a suggestion to give you an idea of what to say. These words can be modified according to the needs of your client.

Say, *"I would like to ask all parts of the mind who are involved in this memory for permission to work on this today. Is this okay with all of you?"*

_____

_____

Safety

Step 2. As with any therapy intervention, it is important that the client be aware of the *objective* safety of the therapist's office. If the client seems unsure of the physical or interpersonal safety of the present situation, this issue should be addressed directly. Sometimes it is necessary through observations, questions, and discussion to help the client see that the fears that are being experienced in the present actually are the direct result of a past event, one which ended long ago and, often, took place far away. This cognitive orientation to present reality does not necessarily have to be accompanied by feelings of safety, but it should be clearly established in the client's intellectual understanding. If the client is uncertain about the actual safety of your office, fears and concerns, including transference and countertransference issues, should be explored and resolved before attempting trauma work. If, on the other hand, the therapist is simply unsure about the client's degree of contact with the reality of the safe office, the questions in Step 3 can be asked to clarify the situation.

Strengthening Present Orientation

Step 3. To assess and further strengthen the person's sense of present orientation, the therapist may ask a series of simple questions relating to the client's present reality in your office, with each client's answer followed by a short set of eye movements (EM). When the client responds to these simple questions, the therapist says, "Think of that," and initiates a short set of EM. The therapist can chose questions that are appropriate to the client or make ones that are suitable for the same goal of grounding the client in the office. Sample questions are the following:

Say questions such as, *"Where are you right now, in actual fact?"*

_____

_____

Say, *"Think of that."* (Do a short set of BLS.)

_____

_____

Say, *"What do you think of that picture over there?"*

_____

_____

Say, *"Think of that."* (Do a short set of BLS.)

_____

_____

Say, *"Can you hear the cars going by outside?"*

_____

_____

Say, *"Think of that."* (Do a short set of BLS.)

_____

_____

Say, *"Can you find the flaw in the design in this rug?"*

_____

_____

Say, *"Think of that."* (Do a short set of BLS.)

_____

_____

Say, *"How many tissue boxes do I have in this room?"*

_____

_____

Say, *"Think of that."* (Do a short set of BLS.)

_____

_____

The therapist can use the above questions or add relevant questions for the client. In this way, the client's subjective sense of being present is strengthened.

Say, *"What's good about being here right now, instead of somewhere else?"*

_____

_____

Of course it is much better to be in the relatively safe present than to be reliving a traumatic event, so (usually without much direction) the client is able to say something like, "I am comfortable here." Or, "I know I am safe here," and this positive information can then be strengthened with additional BLS.

Say, *"Go with that."*

_____

_____

If the client is confused about why the therapist is asking these simple questions, the purpose can be explained.

Say, *"A firm grounding in present reality is an essential precondition for the use of EMDR to resolve old disturbing memories. The way EMDR works is 'one foot in the present; one foot in the past'."*

_____

_____

One particularly useful method of assisting the client in orienting to present time is to engage in a game of catch with a pillow or a small soft object.

Say, *"Can you catch this pillow?"*

_____

_____

Say, *"Good, now toss it back. That's right* (repeated 1 to 10 times, as necessary)."

_____

_____

Say, *"Where are you on the line now* (Back of the Head Scale)*?"*

_____

_____

Or ask the client to *"Take a drink of water."*
Or say, *"Hold this drop of water or ice cube in your hand."*
Or say, *"Hum a song and then count to 10."*

The game of catch, in particular, seems to quickly and reliably reverse the derealization experience in many clients. The action of tossing an object back and forth pulls the person back to the present. Playing catch is an easily performed task and seems to require the individual to neurologically activate the orienting response (OR) in order to follow the trajectory of the tossed object. We can speculate that this procedure reciprocally inhibits (Wolpe, 1958) the activation of excessive traumatic material, which in turn allows the client to be more aware of the actual safety of the therapist's office. Other similar procedures are taking a drink of water, holding a drop of water or an ice cube in their hand, or alternately humming a song and counting to 10. Each of these procedures can bring about a *state change* back to orientation to present safety, which then empowers the client to be able to proceed with processing trauma material.

The Back of the Head Scale (BHS) and CIPOS

Step 4. Through the use of the BHS, the therapist is able to assess the effectiveness of the CIPOS interventions. In this way, it can be insured that the client is remaining sufficiently grounded in emotional safety, so that reprocessing of the trauma can occur. The BHS is a way of making sure the client remains safely in the zone of dual attention; continuing connection with present safety while accessing traumatic memory information.

An example of how to use BHS to assess the effectiveness of the CIPOS intervention occurred in Step 3.

Say, *"Can you catch this pillow?"*

_____

_____

Say, *"Good, now toss it back. That's right* (repeated 1 to 10 times, as necessary).*"*

_____

_____

Say, *"Where are you on the line now* (Back of the Head Scale)*?"*

_____

_____

According to the BHS above, by engaging the client in a CIPOS question and action and then asking the client to bring into awareness where she is in present time, the therapist and the client are able to know if the client is sufficiently present to begin or to continue trauma processing. Seen from another angle, this procedure allows both therapist and client to monitor whether the client is experiencing derealization due to high levels of intrusive, post-traumatic disturbance. This information informs the next step of the therapy.

If the client is in a state of derealization or going into one, the therapist works to engage the client back into present time.

If the client is experiencing sufficient orientation to present time, based on the therapist's judgment and the agreement of the client, they can proceed to do some trauma work.

Beginning Trauma Work Slowly

1. When present orientation is sufficiently established, say the following:

Say, *"Are you willing to go into your memory image for a very brief period of time* (e.g., perhaps up to 10 seconds)*?"*

_____

_____

Say, *"Good, go ahead and do this for _____ (state how many seconds) seconds."*

_____

_____

Keep track of the time. This is essentially a carefully controlled dissociative process. Immediately following the end of this period of seconds, use soothing but repetitive and emphatic words as in the following:

Say, *"Come back into the room now, okay, now come back here, just open your eyes, find your way back here now, that's right, just open your eyes."*

Do this until the client's eyes open and they are looking out into the room again.

Importance of Encouragement

2. At this point, give encouragement.

Say, *"Good,"* or *"That's right."*

Then resume the CIPOS interventions.

Say, *"Where are you right now, in actual fact?"*

_____

_____

CIPOS Method – sequence of procedures

Fully present • ----------------------------------- • *Dissociated*

Use the Back of the Head Scale to check for Orientation to Present Safety, then pair safety with BLS

2-10 seconds of deliberate dissociation into traumatic material in a way that preserves present safety – No BLS

Repeat 4+ times

Orientation to Present Safety

Paired with BLS

2-20 seconds of deliberate dissociation into traumatic material while preserving safety - No BLS

Continue repeating as necessary while preserving present orientation

Orientation to Present Safety

More than 20 seconds in trauma _with BLS_ ---Standard EMDR Desensitization Phase

Figure 18.1 The method of constant installation of present orientation and safety (CIPOS).

Say, *"Go with that."* (Do a short set of BLS.)

_____

_____

The CIPOS interventions are continued until the client is able to report, using the BHS, that she is oriented once again toward the present reality of the therapist's office. At this point, Step 5 (trauma work) can be repeated. The idea is to go back and forth between pairing Present Safety with BLS and then experiencing the trauma for up to 10 seconds with no BLS.

As this process continues, the client develops increasing ability to stay present as well as greater confidence and a sense of emotional control in confronting the disturbing memory. This opens the door to the use of the 11-Step Standard Procedure and directly pairing bilateral stimulation with traumatic material. Figure 18.1 illustrates the sequence of steps in this procedure.

19

Installation and Transmission of Current Time and Life Orientation

Joanne Twombly

Installation and Transmission of Current Time and Life Orientation Script Notes

Clients with dissociative identity disorder (DID) or dissociative disorder not otherwise specified (DDNOS) live with a multiple reality disorder (Kluft, 1989) where parts are often living in the past and are not aware of where they are, the current date, or the time. The goal of this resource is to reduce the anxiety of parts living in the past and increase the client's ability to differentiate the past from the present. This is done in the following manner:

1. Make a list of all the information that allows parts to know where they are in present time or list the information that the disoriented parts specifically need to have.
2. Install the information with dual attention stimulation (DAS).
3. Use DAS to facilitate internal communication among the parts.

Making this list with the adult, host, or oriented parts is useful in itself; often, even oriented parts, feel the anxiety of disoriented parts and might even say, "Nothing's different, nothing's safe" and will need coaching to come up with a list. When communicating the list to part(s) not oriented to the present, it is helpful to tell them they do not need to believe the information but can just listen and watch.

As always, it is important to attend to the timing and use of this resource as it increases the system's overall awareness of the present. If it is too stressful for the client or different parts of the client to tolerate, postpone the use of this resource until a later time when the client can tolerate greater awareness.

Installation and Transmission of Current Time and Life Orientation Script

Beginning with the host, adult, or other oriented parts, make a list of information that the disoriented parts need to be oriented and to decrease anxiety. There are two steps to this process: first install the list with the host, adult, or other oriented parts and then second with any of the other parts that are ready to hear. This process can be done with the goal of orienting all parts to the present, or, if there's a specific need, with smaller groups of parts.

Say, *"We're going to work on orienting parts to the present. Is that okay?"*

_____

_____

Once you have identified with whom you'll be working, say the following:

Say, *"Okay _____ (name the host or other oriented parts identified), we're going to start by making a list of all the information that allows you to know where you are in present time or is information that the disoriented parts specifically need to have. This information usually includes concrete items, for example, where you live now versus where you grew up, with whom you live, and how you know the person is not abusive. Other choices for your list could be about your abilities like driving and working, and how long it has been since you have been abused. Some parts will need different information than other parts. What should we put on the list or is information that you all need to have?"*

_____

_____

_____

_____

Once the list is developed, install the list using dual attention stimulation (DAS). It is most useful if the items on the list are installed in words and images, for example, where the client now lives can be described in words, visualized as a picture, or further described by a "fast forward movie." For example, a man lived in a house for 10 years. He started with visualizing what it was like when he first moved into the place, and then visualized a number of things that indicated the passage of time such as his children growing, the house being painted, and a list of the years up to the present, just like running a DVD, or movie.

Say, *"Now we're going to install the list. I'll read the first one and you can install it by thinking about it in words, imagining pictures of it, or a fast forward movie. A fast forward movie is when you think of the first time you experienced _____ (state what you will be working on) and move through the experiences you have had there until present time. Let me know when you're done with the one we are working on and I'll stop the DAS. I'll check in with you and see how it went or if anything came up and we'll go on to the next. Is that okay with you?"*

_____

_____

Say, *"Now we're going to install the list. I'll put the DAS on and then read the list to you slowly and as I read it install each one with words and images. At the end of the list, I will stop the DAS."*

_____

_____

Turn on the DAS and read the first one on the list.

Say, *"The first one is _____* (state the first on the list). *Let me know when it's installed."*

_____

_____

Continue until all information on the list is completed then say the following:

Say, *"The next one is _____* (state the next on the list). *Let me know when it's installed."*

_____

_____

For some clients, it helps to turn the DAS off after each item on the list. Notice what works best for your client.

Sometimes it helps to check in.

Say, *"What do you notice?"* Or say, *"Did anything else come up?"*

_____

_____

Once the list is installed with the adult or host, then say the following:

Say, *"Now let's communicate the list to all the other parts who are willing to listen and watch the information. If some of you don't want to, that's okay but if you can it would be helpful."*

_____

_____

Say, *"You do not have to believe him or her, just take in the information. Once you have gotten the information, you can ask any question you have. When you leave here, I want you to please check out the information for yourselves. Next week it will be interesting to hear what you agree or disagree with. Do you have any questions before we start?"*

_____

_____

If you notice that something is going wrong (like the client is getting flooded) stop the DAS and check.

Work with each item until the whole list or whatever seems suitable is communicated to all the parts using the script above.

Examples of common items on lists include:

Say, *"It's been _____ (state how many years) years since you were last abused, do a fast forward movie from when you were _____ (whatever age the client was the last time he was abused) to now."*

_____

_____

Then begin DAS and continue until the client indicates he is done with that point.

Say, *"What did you notice?"*

_____

_____

Say, *"You've been living in this _____ (state a descriptor of the place the client lives, e.g., a brown house) for _____ (state the number of years) years and it's always been safe. Do a fast forward movie of those _____ years."*

_____

_____

Say, *"Okay, go with that."*

_____

_____

Use as many DAS sets as you need.

Say, *"What did you notice?"*

_____

_____

Say, *"You live in _____ (state where client lives) with _____ (state the name of with whom the client lives) who doesn't hurt you. Visualize the time spent with the person and the significant incidents such as positive experiences, changes, arguments that happened without physical violence, and so on _____ (or whatever is appropriate for your client)."*

Begin DAS.

Stop DAS and say, *"What did you notice?"*

_____

_____

Useful items tend to be concrete (parts are often quite concrete) and help differentiate the past from the present. If the client is being abused in some way in the present, often there are ways to differentiate the past from the present. For instance, a woman being verbally abused whose husband demanded sex had these items on her list: our husband screams at us, but he never hits us; when my husband has sex with me, there is never bleeding afterward.

Child parts may need a child friendly list such as the following: pets now versus in the past and that now they get specific needs met. Often, as the list is made or being communicated, additional items will come up and you can add them to the list. This is helpful as you are responding to and involving parts.

Say, *"How is your life organized so you are safe now? Please visualize the details of how you accomplish this."*

_____

_____

Begin DAS.

Stop DAS and say, *"What did you notice?"*

_____

_____

Once the list has been communicated with the parts, say the following:

Say, *"How did you _____ (state the host or other oriented parts) think the process went?"*

_____

_____

Say, *"Do those of you who received the information have any other questions or is there anything you want to say about it?"*

_____

_____

Some parts will verbalize disbelief or feel tricked, and others will feel some tentative relief.

Say, *"I'd like all of you to check this information out between now and when we meet next. If there's anything you notice that's different I'll be interested in hearing about it next week."*

_____

_____

Most often, it is the parts that have not been noticing how the past is different from the present, but there are times when the oriented part also has not been noticing something important. This is why it is helpful to say the following:

Say, *"I'm very interested in all of you being safe and if there's something about the information you took in today that's not right, I want to know about it."*

_____

_____

It's also helpful to ask the host or other oriented parts to point out important things.

Say, *"While you're driving home today and during the week, it would be helpful if you could point out things to the parts like where you live now and evidence that it is _____ (state the year)."*

Once the client has some success with this exercise, you can suggest:

Say, *"You can use this technique on your own when a part becomes triggered. Just remind the triggered part about the present and use tapping, walking, standing, and shifting your weight from one foot to the other as the DAS to facilitate that. For instance, if a part or parts are anxious and fearful at home, walk around the house and talk to parts about how you know it's safe to be there. Show them locked doors and windows and talk about who lives there with you."*

Parts often need to be oriented over and over, as unprocessed traumatic material tends to cause them to slide back into the past. It appears that this process makes it easier to reorient parts and is a useful coping skill for clients to have.

Height Orientation

Joanne Twombly

Height Orientation Script Notes

Parts, alters, and ego states often believe they are living in the past and they are child sized. Orienting them to adult height can lessen anxiety and gives them more concrete proof that the past is different from the present. Child parts are often surprised when they can reach higher than they thought. This adult perspective is reinforced when using dual attention stimulation (DAS).

Responses to this exercise will be specific to the part. The parts' perceived ages rarely appear to change, with their change in perceived body height, for example, one part needed to be told that even if he was adult height, he was too young to drive.

Note: This resource is not appropriate for parts that think growing up is dangerous. Also, sometimes the delusion of child height will be so strong that the part will not be able to reach any higher than an actual child.

Height Orientation Script

Say, "_____ (address part), *would you be willing to volunteer to try an experiment or be coconscious with an adult part, and with that support try to see if you can reach something? Do you think you can reach the top shelf of the bookcase? Or, how high can you reach on the door?"*

_____

_____

If yes, say the following:

Say, *"Ok, just go over to the bookcase* (or door) *and notice how high you can reach."*

_____

_____

Say, *"What are you noticing?"*

_____

_____

If the part is noticing and feeling positive feelings such as "Wow, I can reach all the way to the top of the door!" Use short sets of DAS to install the positive feelings or experience.

Do bilateral stimulation (BLS).

Clients can use this resource at home after having a successful experience in the office with the therapist. For example, an older part or host could help a child part learn that the part is tall enough to reach up, open, lock, and unlock all the doors in his house.

Say, *"You can try this out at home. Help all the child parts experiment with how high they can reach on all the doors in your home. You can show them how to lock and unlock the doors too. This might help them feel less trapped and anxious and if they feel less anxious then you all will feel less anxious. Let's talk about how it goes next week when we meet."*

Safe Space Imagery (SSI)

Joanne Twombly

Safe Space Imagery Script Notes

Since people with dissociative disorders rely on autohypnotic defenses (Kluft, 1994), this version of SSI uses hypnotic language to teach the client to block out intrusive thoughts and feelings and learn how to get their body to a state of deep relaxation. Regular practice of SSI supports the client's stability and becomes a coping skill used for self-soothing, symptom management, and eventually as an integral part of trauma processing. The teaching of SSI early in the treatment begins to give the client a way to manage symptoms, often resulting in a sense of hope and mastery and facilitating development of a positive connection with the therapist.

The SSI method is different from the Safe Place Protocol that is routinely taught in the EMDR Institute Basic Training. The SSI protocol is useful for many clients with trauma histories and for those with dissociative disorders.

Goals for Using SSI

The goals for using SSI are the following:

- Enhance or develop the client's ability to bring his body to a calm, relaxed physical state of being.
- Develop the client's ability to use SSI for self-soothing and for symptom management.
- Create safe spaces for all parts of the mind. Parts may need to be in one together or need different ones.
- Help the client develop the ability to adjust and develop new safe spaces as needed.

Script Notes for Developing Safe Spaces When Working With Clients Diagnosed With Dissociative Disorders

Helpful suggestions when working with clients diagnosed with dissociative disorders:

- *Use hypnotic language.*
- *Adapt language to fit the client.* For instance, if the word "safe" is triggering for the client (or for a part of the client), find a different word, for example, "comfort." Also, keeping track of and using words that the client has used to describe the safe space will deepen the experience.
- *Use positive language.* This deepens and facilitates the process as people with dissociative disorders often experience considerable hopelessness. Thus, saying, "You will notice" instead of "Try and notice" will more often lead to positive results.
- *Address all parts directly when developing resources.* For example, "I want all of you to listen." This is important because many parts of the mind will not listen unless spoken to directly. Clinical judgment is used to decide when communication should not include all parts.
- *Use language that supports inclusion of all parts.* For example, using the words "You all" will remind the client that you are addressing the client as whole person, that is, all parts of the mind.
- *Rework dissociative symptoms into coping skills.* For example, amnesia for the early years can be developed into container imagery used to store painful traumatic material.
- *Start with a space or a place a client has felt safe in before or wants to be able to feel safe in* (many clients have never felt safe anywhere). It doesn't have to be a real place, or a place at all. Some clients have used being surrounded by music, feelings, different dimensions, different planets, and so forth.
- *Assist the client in choosing a safe space that is not from the client's childhood or a space where any danger has previously occurred.*
- *Check in regularly.* Make sure that the process is going smoothly internally and, if not, make suggestions to support the client and the process.
- *Give choices.* As clients were often not given alternatives and forced to be compliant, it is important that the invitation to make choices is part of their treatment.

When working with dissociative disordered clients with SSI, it is possible either to work with all of the parts at the same time or to work with one volunteer while the others watch or choose not to be a part of the process. If there are suspicious or protective parts that need to be hypervigilant, it is helpful to use the SSI script for one part.

When reading the script, note the following:

- Pauses are indicated by ". . . ."
- You will get a sense for how much time your client needs and can pace the process accordingly.
- Take note of the words your client uses to describe the Safe Space and use the same language to deepen his experience, for instance, if the client says, "I see flowers, and ferns, and oak trees," use those words.
- Short sets of dual attention stimulation (DAS) are used only after the Safe Space is established and all intrusions are addressed to install the feelings of being in the Safe Space, the ability to do SSI, and to communicate it to other parts across the whole system.

Safe Space Imagery for All Parts Simultaneously Script

Note: Some clients have very large internal systems. If it gets too complicated, try this process with a smaller group of volunteer parts, or try the SSI for One Part (shown later in this chapter).

In the beginning, it helps to tell the client that intrusions often happen. Ask the client to let you know when there are intrusions. Working on intrusions in the session will help the client learn to get rid of them outside of the sessions.

Say, *"This process works differently for different people. Some find a space that feels safe and comfortable right away while others may get intrusions and need to work on learning to block them out. Either way is just fine. We're going to work on SSI together. I'd like all of you who are willing to work on this to follow along with me. Pick a space or a place—NOT from your childhood—where nothing bad has ever happened, where you have felt safe before or would like to be able to feel safe, a place or space that is completely or partially made up."*

Pause

Say, *"So, where would you all like to start?"*

_____

_____

If needed say the following:

Say, *"You all could try what it's like to visualize being on a beach, in a cabin surrounded by a force field, in a different dimension, or something like a condo complex with separate spaces for all and a common room for meetings. What do you think?"*

_____

_____

Say, *"During the process, you can keep your eyes open or closed, or experiment and find what's right for you. Also, we will talk back and forth during the SSI, if any of you have any questions or concerns or something isn't working let me know."*

_____

_____

Say, *"Imagine or put yourself in your Safe Space(s) _____ (use wording that your client and parts have used to describe the Safe Space) and look around with all your senses and notice everything about it that makes it safe to be _____ (state where the client has chosen to be)."*

_____

_____

Note: This is a positive suggestion to front load positive imagery.

Using as many senses as possible enhances the imagery and deepens the experience. Also, it is helpful to repeat back to the client what you hear that he said.

This also lets the client know that you are with him and this process supports your relationship.

For example, if the client says, "I'm on an island, there's no one else on it, and there are palm trees."

The therapist can say, "Okay, so you're on an island, no one else is there, there are palm trees."

Or say, "_____ (repeat back to the client what he has said)."

Then say, *"Look around with all your senses, perhaps you can describe what else you are noticing."*

_____

_____

To check for intrusions, say the following:

Say, *"Look around your Safe Space with all your senses and notice if there's anything any of you are seeing* (hearing, smelling, tasting, touching) *that does not feel quite right."*

After pausing to allow time for the client to notice, say the following:

Say, *"What are you noticing?"*

_____

_____

Several parts may be doing fine while others may have intrusions!

Script for Intrusions, Negative Beliefs, or Problems

This script is set apart for easier reading, it does not imply that intrusions, negative beliefs, or problems are unusual; in fact, it would be more unusual for them *not* to occur.

If the client notices something, say the following:

Say, *"Just look around and as you look around you will either see* (hear, smell, taste, touch) *something that will help, or some thoughts will occur to you that will help . . . What are you noticing?"*

_____

_____

Then say, *"Focus on it and notice what changes."*

_____

_____

Or say, *"What ideas come to mind? Focus on them and notice what changes."*

_____

_____

Most of the time, the client will be able to come up with something himself. If that happens, make an ego-strengthening comment.

Say, *"You've just been learning how to do this and already you are able to block out intrusions."*

_____

_____

Or if some of the intrusion remains, say the following:

Say, *"You are just learning about the Safe Space and already you have been able to get rid of some of that intrusion. Keep looking around with all your senses and notice what else helps you."*

_____

_____

Continue this process until no negative feelings or imagery remains. If unsafe imagery continues to come up, you can ask the following:

Say, *"Would you like to continue to work with this Safe Space or would you like to move on to a new one that is even safer?"*

_____

_____

Or if the Safe Space is too contaminated, say the following:

Say, *"You will find yourself moving away from this Safe Space and as it is getting further and further away you are getting closer and closer to a new even safer Safe Space."*

_____

_____

If the client is unable to get rid of an intrusion, work with him by making suggestions to add or subtract something that makes it safer. This teaches the client a problem-solving process to deal with intrusions as he works on SSI at home.

Say, *"First look around and you will see something."*

_____

_____

Or say, *"A thought will occur to you."*

_____

_____

Or say, *"You can try adding or subtracting something."*

_____

_____

If that does not work then move to a new even safer Safe Space.

Say, *"Sometimes it helps to draw a picture of it and draw in improvements."*

_____

_____

You may need to repeat this process to get rid of additional intrusions. When the intrusion(s) are gone, say the following:

Say, *"Every time you block out intrusions you all will get better and better at it."*

_____

_____

Once all the intrusions are gone, say the following:

Say, *"Focus on what you're feeling and describe what you're feeling."*

_____

_____

If there is still any discomfort continue asking him to look around with all his senses, until intrusions are dealt with and then, say the following:

> Say, *"You can just settle in to being* _____ (state the name of client's Safe Space), *breathing in all the feelings of* _____ (state whatever the client has identified) *and feeling those feelings settle deep inside all the cells of your body."*

_____

_____

After the part has developed a Safe Space with no intrusions, continue with the following script.

Using words the client has used, say the following:

> Say, *"Just settle there surrounded by all the feelings of* _____ (state whatever words the client has used), *breathe in the* _____ *and let these feelings settle deep inside you, deep inside all the cells of your body."*

_____

_____

Once the intrusions are gone or if everything is fine, get more description of the Safe Space.

Say, *"Focus on what you're feeling and that feeling will get clearer and clearer."*

_____

_____

Use words that the client has used to support and deepen the experience. Once the Safe Space is developed, use DAS to install it and the ability to do SSI.

Say, *"Let's install the _____ (use client's words) you feel and your ability to develop a Safe Space. Focus on the feelings and your ability and go with that."*

_____

_____

Comments like, "As you practice learning SSI you will be learning more and more about how today is different."

They are useful in helping parts that have been dissociated and living in the past to become oriented to the present.

Let them stay in the SSI for at least a couple of minutes. Before ending the exercise, say the following:

Say, *"You have just started learning this and already you are learning to create an environment in which you can really relax. As time passes you will find more and more ways to use the Safe Space Imagery in your daily life."*

Or say, *"As you continue to practice the Safe Space Imagery, you will notice that every time you block out intrusions you get better and better at it."*

_____

_____

Once all intrusions are dealt with, DAS can be used to install the feelings of being in the Safe Space. It is usually helpful to also say the following:

Say, *"DAS will help install the feelings of being in the Safe Space and also the ability to do Safe Space Imagery."*

_____

_____

Short sets can be done to install and enhance the feelings.

To end the exercise, it is important to give the part(s) his, her, or their own control over being in the Safe Space and getting out of the Safe Space.

Say, *"In a way that is right for all of you, you will find you can bring yourselves back from your Safe Space to this office."*

_____

_____

Ask for feedback.

Say, *"Do any of you have any questions or feedback about the exercise?"*

_____

_____

Use the following instructions between sessions:

Say, *"I'd like all of you to practice the Safe Space Imagery everyday, whether or not you feel stressed. The more all of you practice the easier it will be to use SSI when you feel stressed. Also, remember to do SSI only when you're at home or in another safe place. Some of the small parts may want to stay in their Safe Space when the older ones are doing something like working, you can practice that too."*

_____

_____

When clients are new to SSI, it is also necessary to say the following:

Say, *"If it does not work or if at any step along the way it gets too scary, stop and write down what happened and we will work on it next session. This will give us information about how your intrusions work for you. Either way, we'll work on it next week too."*

Safe Space Imagery for One Part Script

In this Safe Space Imagery exercise one part volunteers to go first while the others watch. This approach works well when you want to begin to teach a DD client SSI and there are protective or suspicious parts that need to stay hypervigilant. Their need to be hypervigilant is used in the service of healing by asking them to watch carefully and learn how to do or use SSI. In addition, this approach models one of the ways of using SSI to cope with daily life, such as having one or more triggered parts use their Safe Space while others handle daily life situations (parenting, work, or driving). The exercise is essentially the same as the one for Safe Space Imagery for all parts simultaneously, except for a different introduction to the task.

Say, *"Who would be willing to try this Safe Space exercise?"*

_____

_____

When you get a volunteer, say the following:

Say, *"Okay, great, I am going to talk directly to _____* (state the name of the part) *now everyone else can listen and watch how it is done so later you can help each other learn how to do it."*

_____

_____

It is helpful to begin by alerting that intrusions may occur during this work, that they are not unusual, and that clients can tell the therapist so that they can work on them together.

Say, *"This process works differently for different people. Some find a space that feels safe and comfortable right away while others may get intrusions and need to work on learning to block them out. Either way is just fine. We're going to work on SSI together. Pick a space or a place—NOT from your childhood—where nothing bad has ever happened, where you have felt safe before or would like to be able to feel safe, a place or space that is completely or partially made up."*

_____

_____

Pause

Say, *"So, where would you like to start?"*

_____

_____

If needed, say the following:

Say, *"Here are some examples like the beach, a mountain top, an island, another planet, surrounded by music, soft blankets, or something like a condo complex with separate spaces for all and a common room for meetings. What do you think?"*

_____

_____

Say, *"During the process, you can keep your eyes open or closed, or experiment and find what's right for you. Also, we will talk back and forth during the SSI, if you have any questions or concerns or something isn't working let me know."*

_____

_____

Say, *"Imagine or put yourself in your Safe Space _____ (use wording that your client used to describe the Safe Space) and look around with all your senses and notice everything about it that makes it safe to be _____ (state where the client has chosen to be)."*

_____

_____

Note: This is a positive suggestion to front load positive imagery.

Use as many senses possible to enhance the imagery and deepen the experience. Also, it is helpful to repeat back to the client what you hear that he said. This also lets the client know that you are with him and this process supports your relationship.

For example if the client says, "I'm on an island, there's no one else on it, and there are palm trees."

The therapist can say, "Ok, so you're on an island, no one else is there, there are palm trees."

Or say, "_____ (repeat back to the client what he has said)."

Then say, *"Look around with all your senses, perhaps you can describe what else you are noticing."*

_____

_____

To check for intrusions, say the following:

Say, *"Look around your Safe Space with all your senses and notice if there's anything you are seeing* (hearing, smelling, tasting, touching) *that does not feel quite right."*

After pausing to allow time for the client to notice, say the following:

Say, *"What are you noticing?"*

_____

_____

Script for Intrusions, Negative Beliefs, or Problems

This script is set apart for easier reading, it does not imply that intrusions, negative beliefs, or problems are unusual; in fact, it would be more unusual for them *not* to occur.

If one or more parts notice something, say the following:

Say, *"Just look around and as you look around you will either see* (hear, smell, taste, touch) *something that will help, or some thoughts will occur to you that will help . . . What are you noticing?"*

_____

_____

Then say, *"Focus on it and notice what changes."*

_____

_____

Or say, *"What ideas come to mind? Focus on them and notice what changes."*

_____

_____

Most of the time the client (or parts) will be able to come up with something. If that happens, make an ego-strengthening comment.

Say, *"You've just been learning how to do this and already you are able to block out intrusions."*

_____

_____

Or if some of the intrusion remains, say the following:

Say, *"You are just learning about the Safe Space and already you have been able to get rid of some of that intrusion. Keep looking around with all your senses and notice what else helps."*

_____

_____

Continue this process until no negative feelings or imagery remains. If unsafe imagery continues to come up you can ask the following:

Say, *"Would you like to continue to work with this Safe Space or would you like to move on to a new one that is even safer?"*

_____

_____

Or if the Safe Space is too contaminated, say the following:

Say, *"You will find yourselves moving away from this Safe Space and as it is getting further and further away you are getting closer and closer to a new even safer Safe Space."*

_____

_____

If clients are unable to get rid of an intrusion, work with them by making suggestions to add or subtract something that makes it safer. This teaches the clients a problem-solving process to deal with intrusions as they work on SSI at home.

Say, *"First look around and you will see something."*

_____

_____

Or say, *"A thought will occur to you."*

_____

_____

Or say, *"You can try adding or subtracting something."*

_____

_____

If that does not work then move to a new even safer Safe Space.

Say, *"Sometimes it helps to draw a picture of it and draw in improvements."*

_____

_____

You may need to repeat this process to get rid of additional intrusions. When the intrusion(s) are gone, say the following:

Say, *"Every time you block out intrusions you all will get better and better at it."*

_____

_____

Once all the intrusions are gone, say the following:

Say, *"Focus on what you're all feeling and describe what you're feeling."*

_____

_____

If any parts are experiencing any discomfort, continue asking them to look around with all their senses until intrusions are dealt with and then, say the following:

Say, *"You all can just settle in to being* _____ (state the name of client's Safe Space)*, breathing in all the feelings of* _____ (state whatever the client has identified) *and feeling those feelings settle deep inside all the cells of your body."*

After the client and parts have developed a Safe Space with no intrusions continue with the following script.

Using words the client has used, say the following:

Say, *"Just settle there surrounded by all the feelings of* _____ (state whatever words the client has used), *breathe in the* _____ *and let these feelings settle deep inside you, deep inside all the cells of your body."*

_____

_____

Once the intrusions are gone or if everything is fine, get more description of the Safe Space.

Say, *"Focus on what you're feeling and that feeling will get clearer and clearer."*

_____

_____

Use words that the client has used to describe the experience to support and deepen the experience. Once the Safe Space is developed, use DAS to install it and the ability to do SSI.

Say, *"Let's install the _____ (use client's words) you feel and your ability to develop a Safe Space. Focus on the feelings and your ability and go with that."*

_____

_____

You can make comments, as in the following, to help a part that has been dissociated and living in the past to become oriented to the present.

Say, *"You'll notice more and more about how today is different from the past as you practice Safe Space Imagery."*

_____

_____

Let him stay in the SSI for at least a couple minutes. Before ending the exercise, say the following:

Say, *"You have just started learning this and already you are learning to create an environment in which you can really relax. As time passes you will find more and more ways to use the Safe Space Imagery in your daily life."*

Or say, *"As you continue to practice the Safe Space Imagery, you will notice that every time you block out intrusions you get better and better at it."*

Once all intrusions are dealt with, DAS can be used to install the feelings of being in the Safe Space. It is usually helpful to also say the following:

Say, *"DAS will help install the feelings of being in the Safe Space and also the ability to do Safe Space Imagery."*

_____

_____

Short sets can be done to install and enhance the feelings.

To end the exercise, it is important to give the part his own control over being in the Safe Space or taking himself out of it.

Say, *"In a way that is right for you, you will find just the right way to bring yourself back to this office."*

Ask for feedback.

Say, *"What was that like for you?"*

_____

_____

Say, *"Do you have any questions or feedback about the exercise?"*

_____

_____

Then ask for feedback from all the other parts that watched the exercise.

Say, *"What was it like for all of you to watch* _____ (state name of part that did exercise) *do this exercise and what did you notice?"*

_____

_____

The following instructions are for between sessions:

Say, *"Try and practice the Safe Space Imagery everyday whether or not you feel stressed. The more you practice, the easier it will be to use SSI when you feel stressed. Also, remember to do SSI only when you're at home or in another safe place."*

When clients are new to SSI it's also necessary to say the following:

Say, *"If it does not work or if at any step along the way it gets too scary, stop and write down what happened and we will work on it next session. This will give us information about how your intrusions work for you. Either way, we'll work on it next week, too."*

Variations and Additions to SSI

Sometimes, it is helpful for the therapist to suggest adding concrete information about the present to assist in orienting parts to present time (e.g., a current calendar, image of current home). This is most often done when the part that is developing the Safe Space is not oriented to the present. If the part you are working with is not oriented to the present, elicit the help of a part who is to help determine what would be useful to add to the Safe Space.

Say, *"Often it is helpful to have a current calendar or an image of your current home* _____ (or any other appropriate example for your patient). *What would be helpful for you?"*

_____

_____

To support the client's connection with the therapist, orientation to the present, and dual awareness, the client can imagine a picture of the therapist on the wall of the Safe Space along with a calendar with appointment dates listed. This promotes the SSI as a transitional object between sessions.

Say, *"If you would like, you can imagine a picture of me on the wall of your Safe Space along with a calendar with all of our appoint-*

ment dates listed so that you can have me with you between our sessions."

_____

_____

Support growth and learning by including whatever may be needed to facilitate a state of support and well-being for the client.

Say, *"You can also include anything that gives you feelings of support and well-being. What might they be?"*

_____

_____

Appropriate safe places can be developed by the host or adult part for other parts that are too young or too distressed to develop their own safe places. In this case, work with the adult part.

Say, *"As you focus on the child part, notice what kind of space the child needs to start to feel safe."*

_____

_____

If the adult doesn't know, say the following:

Say, *"Try starting by putting the child in a room with a soft carpet, warm light, a soft blanket, nice chair, and some stuffed animals. How does the child feel now?"*

_____

_____

Then you and the adult part can add and subtract things and can figure out what the child needs.

If it is a child part that is making the system of parts anxious, it can help to put *sound and feeling proofing* in the wall as the safe space. This step is also very helpful to have in place when the client begins to do trauma processing. The sound and feeling proofing are used to protect some of the parts from the trauma processing and to help maintain stability. Adjust the words to fit the kind of safe space the part has developed.

Say, *"Notice that there is sound and feeling proofing in the walls of the Safe Space."*

In the case of distressed parts, the part(s) may not be able to calm down and you can end in the following way:

Say, *"As the part is in _____ (his or her) Safe Space _____ (he or she) will learn more and more about how today is different from the past and will find out more and more about what helps _____ (him or her) feel calmer and calmer."*

Safe Space Imagery becomes a resource that is used by clients to help manage symptoms and daily life issues, to help with trauma processing, and to provide respite for parts who have worked on traumatic material in session.

Installing Therapist, Therapist's Office, and Maintaining Duality

Joanne Twombly

Clients with dissociative disorders (DD) or complex post-traumatic stress disorder (C-PTSD) often have issues concerning the "therapist's trustworthiness, inherent dangerousness and potential abusiveness" (Loewenstein, 1993, p. 66). Goals of this exercise are the following:

1. Increase cooperation between the therapist and the dissociative system by communicating knowledge about the therapist, the office, and experience in treatment to all parts of the system.
2. Maintaining the client's dual awareness while processing information concerning trauma in the past. It is essential for these clients to maintain their connection to the therapist and the present.

Dual attention stimulation (DAS) is used to install and communicate the information.

Installing Therapist, Therapist's Office, and Maintaining Duality Script Notes

As with the orienting exercise (see chapter 19), first make a list with the part or parts who have had sufficient experience with your office and you in the present. The types of information to install fall into five categories:

1. Information about the concrete appearance of the office. Highlight anything that indicates differences between current time versus the past, including things like calendars, push button phones, and other technical equipment.
2. Any experiences about you that indicate safety, boundaries, and respect.
3. What you look like and the sound of your voice.
4. Years in treatment with you from the beginning of treatment to the present. This often helps parts that tend to be hypervigilant to start to see that there is a history of safety in the relationship.

269

5. Other information that is client specific, for example, one client had a part who needed to install that the door to the waiting room was never locked.

Then install the list with the part(s) who helped you develop it. For some clients, it is necessary to install each point separately, starting and stopping the DAS with each point. With others, the whole list can be installed at once. Then the list can be reinstalled with the instruction to send it to all parts who are willing to take in the information. Deal with questions. Then for homework, parts can notice and think about all the information they received and check it out for themselves. This helps parts continue to get oriented to the present. One client installed the following items:

1. We've been working together for 4 years and nothing dangerous has ever happened here.
2. No one has ever found out about anything we've talked about except for when I got hospitalized and gave you permission to talk to the in-patient therapist.
3. Once you patted me on the shoulder, it scared some parts and you apologized. Sometimes we shake hands.
4. When I picture you, I picture your curly hair, glasses, and that you're tall.
5. The sound of your voice.
6. I usually sit on the couch and you always sit on your chair by the desk. There is a 2009 calendar on the wall, cordless phone, and a fax machine. We didn't have them when I was little.
7. When you go on vacation you always come back.
8. Usually we don't get mad at each other, but that time you got mad you apologized and we talked about it. When I got mad because you forgot to call me, nothing bad happened. We talked about it.

Note: Some clients or parts of the client may refuse to try this exercise. In this case the therapist should tell the parts they don't have to participate until they're ready or decide to wait till there's greater cooperation.

Installing Therapist, Therapist's Office, and Maintaining Duality Script

Information About the Office

Examples of things to notice are the following: pictures on walls, the carpet, a stuffed animal, the wallpaper, where therapist sits, where client sits, typical sounds, and any things in your office that indicate it's not the past, like a computer, cordless phone, fleece blanket, and so forth. Safety-oriented information is also important.

Say, *"Look around the office. What are the things you notice that tell you that you're here in my office in _____ (name what year it is)?"*

_____

_____

_____

_____

Experiences the Client Has Had With the Therapist

This becomes a discussion between client and therapist, remembering and listing experiences during the therapy. For example, when you went on vacation and returned; that you return calls when asked to—except for the time you forgot to and apologized; any disagreements and their resolution, positive experiences.

Say, *"What are the experiences that stand out for you all throughout the time we've worked together? Let's make a list together."*

_____

_____

_____

_____

_____

_____

Once the client has answered say the following:

Say, *"When I think of our work together, I remember the time when _____ (state a time that you remember)."*

_____

_____

The Therapist Appearance and Voice Quality

Say, *"When you picture me what do you think about?"*

_____

_____

Say, *"Let's also install the sound of my voice. What does it sound like to you?"*

_____

_____

Fast Forward Video (DVD or Movie) Treatment

You can use a fast forward video of the years in treatment with you, perhaps how they came into treatment with you, and that no one gets hurt in your office.

Say, *"Let's also install a fast forward video of how you came to work with me, the time when we started, and the experiences that we have had up until now as we have worked together. You could picture a calendar with months flipping by or whatever works for all of you."*

_____

_____

Once the list is established, the list is installed with the host or parts that have helped establish the list. It is most useful if the items on the list are installed in words and images. For example, the course of treatment with the therapist can be described in words, visualized as a picture, or further described by a fast forward video. This might include the first call to the therapist, including the first meeting and through the different experiences he has had over the time in treatment up to the present time—just like running a video, DVD, or movie.

Say, *"Now we're going to install the list. I'll read the first one and you can install it by thinking about it in words, by making or seeing pictures of it or a fast forward video. A fast forward video is when you think of the first time you experienced _____ (state what you will be working on) and moving through the experiences you have had there until present time. Let me know when you're done with this one and I'll stop the DAS. I'll check in with you and see how it went or if anything came up and we'll go on to the next. Is that okay with you?"*

_____

_____

Say, *"Now we're going to install the list. I'll put the DAS on and then read the list to you slowly and as I read it, install each one with words and images. At the end of the list, I stop the DAS."*

_____

_____

Turn on the DAS and read the first one on the list.

Say, *"The first one is _____ (state the first on the list). I am turning on the DAS and go with that."*

_____

_____

Continue until all information on the list is completed, saying the following:

Say, *"The next one is _____ (state the next on the list). I am turning on the DAS and go with that."*

_____

_____

Sometimes it helps to say, "What do you notice?"

Or say, *"Did anything else come up?"*

_____

_____

Once the list is installed with the adult or host, say the following:

Then say, *"Now, communicate the list to all parts of the mind who are willing to take it in. Let the parts know, they don't have to believe the information, just take it in and check it out for themselves."*

As you read the first item on the list, begin the DAS. Then the *oriented part* can repeat the first item, visualize it, and communicate it to the parts that are taking the information in. DAS can be started and stopped after each item on the list or be used for the duration of the whole list. With clients who have fewer resources and are less stable, start and stop DAS for each item.

Say, *"Okay, now I'll start the DAS and read the first item on the list and you can communicate it in words or pictures to all the parts who are willing to listen* (or a fast forward video). *Let me know when you have communicated the information."*

_____

_____

Use as many DAS sets as you need. Stop the DAS when the adult, host, or oriented part has communicated this to the parts. If you notice that something is going wrong (like the client is getting flooded) stop the DAS and check.

Say, *"Okay, now I'll continue with the DAS and read the next item on the list and you can communicate it in words or pictures to all the parts who are willing to listen* (or a fast forward video). *Let me know when you have communicated the information."*

_____

_____

If it is helpful, after each item say, "What did you notice?"

Work with each item until the whole list or whatever seems suitable is installed using the script above.

Once the list has been communicated with the parts

Say, *"How did you _____ (state the host or other oriented parts) think the process went?"*

_____

_____

Say, *"Do those of you who received the information have any other questions or is there anything you want to say about it?"*

_____

_____

Most often, it is the parts that have not been noticing how the past is different from the present, but there are times when the oriented part has not been noticing something important. This is why it's helpful to say the following:

Say, *"I'm very interested in all of you being safe and if there's something about the information you took in today that's not right, I want to know about it."*

_____

_____

Say, *"I'd like everyone who took information in to watch and check everything out. You may come up with other things about our work together to install or come up with questions for us to talk about next week."*

_____

_____

This exercise helps orient parts to the therapist and ground the client in the therapist's office. As with all orienting exercises, it can be very helpful and can make it easier to reorient parts that have slipped back into the past. Parts will continue to need to be oriented one way or another until all traumatic material is processed.

23

The Absorption Technique

Arne Hofmann

The Absorption Technique Script Notes

The Wedging or Strengthening Technique (Kiessling, 1999) has been modified in Germany and is called The Absorption Technique to create resources to deal with what the client is concerned about in the future, for example, a stressful partner, a problematic child, stressful work, or a stressful boss, and so forth, or having stress about working with EMDR in the future, a present trigger or even an intrusive memory (past).

Having clients imagine a strength or skill that would help them during the problem often helps them to reduce their anxiety. Focusing on a specific strength or coping skill may create a wedge of safety or control that will assist clients with the difficult situation in the future. Use short sets of 3 to 12 bilateral stimulation (BLS) to assist in generalizing the resource.

The Absorption Technique Script

Skill or Strength

Say, *"What is the issue in the future* (present/past) *that you want to focus on?"*

_____

_____

Say, *"If you think of that situation now, how stressful is that to you on a scale of 0 to 10, where 0 is no disturbance or neutral and 10 is the highest disturbance you can imagine, how disturbing does it feel now?"*

0	1	2	3	4	5	6	7	8	9	10

(no disturbance)   (highest disturbance)

The following is a list of three positive abilities or needed resources.

Say, *"What skills would you need to deal with that issue of* _____ (state the past/present/future concern) *better?"*

_____

_____

It is helpful to just get a theoretical answer from the head or cortex of the patient.

1. _____

2. _____

3. _____

First Ability

Say, *"Think of the FIRST ability. In the last few years or so, was there ever a situation or time in your life where you remember having or feeling this ability?"*

_____

_____

Say, *"Can you think of an image that represents that situation?"*

_____

_____

Say, *"When you focus on the image, at that specific moment of time* (make sure your voice reflects or stresses this point), *where do you feel that you had some of that skill in your body of* _____ (name the resource chosen)?"*

_____

_____

Enhance

Say, *"Think of that _____* (name the resource), *the image, and the feeling in your body and go with that."*

_____

_____

Do 4 to 6 BLS.

Say, *"What are you noticing?"*

_____

_____

If the feeling is positive, do another set.
If it has not changed, do another set.

Say, *"Go with that."*

_____

_____

If it changes to a negative feeling, look for another resource and start from the beginning again.

Second Ability

Say, *"Think of the SECOND ability. In the last few years or so, was there ever a situation or time in your life where you remember having or feeling this ability?"*

_____

_____

Say, *"Can you think of an image that represents that situation?"*

_____

_____

Say, *"When you focus on the image, at that specific moment of time* (make sure your voice reflects or stresses this point), *where do you feel that you had some of that skill in your body of _____* (name the resource chosen)?"

_____

_____

Enhance

Say, *"Think of that _____* (name the resource), *the image, and the feeling in your body and go with that."*

_____

_____

Do 4 to 6 BLS.

Say, *"What are you noticing?"*

_____

_____

If the feeling is positive, do another set.
If it has not changed, do another set.

Say, *"Go with that."*

_____

_____

If it changes to a negative feeling, look for another resource and start from the beginning again.

Third Ability

Say, *"Think of the THIRD ability. In the last few years or so, was there ever a situation or time in your life where you remember having or feeling this ability?"*

_____

_____

Say, *"Can you think of an image that represents that situation?"*

_____

_____

Say, *"When you focus on the image, at that specific moment of time* (make sure your voice reflects or stresses this point), *where do you feel that you had some of that skill in your body of* _____ (name the resource chosen)?"

_____

_____

Enhance

Say, *"Think of that* _____ (name the resource), *the image, and the feeling in your body and go with that."*

_____

_____

Do 4 to 6 BLS.

Say, *"What are you noticing?"*

_____

_____

If the feeling is positive, do another set.
If it has not changed, do another set.

Say, *"Go with that."*

_____

_____

Getting the Resources Together

Say, *"Think of the three abilities together and where you felt them in your body. Just nod if you are in contact with all three body feelings."*

_____

_____

Only use the successfully installed resources.
If the patient nods stimulate with a short set of BLS.

Say, *"Go with that."*

_____

_____

Check for the Issue

Say, *"As you are feeling your resources, take a look back at the issue that troubles you, how stressful is that to you on a scale of 0 to 10, where 0 is no disturbance or neutral and 10 is the highest disturbance you can imagine, how disturbing does it feel now?"*

   0   1   2   3   4   5   6   7   8   9   10
(no disturbance)   (highest disturbance)

During the Future Phase of the Inverted Protocol for Unstable C-PTSD use the Absorption or Wedging Technique to develop as many different resources for the different issues about which the client might be concerned. The goal is to make sure that the client's day-to-day life is calm enough to move on to trauma work.

24

Modified Resource Development and Installation (RDI) Procedures With Dissociative Clients

Don Beere

The most critical therapeutic work with dissociative clients is stabilization. The modified RDI procedures (Shapiro, 2001, pp. 234–244) described here can help such clients slowly develop skills that lead to this kind of stabilization. There are many reasons stabilization is a central facet of work with the dissociative disorders:

1. *Dissociative clients present in turmoil—usually internal turmoil that is a reaction to an external trigger.* Frequently, there are physical symptoms (body memories), visual intrusions (visual flashbacks), sleep difficulties (anxiety or vigilance stemming from nighttime abuse), nightmares (often relived trauma), barraging inner voices (upset alters who attack or threaten), and other negative affects. Such extensive negative affect makes therapeutic work impossible and requires stabilization and symptom reduction. This author conceptualizes the cause of the particular kinds of negative affect listed above as consequent to intrusions from or responses to activated traumatic memory. When most other clinicians write about and discuss intrusions, almost no one conceptualizes the distress or other negative affects as a response to whole or fragmentary intrusions of traumas that then lead to all kinds of other difficulties such as alters switching in and out, emotional reactions to the intrusions, avoidance, and acting out to blunt or distract. The clinical power of this way of thinking is to address those intrusions that—when successful—rapidly lead to state shifts, in other words, distress and symptom reduction.

2. *Most dissociative clients are affect phobic.* Managing the intense negative affects associated with EMDR is not yet part of the client's repertoire. Such capacities must be developed for the client to use EMDR effectively. Also, the client must be aware of what is occurring internally both negatively and positively (thoughts, feelings, sensations, pictures, sounds, sights, smells). These negative internal experiences inevitably trigger earlier traumatic

experiences and their associated emotions and sensations. Often, internal positive experiences can be problematic as a result of the meaning that it is given by any of the internal states; especially since positive experiences were often followed by intensely negative ones. Dissociation, by definition, disintegrates consciousness so the individual becomes unaware of (dissociates) what has been overwhelming. Teaching the dissociative client how to track or be aware of what is happening inside without dissociating is essential. Furthermore, to effectively use EMDR, a client must be able to be here in the present while back there in the targeted situation. In other words, be in the present and the past at the same time. This is difficult for dissociative clients when traumatic material begins to surface. They can get pulled into it and relive it easily.

3. *Dissociative clients, frequently, do not have a support network, do not engage in self-caretaking, and do not have "fun."* Such activities are crucial in moderating the strong pull of isolation, caution, and depleted resources that often go along with this disorder. Learning how to support and provide self-care can result in present time satisfactions and the decrease in the experience of negative affect.

Modified Resource Development and Installation (RDI) Procedures Script Notes

The Resource Development Installation (RDI) intervention described below focuses on helping the client develop resources to address the above issues. There are three steps to the intervention:

Step 1. Introduces EMDR and the procedure.
Step 2. Introduces inner focus and allowing whatever emerges in experience to emerge, just noticing without eye movements.
Step 3. Applies the EMDR intervention when an appropriate target emerges during a session.

There are two important concerns when using the modified RDI Protocol with clients:

1. *Speed.* In this author's clinical experience, most dissociative identity disorder (DID) clients process very intensely and very quickly with eye movements (EMs). It neither takes many EMs, nor does it need to be fast to get a potentially strong response. The super slow EMs are designed to reduce the possibility of such processing. For the purposes of the RDI intervention, short sets support installation of the resource without moving into further processing and possible distress.

2. *Too much positive.* With nondissociative clients, we want to maximize the positive strengthening. Consider, however, with the dissociative client, that there is an inner unstable stability. To an outsider, many DID clients appear unstable or in chaos. The clinical experience of this author suggests that this instability results in an inner cycling that maintains an inner balance in the DID system. This is different from crises—precipitated from the outside—which destabilize the client. As well, historically, the DID individual has not lived without threat or vulnerability. As an explanatory model, imagine a mobile that has static shapes linked to a stable support. The different pieces all move in response to outside air currents (if it helps, consider this a three-dimensional tinker toy arrangement). From the outside, we have a

small fixed window that allows us to see only part of the mobile as it moves. From the outside we assume it is a single entity with a singular identity; as the mobile moves what we see changes and transforms. If we change the static pieces to active and alive beings, the mobile now begins to move as those alive parts shift around. In all of these situations, the mobile oscillates around a center point, though from a small outside perspective it seems chaotic and unstable. Whoever is the recipient of the enhanced resource will unbalance internal homeostasis by feeling better, stronger, hopeful, safer, or whatever might be the outcome. In this regard, especially early on, we need to slowly and incrementally develop resources. If the outcome is too positive, it can lead to a negative rebound.

Modified Resource Development and Installation (RDI) Procedures Script

Step 1: Introduction to EMDR

Say, *"I am trained to do EMDR. After we discuss it, I will ask you if you would be willing to try EMDR. Of course, you would have to be comfortable with it first. I will answer any questions you might have. As well, I would stop during the time we are doing EMDR immediately, any time you asked. Is it okay for me to continue telling you about EMDR?"*

_____

_____

Wait for an answer and explore any ambivalence or caution.

Say, *"EMDR is a therapeutic method developed by Dr. Francine Shapiro as the result of her own discovery that it reduced her own distress. Most of the research is on trauma and research has begun on using EMDR to install resources. This is how we are going to use it today. We are going to use eye movements and bilateral stimulation (BLS) to enhance resources that you have at times during the session, if that is okay with you."*

_____

_____

Say, *"One way I think of EMDR is that it helps the brain process and reprocess experience and memory. It seems to allow connections to form. All you need to do is allow it. There is nothing for you to do but follow my fingers with your eyes* (or any other BLS) *and notice whatever seems to come to your awareness.*
We will practice this without the eye movements first, so that you can understand what we will do and then add the eye movements later. Just to let you know, we would not set up resources without your permission and we would not do it all the time, only when it seemed appropriate to do it. We can install resources as they come up during the session if you are okay with that."

_____

_____

The reason for using eye movements instead of tapping or sound is because the therapist wants the client to be located strongly in the present and not drift inward or into a dissociated state.

Say, *"To install the resources during our session, the therapist might say, 'okay, notice that' and then ask you to follow my fingers a few times. Are you alright with following my fingers right now so you can see what that would be like?"*

_____

_____

Note: Alternative BLS like tapping or tones is possible. However, this author has found that the slow eye movements work in a way that allows for closer tracking of both "zoning out," which is a frequent occurrence for patients with dissociative disorders and other affective reactions. It is especially important to do this kind of tracking to monitor what is going on with your client in the early stages of installing an RDI.

If yes, continue.

If no, say the following:

Say, *"What are your concerns?"*

_____

_____

Wait for a yes answer and be sure to explore and deal with any ambivalence or caution.

Say, *"Okay, look straight in front of you, chin and belly button lined up. Now look at my fingers without moving your head. Are you okay with my holding my hand this way? How does that feel to you?"*

_____

_____

Notice whether the presence of a raised hand creates some reaction. If it does, find a different object on which the client can focus. You could use a pencil's eraser, a cup, a vase, a piece of paper, or whatever your creativity and client come up with. This author has discovered that clients can track fingers or other objects from across the room and still process effectively. If nothing reduces distress or negative reaction, do not proceed. At that time, it is appropriate to return to debriefing what happened and being alert to any sequela from the introduction to the RDI. If the client asks about the shift, say the following:

Say, *"As we were working, I realized that my timing did not fit right now, so we can return to what we were doing before we started the RDI."*

Introductory EM

Very slowly make only *one* round trip, about 20 seconds total; notice that is a count of 5 for one-quarter round trip.

Say, *"Okay, let's start by your following my fingers for a moment, then tell me what it is like for you?"*

_____

_____

Track your client carefully, especially in the first quarter to half round trip. Did the EM (or other BLS) activate any material or any negative responses? This should activate nothing. If it activates any processing or anything negative, this is very helpful because it lets you know that the client is in need of more practice in tolerating affect or working internally. The objective is to help develop positive resources; the activation of negative material or distress indicates that there is a current difficulty using this method to develop positive resources. This might be because the client has stuff going on inside. If so, wait for a more settled time and try again.

Follow up.

Say, *"What was it like for you to do the eye movements* (or other BLS)?"

_____

_____

After you have gotten a sense of this from your client, use the following assessment question. The Subjective Units of State Strength Scale (SUSS) was developed as a way to communicate to the therapist that it is important to assess the effect of the RDI. It is similar to the subjective units of disturbance (SUDs) measure in the Standard EMDR Protocol but, by contrast, is administered after every BLS and uses a different scale. The SUSS assesses how strong the state is for the client. It is a 3-point scale that consists of the following points: weaker, same, and stronger. It is helpful to vary the order in asking about them to reduce an order effect that might influence the client. The SUDs scale is not used because the idea is to have only a small shift—that is what a 3-point scale implies.

Say, *"Notice the way you feel right now. Comparing this to how you felt before we did the eye movements, is it stronger, weaker, or the same?"*

_____

_____

This question introduces the client to what you will ask after every modified RDI set.

Knowing when to try again is a clinical judgment call. There are four types of responses to consider:

1. *Negative responses:* Any negative or weakening response indicates that the RDI is not increasing resources but diminishing them. A negative response (anxiety, distress, just feeling a little out of sorts) implies that stored materials linked to those emotions have been activated; this is not the goal. More BLS would simply continue the activation and processing of that material and weaken it even more. In this situation, a weaker response suggests waiting before continuing with the RDIs.

Say, *"As we were working, I realized that my timing did not fit right now, so we can return to what we were doing before we started the RDI."*

2. *Positive responses:* When there is positive affect over increasingly longer intervals and the client can feel good, successful, happy, satisfied, competent, and so forth without negative backlash, means that installing positive resources will go easily. When this occurs, say the following:

Say, *"Go with that."*

_____

_____

Continue to install several times to reinforce the positive experience.

3. *Tentative positive responses:* If the client expresses a reduction in the intensity and emotional quality ("Yeah, I guess I feel okay about it") and the time it lasts ("It doesn't last very long, maybe 15 minutes at most"), then the therapist can try a tentative RDI.

Say, *"Okay, if you think about that, what do you notice?"*

_____

_____

Say, *"And when you remember it, does it bring back the way your body felt, your emotions, the way you thought?"*

_____

_____

Say, *"Okay, just remember it and follow my fingers."*

_____

_____

4. *Tentative negative responses:* If the client responded to the question about feelings and emotions with "No not really"—meaning there is no activation of a positive body or emotional state—then the RDI would probably not be successful. However, that does not mean it is not possible to continue. Just recalling the situation and doing the slow BLS can begin to install it. Just be alert for negative shifts.

Say, *"Okay, just notice* _____ (state the situation) *and go with that."*

_____

_____

Step 2: Introducing Inner Focus

Say, *"You remember our having talked about EMDR?"*

_____

_____

Say, *"Would you be alright taking the next step, but without any eye movements?"*

_____

_____

Whenever the answer is no, say the following:

Say, *"Do you have any concerns or misgivings?"*

_____

_____

Explore them until resolved. Never impose or force.

Say, *"Sometime during our session today I might ask you to simply notice something, and, after you notice it, simply to be openly aware of whatever comes up in your mind and body. Don't hold on to what I asked you to notice, just let things flow so that you let whatever happens happen. There are no 'shoulds.' Then, when it feels right to you, let me know what it was like to notice what comes up inside. Can you do that? Do you have any issues or concerns?"*

_____

_____

Say, *"Let's practice right now. Are you willing? Any concerns before we start? What are you noticing right now?"*

_____

_____

Say, *"Just notice how it feels and what it is like mentally to agree to do this. Whatever is there right now is just fine. Just be aware of it. And as you are aware of it, notice whatever else comes up. Remember, there are no shoulds."*

_____

_____

Track the client closely, ending the processing if there are signs of distress. Make the self-observation interval short, 10 to 20 seconds.

Say, *"Okay, stop and take a breath."*

_____

_____

Wait for the client to reorient to you.

Subjective Units of State Scale (SUSS)

Say, *"In comparison to how you felt when we started, is it weaker, stronger, or the same?"*

_____

_____

Wait for an answer. If weaker, do not do this again for a while.

Say, *"What was that like?"*

_____

_____

Say, *"Would it be alright to use this later today or during future sessions?"*

_____

_____

Caution: For severely traumatized individuals, allowing the mind to flow freely and to observe that flow can open up traumatic material. It is possible that this can happen with this procedure and becomes an even more significant issue during EMDR processing when open and noncontrolling inner observation is necessary. Teaching this kind of inner awareness to clients prepares them for future EMDR. Initially, however, this might be a problem. Therapists should be attentive to traumatic disruption in the early practice of this aspect of the RDI. In the event of disruption, the therapist and client have the opportunity to develop coping mechanisms to manage traumatic intrusions.

Step 3: Modified RDI

As a session unfolds, be on the lookout for a moment when the client refers to a positive experience. It can be anything that could be a component of stabilization: success in listing a few targets, demonstrating an ability to manage distress, experiencing a feeling of strength, a positive feeling, an increase in self-esteem, acting in a self-assertive manner, doing self-care, being able to cope with something well, and so forth. Before the experience shifts or fades and without startling your client, have the client engage in the modified RDI to install the resource as above. The resource from a client will be used here, followed by the script:

Client: "I was really distressed earlier in the evening. I just couldn't get my mind off what happened. I tried to watch TV. I paced. I started smoking and eating. And then I don't know what happened but it just changed and later on I was able to go to sleep. This almost never happens to me."

Say, *"Tell me about the resource that you would like to use."*

_____

_____

Say, *"Okay, so the resource for you was* _____ (state your understanding of the resource). *Did I get it right?"*

_____

_____

If not, clarify it further:

Say, *"Tell me again what it is so we are as clear as can be."*

_____

_____

After the resource is clarified, say the following:

Say, *"Notice that. Now follow my fingers and just observe whatever comes. Good. That's right. What do you notice?"*

_____

_____

Do, at most, three back and forth BLS sweeps. Frequently, this author will only do one quarter or one half of a sweep the very first time. Track the client closely, especially if this is an early RDI, to assess its impact on the client. Stop the EM and wait between 10 and 30 seconds. Usually the client will look up signaling a return to regular interaction with the therapist.

Say, *"Is that weaker, the same, or stronger than before?"* (SUSS)

_____

_____

If stronger, do another set. Do, at most, three sets. Use your clinical judgment to decide how many sets and how many round trips to do.

If weaker or the same, do NOT do another set. Simply say, "Okay," and segue back to what was happening in the session just prior to the RDI. This will not have taken more than 2 minutes and probably about 45 seconds. The thread of the session will not have been lost.

Constructive Avoidance of Present Day Situations: Techniques for Managing Critical Life Issues

Carol Forgash

Constructive Avoidance of Present Day Situations Script Notes

The purpose of the constructive avoidance script is to assist clients in dealing with their anxiety or stress-provoking present day situations. Dissociative clients generally are phobic or avoidant of many activities such as medical procedures, going to the dentist, taking examinations, going for job interviews, and so forth due to the complex nature of their traumas, panic, anxiety, and other trauma-related problems. Despite their difficulties, clients in treatment still have to function in their communities, jobs, roles, and deal with situations that cause anxiety, triggering, stress, and so forth in their current lives. Given that many of them need a lengthy stabilization period, trauma processing and resolution may not take place for quite a while. However, toothaches, medical tests, job-related interviews, and so forth will not wait for trauma resolution and subjective units of disturbance (SUDs) of 0 or validity of cognition (VoC) equal to 7. Many clients with severe ego state disturbances or dissociative symptoms do not have the skills to cope with these situations. As a consequence of these trauma symptoms, many of these clients have poor health, do not allow themselves to advance at work, and so forth. When the client and ego state system realize that only the adult has to deal with the situation, and that child, traumatized, or dissociated parts can stay in Home Base, life can run more smoothly.

Clients can become very adept and creative about situations and events in which they have previously been uncomfortable by following the Constructive Avoidance Protocol. When the client is going to encounter a situation that has caused high stress or triggering in the past (doctor visits, interviews, exams) and has not completed (or begun) an EMDR target focusing on that issue, chances are that the ego states involved are not yet ready to deal with the situation. They can stay at the Home Base while the client deals with the present situation. The client can practice with the parts before the upcoming event in sessions and as homework between sessions. This protocol assumes that clients have already established a Home Base and Workplace (see chapters 14 and 15 by this author).

Constructive Avoidance of Present Day Situations Script

Say, *"Okay, now that you have been working with Home Base for awhile, let us put it to use in this situation of _____ (state the current situation that the client is concerned about)."*

_____

_____

Say, *"If no real event is going to occur soon, you can make one up just for practice. What would you like to use for a practice situation?"*

_____

_____

Say, *"Chances are some of your ego states are not ready to deal with this situation. How about this? They will remain at Home Base while you deal with the present situation and go to _____ (state the current situation that the client is concerned about)."*

_____

_____

Say, *"Now, could you ask them to come to the Workplace? You could say that you would like to tell them about a new way to work with _____ (state the upcoming situation). Let them know if this is just an imaginary practice session. You can remind parts that they don't have to listen if they don't want to. Is that all right with everyone?"*

_____

_____

If appropriate, say the following:

Say, *"Tell them that they have the choice of watching what will happen on a screen or not watching. Or you could ask them what would they like to do while they are at Home Base and you are at _____ (state where you will be)."*

_____

_____

Say, *"Okay, tell the parts that you will always, when possible, tell them when you are going to have a situation that you have to deal with but for which they don't need to be present. They can stay 'home'."*

_____

_____

Say, *"Remind them that they are always with you, but by staying 'at home,' they don't have to 'be' at the _____ (state the kinds* of situations that they might have to encounter) *or even pay attention to the situation while it is happening."*

_____

_____

Say, *"Also, you might tell them that you will always let them know when the situation or event has been completed. If you would like, you can ask them what they think about this idea?"*

_____

_____

Say, *"Another choice is to let the parts know that sometimes they might want one part to take care of everyone while you are at the* _____ (state where you will be). *Who could that be? Does anyone want to volunteer?"*

_____

_____

Say, *"Tell the parts in words they can understand, what is going to occur. For example, if you are going for a dental checkup and you know that in the past you have felt some anxiety but not too much, let them know this is what usually happens. Otherwise use a practice situation."*

_____

_____

Say, *"Let's practice by imagining together that* _____ ('I am going to the dentist in two weeks' or use as an example any appropriate task that needs to be done). *It's only for* _____ (a checkup or state the purpose). _____ ('the dentist will just look at my teeth and take an x-ray' or state the appropriate task). *What would you like to do at home while I'm getting my* _____ (checkup or state the activity)?"*

_____

_____

Say, *"Tell them, if they like, that they can watch the TV screen now and you can show them what the* _____ (checkup or state the activity) *will look like."*

_____

_____

Say, *"Anyone who doesn't want to watch doesn't have to. Remind them that they can say, 'Stop!' at any time. Play a short movie* _____ (of going to the dentist, sitting in the waiting room, or state the appropriate task). *Going into the* _____ (office or other relevant area). *Telling the* _____ (dentist or relevant person) *that you want them to 'Stop!' when you put your hand up and to always tell you what will be happening.* _____ (show the dentist looking at your teeth and the hygienist taking an x-ray or whatever relevant action). *Let them see your leaving* _____ *(the office or the relevant area). Ask them what they noticed about how things went. You can go ahead and do that now."*

_____

_____

Say, *"Do you have any questions before you start?"*

_____

_____

Say, *"Is there anything else they need to help them be okay that day?"*

_____

_____

Say, *"If all is well, ask them what feels good about what they did today."*

_____

_____

This can be enhanced with a few short sets of BLS.

Say, *"When the day of the appointment arrives, tell the parts 'I'll tell you when I'm leaving to go there and I'll let you know when I leave the* _____ *(dentist's office or wherever they are going). Is that okay with all of you?'"*

_____

_____

Say, *"Remind them that there will be opportunities to practice at the next session and at home. Ask if there are any more questions and if there are, go ahead and discuss them."*

_____

_____

Debrief with relaxation exercise and reminder to practice at home.

Say, *"Is there anything else that happened today that you feel is important and we should address or are there any parts who have something to say or have questions?"*

_____

_____

Say, *"Okay, let's end with a relaxation exercise. You can choose from the ones that we have worked on before such as your safe or comfortable space, progressive muscle relaxation, slow deep breathing, yoga breathing (breathe in to the count of 4, hold to the count of 4, breathe out to the count of 4), finding the relaxed place in the body and gently focusing on that place or another one that you would find helpful, or any other relaxation exercises. Which one would you like to do today?"*

_____

_____

When the client chooses one, go through the closing exercise. Always use this as a time to check in with the system to make sure that everyone is okay before leaving the session. This is a good safety measure and models how to take care of themselves.

After doing the closing exercise, say the following:

Say, *"Okay, I would like to check in with everyone to make sure that all of you are okay before you leave the session. How are you doing?"*

_____

_____

Say, *"I would like to remind you before you leave that you can practice this exercise at home this week."*

_____

_____

Initial Targeting of Traumatic Material: Steps

Joanne Twombly

Initial Targeting of Traumatic Material Script Notes

Clients are ready to begin preparation for working on traumatic material when they have some internal communication and cooperation and have developed coping skills, which they are able to use during their daily lives to manage symptoms. Preparation for trauma work may take a short or long time depending on the needs of your client. The process of preparation involves making sure all the resources are in place that the client needs to be able to process traumatic material without becoming overwhelmed or destabilized. It is helpful to use the standard resources frequently used with clients with a dissociative disorder (DD) during processing, for instance, the *affect dial* to modulate painful affect (Brown & Fromm, 1986); *container imagery* (Kluft, 1989); and *deep-trance dreamless sleep* (Kluft, 1988); or any other techniques that are applicable for your client. Also, it can help to reinstall the presence of the helpers, therapist, and therapist's office that you have already installed (see chapters 19, 21, and 22). Another important resource is installing teams of parts when clients have a complex system with many parts. The idea of teams here is having a team of parts who handle daily life or work and can make functioning more efficient.

The protocol for this author's work with clients with dissociative disorders diagnoses differs from standard EMDR procedure. For instance, emotions, sensation location, and negative or positive cognitions are not asked for because of the need to maintain stability. Asking parts to picture the image that brings up the most negative affect can also result in instant flashbacks. Concern for client stability requires leaving out some steps from the Standard EMDR procedure, and adding others. As your client works through traumatic material, it might become possible at times to use more steps from the Standard EMDR Protocol, however as new groups of parts come up or begin work with traumatic material, it is most often necessary to return to the protocol that provides for the most stability.

Phase 2: Preparation

Earlier chapters by this author and others in this section of the book will help with preparation (see chapters 13–31). This phase can take weeks or months to

297

accomplish. Spending time on it will increase the possibility of the processing being productive. For clients with complex systems of many parts, it is helpful to have experience in developing teams of parts. In the initial stages of developing coping skills, teams often developed to help with daily life functions such as: work, parenting, and driving. This is useful in situations where parts do not know how to do something join in inappropriately, such as a child part speaking up at a work meeting. Sometimes, other parts stay in their safe spaces when a team is handling whatever its function is. The following script details team building.

Installing Team of Parts Script

First identify what kind of team needs to be developed.

Say, *"Let's decide what kind of team we need today for* _____ (state the task ahead).*"*

_____

_____

Then say the following:

Say, *"Who helps with* _____ (state where help is needed)*?"*

_____

_____

Say, *"Is there anyone else who needs to be part of this team?"*

_____

_____

Say, *"How does it feel?"*

_____

_____

Say, *"Is there anyone else who needs to be part of this team?"*

_____

_____

Say, *"Okay, let's install the team and its function."*

_____

_____

Say, *"Ask if other parts would be willing to allow this team to handle* _____ (state what they will be handling).*"*

_____

_____

Ask, *"Are there any concerns or comments?"*

_____

_____

Say, *"See how it goes at* _____ (state the situation) *this week. Remind everyone that the* _____ (state the type of team) *team will be handling* ____ (state the situation), *and if there are any adjustments that are needed, make them, and we can talk about it next week."*

_____

_____

During trauma processing, it can be very helpful to dissociate any daily life teams from the trauma processing by having them stay in a Safe Space with sound and feeling proofing in the walls during the processing. This protects them from exposure to the traumatic material that can be destabilizing and maintains their ability to handle daily life. Their trauma work is put off until many of the other parts have completed their work and gotten stronger. Other parts that are not ready to do trauma work, or parts that were not involved in whatever traumatic material is being processed, can also stay in their safe spaces during the processing.

Targeting of Traumatic Material Script

Picture in Picture (PIP) Imagery

The Standard EMDR Protocol allows the processing to flow, while this protocol tightly controls processing to prevent destabilizing the client. This is facilitated by teaching the client the Television Technique (Brown & Fromm, 1986) that uses PIP imagery (Twombly, 2005). There are two steps to PIP:

Step 1. The client learns to visualize being in a safe room and turning a visualized television on to a screen of the therapist's office (previously installed, see chapter 22) with the therapist and client sitting in it. Some clients may prefer to turn the TV on to a screen of their safe space or to some other picture. The goal is for the client to have a default image that brings them stability and maintains duality. If the client prefers a different image, adjust the wording to reflect that.

Step 2. The client is taught to turn the PIP on and off with a small screen in the corner of the large screen. The PIP is where the trauma processing will be done. This process also helps the client maintain duality.

Remember, as with all resource work, ask all the parts to take part in learning this coping skill, or one part can do it while all others are watching and learning.

Say, *"Picture that you're all in a safe room, sitting in a chair across from a TV. You have the remote and when you're all ready, turn the TV on to an image of this office with you and me sitting here together so that this picture fills the whole screen. Now practice turning the TV on and off."*

_____

_____

Once the client has practiced visualizing turning the TV on and off, install this ability using dual attention stimulation (DAS) and communicate it to all parts.

Say, *"Focus on your ability to turn the TV on and off and everyone can install it. Go with it."*

Say, *"How was that? Does anyone have questions?"* (Have the client practice until this is mastered.)

_____

_____

Say, *"Okay, you have the scene of the office with you and me in it on the TV, now we'll practice turning the PIP on and off. What is a benign image you can practice with? Something like a picture of a flower garden or a pet?"*

_____

_____

Say, *"Now turn on the TV to the scene of the office with you all and me in it and then turn on the PIP to the picture of _____ (whatever the client came up with)."*

_____

_____

Say, *"Okay, is it on?"*

_____

_____

Say, *"Okay, now turn it off. Practice turning it on and off. That's great!"*

_____

_____

Once the client is good at turning the PIP on and off, install his ability using DAS.

Say, *"Focus on your ability to turn the PIP on and off and go with that."*

_____

_____

Say, *"How was that?"*

_____

_____

Now, with the client, identify something that is mildly annoying to him and have him practice turning the PIP on to the image of the annoying scene then off again.

Say, *"Pick something that is mildly annoying to see in the PIP and practice turning the PIP on and off to the scene of _____."*

_____

_____

Say, *"How was that?"*

_____

_____

Sometimes clients need to make adjustments to the PIP. For a group of parts in one client, the outline of the PIP needed to be made into strong bars to prevent it from filling the whole screen.

If necessary, say the following:

Say, *"Sometimes, it is helpful to make adjustments to the PIP. Is there something that you would like to do to the PIP to make it work better for you?"*

_____

_____

Phase 3: Assessment

Choosing an Initial Target

Ideally, it is helpful to begin with a less difficult piece of traumatic material. This might be something that happened once, something that happened outside the family, or something that happened later in the client's life. Help clients choose this initial target based on your clinical judgment concerning what you know about them and their preferences. Be aware that even targets that seem simple on the surface can be quite complex if some of the traumatic material is dissociated.

Say, *"Do you have an idea of something we can start with?"*

_____

_____

If the client doesn't have an idea, you can make suggestions and discuss possibilities until one is chosen.

Or say, *"Let's pick a piece of traumatic material that is less difficult to start our work with EMDR. If possible, let's work on something that does not involve the parts of you who take responsibility for your daily functioning. The reason for this is we want to support your continuing to function at the highest level possible. If we start with a less difficult piece of work and with parts not vital to your daily functioning, it will give us a way to see how EMDR works for you with the least amount of interference with your day-to-day life. Would it be okay for us to proceed?"*

_____

_____

If the parts that help with daily life are not willing to be dissociated from the processing, take extra care to maintain the client's stability. One possibility is to ask them if they would be willing to watch the processing from behind a shield that protects them from the traumatic feelings.

Say, *"I want to make sure that you are all protected while we work on this issue. Sometimes, people have found that watching from behind a shield that protected them from traumatic feelings was helpful, would you like to try that?"*

_____

_____

If they are not willing to stay behind a shield say the following:

Say, *"If not, what would work for you to help maintain your stability?"*

_____

_____

Determining Which Parts Are Involved in Processing

Once the initial target is chosen, ask the following:

Say, *"Who needs to be involved in processing this target?"*

_____

_____

Enlisting Parts as Helpers

Helper parts are parts that are not involved with daily life or the chosen target who can be there to support the client in remaining grounded and to remind parts about their coping skills. Helper parts also can let the therapist know if there is a problem.

Say, *"It would also be helpful if two or three parts who also aren't involved with daily life or this bit of traumatic material would be willing to volunteer to help. These helper parts will be there to support your remaining grounded and will remind the parts working on the traumatic material about their coping skills. Also, they will be able to warn me if there is a problem. Who do you think could be good helper parts, or are there any volunteers?"*

_____

_____

Protecting Parts Not Involved in the Processing

Request that all parts not involved in the processing of this target go to their Safe Spaces and put sound and feeling proofing up. This protects the parts from being involved in the processing by isolating themselves from hearing or watching the processing. Address questions and concerns.

Say, *"I'd like everyone who isn't involved in this target to go to their safe spaces and put sound and feeling proofing up. Does anyone have questions or concerns?"*

_____

_____

Then ask the group of parts who will be processing the target and the helper parts to check and see if there are any other parts present who need to go to their safe spaces, or have ones developed. If there is any sense that there are unidentified parts floating around, develop a wall around them that contains sound and feeling proofing.

Say, *"How does that feel? Check around and notice if there are any parts present who need to go to their safe spaces or who don't have a safe space and need one. Are there any there? And, if so, who is there?"*

_____

_____

As mentioned before, if parts that manage daily life aren't willing or able to go to their safe spaces during the processing, extra caution must be used to protect stability. Sometimes extra protection can be built in, for example, by suggesting they watch from behind a shield that protects them from strong affects.

Say, *"Visualize that you* (all the daily life parts) *are behind a shield with feeling proofing to protect you from the feelings involved in the trauma processing. What's that like?"*

_____

_____

It is important to recognize that if the host or daily life team are not willing or able to work in this way, all trauma processing must be done more slowly and carefully.

Say, *"This means we will proceed very carefully so that we do not interrupt any of your current life functioning."*

_____

_____

All safe spaces, walls, and resources can be installed using DAS.

Fractionating the Initial Target

The initial target is then further fractionated (Kluft, 1988; Fine, 1991) to provide additional safety and control. Targets can be fractionated by deciding to focus on one BASK dimension (the BASK model stands for four dimensions of traumatic material: behavior, affect, sensation, or knowledge; Braun, 1988), by parts going one at a time or any other way that makes sense.

Say, *"Let's decide how we are going to break up the trauma work so that it's in manageable amounts. We have some choices: each part can proceed one at a time; or we can focus on either the behavior, affect, sensation, or knowledge dimension of the memory; we can take one aspect or section of the trauma at a time. Another possibility is to store everything in a container and work on one chunk at a time. What feels best?"*

_____

_____

Say, *"Okay, so today we will be working on _____* (state the work or issue)."*

_____

_____

Installing the Therapist's Voice and Key Comments for Reprocessing

During the implementation of the Standard EMDR Protocol, the therapist makes as few as possible comments during the processing; however, with this population, the therapist makes frequent comments during processing to help clients maintain duality (one foot in the present and one in the past). It is helpful to ask clients if there are any comments that would specifically be helpful to them, then install the sound of your voice making these comments.

Say, *"As you're doing the processing I'll be keeping track of time, reminding you of whatever is helpful. I'll probably say things like, 'It's old stuff,' 'You're here in my office,' and 'You can stop anytime you want.' I want to make sure that you have as many phrases as you need for support. What else would you like me to say to remind you that we're here together in the present?"*

_____

_____

Say, *"Let's install the phrases that you've chosen. Go with that."*

_____

_____

Use DAS.

Say, *"Are all of the resources you all need in place or is there something else you can think of that would help before we begin?"*

_____

_____

If so, follow the guidelines for developing resources from this section of the book (see chapters 13–31), or other appropriate resources. If nothing new is needed, continue on to the Assessment Phase.

Negative and Positive Cognitions

Much of the time when beginning to process traumatic material with this client population, this author does not ask for positive and negative cognitions as to do so can be destabilizing and sometimes the material is not available (e.g., it might be put away in a container or dissociated). Instead, it is helpful to use a statement about the intention of the trauma work such as the following:

Say, *"This _____ (state the traumatic material) makes you have symptoms such as _____ (name them). Once we finish processing it, you will feel better."*

_____

_____

Or say, *"We are going to process this past traumatic event so it goes from feeling like it is occurring in the present to realizing it really happened in the past. Which one works for you or is there another one that works better?"*

_____

_____

Phase 4: Desensitization Beginning Processing

Trauma processing begins with parts involved in the processing practicing turning the PIP on for 2 seconds of traumatic material and then turning it off. It does not matter specifically what comes up, the goal is that the client can control accessing it and shutting it off.

Say, *"Now we're going to use the PIP to process 2 seconds of traumatic material. I'll count the seconds off and then I'll remind you to turn the PIP off. Do you have the whole screen turned on to us here in the office?"*

_____

_____

Say, *"Good. Ready? I'll turn the dual attention stimulation (DAS) on, now tell me when you've turned the PIP on and then just let whatever comes up come up and go by."*

_____

_____

Once the client tells you it is on, count the 2 seconds off and remind client to turn the PIP off.

Say, *"Okay, 1 second, 2 seconds. Okay, turn the PIP off. Is it off?"*

_____

_____

Once the PIP is off, turn the DAS off.

Say, *"Great, take a deep breath in, let it out. What came up?"*

_____

_____

Coping skills may need to be adjusted or developed, a part may be discovered who needs a Safe Space, and so forth. Note: Usually the client will keep the TV imagery on to the image of sitting in therapist's office.

Say, *"Is there anything else that we need in place to continue?"*

_____

_____

If so, do what is needed to support the client and their process. After the adjustments have been made and the processing has gone smoothly, do 2 more seconds of processing.

Say, *"I'll turn the DAS back on, let me know when you turn the PIP on and we'll do 2 more seconds of processing; 1 second, 2 seconds, okay, turn the PIP off. Are you back to the whole screen of us in the office?"*

_____

_____

Turn off DAS when the client has turned the PIP off.

Say, *"Take a deep breath in, let it out. How did you do?"*

_____

_____

Say, *"Let's try it again."*

_____

_____

Repeat the process with 2 more seconds of traumatic material.

Say, *"I'll turn the DAS back on, let me know when you turn the PIP on and we'll do 2 more seconds of processing: 1 second, 2 seconds, okay, turn the PIP off. Are you back to the whole screen of us in the office?"*

_____

_____

Turn off the DAS when the client has turned the PIP off. Practice this until the client has confidence in his ability to control the PIP. Then increase the length of sets to 5 seconds.

Say, *"I'll turn the DAS back on, let me know when you turn the PIP on and we'll do 5 seconds of processing; 1 second, 2 seconds, 3 seconds, 4 seconds, 5 seconds, okay, turn the PIP off. Are you back to the whole screen of us in the office?"*

_____

_____

Turn off the DAS when the client has turned the PIP off.

Say, *"Take a deep breath in, let it out. How did you do?"*

_____

_____

Say, *"Let's try it again."*

_____

_____

Repeat the process with 5 more seconds of traumatic material.

Say, *"I'll turn the DAS back on, let me know when you turn the PIP on and we'll do 5 more seconds of processing: 1 second, 2 seconds, 3 seconds, 4 seconds, 5 seconds, okay, turn the PIP off. Are you back to the whole screen of us in the office?"*

_____

_____

Turn off the DAS when the client has turned the PIP off. Repeat processing for 5 seconds until the client feels confident and then lengthen the sets. As the length of sets increases, the processing will look more like the Standard EMDR Protocol, with the exception that the PIP is being turned off between sets.

If it appears that the first chunk of traumatic material is completed, say the following:

Say, *"Does it feel like you're done with this piece?"*

_____

_____

If the parts agree, say the following:

Say, *"What did you get out of processing this piece?"*

_____

_____

It is often possible to install the answer. Use clinical judgment.

Say, *"Go with that."*

_____

_____

If there is enough time remaining in the session, another chunk of the target may be processed.

Ending the Trauma Processing Portion of the Session

Make sure you end the trauma work portion of the session with enough time to ensure the client's stability when he leaves the office. Most often, targets will take more than one session to complete.

Incomplete Targets

If the processing is incomplete, ask the helpers and processing parts what was the most important thing they learned and install that with DAS (Shapiro, 2001).

Say, *"What is the most important thing you've gotten from this so far?"*

_____

_____

Say, *"Go with that."*

_____

_____

Then have the parts put the remaining traumatic material back in the container with a commitment built into the container to return to work on it when the time is right.

> Say, *"Okay, I would like to ask all of the parts to put the remaining trauma back into the* (preestablished) *container with the commitment built into it that we will return to work on everything stored inside of it when the time is right."*

> Say, *"Are there any questions or concerns?"*

Trauma processing is often exhausting. It is helpful to suggest that the parts that were involved in the processing go to their Safe Spaces and rest, unless there is some reason why that is not appropriate, or they may wish to use another resource. If you are working with parts that are not parts who manage daily life, say the following:

> Say, *"What would you like to do now? You have worked so hard today. It might be helpful to go to your Safe Spaces and take a rest."*

Then request that all parts who were not involved in the processing return from their safe spaces so they can be updated, and ask questions.

> Say, *"I'd like everyone else to come out of their Safe Spaces* (if appropriate). *Do you have any questions or concerns?"*

If parts want to know what was worked on, give general information such as the following:

> Say, *"We worked on some traumatic material and the parts did great. We processed a chunk and will continue."*

Providing more information or specific information can be destabilizing. Once the traumatic material is fully processed, usually the processed material will become known to the other parts either immediately or over the next week(s). Check to make sure that the system is stable, and set up the plan for the next session.

> Say, *"Check inside, are there any other concerns or questions? How are you all feeling now?"*

It's often helpful to set up a general agenda for the next session.

Say, *"Next time we'll check with the parts who did the work to see how they are doing and then decide how we want to proceed. Does that sound okay?"*

_____

_____

Check to see that whoever leaves the session is able to manage daily life.

Say, *"Who's here now?"*

_____

_____

Completed Targets

When the target has been fully processed, discuss with the group of parts what can be installed. Often there are evident positive feelings like relief, a sense of control, or some kind of positive cognitions such as "It wasn't my fault!"

Say, *"What's different now that you've processed that target?"*

_____

_____

Or say, *"What do you notice?"*

_____

_____

Or say, *"What did you get out of processing the target?"*

_____

_____

Install the positives with DAS.

Say, *"Go with that."*

_____

_____

Note: Phases 5 and 6 of the Standard EMDR Protocol generally are not done unless you are extremely sure of the stability of your client. It is important to remember that the target is only one target in a web of targets in a system of dissociated parts. Referring back to something traumatic, doing body scans at the end of sessions can easily link into the next target(s) and be destabilizing. It is generally safer to install positive learning and ensure stability. Also, asking for a SUD can be depressing for the client unless you are sure there is a positive change.

Say, *"What positive learning did you have today?"*

_____

_____

Say, *"Go with that."*

_____

_____

Do DAS.

As targets are fully processed, the parts that were involved in the processing may spontaneously integrate. It is important to recognize when this happens so the change can be discussed with the rest of the system. Parts that have finished working on some traumatic material can become valuable helpers as other groups of parts begin working on targets.

Notes on Future Targeting

As groups of parts successfully work their way through processing targets, they will gain stability and confidence. However, you will notice that this sometimes leads to new material coming up or to groups of parts being accessed that had been dissociated on deeper levels. When this happens, the client may look destabilized, although in this instance, it would be because progress made it possible to reach a deeper level of work. Sometimes, new layers of parts will have no connection to the treatment and will need to establish relationships with the client and therapist and develop coping skills. It is useful to remember that although the treatment can seem complicated, the majority of these clients heal in the right kind of treatment. When done in a way that protects the clients' stability, EMDR processing facilitates progress.

The Inverted EMDR Standard Protocol for Unstable Complex Post-Traumatic Stress Disorder

Arne Hofmann

Often in the treatment of complex post-traumatic stress disorder (C-PTSD), there is a situation where the affect tolerance of the client is compromised and the client is flooded by trauma-based symptoms at the same time. In one group of these clients, the EMDR Standard Protocol approach works well (van der Kolk et al., 2007), especially in moderately stable outpatients. For those clients who are unstable, however, clinical complications can come up and the EMDR process is not as efficient anymore or gets stuck completely.

The Inverted EMDR Standard Protocol

The Inverted EMDR Standard Protocol for C-PTSD is a structured way to assist these clients to reduce their symptoms to the point where they are stable enough to work with more and more of their old memory clusters of the past (most often childhood abuse, neglect, and numerous secondary traumas after that). The proposed tests of the protocol are a way to ensure the client is neither kept too long in affect—avoidant stabilization nor pulled too early into trauma—work that overwhelms her. The protocol seems to be especially useful in clients with psychiatric hospitalization histories or inpatient settings.

The Inverted EMDR Standard Protocol Script Notes

There are three foci for the Inverted Standard Protocol for unstable C-PTSD based on inverting the EMDR Standard Protocol to meet the needs of unstable C-PTSD clients: the future, the present, and the past.

Future

Goal

1. To attain or support calm day-to-day living.

Targets

These clients often present with problems concerning triggering of traumatic memories or traumatic relationships (some of them transferences) as well as compromised affect regulation regarding these situations in their everyday life.

Clients typically present with problems represented by the following examples:

1. *My stressful child* (e.g., a tired, working mother comes home, finds that her child did not do his homework and this escalates into a fight).
2. *My stressful partner* (e.g., a wife has cooked a full dinner and her husband does not call to say he is late and a fight ensues).
3. *My stressful workplace* (e.g., stress with boss or customers).

These stressful events are anticipated in the near future (next days or weeks) and adequate resources are activated and connected with them.

Resources Used

1. Absorption Technique (using resources like the ability to distance oneself, inner strength, the ability to control oneself, etc.).

Present

Goals

1. To make everyday life more calm and stable.
2. To work with any triggers that remain after working with the future focus, that is, work with any other issues that prevent a more calm daily life.

Targets

1. Every day life targets where more change is needed after the use of the Absorption Technique.
2. Secondary trauma targets that produce symptoms in present time (e.g., sociophobic symptoms).

Resources Used

1. "The Method of Constant Installation of Present Orientation and Safety (CIPOS)" (chapter 18). This technique is a mixture between resource work and a fractionated abreaction (Fine, 1991; Kluft, 1988). The CIPOS method assists clients in reducing the stress of triggers of older trauma material in a more controlled manner without getting overwhelmed by the old material.

Past

Goal

1. To work with the past traumatic material when the client has better affect tolerance.

Criteria for Working on Past Memories or Issues

Work in the past is only done after the client passes each of the criteria in the following four tests:

1. Every Day Life Test

   a. The client does not go from crisis to crisis.
   b. The client maintains some energy reserves.
   c. Every day life has some effective routine.

2. Safe Place Test

   a. The client is able to activate a solid resource that is anchored or felt in the body.
   b. The client is able to use this resource to close down a difficult or affectively laden session.
   c. The client can elicit a resource state and stay there for a time (even if initially only in the session).

3. Stimulation Test

   a. The client uses resource work such as the Absorption Technique in a positive manner to access positive resource states without falling into emotional swamp holes after stimulation.

4. History-taking Test

   a. The client can briefly look at the past traumatic event that she will work on and say a few sentences about it—without details—without decompensating.
   b. The client is able to talk (briefly) about the traumatic event without dissociating or decompensating afterward.

Note: If the client does decompensate or dissociate in this test, it means that more stabilization techniques should be considered.

Targets

1. It is important to look at where the traumatic material comes from. It is not always the primary clusters such as childhood abuse or neglect but secondary trauma from adolescence or later in life as in the violence in school or in a marriage that keeps the PTSD symptoms active. Start with smaller single incident active targets (preferably secondary trauma).
2. After some work has been done with the secondary trauma(s) the affect tolerance is often strong enough and it is possible to confront the primary clusters.

The early neglect cluster is a special case and there are two possibilities:

1. The patient has good, stable, and present social relationships. In this case, this cluster can be addressed early in the treatment.
2. The patient has few—or no—good and stable social relationships. In this case the present must be stabilized first before the past can be addressed successfully.

Resources

1. Resource Development
2. CIPOS
3. The Standard EMDR Protocol

Note: Very stable complex PTSD clients with good stability in their daily lives, a strong social network, ability to remember many neglect or abuse memories, and who pass the four tests to work with past material stated above, often, can work with the Standard EMDR Protocol more quickly, although it is often helpful to teach the resources of the Absorption Technique, Strengthening or Wedging (Kiessling, 1999) and use CIPOS in the first work with old memories.

The Inverted EMDR Standard Protocol Script: Future

The Wedging or Strengthening Technique (Kiessling, 1999) has been modified in Germany and is called The Absorption Technique to enhance resources in order to deal with what the client is concerned about in the future, such as a stressful partner, a problematic child, stressful work, a stressful boss, having stress about future EMDR-work, a present trigger, or even an intrusive memory (past). Having clients imagine a strength or skill that would help them during the problem often helps them to reduce their anxiety. Focusing on a specific strength or coping skill may create a wedge of safety or control that will assist clients with the difficult situation in the future. Use short sets of 3 to 12 bilateral stimulation (BLS) to assist in generalizing the resource.

The Absorption Technique

Skill or Strength

Say, *"What is the issue in the future* (present or past) *that you want to focus on?"*

_____

_____

Say, *"If you think of that situation now, how stressful is that to you on a scale of 0 to 10 if 0 is no disturbance at all and 10 is the worst you can imagine?"*

0	1	2	3	4	5	6	7	8	9	10
(no disturbance)								(highest disturbance)		

List of Three Positive Abilities Needed

Resources

Say, *"What skills would you need to deal with that issue better* (state the future concern)*?"*

_____

_____

The idea is to just get a theoretical answer from the head or cortex of the client at first.

1. _____

2. _____

3. _____

First Resource

Say, *"Think of the first resource. Was there ever a situation in your life where you felt you had some of this ability already?"*

_____

_____

Say, *"Can you think of an image of that situation?"*

_____

_____

Say, *"As you focus on the image, where do you feel some of that skill of _____ (name the resource) in your body that you had at that moment?"*

_____

_____

Enhance

Say, *"Think of that image of ____ (state the resource), the body feeling, and that you had some of the resource and _____ (state what BLS you are using). What are you noticing?"*

_____

_____

If the feeling is positive, do another set.
If it is not changed, do another set.
If it changes to a negative feeling, look for another resource.

Second Resource

Say, *"Think of the second resource. Was there ever a situation in your life where you felt you had some of this ability already?"*

_____

_____

Say, *"Can you think of an image of that situation?"*

_____

_____

Say, *"As you focus on the image, where do you feel some of that skill of _____ (name the resource) in your body that you had at that moment?"*

_____

_____

Enhance

Say, *"Think of that image of ____ (state the resource), the body feeling, and that you had some of the resource and _____ (state what BLS you are using). What are you noticing?"*

_____

_____

If the feeling is positive, do another set.
If it is not changed, do another set.
If it changes to a negative feeling, look for another resource.

Third Resource

Say, *"Think of the third resource. Was there ever a situation in your life where you felt you had some of this ability already?"*

_____

_____

Say, *"Can you think of an image of that situation?"*

_____

_____

Say, *"As you focus on the image, where do you feel some of that skill of _____ (name the resource) in your body that you had at that moment?"*

_____

_____

Enhance

Say, *"Think of that image of ____ (state the resource), the body feeling, and that you had some of the resource and _____ (state what BLS you are using). What are you noticing?"*

_____

_____

If the feeling is positive, do another set.
If it is not changed, do another set.
If it changes to a negative feeling, look for another resource.

Getting the Resources Together

Say, *"Think of the three abilities together and where you felt them in your body. Just nod if you are in contact with all three body feelings that go with them (just take the successfully installed resources)."*

_____

_____

If the client nods, stimulate.

Say, *"Go with that."*

_____

_____

Use a short set of BLS.

Check for the Issue

Say, *"While you are now in contact with your resources, take a look back at the issue that troubles you. How stressful is it for you now on*

*a scale from 0 to 10, where 0 is no disturbance or neutral and 10 is
the highest disturbance you can imagine?"*

0	1	2	3	4	5	6	7	8	9	10
(no disturbance)										(highest disturbance)

During the Future Phase of the Inverted Protocol, use the Absorption Technique
to develop as many different resources for the different issues about which the client might be concerned. The goal is to make sure that the client's day-to-day life is
calm enough to move on to trauma work.

Present

During the present phase of the Inverted Protocol, the idea is to create resources for
present daily life. These are issues that get in the way of the client having a calm
daily life. The first technique to use is the Absorption Technique to see if the client
needs resources for present triggers.

Targets are everyday life targets that should change more after the use of the
Absorption Technique. Work with secondary trauma targets that produce symptoms in present time first (e.g., a clear transference situation where experiences
with an abusive brother are transferred onto the client's boss). Since CIPOS allows
for affect bridging to be better controlled, the focus of the boss can be selected
without getting overwhelmed by the brother material.

The Back of the Head Scale (BHS) and the Method of Constant Installation of Present Orientation and Safety (CIPOS) Script

Two other ways to create resources and to help ground the person in the present or to understand when they are not grounded in the present are the Back of the Head Scale and the Method of Constant Installation of Present Orientation and Safety developed by Jim Knipe (see chapters 17 and 18). When a client is able to use these techniques, they are less likely to be retraumatized if a disturbing memory appears as they have a way to keep connected to present reality. It is helpful for the therapist and the client to know when the client is drifting into derealization, that is, the client is losing a felt sense of the reality and safety of the present situation. For clients who are potentially dissociative, the degree of orientation to the present situation can be assessed through the use of the BHS. This procedure is introduced to the client during the Preparation Phase, before any desensitization of trauma is begun.

> Say, *"Think of a line that goes all the way from here* (hold up two index fingers about 15 inches in front of the person's face) *running right from my fingers to the back of your head.*
>
> *Let this point on the line* (move your fingers to indicate the point 15 inches in front of the person's face) *mean you are completely aware of being present here with me in this room, you can easily listen to what I am saying, and you are not at all distracted by any other thoughts. You are completely present.*
>
> *Let the other point on the line at the back of your head* (in order to not be intrusive into the space of the client, the therapist points to the back of his own head) *mean that you are so distracted by disturbing thoughts, feelings, or memory pictures that you feel like you are somewhere else. Your eyes may be open but your thoughts and your awareness are completely focused on another time, place, or experience. At this very moment, show with your finger where you are on this line."*

The therapist should check to make sure the client understands this idea. Most clients who have dissociative experiences will quickly recognize this procedure as a way of measuring and expressing a familiar aspect of their mental life. The assumption is that the more the person points toward the most present end point of the line, the safer it is to do trauma work with BLS. Clients seem to be able to easily assess the full range of dissociated experiences, either pointing to a place in front of the face, to a place parallel with the eyes, to the temple, or to an area further back in the head, according to what they are experiencing.

As a rough rule of thumb, it is assumed that it is necessary for the client to point to a position at least three inches in front of the face in order for trauma-focused work to proceed, although, this may vary from client to client. The use of the BHS throughout a therapy session can be very useful in insuring that the client is staying present while reprocessing disturbing memories.

Working With the Method of Constant Installation of Present Orientation and Safety

The next step during this Present Phase of the Inverted Standard Protocol for unstable C-PTSD is to work with the CIPOS method. The CIPOS method is used in conjunction with the BHS, and basically consists of using BLS to strengthen or install in the client's awareness the resource of a clear subjective sense of being present in the immediate real life situation (i.e., the therapy office as resource). This method may be used in the Preparation Phase prior to the desensitization work or during the actual desensitization of a particular, highly disturbing traumatic memory. By constantly strengthening the person's present orientation through BLS, processing of the memory can proceed more safely with much less danger of unproductive, dissociated reliving of the traumatic event.

The CIPOS steps in the Inverted Standard Protocol for unstable C-PTSD:

Step 1. Obtain full permission from the client to work on a persisting present trigger (or later on a highly disturbing memory) in a gradual and safe way, with ample time in the therapy session to complete the work regardless of whatever unexpected traumatic material may emerge during processing. For more dissociated clients or with clients who have dissociated ego states, it is necessary to also ask for and obtain permission *from any other parts that are involved in this memory.* If some parts of the system do not wish to participate, that is fine, but there should be a commitment from the whole system to allow processing of the memory. Since the way to ask the system for permission can be quite variable, with the words for one not necessarily appropriate for another, the following is only a suggestion to give you an idea of what to say. These words can be modified according to the needs of your client.

Say, *"I would like to ask all parts of the mind who are involved in this memory for permission to work on this today. Is this okay with all of you?"*

_____

_____

Step 2. As with any therapy intervention, it is important that the client be aware of the *objective* safety of the therapist's office. If the client seems unsure of the physical or interpersonal safety of the present situation, this issue should be addressed directly. Sometimes it is necessary, through observations, questions, and discussion, to help the client see that the fears that are being experienced in the present actually are the direct result of a past event, one that ended long ago, and often took place far away. This cognitive orientation to present reality does not necessarily have to be accompanied by feelings of safety, but it should be clearly established in the client's intellectual understanding.

If the client is uncertain about the actual safety of your office, fears and concerns (including transference and countertransference issues) should be explored and resolved before attempting trauma work. If, on the other hand, the therapist is simply unsure about the client's degree of contact with the reality of the safe office, the questions in step 3 can be asked to clarify the situation.

Step 3. To assess and further strengthen the person's sense of present orientation, the therapist may ask a series of simple questions relating to the client's present reality in your office with each client answer followed by a short set of eye movements (EMs). When the client responds to these simple questions, the therapist says, "Think of that," and initiates a short set of EM. The therapist can chose questions that are appropriate to the client or make ones that are suitable for the same goal of grounding the client in the office. Sample questions follow:

Say questions such as, *"Where are you right now, in actual fact?"*

_____

_____

Say, *"Think of that"* and do a short set of BLS.

_____

_____

Say, *"What do you think of that picture over there?"*

_____

_____

Say, *"Think of that"* and do a short set of BLS.

_____

_____

Say, *"Can you hear the cars going by outside?"*

_____

_____

Say, *"Think of that"* and do a short set of BLS.

_____

_____

Say, *"Can you find the flaw in the design in this rug?"*

_____

_____

Say, *"Think of that"* and do a short set of BLS.

_____

_____

Say, *"How many tissue boxes do I have in this room?"*

_____

_____

Say, *"Think of that"* and do a short set of BLS.

_____

_____

The therapist can use the above questions or add relevant questions for the client. In this way, the client's subjective sense of being present is strengthened.

Say, *"What's good about being here right now instead of somewhere else?"*

_____

_____

Of course, it is much better to be in the relatively safe present than to be reliving a traumatic event, so (usually without much direction) the client is able to say something like "I am comfortable here." Or "I know I am safe here," and this positive information can then be strengthened with additional BLS.

Say, *"Go with that."*

_____

_____

If the client is confused about why the therapist is asking these simple questions, the purpose can be explained.

Say, *"A firm grounding in present reality is an essential precondition for the use of EMDR to resolve old disturbing memories. The way EMDR works is 'One foot in the present; one foot in the past'."*

_____

_____

One particularly useful method of assisting the client in orienting to present time is to engage in a game of catch with a pillow or a small soft object.

Say, *"Can you catch this pillow?"*

_____

_____

Say, *"Good, now toss it back. That's right* (repeated 1 to 10 times, as necessary).*"*

_____

_____

Say, *"Where are you on the line now* (Back of the Head Scale)*?"*

_____

_____

Or ask the client to *"Take a drink of water."*

_____

_____

Or say, *"Hold this drop of water or ice cube in your hand."*

_____

_____

Or say, *"Hum a song and then count to 10* (and so forth).*"*

_____

_____

The game of catch, in particular, seems to quickly and reliably reverse the derealization experience in many clients. The action of tossing an object back and forth pulls the person back to the present. Playing catch is an easily performed task and seems to require the individual to neurologically activate the orienting response (OR) in order to follow the trajectory of the tossed object. We can speculate that this procedure reciprocally inhibits (Wolpe, 1958) the activation of excessive traumatic material, which in turn allows the client to be more aware of the actual safety of your office. Other similar procedures are taking a drink of water, holding a drop of water or an ice cube in the hand, or alternately humming a song and counting to 10. Each of these procedures can bring about a state change back to orientation to present safety, which then empowers the client to be able to proceed with processing trauma material.

Step 4.   Through the use of the BHS, the therapist is able to assess the effectiveness of the CIPOS interventions. In this way, it can be insured that the client is remaining sufficiently grounded in emotional safety so that reprocessing of the trauma can occur. The BHS is a way of making sure the client remains safely in the zone of dual attention: continuing connection with present safety while accessing traumatic memory information.

Step 5.   When present orientation is sufficiently established, say the following:

Say, *"Are you willing to be in contact with your memory for a very brief period of time* (e.g., perhaps only 2 to 10 seconds).*"*

_____

_____

Say, *"Good, go ahead and do this for* _____ (state how many seconds) seconds.*"*

_____

_____

Keep track of the time. This is essentially a carefully controlled dissociative process. Immediately following the end of this period of seconds, use soothing but repetitive and emphatic words.

Say, *"Come back into the room now, okay, now come back here, just open your eyes, find your way back here now, that's right, just open your eyes."*

_____

_____

Do this until the client's eyes open and they are looking out into the room again.

Step 6.   At this point, give encouragement:

Say, *"Good,"* or *"That's right."*

_____

_____

Then resume the CIPOS interventions as in the following:

Say, *"Where are you right now, in actual fact?"*

_____

_____

Say, *"Go with that* (do a short set of BLS)."

_____

_____

Using the BHS, the CIPOS interventions are continued until the client is able to report that they are once again oriented toward the present reality of your office. At this point, Step 5 can be repeated. The idea is to go back and forth between pairing Present Safety with BLS and then experiencing the trauma for 2 to 10 seconds with no BLS.

Step 7. As this process continues, the client develops increasing ability to stay present as well as greater confidence and a sense of emotional control in confronting the disturbing memory. This opens the door to the use of the 11-Step Standard Procedure and directly pairing bilateral stimulation with traumatic material.

Past

Test to see if the client has good enough affect tolerance to work with past traumatic material. The client needs to pass the following four tests. Though the therapist evaluates the three tests, it may be helpful to ask the clients the following questions.

Every Day Life Test

Say, *"How has your life been going over the past few months?"*

_____

_____

Say, *"Have you been able to cope with the normal stressors of life or are you finding them overwhelming?"*

_____

_____

Say, *"Do you find yourself going from crisis to crisis or is life relatively calm and has some routine for you?"*

_____

_____

If the client has not been going from crisis to crisis, say the following:

Say, *"How have you been feeling emotionally and physically? Do you have enough energy for the things that you need to do in your life."*

_____

_____

If the answer is "Yes" (and the therapist agrees), the client has passed the first test, and is demonstrating the affect tolerance and enough energy to do the trauma work.

If the answer is "No," then the therapist can spend the rest of the session time working on resources and stabilization.

Safe Place Test

The safe place test is done without BLS. Use of BLS occurs later during the stimulation test. This is because some clients can do the safe place but they do not tolerate stimulation (yet).

Say, *"I'd like you to think about some place you have been or imagine being that feels very safe or calm. Perhaps being on the beach or sitting by a mountain stream."*

_____

_____

Pause

Say, *"Where would you be?"*

_____

_____

Emotions and Sensations

Say, *"As you think of that safe place, notice what you see, hear, and feel right now."*

_____

_____

Pause

Say, *"What do you notice?"*

_____

_____

Enhancement

Say, *"Focus on your safe place, its sights, sounds, smells, and body sensations. Tell me more about what you are noticing."*

_____

_____

Cue Word (Optional)

Say, *"Is there a word or phrase that represents your safe place?"*

_____

_____

Observe if the client is able to activate the image and the body feeling associated with the safe place and hold it for some time. If she can do this—or even reports that she can do that at home—the safe place test is positive. If the client is unable to pass the safe place test, continue working at establishing resources and stabilization.

The Stimulation Test

The question to pass the stimulation test is the following: "Has the client been able to use the Absorption Technique in a session and accessed positive resource states without ending the process in negative material or decompensating?" The answer will be based on the work that you have done in the Future and Present Phases.

If the answer is "Yes," the client can proceed to the history-taking test.

If the answer is "No," continue working at establishing resources and stabilization.

History-Taking Test

This test asks that the client look briefly at a past traumatic event that will be the first event that she will work on. Then she will say a few sentences about it without details.

> Say, *"Would it be okay for you to talk about one of the past traumatic events* (about 2 to 5 minutes) *that happened to you that is about a 7 on our 0 to 10 scale where 0 = no distress and 10 = the most distress?"*

_____

_____

> If yes, say the following:

> Say, *"Okay, please tell me a few sentences about it without details."*

_____

_____

> Say, *"How do you feel on the inside when talking about the trauma? How are the other parts feeling? Is this something that you and they are ready to move forward on or do you or any of the others need to do more resource work before we begin the trauma work?"*

_____

_____

If the client (or the parts of the client) are able to do this and they come back to the next session and do not report any major setbacks, then you can contract to do further trauma confrontation work. The rationale is that a client needs affect tolerance while in contact with the memory. In this way, she is able to build a step-by-step sense of mastery. If the client does have difficulty, praise her for letting you know that more stabilization work is needed and continue with that work.

When the client has passed the four tests from this last section, she is ready to move on to work on her trauma with the EMDR Standard Protocol. However, it is helpful to maintain practice using the resources at intervals or as needed.

Often, therapists begin trauma work with early childhood clusters of negative events such as violence, sexual abuse, and severe neglect. Instead of going into the past to begin trauma work with the client, it is safer to start by creating a trauma map that is a list of traumatic events that are rated on the SUD scale and are plotted on a timeline from birth to the client's current age (see Hofmann & Luber, 2009). The idea is to focus on the events first that still produce symptoms in present time. These may be not only PTSD symptoms, but also phobic symptoms (Cloitre, 2008). Past work can be accomplished when the client has gained the affect tolerance learned in the Inverted EMDR Standard Protocol for C-PTSD in the Future and Present Phases.

The Wreathing Protocol: The Imbrication of Hypnosis and EMDR in the Treatment of Dissociative Identity Disorder, Dissociative Disorder Not Otherwise Specified, and Post-Traumatic Stress Disorder

Catherine G. Fine

The Wreathing Protocol has been designed as a thorough, planful, and parsimonious way to protect trauma patients from decompensation during the middle phase of trauma. This protocol helps trauma patients not only approach abreactive material with safety but it also furthers more complete metabolism of their dissociated conflictual experiences. It presumes sophistication and fluency on the part of the clinician who ought to be skilled in advanced hypnosis techniques, ego state therapy, and controlled fractionated abreactions *without* the use of formal hypnosis or EMDR. To best illustrate the discrete interventions amidst the complexity of dissociative responses, the operationalized EMDR protocols will be exemplified in the paradigmatic dissociative disorder, dissociative identity disorder (DID); however, they also apply for lesser dissociative disorders, dissociative disorder not otherwise specified (DDNOS) and post-traumatic conditions particularly when using an ego state model as an organizing principle in the treatment.

The Wreathing Protocol Script Notes

Basic Concepts

- *BASK model of dissociation.* Combining both hypnosis and EMDR methodologies in a structured DID treatment seem like a natural and organic development in a therapy in which traumatized patients live in a dissociative field. The Wreathing Protocol is designed to create an organizing scheme, based on the BASK (dimensions of behavior, affect, sensation, and knowledge) model of dissociation (Braun, 1988), for planned fractionated work in the structured treatment of DID (Fine, 1990, 1991; Kluft, 1988). The Wreathing Protocol helps organize the abreactive work by means of hypnotic interventions and EMDR methodologies used jointly. How each Wreathing Protocol evolves will naturally be dictated by the needs, deficiencies, and ego strengths of the individual DID patient. It represents a skeletal structure around which complex dissociated elements of personality can regroup, blend, and integrate after detoxification and transformation of the traumatic material. The goal of treatment for a patient with DID is to achieve a congruence of purpose and motivation between the various personalities (Kluft, 1984). Restated in cognitive behavioral terms: "all personalities need to be congruent and similar in Behavior, Affect, Sensation and Knowledge" (BASK; Braun, 1988; Fine 1990, 1991, 1992). This definition is fitting because the case conceptualization for the Wreathing Protocol is cognitive–behavioral in structure, even though it incorporates and respectfully acknowledges and works with the relational dynamics within and between the personalities.
- *Fractionated abreactions.* In the beginning of treatment for DID and complex PTSD, stabilization is promoted before moving onto working with the traumatic material through the use of "fractionated abreactions" (Fine, 1991; Kluft, 1988). This is an ecological concept that supports working with a smaller piece of traumatic material first as a way to help the patient to successfully process and metabolize increasingly painful material and then successively manage larger and larger amounts of upsetting memory. Understanding the BASK dimensions (their presence or seeming absence) when working with the various individual personalities or clusters of ego states enables the therapist to keep track of the complexity and fragmented nature of experience of a patient with a diagnosis along the dissociative spectrum.
- *Spontaneous trance.* Having a way to understand the structure of the DID experience is essential because of the hypnotic nature of dissociative occurrences and because of the frequent intrusions of spontaneous trance in the DID patient as a way of coping with life stressors. An essential prerequisite treatment element is to assist the patient in the identification, management, and mastery over spontaneous trance (Kluft, 1982). Without this skill the dissociative patient is left to the vicissitudes of spontaneous abreactions and therefore vulnerable to retraumatization. Indeed, unplanned abreactive work can promote regression, decompensation, and uncontrolled affect bridges with potential reemergence of post-traumatic symptoms. If premature or misaligned abreactive work occurs, the message to the DID patient is that past experiences contained within parts of the mind remain overwhelming and unmanageable, and that these experiences should continue to be avoided at all cost (Fine & Berkowitz, 2001). It is important to keep this in mind when working with EMDR because it is such a powerful methodology. It is also important to keep in mind that regardless of the therapist's and patient's better efforts, it is unrealistic to assume that the patient will not be transported in their minds to an alternate reality where they may lose duality (since many have multiple reality disorder). The art of using EMDR in these

circumstances is to assure that they will return to the present after the EMDR and before the therapy session ends.

- *BASK dimensions versus EMDR assessment.* Because of the fragmented nature of the patient's experiences for both traumatic and nontraumatic events, the BASK conceptualization serves as a benchmark. The BASK model helps the patient and the therapist jointly assess those parts of the trauma puzzle the patient is able to access and those he is not. Therefore patients can a priori have a sense of where the most dissociation lies because they will have learned in the talk therapy that the most dissociated material is potentially the most traumatic for their mind. The metabolism of a traumatic incident (captured by a BASK dimension) is considered to be complete when the patient knows, understands, and has experienced all parts of the traumatic BASK event. Because the patient often presents with only one element (perhaps two) of a BASK event, it may prove helpful to use BASK dimensions as psychological yard sticks rather than using the formal EMDR assessment to better understand the patient's experience. Using the BASK foundationally would allow for a better positioning of hypnotic interventions and a better inclusion and appropriate targeting of EMDR modules. When working with the Assessment Phase of EMDR, the image, negative cognition/schema, emotions, and sensations of the target incident are typically elicited. The problem with the standard EMDR conceptualization in the initiation of trauma work for DID patients (in the middle stage of treatment) according to this author is that initially the dissociative system may be too fragmented and the personalities too afraid to bring this material together in such a holistic way. Therefore, it is anticipated that many imbricated partially processed BASK experiences will temporarily remain in limbo with incompleted EMDR processing. Because the patient is operating in a dissociative field, is trauma phobic, and prone to cascading abreactions, the therapist must expect seemingly stagnant in situ temporarily frozen BASKs while other BASK processing takes place as the patient or the personality builds more affect tolerance or sensation tolerance as they improve their ability to know what happened to them. The use of the BASK dimensions allows the therapist to help the patient and personality focus on whichever element(s) of BASK can serve as most appropriate targets at that time, and titrate the experience with a systematic desensitization approach in mind rather than one of full flooding. Important elements of the BASK model are as follows:

- *Traumatic and nontraumatic experiences.* Implied in the use of BASK as a benchmark structure is that both traumatic and nontraumatic experiences are distributed across these four dimensions. Because the DID patients' or the chronic post-traumatic stress patients' minds are primarily operating in a dissociative field, multiple pieces of their experiences (both traumatic and nontraumatic) represent pieces of cognitive memory, memory in feeling form, sensation form, as well as kinesthetic memory, which have to be found, aligned, reconnected, and integrated.
- *Trauma-based versus nontrauma-based BASKs.* The patient/therapist dyad will likely encounter and alternately work within both trauma-based BASKs and nontrauma-based BASKs. The therapist needs to expect that over time, the linking between trauma-based BASKs and nontrauma-based BASKs, though not officially defined as traumatic in and of itself (because it may not involve attack, violence, witnessing of overwhelming events, or anything of the like) may actually be more strenuous and overwhelming because it directly undermines the patients' notions of their lives, their meaning making, and ultimately their self-identity.

- *Use of Standard EMDR Protocol.* When these caveats have been understood by the therapist and when the DID patient is more integrated and able to access the full material used in the Assessment Phase, the Standard EMDR Protocol can be used.

Note: This work presupposes that the therapist already has working knowledge concerning the use of heterohypnosis, of processing experiences to decrease and eliminate minor post-traumatic symptoms, and of the controlled negotiation of fractionated abreactions without EMDR. Reconfiguration of ego states through techniques such as shuffling the deck, safe place, permissive amnesia, providing sanctuary, fantasy trip, pseudo-orientation in time, vault maneuver, split screen, or some other distancing interventions, for example, require advanced training in hypnosis without which this whole protocol should not be attempted (Fine, 1991, 1993b; Kluft, 1982, 1988; Phillips & Frederick, 1995); it is questionable whether any therapy for complex post-traumatic stress and dissociative disorders ought to be initiated when the therapist does not know the language of the patient, which is the language of hypnosis.

Entering into the imbricated Wreathing Protocol in the middle phase of trauma treatment may be initiated with or without formal hypnosis but presupposes the possibility of the following:

1. *A hypnotic reconfiguration may be required at protocol onset.* This circumstance could arise when the abreactive work that needs to be done is contained within an alter personality behind the host personality who is the one in executive control of the individual most of the time. The host personality may be geared to functioning in the outside world and may need to step back to allow for the alter personality to step forward and officially engage in the EMDR work to process traumatic material less readily available to the host personality. Once the EMDR work is done, the alter personality steps back again and the host personality resumes his or her front and center position. For example, the therapist could prepare for the EMDR initiation by asking, "_____ (specify Part A) kindly step away from front and center temporarily as has been agreed upon, so that _____ (specify Part B) can come forward to do the EMDR." Once Part B is front and center, the EMDR protocol described later in this script is initiated and completed to the satisfaction of therapist and alter. Then the therapist may say, "Thank you Part B for your work today, you may want to rest in the background listening in if you choose, while Part A comes front and center again. Part A could you kindly move forward as Part B steps back."

2. *A spontaneous reconfiguration during the course of the EMDR.* Sometimes the host personality is prepared to do the EMDR work himself. He may be in touch with the alter personalities whose memories or experiences he feels in a diffused and limited way, or he may not want to turn over the spotlight of the therapy to the alter personalities because of his control issues. EMDR is set up as described later but the therapist ought to expect that the host personality may get sufficiently overwhelmed to spontaneously, in the midst of the EMDR processing, step back and leave the space to the alter personality containing the traumatic material. If the alter personality is processing well after the spontaneous shift, continue the EMDR. If the alter personality is getting overwhelmed as well, then the EMDR needs to be shut down, the alter needs to get regrounded and then needs to step back as the host personality comes forward again.

3. *Passive influence phenomena affecting the personality or group of personalities that are up front doing the work with the therapist.* This circumstance is not unlike the previous one, however potentially more confusing. Unantici-

pated or unknown alters from the background may begin to influence the EMDR processing that was planfully and directly set up either with the host personality or with a known alter. Once the EMDR sweeps or taps have begun, it is as if by affective or sensation bridges, alter personalities are drawn to the EMDR "by surprise." The therapist needs to monitor the capacity of the patient to tolerate this additive process. Sometimes this spontaneous joining is welcomed because it is organic and smooth; at other times, it is overly strenuous to the dissociative defenses of the DID patient and the EMDR needs to be stopped and all the personalities regrounded. It behooves the therapeutic dyad at this point to examine the reason for the surprising development and understand it fully before attempting EMDR in this fashion again. It is not uncommon for the therapist at this point to resume talk therapy directed at further mapping of personalities and exploration of relationships between parts. This continued mapping may lead to the realization that there are layers of personalities or ego states in the background that need their own separate EMDR assessments, BASK assessments, and further trauma-based processing prior to returning to the initially organized EMDR set up. Months may lapse before this kind of retargeting may occur.

The Wreathing Protocol Script

Determine which BASK dimension of the traumatic experience carries the highest level of distress at the time of the session.

Say, *"Which personality or group of personalities will step forward to work on a piece of trauma or a piece of upsetting material today?"*

_____

_____

This material can be from the past or could be current. If the material is from the person's present life, once the neural network is engaged it may lead the client to a past similar or parallel event on whichever BASK dimension is relevant. If the material is already understood as from the person's past then it will, from the beginning of the protocol, be contextualized as such.

Say, *"Let's talk about which trauma is the most relevant for* (all of) *you to work on today. What would you be willing to use as a target today?"*

_____

_____

Note: Regardless of the stated dimension that was chosen, there may remain last minute interruptions, interlopers, and passive influence experiences that may require several retargetings prior to actually engaging either formal or informal hypnosis or EMDR.

Notice which BASK dimension is chosen as most salient. Is it the *behavior* that occurred today or one that patients remember from childhood? Is it the *affect* experienced in a distant past or yesterday in a circumstance that they cannot relate to their past at all? Is it the *sensations* experienced in some part of their body that may or may not make sense to them? Or is it the *knowledge* of what happened that is most distressing for the patient? Note what will potentially be targeted at the beginning or the EMDR sequence.

Behavior: _____
Affect: _____
Sensation: _____
Knowledge: _____

Working From the Knowledge (K) Dimension of BASK

In the Wreathing Protocol, at first, the relevant dimension of the BASK is targeted to access the appropriate neural network; it may also be used for ongoing targeting and retargeting as the Wreathing Protocol unfolds. A positive cognition (PC) may not initially be accessible to the patient until the subjective units of disturbance (SUD) level of the experience being processed has reached less than 40% of its original value; the patient may, only then, be better able to *spontaneously* generate a PC.

Note: The fact that a patient with DID often is demand characteristic sensitive, the initial PC that he might report if pressured by the therapist may be the PC that he thinks that the therapist wants to hear and therefore not truly come from the self. Therefore, sensitivity to the DID patient's suggestibility allows for more accurate targeting.

Say, *"When you think of _____* (state which element(s) of the BASK you are targeting), *on a scale of 0 to 10, where 0 is no disturbance or neutral and 10 is the highest disturbance that you can imagine, how disturbing is this to you* (do not use the word feel) *now?"*

0   1   2   3   4   5   6   7   8   9   10
(no disturbance)   (highest disturbance)

Note: The word "feel" is not used in the elicitation of the SUD for the BASK element. This is because if it were to be used, it would shift the BASK to Affect when that might not be what the patient wants or is ready to work on.

The next important step is the decision of whether to start with EMDR or hypnosis. Take into account:

1. The alter who will primarily be engaged in the work for this set of EMDR.
2. The system of alters that may be in back of the alter doing the work.
3. The whole system of alters as the therapist and the patient know them as well as.
4. The overall ego strength of the patient as a whole—this will hold true whatever BASK dimension the therapist chooses to engage.

- *Start with hypnosis.* If the disturbance is too high (SUD > 7) or uncontained, the affect or sensation bridges may occur among alters.

Say, *"You may remember that we have been speaking about your being ready to explore this traumatic event from your past _____* (specify the issue). *Even though you understand that this happened to you many years ago and it is a memory, it is currently still so overwhelming that you and I together have to make some decisions before we explore this with EMDR."*

Say, *"You report seeing a picture of yourself in your mind's eye and with that picture comes the K—Cognition _____* (state the relevant cognition such as 'I am a bad boy'). *You say _____* (state what is said such as 'It's too much')."*

Say, *"We may choose to deal with the thought of _____* (state the thought such as 'I am a bad boy') *or with the feeling _____* (state the feeling such as 'It is too much'), *which one is more important to you right now?"*

If yes, continue to read protocol for cognition.
If no, skip to protocol for affect.

Say, *"Since you have chosen to deal with the thought _____* (state the thought using) *we have several options using hypnosis. We may want to do one of the following:*

1. *Address this cognition from the perspective of a part of you that knows you feel that way, who can target that cognition but who does not feel the same intensity surrounding it by reconfiguring the personalities; ____* (he or she) *would be forward and you would be in back of _____* (him or her) *to do the EMDR.*
2. *Have this other personality step close to you when you target the cognition _____* (state the cognition), *___* (he or she) *can stand with you, in the*

same spot in your mind, and through passive influence help modulate the processing of that thought with you when we do the EMDR.

3. *A third alternative may be to project onto a screen in your mind the sentence _____ (state the cognition) and begin to change the font of the writing from large to small until it is sufficiently small that though readable it is less overwhelming and initiate EMDR from the K cognition as represented in small print.*

4. *A further alternative is to leave that sentence on the screen and to notice slowly that the screen that was initially large and broad recedes more and more in the distance until it is sufficiently far in the distance that its words seem less powerful. Initiate EMDR from there. These are only a few of the hypnotic interventions that we can use together to better contain and modulate powerful thoughts and have them safely accessible to you so that you can do the EMDR."*

- *Start with EMDR.* If the disturbance is low (SUD < 7) and affect can be contained consistently, say the following:

  Say, *"Focus on the thought that came to mind and that you brought to my attention. Let's use that as a target and see what we can learn and what your mind can teach us."*

Start with 10 to 15 sweeps if the patient is new to EMDR and get feedback early as a double check to the patient's resilience in the work.

Note: If we were starting from Affect or Sensation, the initial sweeps would be less than 10 to 15; this author prefers to use 5 to 8.

  Say, *"Let's do a few sweeps of EMDR and see what you can learn. You chose as a target the thought _____ (state the cognition). Notice what happens as we initiate the EMDR."*

_____

_____

The goal is for the patient and alter(s) or ego state(s) to have a successful experience when encountering a dimension of the traumatic event from his past. At this point, the EMDR may stay in the cognitive realm or may switch to affect or sensation and would be tracked according to the Standard EMDR Protocol.

What this author considers falling into the K or cognitive dimension of BASK are the following:

1. Formulated thoughts and sentences.
2. Banner statements "Let's do it!" "Faster is better," "Drop dead," and so forth.
3. Dream stories (broken down into dream segments).
4. Fantasies (segmented).
5. Fantasized role-plays, to name a few.

Sometimes it is hard for a patients with DID to focus in on a cognition as an initial target since their mind is blank, or there is too much reported noise in the head making it hard to focus, you have one of two choices:

1. You may have the patient or personality focus on "blank" and monitor what evolves. The patient may track either increased blankness (i.e., increased

dissociation as a resistance or as a measure of overwhelm) or may shift to another BASK dimension.

Say, "_____ (state name of patient or personality) *focus on that experience of _____* (blankness or whatever words the patient uses) *and just notice what happens.*"

_____

_____

Sometimes if patients speak of blankness, ask whether it has a shape, a form, a texture, a color, and so forth. Do not ask about smell unless you are prepared to continue fairly immediately to work with the S dimension of the BASK.

Say, "_____ (state the name of the patient or personality) *can you describe the shape of the blankness to me. Let's focus on that experience of _____* (whatever words the patient uses to describe the shape) *and just notice what happens.*"

_____

_____

Say, "_____ (state the name of the patient or personality) *can you describe the form* (i.e., angular, sharp) *of the _____* (blankness or whatever words the patient uses) *to me? Let's focus on that experience of _____* (whatever words the patient uses to describe the form) *and just notice what happens.*"

_____

_____

Use similar verbalizations for texture, color, movement, or stillness of the blankness. Sometimes to bring the blankness into better focus and better targeting, the therapist can accumulate all the descriptors the person or personality brings to the therapy moment to describe the totality of the blank (or whatever words the patient uses) experience.

Say, "_____ (state the name of the patient or personality) *can you describe the shape, form, color, texture of the _____* (blankness or whatever words the patient uses) *to me? Let's focus on that experience of _____* (state whatever words the patient uses to describe the complete ensemble of the blank description) *and just notice what happens.*"

_____

_____

Again be prepared that if the person or personality brings any affect or body sensation to the experience of blankness (or whatever words the patient has used) on a cognitive dimension of BASK, the Wreathing Protocol will be shifting to a separate BASK dimension fairly rapidly (if not immediately). In this case, attend to the following:

2. You may immediately guide the patient to another dimension of the BASK. It is also common for the DID patient to be so overtaken by an Affect or a Sensation that targeting a cognition or knowledge proves impossible.

Say, *"Clearly the fact that we started by directing our attention to _____ (blank or state the wording the patient used) and that very rapidly you noticed _____ (specify feeling, sensation, or pressure to behave or act in a particular way, or experienced by patient), tells us that we are on the right track. Let's focus on _____ (choose the most relevant BAS dimension for the patient)."*

_____

_____

For how to initiate EMDR from BAS dimensions, see below.

Targeting A (Affect) of BASK

Say, *"When you feel _____ (state the affect using the patient's own words) on a scale between 0 to 10, where 10 is the worst feeling like this you can have and 0 is feeling this feeling in a neutral manner, how disturbing does it feel to you right now?"*

0	1	2	3	4	5	6	7	8	9	10
(no disturbance)								(highest disturbance)		

Note: It is important for the therapist to *not* say, "Zero is not feeling this feeling." This is because the patient may interpret that the therapist is suggesting that not feeling the feeling is the goal.

Use the same script as for targeting S of BASK after asking for the SUD (see immediately below).

Targeting S (Sensation or Somatic Experience) of BASK

Say, *"When you experience _____ (state the experience in the patient's body in their own words, perhaps with more specificity about the exact location[s] through clarification with the patient for better targeting of the specific neural network/state the affect) on a scale between 0 and 10, where 10 is the worst sensation or somatic experience of this kind you have ever experienced and 0 represents noticing this sensation in a neutral manner, how disturbing is this sensation right now?"*

0	1	2	3	4	5	6	7	8	9	10
(neutral sensation)								(worst sensation)		

Again, when working with either the Affect or Sensation dimensions of BASK like when working the Knowledge dimension, the initial step is the decision of whether to start the abreactive work with EMDR directly or to insert hypnosis into the protocol to mediate the potentially overwhelming reaction to the EMDR. As the therapist makes this determination, take into account:

1. The alter who will primarily be engaged in the work for this set of EMDR.
2. The system of alters that may be in back of the alter doing the work.
3. The whole system of alters as the therapist and the patient know them as well as
4. The overall ego strength of the patient as a whole—this will hold true whatever BASK dimension the therapist chooses to engage.

- *Start with hypnosis.* If the disturbance is too high (SUD > 7) or uncontained, the affect or sensation bridges may occur among alters.

Say, *"You may remember that we have been speaking about your being ready to explore this traumatic event from your past _____ (specify the event). Even though you understand that this happened to you many years ago and it is a memory, it is currently still so overwhelming that you and I, together, have to make some decisions before we explore this memory with EMDR."*

_____

_____

Note: Emphasize that they now have choices. They were alone then and are no longer alone now to face the traumata.

When dealing with the Affective dimension:

Say, *"Let's choose a 'feeling target' together that captures a small aspect of the memory that you described."*

_____

_____

Say, *"We can do a small piece of work at a time making sure that we are working with an alter that is both available, ready, and appropriate to engage in the processing work."*

_____

_____

For example, say the following:

Say, *"You report seeing a picture of yourself in your mind's eye."*

_____

_____

This could be a cognitive dimension, but in this situation it is not; this is because the patient follows with "I can't keep the picture in focus." The patient reports that with this picture of her, there are no thoughts just feelings (or sensations).

Say, *"Is your experience too much for you right now."*

_____

_____

Say, *"We have a decision to make. Do we move forward with the _____ (specify affect or sensation) associated with this picture or do we modify it a bit so that you can process _____ (specify affect or sensation) with greater ease?"*

_____

_____

Say, *"How intensely do you feel* _____ (specify the affect or sensation)*?"*

_____

_____

Say, *"If your SUD level is less than 7, we will start the EMDR, if the SUD level is more than 7, we may want to consider some hypnosis to initially attenuate the intensity of the processing, until you have more affect* (or sensation) *tolerance for this picture* (event)*."*

_____

_____

Like working with cognition, the therapist wants to explore whether the appropriate ego state or personality is present to do the work. Make sure to get the name or descriptor of the part.

Say, *"Who will participate in this piece?"*

_____

_____

Have them specify groups or personalities.

Say, *"Who will not participate in this piece of work?"*

_____

_____

Say, *"Is* _____ (name or describe the part) *the one who needs to be forward now to work with* _____ (name the affect or the sensation)*?"*

_____

_____

If the answer is yes, proceed.
If the answer is no, do a reconfiguration of personalities.

Say, *"I understand from what* _____ (name the part) *just said that you may not be prepared right now to explore this* _____ (name feeling/sensation). *Is there anyone or part near you for whom this is relevant and who is ready to do the work?"*

_____

_____

If no, go back to square one. You have missed something or there is interference, resistance, or impediment by an obstructionist alter. If yes, say the following:

Say, *"Could* _____ (name Part 1) *kindly step back for right now as* _____ (name Part 2) *steps forward."*

_____

_____

Say, *"To make sure that we are all on the same page, let's revisit the SUD measures again with you _____ (name part 2) as we did with _____ (name part 1)."*

_____

_____

Say, *"When you experience _____ (state the experience in the patient's body in their own words or state the affect) on a scale between 0 and 10, where 10 is the worst sensation or somatic experience of this kind you have ever experienced and 0 represents noticing this sensation in a neutral manner, how disturbing is this sensation right now?"*

0   1   2   3   4   5   6   7   8   9   10
(neutral sensation)   (worst sensation)

Apply the same SUD considerations as previously discussed, never initiating EMDR until the SUDs level is below 7.

In some poly-fragmented DID patients, it may be necessary to negotiate technique dense hypnotic interventions prior to starting EMDR processing with each hypnotic intervention building on the other to distance the affect or the sensation sufficiently. If hypnosis is used, it will always be essential when the EMDR is finished to backtrack each hypnotic step. Sometimes the therapist will find that through the use of EMDR there have been some healthy integrations or blendings of personalities or alters during the course of the processing; at other times, each hypnotic step will remain present and intact with some metabolism of affect or sensation in the alters involved but many hypnotic steps having remained the same.

- *Start with EMDR.* If the disturbance is low (SUD < 7) and affect or sensation can be contained consistently.

Say, *"Focus on _____ (name affect or sensation) that came to mind and that you brought to my attention. Let's use that as a target and see what we can learn and what your mind can teach us."*

_____

_____

Start with 5 to 8 sweeps if the patient is new to EMDR. Get feedback early as a double check to the patient's resilience in the work.

Say, *"Let's do a few sweeps of EMDR and see what we can learn."*

_____

_____

Say, *"Tell me what you noticed."*

_____

_____

Say, *"You chose as a target the feeling or sensation _____ (name it). Notice what happens as we initiate the EMDR and do a few eye movements."*

_____

_____

Say, *"Tell me what you notice, now."*

_____

_____

The goal is for patients, alter(s), or ego state(s) to have a successful experience when encountering a dimension (here affect or sensation) of the traumatic event from their past. At this point, the EMDR may stay in the affect realm, may switch to sensation or may alternate between the two. The tracking can follow the Standard EMDR Protocol.

For both Sensation and Affect do not initiate a large number of sweeps, taps, or tones without having tested out a smaller number of them first.

Say, *"How many sweeps or taps would you like to start with to verify that all is stable that needs to be stable for our next processing of _____ (state affect or sensation in the patient's words)?"*

_____

_____

Make note of what they report on the lower end and start there. This author likes to test around 5 to 8 sweeps of eye movements before moving up to the 20 to 30 sweeps, which is the number of sweeps this author typically favors with DID patients.

Say, *"So, let's start with _____ (number of sweeps or taps) to verify that all is stable that needs to be stable for our next processing of _____ (state affect or sensation in the patient's words)."*

_____

_____

Say, *"Go with that for _____ (number of sweeps or taps)."*

_____

_____

Say, *"What did you notice?"*

_____

_____

If the patients want to just "Go for it," consider that they may be responding

1. To a personal sense of mastery.
2. To a wish.
3. To internal pressure from another (perhaps ill intended) personality.
4. To a desire to please, you, the therapist. Make note of their request and proceed slowly as planned.

If the initial sequence of sweeps does not go well and an affect or sensation bridge seems imminent or already in progress, say the following:

Say, *"We must temporarily stop the EMDR right now and see why you are getting so overwhelmed."*

_____

_____

At this point, the therapist and patient may need to verify the appropriateness of the configuration of alters, look for copresence phenomena, sabotaging alters who may have snuck into the mix of alters planning to participate in the EMDR, or any number of the usual conflagrations DID therapists would encounter in regular talk therapy for DID. (It may also be appropriate at this point to reconsider the use of hypnosis.) Noticing and reflecting back on the appropriateness of the EMDR target for each sequence of new sweeps and new targets is essential at the initial sequence of EMDR and all sequences thereafter.

If the initial sequence of sweeps seems to go well and no affect or sensation bridge seems imminent, the therapist may say the following:

Say, *"I am pleased to see that you are doing well with these initial few sweeps. Let's see whether little by little we can increase the number of sweeps in a helpful way for your learning."*

_____

_____

Say, *"Let's take our time and make sure that we start with fewer sweeps rather than a larger number of sweeps and check your responses out each time."*

_____

_____

At each increase in the number of sweeps (which is not based on a prescription in the therapist's mind but truly reflects the tolerance of the patient), include the patient in the self-observation. The therapist may say the following:

Say, *"You did well with* _____ (specify number of sweeps or taps), *can we add two more sweeps or should we repeat the EMDR with this past number* ____ (specify number of sweeps or taps) *or do we temporarily decrease the number of sweeps or taps for right now?"*

_____

_____

If the patient is ready to add more sweeps:

Say, *"Please target* _____ (specify affect or sensation) *again and let's start EMDR here* _____ (specify number of sweeps or taps plus 2 or 4 [whatever is agreed upon by treatment dyad]) *again."*

Say, *"What do you notice?"*

_____

_____

If the patient is satisfied with the processing at that number of sweeps or taps, the therapist resumes the EMDR at that level until further notice.

Ultimately, the therapist goes back again and again to the targeted affect or sensation increasing systematically the number of sweeps as the patient rapidly or slowly gains mastery over the affect or sensation that is being targeted. Once the DID patient is tolerating 20 or more sweeps, say the following:

> Say, *"You have truly made great strides in facing _____ (specify feeling or affect); it is an accomplishment and you are demonstrating increased mastery at every set of EMDR sweeps."*

_____

_____

> Say, *"When you are ready we can revisit this _____ (specify feeling or sensation) again and again until the 20 sweeps of EMDR no longer elicit much response from you; at this point we may decide to work in sets of 20 sweeps for that same _____ (specify the affect or sensation) to verify whether it is all detoxified or whether some _____ (affect or sensation) remains."*

_____

_____

The therapist repeats as anticipated one set of 20 sweeps and then begins by adding a few sweeps on the second set of EMDR for the specified affect or sensation and so on until two sets of sweeps is comfortable for the patient. The therapist will continue adding sets of sweeps surrounding a targeted affect or sensation until the SUDs value of the target is 0 or 1.

Targeting B (Behavioral Dimension) of BASK

Though not necessarily considered part of sensorimotor treatments, the Wreathing Protocol—which can target a Sensation (as addressed earlier)—can also be initiated by targeting a Behavior or a behavioral cluster; however, appropriate precautions must be in place.

- Starting EMDR from the B of the BASK is not recommended for DID patients prone to behavioral reenactment, fugues, and ongoing behavioral dyscontrol.
- EMDR starting from the B of the BASK is helpful for the DID patient who has no particular thoughts, feelings, sensations, or understanding of why they find their body positioned in a particular way again and again.
- EMDR starting from the B of BASK may be useful for the DID patient who avoids or is scared of the following:

  1. Experiencing certain body positions.
  2. Witnessing them in others.
  3. Concerned about "bumping into these (observed) behaviors" in a naturalistic setting or over the TV and is preemptively interested in finding out more about these situations.

> Say, *"Place your _____ (specify body part) in a way that you feel compelled to place it at this time or want to avoid placing it at this time. On a scale between 0 and 10, where 10 is the most compelling desire to engage in this behavior or the most compelling desire to avoid this behavior and 0 represents noticing this behavior in a*

neutral manner, how compelling is this behavior or avoidance of behavior right now?"

0	1	2	3	4	5	6	7	8	9	10
(neutral desire)								(highest desire)		

Say, *"Are you prepared to discover how this behavior is relevant to some current or past experience in your life?"*

_____

_____

Say, *"Can you now put your body in that* (behavioral) *position _____ (specify behavior)?"*

_____

_____

Note: If you have the patient "imagine putting their body in a certain position" rather than going into the actual behavioral position, use the Wreathing Protocol according to the directives for the K dimension of BASK as described above. Starting EMDR from imagining a behavior rather than participating in the behavior would be a cognitive rehearsal that would likely rapidly lead to the affect or sensation associated with the imagined behavior.

If the SUD level is above 7, a reconfiguration of personalities or some other hypnotic intervention may be necessary to decrease the likelihood of behavioral dyscontrol.

Say, *"You may remember that we have been speaking about your being ready to explore this behavior associated with _____ (specify the event) that seems more anchored in your body than in your thoughts or than in historical memory."*

_____

_____

Some patients just have the behavior with no specific associated conscious memory, then say the following:

Say, *"You may remember that we have been speaking about your being ready to explore _____ (specify behavior), which seems so unexplainable or curious to you."*

_____

_____

Then continue with the following:

Say, *"Even though you understand that this is not a behavior congruent with sitting in the office with me, it is currently overwhelming you sufficiently that you and I, together, have to make some decisions before we explore this memory with EMDR."*

_____

_____

Note: Emphasize that they now have choices. They no longer have to reenact the solitude and abandonment of the trauma situation.

Do not initiate EMDR from the Behavioral dimension with a SUD over 7. Therapists will in this case revisit their interventions in the same way and consider the same steps as when working with the Affective or Sensation dimensions of BASK when the SUD level was over 7.

Only initiate EMDR when the patient is displaying the targeted behavior and the SUD level is 7 or below.

Say, *"When you target _____ (specify the behavior that the patient is doing or enacting), tell me what you notice."*

_____

_____

Carry on with anticipated EMDR sweeps, taps, and tones as the DID patient begins to piecemeal an experience together. In parallel with working with the Sensation or Affect dimension of BASK using the Wreathing Protocol, you build up the number of sweeps and increase the number of sets of sweeps until the SUD value is 0 or 1, which would indicate that disconnected behavior segment is detoxified.

Therefore, any dimension of BASK, whether it be K, A, S, or B can serve as a target for initiating EMDR as described above. As in the Standard EMDR Protocol, the actual processing of the traumatic or overwhelming experience will shift from the initial dimension to eventually include all other BASK dimensions. What the Wreathing Protocol offers is a flow chart of imbricated and truncated EMDR experiences managed through hypnotic interventions. Both EMDR and hypnosis "slalom" through traumatic and nontraumatic experiences weaving together a clearer, more contained representation of the patient's life. The hypnotic interventions support the truncated EMDR processes, contain them until they are ready to be revisited again at a later point in time with EMDR. The EMDR, smoothly interwoven—wreathed—in this manner supports more complete metabolism of the experiential content because the Wreathing Protocol, thanks to its tailoring and precision, decreases the likelihood of redissociation. Therefore in using the Wreathing Protocol, a therapist would expect to alternately do hypnosis, followed by EMDR, and followed by hypnosis and then EMDR and so on, until the segment of planned work is done. Sometimes a complete traumatic experience can be processed in this manner, from start to finish, in one session; this is not normative. At the end of any Wreathing Protocol procedure—irrespective of the BASK dimension at which the hypnosis or the EMDR was started—it is not only essential but more so *imperative* that a hypnotic shutdown be inserted to protect patients by reorienting them to current day reality as they will often lapse into various degrees of trance as they discuss and process their memories. This is in line with Kluft's (2006) strong recommendation about the importance of dehypnosis with all patients.

Say, *"As all parts of the mind listen in, I would like to thank all of the parts who participated in the work today as well as those who observed from a distance. I would like to make sure that the part who came into the session, _____ (specify name, identifier, or Part A) is also the one who leaves, therefore as I count back from 1 to 10, I would like _____ (specify name, identifier, or Part B) to step away from the sound of my voice making room as I count _____ (Part A) forward from 10 to 1."*

_____

_____

Hypnotic shut downs are important in the field of hypnosis and even more critical when using EMDR under any form.

Though very tempting, describing the exact hypnotic interventions to use in the Wreathing Protocol defies its purpose as a "one size fits all" hypnotic intervention package that would accommodate both the patient's personal and identifiable characteristics and their specific traumas. The art of hypnosis is the tailoring of the intervention to the need of the patient in that moment. Additionally, describing detailed hypnotic interventions in a nonhypnosis book violates American Society of Clinical Hypnosis (ASCH) code of ethics.

The Wreathing Protocol in some ways is no different than the early protocols (Shapiro, 1995) for the use of EMDR in the treatment of PTSD in that it promotes the activation of the neural network for an experience and allows for the inclusion of complex dimensions of that experience to be awakened and metabolized. In other ways, the Wreathing Protocol is quite different in that it addresses the far more overwhelming nature of the experiences of patients diagnosed with dissociative disorders and furthers not only a sense of mastery in the processing of the traumatic material but also mastery in a contained approach to the traumata addressed in smaller bytes and more manageable pieces. The Wreathing Protocol not only weaves traumatic experiences together as one dimension after another of memory folds in, the Wreathing Protocol promotes more control, more modulation, and the ability for the therapeutic dyad to better fractionate the work. The Wreathing Protocol furthers the safe, planful, and timely processing of material based on therapeutic readiness rather than on the potential "Nantucket Sleigh ride" of the standard methodology with this highly traumatized population.

The Bottom-Up
Processing Protocol

Ulrich Lanius

Different experiential, psychophysiological, and neurobiological responses to traumatic symptom provocation in post-traumatic stress disorder (PTSD) have been reported in the literature. Two subtypes of trauma response have been hypothesized, one characterized predominantly by hyperarousal and the other primarily dissociative, each one representing unique pathways to chronic stress-related psychopathology (Lanius, Bluhm, Lanius, & Pain, 2006; Lanius, Bluhm, & Lanius, 2007). Dissociative responses to trauma, particularly depersonalization and out-of-body experiences, often pose a significant treatment challenge. While the Standard EMDR Protocol includes a significant focus on the body, this can sometimes be insufficient for clients to continue effective processing in cases of significant depersonalization (Lanius, 2000).

The term bottom-up processing is used in sensorimotor psychotherapy, a somatic (body) approach to facilitate processing of unassimilated sensorimotor reactions to trauma (Ogden & Minton, 2000). Lanius (2000) found this approach useful in dealing with dissociative symptoms and adapted it to be used in conjunction with bilateral stimulation (BLS), as part of a comprehensive treatment approach for individuals with complex PTSD and dissociative symptoms. When we use the Standard EMDR Protocol, we work with sensorimotor, emotional, and cognitive aspects of information. These correlate with the three levels of brain architecture described by MacLean (1990):

- Sensorimotor level of information processing (including sensation and programmed movement impulses) is initiated primarily by lower rear portions of the brain.
- Emotional processing by more intermediate limbic parts of the brain.
- Cognitive processing by the frontal cortical upper parts of the brain.

These three levels interact and affect each other simultaneously, functioning as a cohesive whole with the degree of integration of each level of processing affecting the efficacy of other levels (e.g., Damasio, 1999; Schore, 1994).

The Bottom-Up Protocol differs from the Standard EMDR Protocol in the following ways:

- *Integrated versus sensory.* Whereas the Standard EMDR Protocol integrates cognitive, emotional, and sensory information, bottom-up processing initially focuses on sensory and sensorimotor processing only and then turns to sequentially processing emotional and cognitive elements of traumatic experience. Bottom-up processing is a way to work with issues of dissociation.

- *Simultaneous versus fractionated.* Whereas the Standard EMDR Protocol integrates all levels of processing simultaneously, bottom-up processing fractionates sensorimotor from emotional and cognitive processing by moving through these aspects of experience sequentially.
- *Rapid versus slow.* As this process necessarily occurs slowly, bottom-up processing may avoid excessive emotional arousal or hyperarousal that interferes with the integration of information.
- *Facilitates emotions.* With a pronounced focus on the body, it likely facilitates the experience of emotion—that is without a sense of the body and sensory perceptions it will be difficult to experience feelings.
- *Reduces dissociative responses.* It further reduces the likelihood of dissociative responses through the pervasive focus on the body: the client is encouraged to track even minimal physiological sensations in their body and therefore continues to be mindful of the present. Thus the idea is to target physical sensations, as is frequently done in body therapies. Further, focusing the Standard EMDR Protocol on physical sensations alone, or alternatively, modifying the Standard EMDR Protocol so that neither traumatic events, associated cognitions, or emotions are targeted initially, is based on the notion that all unprocessed traumatic experience is to some extent sensory and experienced somatically, as well as frequently lacking a narrative (e.g., speechless terror).
- *Integrates fixed action patterns.* Overall, bottom-up processing is considered foundational to emotional and cognitive processing. It includes not only overall body processing, but also allows the client to integrate fixed action patterns seen in active defenses (e.g., the startle reflex and the fight, flight, or freeze response), changes in breathing and muscular tonicity, as well as autonomic nervous system activation.

Affect and the Body: The Importance of Subcortical Processes

While the experience of day-to-day, nontraumatic events are commonly integrated into consciousness without the sensory aspects of the event being registered separately (van der Kolk, 1996), traumatic memories seem to be different in nature, for example, flashbacks lack such integration of experience. Traumatic memories appear to be timeless, predominantly nonverbal, and imagery-based (van der Kolk & Fisler, 1995). Somatic memory is an essential element of traumatic memory; trauma memories, at least in part, are encoded at an implicit level (Brewin, Dalgleish, & Joseph, 1996).

Dissociation in particular, results in an alteration in consciousness that disrupts the integration of information, resulting in an inability to integrate memories into the present context, as well as an inability to integrate the totality of what is happening into personal memory and identity. Thus these memories remain isolated from ordinary consciousness (e.g., van der Hart, van der Kolk, & Boon, 1998). Under increased levels of stress, brain areas involved in higher levels of information processing, for example, cognitive and emotional processing, become increasingly less active, thus resulting in diminished information processing. Moreover, as emotional numbing and affect intolerance is an integral part of traumatic stress symptoms and one of the hallmarks of dissociation, this seems to be, at least in part, attributable to a disconnection from the body, for example, depersonalization. By focusing on somatic tolerance prior to accessing emotion, we indeed help our clients increase affect tolerance. Panksepp (2001) has cogently argued that affect is largely a subcortical process, a notion that is supported in a neuroimaging study by

Damasio et al. (2000), as well as by animal research. Whereas healthy adults are usually able to control their emotional drives through cognitive processes, they deprive themselves, sometimes, of their emotional needs in the process. Commonly, higher levels of processing can often influence and direct lower levels.

Sensory Fragments and the Subcortical Bridge

In PTSD, the opposite is commonly the case: sensory fragments have usually taken on a life of their own and intrude at any given moment, beyond cognitive control. In this case, lower levels of processing may also influence and direct higher levels. Our understanding of these processes can be informed by research with split-brain patients, who outside the laboratory context still behave in a unified manner during everyday activities, despite the fact that the main transcortical bridge or corpus callosum, for example, the fibers that connect the two halves of the brain has been bisected. In this case, information is conveyed through lower subcortical structures or what has been referred as the subcortical bridge (Austin, 1998, p. 361). Austin (1998, p. 362) suggests that the sorts of messages transferred across the subcortical bridge for the most part are "unconscious or preconscious codes, nuances we can never attach a name to." Similarly, Gazzaninga, Holtzman and Smylie (1987) have suggested that information relayed from right to left hemisphere in this way tends to be noncognitive in nature. Further, when these messages cross over from the left side to the right, they may engage a kind of response readiness. Furthermore, in the left hemisphere this information may facilitate potential speech responses that are already well rehearsed and ready to be uttered. Thus, bottom-up processing may facilitate the integration of traumatic material through the subcortical bridge. This is one possible mechanism by which psychomotor psychotherapy may transform traumatic memories that are experienced as sensory fragments into a coherent narrative.

The Bottom-Up Processing Protocol Script Notes

For bottom-up processing, the Standard EMDR Protocol is adapted to aid clients to stay in touch with their bodies and develop mindfulness re: body. Important elements of the Bottom-Up Processing Protocol are the following:

- *Inverted Standard EMDR Protocol.* Sensory, emotional, and cognitive aspects of traumatic experience are processed consecutively rather than together. A decision to utilize the Bottom-Up Processing Protocol can be either made a priori in conjunction with the client. Alternatively, the therapist may want to switch to somatic processing when a client is abreacting to a point where she is at risk of losing mindfulness and a sense of her body.
- *Slow the process.* The idea is to slow down the material by staying at the sensory level. In this way, the information coming in is titrated and intense abreactions decreased by slowing down the spontaneous integration of affect, cognition, and sensory experience that usually occurs in EMDR.
- *Active Stance of therapist.* The voice of the therapist is used in an active manner (Active Stance) to engage the client during the processing to keep them grounded.
- *Somatic memories.* The Bottom-Up Processing Protocol also lends itself to targeting the relationships with primary attachment figures, and processing the client's somatic response even in the absence of specific images or verbal memories.
- *Sensation focused.* Prior to the client processing material, the therapist actively encourages the client to only focus on body sensations, but not on

emotions, thought, or cognitions. The client is further instructed to blank out any material other than sensory material when it comes up. If such material comes up during processing, the therapist actively encourages the client to drop the content and return to focus on sensory experience alone. This type of processing helps fractionate the traumatic material by separating somatosensory from cognitive and affective processing. This type of processing may be insufficient for the complete resolution of the trauma, but it develops the necessary body mindfulness that is essential for affective and cognitive processing. Consequently, it is suggested that eventually, when the client is able to access the traumatic experience in its entirety, the Standard EMDR Protocol is used to complete processing, though in many cases this may not be necessary.

The Bottom-Up Protocol Script

Identify Presenting Issue, Memory, or Physical Sensation

Say, *"Identify the presenting issue, memory, or physical sensation that you would like to work on today. It can be a picture of _____ (state attachment figure) or any negative belief or issue that is relevant to the issue you came in to work on."*

_____

_____

Then say, *"For now, during this process I would like you to focus on physical sensations alone. So for now, whenever any feelings or thoughts come up, I would like you to go back to the physical sensations in your body. Just stay with the physical sensations in your body only. I will check with you often about what you are experiencing in your body. Remember, if for any reason you need to stop, just hold your hand up like this* (raise hand to demonstrate stop signal).*"*

_____

_____

Do BLS.

Say, *"What do you notice?"*

_____

_____

Location of Body Sensation

Say, *"When you focus on that, what do you get in your body? Where do you feel the sensation or disturbance in your body."*

_____

_____

If the client has difficulty locating the body sensation or is experiencing multiple body sensations, ask the client to put their hand where they are experiencing the most intense physical sensation.

Say, *"Since you are experiencing many body sensations, please place your hand where you are experiencing the most intense physical sensation."*

_____

_____

Do BLS.

Say, *"Go with that."*

_____

_____

Then say, *"What do you get now?"*

_____

_____

While administering bilateral stimulation, the therapist uses Active Stance and keeps talking to the client while administering BLS with phrases such as the following:

Say, *"Focus on your body."*

_____

_____

Say, *"Where in your body do you notice that?"*

_____

_____

Say, *"Stay with your body."*

_____

_____

Say, *"Just follow the physical sensations in your body."*

_____

_____

Say, *"Notice whether it* (the body sensation) *increases, decreases, or stays the same."*

_____

_____

Say, *"Regardless of where the sensation goes, just keep tracking those physical sensations throughout your body."*

_____

_____

Say, *"Just notice the physical sensations in your body."*

_____

_____

Say, *"Just focus on the physical sensations alone."*

_____

_____

If at all in doubt, the therapist checks with the client at regular intervals:

Say, *"Is it okay to continue?"*

_____

_____

Continue processing until disturbance has significantly decreased (sometimes several sessions are necessary) to a subjective units of disturbance (SUD) of 5 or below. Then go to the next part of the protocol following the idea of bottom-up processing.

Emotions or Feelings

Say, *"When you bring up that physical sensation now and those words what emotions do you feel?"*

_____

_____

Say, *"Now, just focus on the physical sensations and the feeling."*

_____

_____

Do BLS.

Say, *"Go with that."*

_____

_____

Say, *"What did you get?"*

_____

_____

Process this until disturbance has significantly decreased. If necessary return to focusing on the body only. Then go on to the next part of the protocol following the idea of bottom-up processing.

Negative Cognition (NC)

Say, *"What negative words or thoughts about yourself go with those physical sensations and those feelings?"*

_____

_____

Say, *"Now, just focus on the physical sensations and the negative words/ thoughts."*

_____

_____

Do BLS.

Say, *"Go with that."*

_____

_____

Say, *"What do you notice?"*

_____

_____

Process this until disturbance has significantly decreased. If necessary return to focusing on the body only. Then go on to the next part of the protocol following the idea of bottom-up processing.

Image or Picture

If no picture has been identified at the beginning of processing, say the following:

Say, *"When you focus on the physical sensation, the feeling _____ (repeat verbatim) and the negative thought _____ (repeat verbatim), what picture or image comes up?"*

_____

_____

Before further processing or desensitization takes place, and in order to aid the client in integrating material, it is sometimes helpful for the therapist to ask the following question:

Say, *"What do you make out of that?"*

_____

_____

Subjective Units of Disturbance (SUD)

Say, *"On a scale of 0 to 10, where 0 is no disturbance whatsoever and 10 is the highest disturbance you can imagine, how disturbing does the original issue feel to you now?"*

0	1	2	3	4	5	6	7	8	9	10
(no disturbance)								(highest disturbance)		

Again process until the SUDs has gone down to 0 or 1, then move to the Standard EMDR Protocol including installation of the positive cognition with a clear Body Scan to complete any additional processing that may be necessary.

Partial Installation

Partial installation can be used in cases of incomplete processing at any time to terminate the session as long as the client is capable of identifying positive cognitions.
Without taking a SUDs prior to end of session, ask the following:

Say, *"Given the work you have done today, what is the most positive statement you can make about yourself now?"*

Eliminate the Body Scan and debrief. The reason to eliminate the Body Scan and SUDs in cases of incomplete processing is to avoid accessing additional traumatic material. Alternatives to this strategy are the use of the Lightstream Technique (Shapiro, 1995), or asking the client to put residual distressing physical sensations, emotions, or negative beliefs in a container for the time being until the next session.

30

ACT-AS-IF and ARCHITECTS Approaches to EMDR Treatment of Dissociative Identity Disorder (DID)

Sandra Paulsen

ACT-AS-IF and ARCHITECTS Approaches to EMDR Treatment of DID Script Notes

This chapter describes key steps, with scripts, for the phases of therapy with a DID client, and for an EMDR session with a DID client. In brief, the method employs the artful use of EMDR and ego state therapy for association and acceleration, and of hypnosis, imagery, and ego state therapy for distancing and deceleration within the context of a trusting therapeutic relationship. It is based upon the Standard EMDR Protocol as much as possible, while taking into account the complexity of the client's self-system and trauma history and the need to ensure client stability. It is also endeavoring to stay close to the treatment guidelines as promulgated by the International Society for the Study of Trauma and Dissociation (2005).

The acronym ACT-AS-IF describes the phases of therapy; the acronym ARCHITECTS describes the steps in an EMDR intervention. Those two acronyms organize the chapter, as well as the approach to treatment at the birds-eye view and the EMDR session viewpoint. Naturally, the ACT-AS-IF phases of treatment cannot include all of the language for a process that takes years, so only a few sample scripts are included for each phase. These acronyms and their processes are discussed in Paulsen (2008a) and Paulsen (2009). The two processes covered by the acronyms ACT-AS-IF and ARCHITECTS, taken together, correspond approximately to the Shapiro eight phases of EMDR, however, extended over years of treatment for highly complex trauma histories.

When working with DID patients, it is crucial that the therapist is knowledgeable in working with alters or ego states. An alter may represent one or more trauma-related neural networks, within the client's polyvagal nervous system

357

(Porges, 1995). The therapist endeavors to keep the client in the optimal arousal range (Ogden & Minton, 2000); that is neither overaroused (flooded and in sympathetic arousal) nor underaroused (numbed and in dorsal vagal shutdown). The therapeutic relationship and the relationship between helpful alters will strengthen and enable the client to stay in the optimal connected and engaged (ventral vagal) state. Dual attention awareness then is key in part because it keeps the ventral vagal nervous system engaged sufficiently to empower the client to sustain the painful processing of dorsal vagal states and sympathetic arousal states.

ACT-AS-IF Phases of Treatment of DID

Trauma work cannot begin for DID clients until preparatory work is well in place. That work may take months or years. Pacing is key to successful treatment outcome, as expressed in Kluft's well-known adage, "the slower you go, the faster you get there" (1993a). The ACT-AS-IF acronym provides an organized, paced, and deliberate approach to that preparation. The phases of ACT-AS-IF therapy are listed below, beside their correlate in the Shapiro eight-phase model of EMDR (1995, 2001):

- Assessment (corresponds to Shapiro's Phase 1—Client History)
- Containment and Stabilization (corresponds to Shapiro's Phase 2— Preparation)
- Trauma Accessing (corresponds to Shapiro's Phase 1—History and Phase 2— Preparation)
- Abreactive Association (corresponds to Shapiro's Phases 3 through 7)
- Skills Building (corresponds in part to Future Template)
- Integration (corresponds in part to Future Template)
- Future Template and Follow-Up (corresponds to Reevaluation and Future Template)

It will be necessary to stop the EMDR processing within session time limits, no matter how far processing has gone. This involves what the author refers to as "quitting while we are behind," whether we get to a resolution or not with enough time to close. The therapist should not expect that a DID client will process a trauma to an adaptive resolution in a single session. The therapist will close down the process by using well-rehearsed language or imagery. The two-step process conditioned in the containment stage is recommended.

ACT-AS-IF Phases of Treatment of DID Script

Assessment (Phase 1—Client History)

Assessment of each client begins from the moment they cross the threshold. In the initial interview, in addition to establishing rapport, getting client history, and clarifying treatment goals, the therapist will be wondering, "How is this self-system structured?" If not highly dissociative, the Standard EMDR Protocol can be used. If there is an index of suspicion in the initial interview for a dissociative disorder, the ACT-AS-IF phases should be used. Key questions will look for degree of dissociation as well as information about affect dysregulation, coping skills, and red flags contraindicating using EMDR in the short term. Some information is not easy to script, including clinician assessment of the client's level of trust and rapport over time. Questions can be imbedded in the initial interview, as follows:

For dissociation, say the following:

Say, *"Do you ever seem to have time missing?"*

_____

_____

Say, *"Do people tell you that you have done things that you don't re-member doing?"*

_____

_____

Say, *"Do you have headaches?"*

_____

_____

Say, *"Do you have nightmares or flashbacks?"*

_____

_____

Other questions may be found in Loewenstein (1991).
For affect dysregulation and coping skills say the following:

Say, *"When things get tough, how do you cope?"*

_____

_____

Say, *"In your life, have you had a lot of emotional pain?"*

_____

_____

Say, *"On a scale of 0 to 10, where 0 is no emotional pain or neutral and 10 is the highest emotional pain you can imagine, how disturbing does it feel now?"*

0	1	2	3	4	5	6	7	8	9	10
(no emotional pain)								(most emotional pain)		

Say, *"Does it vary a lot?"*

_____

_____

Say, *"If you have tried to work on traumatic memories in the past, were you able to cope?"*

_____

_____

Say, *"Do you feel that you have a lot of internal resources and strength or not enough?"*

_____

_____

Red Flags

Both editions of Francine Shapiro's seminal book on EMDR (1995, 2001) have included discussion of red flags and an appendix from the Task Force on Dissociation (Fine et al., 1995, 2001) reviewing indicators of nonreadiness to do EMDR.

Say, *"Have you attempted suicide?"*

_____

_____

Say, *"How recently?"*

_____

_____

Say, *"Do you cut or hurt yourself when you are really hurting?"*

_____

_____

Say, *"Are you living in a safe environment?"*

_____

_____

Containment and Stabilization (Phases 1 and 2—History Taking and Preparation)

This phase may take from months to years for a highly dissociative client. Other chapters in this book refer to important steps including Beere on modified resource development procedures (chapter 24); Forgash on accessing ego states (chapter 13), the use of a conference room (chapter 15), and orienting ego states to present reality (chapter 16); Twombly on safe space imagery (chapter 21), maintaining duality (chapter 22), and orientation to height (chapter 20). For more on ego strengthening and resourcing consult the following resources: Fine and Berkowitz, 2001; Korn and Leeds, 2002; Loewenstein, 2006; Paulsen, 2008a, 2009; Paulsen and Golston, 2005; Phillips and Frederick, 1995; Shapiro, 1995, 2001.

An important step in this phase is to establish a conditioned response or habit of containment at the end of each session in which deep or ego state work is conducted. The method described below has been called the Paulsen Two-Step for ego state containment (Paulsen & Golston, 2005), which employs both containing memories and tucking in ego states.

Step 1: Containing the Memories

Say, *"As we begin to prepare for the end of the session, please glance around the conference room in the mind's eye, and begin gathering up any fragments of memories that have been tugged out by our work today. Parts working together as a team, I'll help as you put them in a container of your choice, putting them in a container. . . . is that happening? . . . . good . . . . and putting the lid on the container, putting the container in a vault, not forever, just until the time is right, closing the door on the vault, sending the vault down an elevator, down, down deeper still, and pulling a heavy velvet curtain in front of the elevator. And what's the conference room like now?"*

_____

_____

Say, *"Good!"*

_____

_____

Once it is established that the conference room has been tidied up, proceed to Step 2.

Step 2: Tucking in the Ego States

Say, *"Now, is there anything that simply must be said before we tuck you in?"*

_____

_____

Provide answers or reassurances to anything an ego state says.
The first time say the following:

Say, *"And what kind of transportation would you like to leave on, fluffy white clouds or something else?"*

_____

_____

Once the method of conveyance has been established:

Say, *"And with great appreciation for all the parts of the self that helped today by talking, listening, supporting, or allowing the work, I'll say goodbye as they climb on board their _____ (state the conveyance) and some may want to go together and some may want to go separately and that's fine."*

If a child part has done particularly difficult work:

Say, *"Is there anything you need _____ (say child part's name) to feel okay?"*

_____

_____

As needed, provide other older parts to go with, to comfort, to protect, or provide another resource, for example, applesauce for a hungry child, a clean warm blanket for a cold child, and so forth.

Say, *"_____ (the name of the metaphor for transportation) takes you deep inside for a deep healing sleep, deeper and deeper still. And _____ (say the front part's name) coming back, coming all the way back. Is that you? Could you take a glance in the conference room and tell me what you see?"*

_____

_____

If a part or parts remain(s), say the following:

Say, *"Hi, is there something you need to say before you go?"*

_____

_____

If protective parts are disinclined to tuck in:

Say, *"Hi, _____ (say protective part's name), I guess you feel you need to stay forward. I know better than to struggle with you, because I know who would win that struggle! Okay, and by the way, on the horizon there is a watch tower, like a ranger station, and if you get tired you can go there, because there is a nice hammock there and binoculars, so you can keep an eye on things and get a nice sleep _____ (say front part's name). Are you fully here? How about pressing your heels into the floor. Are you back? Are you good to go and road worthy?"*

_____

_____

In the first weeks of repetition, telephone contact may be needed to explain again the importance of parts tucking in. Whether on the phone or in the session, if there is continued emotional dysregulation between sessions:

Say, *"Could you glance in the conference room and tell me what you see?"*

_____

_____

If a part is there in distress, inquire about the reason, provide orientation, reassurance, problem solving, and explain the rationale for why it is in this part's interest to tuck in until the next session or when the time is right:

Say, *"Here's the thing, part, if you stay forward and ____ (he or she) feels your pain, I'm afraid ____ (he or she) won't want to come back.*

And if ___ *(he or she)* doesn't bring the body back, since you are in the same body, how can I hear your story? And I do want to hear your story."

_____

_____

With several weeks of repetition, the client will establish a conditioned response that will help with affect regulation, and contribute to containment and stabilization over a number of months or years. Before trauma work per se can begin, however, the trauma must be accessed at a high level, to untangle conflictual dynamics that would stymie trauma processing. High level means not the detailed information channels that will emerge in trauma processing, but rather a "30,000 foot view" of the traumatic experience maintaining distance. This is equivalent to reading the title of a book or the table of contents without reading the chapters.

Trauma Accessing (Phases 1 and 2—History Taking and Preparation)

During prior work, the clinician has learned parts of the system and their functions. In this phase, the understanding of the system, the functions of the parts, and their history deepens. The clinician gets the lay of the land before initiating EMDR. Internal conflicts and double binds will have been revealed and some detangled with orientation and other containment steps. There is no need to get full details of trauma at this time. Rather, one can use a metaphor that keeps the information at a high level to avoid reexperiencing the trauma prematurely.

Say, *"There is a door off the conference room that leads to a library. You don't need to open the door, but simply look through the door's window and glance at the books on the shelves. Without opening the books, you can glance at the titles. The library may be able to tell us if there are many shelves, or many books, and what some of the titles of the books on the shelves may be."*

_____

_____

After information is accessed, say the following:

Say, *"And with appreciation to the library, let's turn out the library lights and pull down the window shade, knowing we'll come back to the library when the time is right."*

One of the most critical steps in trauma accessing is to address perpetrator introjects so that they will be on board before actually initiating EMDR, to the degree possible. When the clinician hears evidence that the client is conflicted about something that reflects a perpetrator's point of view:

Say, *"I'd like to speak directly to the part of the self that has something to say about the* _____ *(name the double bind or conflict). Hi, whoever is there, can you come into the conference room at this time? I'd like to know your concern. And* _____ *(say helper part's name), who do you see?"*

_____

_____

Or if a switch has apparently occurred while discussing a perpetrator, the introject is likely present but won't volunteer unless the part is spoken to directly. Always refer to the introject by appending "part of the self" to the name, to continuously clarify that this is an internal part, not the external perpetrator. For instance, say "Father part of the self," not "Father."

Say, *"Hi!* _____ (state name of perpetrator) *part of the self, is that you? You seem bothered. What's going on? I'd like to understand."*

_____

_____

If the part is hostile, unwilling to talk or otherwise loyal to the perpetrator's point of view:

Say, *"Are you remembering that you are not the external* _____ (perpetrator's name) *but rather an internal likeness of* _____ (him or her)*?"*

_____

_____

See Forgash (chapter 16) and Knipe (chapter 18) in this volume for scripts for orienting ego states to present reality and Twombly (chapter 20) for orienting to present height of the body.

Say, *"Thank you for holding the* _____ (say external perpetrator's name's) *energy all these years. Somebody had to do it. It was completely necessary to keep* ____ (him or her, referring to the client as a whole) *safe. I know the others may not appreciate it, but I'll help them to understand. How old was* _____ (he or she, referring to the client) *when you started holding* _____ (say perpetrator's name) *energy?"*

_____

_____

Whatever age the client provides, say the following:

Say, *"Oh, what a very hard job for such a little* _____ (boy or girl). *You know what that means? Beneath that* _____ (say perpetrator's name) *costume you are wearing, you're a* _____ (little girl or little boy) *too. Would you like help with your burden? I'd like to help you too. What concerns and needs do you have?"*

_____

_____

Provide reassurance and help with solutions. During the course of this conversation, the clinician should watch for subtle signs of an emotional shift from defensiveness or anger to vulnerability and pain. At such a moment of subtle shift, say the following:

Say, *"Only you can decide* _____(say perpetrator part of the self's name), *whether to stay loyal to* _____ (say perpetrator part of the self's name) *or to shift loyalty to the life you are living and the body you live in. If*

you want to feel better, and will allow me to help the others who are
suffering, at any time, whether today or another day, you can take off
that perpetrator costume and hang it on that hook over there in the
conference room. You can always put it back on if you need to."

_____

_____

Once all perpetrator introjects are on board with treatment and sufficient stabilization is present, trauma work per se can begin in earnest with EMDR.

Abreactive Association (Phases 3 Through 7)

This is the phase where EMDR is actually conducted as a modification of the Standard EMDR Protocol. In the Standard EMDR Protocol all information channels are activated to "light up the net" or neural network. This can be understood as an accelerative process. For DID clients, deceleration is needed more than is acceleration usually. For that reason, a fractionated approach is described below in the acronym ARCHITECTS. Those steps are:

- Access (corresponds to Shapiro Phases 2 & 3—Preparation & Assessment)
- Refine the Target (corresponds to Shapiro Phases 2 & 3—Preparation & Assessment)
- Consent (corresponds to Shapiro Phases 2 & 3—Preparation & Assessment)
- Hypnosis/Imagery (corresponds to Shapiro Phases 2 & 3—Preparation & Assessment)
- Titrate (corresponds to Shapiro Phases 2 & 3—Preparation & Assessment)
- EMDR/BLS (corresponds to Shapiro Phase 4—Desensitization)
- Closure (corresponds to Shapiro Phase 5 to 7—Installation, Body Scan omitted, Closure)
- Technology Tranquility (corresponds to Shapiro Phase 7—Closure)
- Stabilize, Synthesize, Soothe (corresponds to Shapiro Phase 8)

ARCHITECTS—The Steps in an EMDR Session for DID Clients

The trauma-processing phase of therapy has been described elsewhere (e.g., Fine, 1993a; Kluft, 1993a; Phillips & Frederick, 1995; Paulsen, 2007, 2009). This discussion describes a session that follows the ARCHITECTS model (Paulsen, 2007, 2009). The ARCHITECTS acronym provides a step-wise approach to conducting an EMDR session once assessment, containment, and stabilization are well established (Paulsen, 2007). Although many metaphors and suggestions are possible (see Hammond, 1990), the following offer a few that often work well. The methods employed are those of ego state therapy (Paulsen & Watkins, 2003a, 2003b, 2003c, 2005; Watkins & Paulsen, 2003; Watkins & Watkins, 1997). The script below includes some of the most likely decision points in the process but by no means all of them.

In the many sessions prior to this first EMDR session, preparation would have included containment and stabilization through resource development and other means, the use of ego state maneuvers including the dissociative table technique, extensive communications with and between parts of the self system, getting perpetrator introjects on board with the treatment, and an explanation of EMDR and how to fractionate it. For a more in-depth look at this material, see Paulsen (2008, 2009).

Note: It is essential that practitioners be trained in the complexities of working with patients with DID or C-PTSD and in hypnosis for psychotherapy before using the following hypnotic material.

A—Access the Client's Self-System

To the part of self who is presenting in the session, say the following:

Say, *"Would you glance into the conference room?"*

_____

_____

Say, *"Hi everyone."*

To the front part that you are speaking through, say the following:

Say, *"Who is there as we begin?"*

_____

_____

Once you are aware of what parts are in conscious mind (that is, in the conference room), say the following:

Say, *"Okay, everyone, first let's tuck ____ (her or him) in so ____ (he or she) can be free to continue to not know and be free to function well and 'do life,' while some of us do the necessary trauma work. _____ (state the name of the front part), are you willing to go off in the mind's eye so we can do some EMDR?"*

_____

_____

Once the part has agreed, say the following:

Say, *"So I'm going to invite _____ (name of front part) to float off on a canoe trip (or say another appropriate metaphor, such as on fluffy white clouds, or the back of a buffalo, or on a bike trip, according to client preferences), hearing the soft sound of the oars in the water as you glide through the reeds to open water in the lake (or whatever metaphor you chose). See you later. That's it and there _____ (he or she) goes . . . and as we watch ____ (him or her) leave on (his or her) journey, I'm going to invite _____ (state the name of a helper part) to step forward to assist. Hi _____ (state helper part's name) is that you?"*

_____

_____

Once confirmed, say the following:

Say, *"_____ (state name of helper part) could you check in the conference room and tell me what you see?"*

_____

_____

Say, *"Thanks _____ (say name of helper part) and thanks everyone for your readiness. Is there any concern that we need to deal with related to how the week went?"*

_____

_____

R—Refine the Preselected Target

Say, *"_____ (state name of helper part) could you check inside and see what memory you can agree to target first? Let's pick one of the smaller ones as a starter. Let me know if you want suggestions."*

_____

_____

The "Star" is a role, not a name. It is the part of the self-executive, or, "looking through the eyes" during EMDR processing. Looking through the eyes, means that a part is fully forward, present in the chair in the office, and executive or in control of the body (to a large extent), this is also the definition of ego cathexis. A part that is looking through the eyes uses "I" to refer to itself, and "he, she, it, or they" to refer to other parts of self that are in objective cathexis or "over there." These little parts are so impoverished of attention that they like being the star usually. After the helper part reports back what memory to target, say the following:

Say, *"Okay, and who will be the star of the EMDR. Who is suffering the most?"*

_____

_____

If the term star is not suitable to this client, find another word. When the helper part identifies the part most needing relief, first in the sequence, or just willing to go first:

Say, *"____ (say selected part's name), is that okay with you, are you willing?"*

_____

_____

The therapist can expect the system to assert changes of plan as internal dynamics dictate.

C—Consent Refreshed

Although it is sometimes enough to just go with consent of the parts in the conference room, in some cases the following more comprehensive consent is better.

Say, *"So, everyone who can hear my voice, whether they are inside the conference room or outside, inside or outside the body, asleep or awake, alive or dead. If anyone hasn't previously heard the explanation of EMDR or voted on whether it's okay to proceed, please let us know with a show of hands in the conference room or showing a red light on the control panel by the door in the conference room. There is a red light and a green light for each one not in the conference room. Red lights mean no, don't proceed, and green lights mean proceed."*

_____

_____

Troubleshoot any red lights or concerns; do not proceed with EMDR without consent from the preponderance of the key alters.

Say, *"Any questions or concerns before we start doing EMDR today?"*

_____

_____

If there are concerns, troubleshoot by providing orientation, solutions, and reassurances or delay the processing if necessary. Reluctant parts mean the client is ambivalent. If parts consent, say the following:

Say, *"And, we've got* _____ (say front part's name) *off on* ___ (his or her) _____ (canoe journey or other metaphoric distancing maneuver that utilizes the dissociation. See also tactical integration, Fine, 1993a)."

_____

_____

Say, *"Now let's tuck in the parts that don't need to be here for this fraction of work. Let's get those kids on the waiting horses* (or other appropriate conveyance), *who will take them to a far away mountain stream* (or other appropriate place), *where they can wait in quiet and safety, while the necessary work happens in the conference room. That's it. There they go, bye kids see you later, not going forever, just until the time is right. And* _____ (say introjects' names, one by one), *are you guys willing to go on a cruise* (or other appropriate conveyance)? *Thanks for allowing the work, as you sail* (or other appropriate means) *away, knowing you can return when you are needed. So long for now, there they go . . .* _____ (say helper part's name). *Have they gone?"*

_____

_____

Do problem solving or accept the presence of any stragglers, asking for their help.

Say, *"*_____ (say helper part's name), *you'll stay on stand-by? And we need our older resource team to help too."*

_____

_____

Ask for volunteers or nominate alters to assist, saying each of their names in turn.

Say, *"Are you willing to sit with* _____ (say star's name) *and give* ___ (him or her) *strength, and* _____ (say another resource part's name)?"

_____

_____

Or say, *"Are you willing to be on standby with _____ (wisdom or com-passion or courage or other resources)?"*

_____

_____

Say, *"Good! And I'll add my energy as well. I'll be with you listening, honoring, and supporting every inch of the way. This time you aren't alone."*

_____

_____

If parts are more hostile than described above, trauma processing is likely premature.

H/I—Hypnosis or Imagery

Training in hypnosis is extremely helpful—even essential—in working with dis-sociative clients, who are themselves products of self-hypnosis, and who engage in hypnosis whether we are trained to recognize it or not. Whether with formal hypnosis or with simple imagery, it will be necessary to use methods to access traumatic material and accelerate processing, and, more likely with dissociative clients, apply the brakes with distancing maneuvers (Hammond, 1990). Most of the devices in the dissociative table method (Fraser, 1991, 2003) are distancing ma-neuvers (Paulsen, 2004a, 2004b, 2007). The resources available in the conference room are limited only by the imagination of the therapist and client collaboratively. It will likely be necessary to debug processing problems during the EMDR by add-ing devices in the conference room and in the skillful interweaving of EMDR and hypnosis (see also Fine & Berkowitz, 2001; Fine, chapter 28, this volume).

Say, *"Okay, then speaking through _____ (say helper part's name), directly to _____ (say star's name), there's _____ (say resource states names) to help you. There's a comfortable chair for you, a microphone to give you a voice, a screen to play the memory at a distance and in black and white if you like. There is a dimmer switch beneath your hand. Anything else you need?"*

_____

_____

If the star of the EMDR is mute, consider blending the part with another part temporarily (Fine & Comstock, 1989) so the mute part has a voice.

Say, *"Is there a volunteer to blend with _____ (say star's name) temporarily to give* (him or her) *a voice?"*

_____

_____

Once a volunteer is identified, say the following:

Say, *"Thank you, part. And is it okay with you, _____(say star's name)?"*

_____

_____

Once the star has nodded consent either in a switch or in the conference room, as reported by another part, say the following:

> Say, *"Okay, the two of you, coming together, to give _____ (her or him) a voice, blending together. Okay, _____ (say star's name), can you talk now with ___ (her or his) help? Good!"*

_____

_____

T—Titrate

Memories can be stored in whatever fashion a child's mind finds it expeditious to store them. They may be stored by channel of information, by age of alter, by perpetrator, type of trauma, or other arrangements. It is helpful to ask a knowing part, if there is such a part, for suggestions as to how the particular memory is stored.

> Say, *"Is there a knowing part who can tell me how this memory is stored? And there may not be such a part and that's okay, but if there is, this is a good time to step forward. Knowing part?"*

_____

_____

If there is no knowing part, proceed with your best guess and be prepared to change plans rapidly. If there is a knowing part, it may be wrong or it may be right. If a knowing part suggests a likely structure for how the memory is stored, utilize that information.

> Say, *"_____ (say star's name), remember there is a dimmer switch, too, under your hand to turn the intensity down. Anything else you need?"*

_____

_____

> Say, *"I think you may have all of the channels of information, the behavior, affect, body sensation, and the beliefs. To break it up smaller still so the work is manageable for you, we can break it into smaller pieces. Just watch as the _____ (body sensations or picture, sound, smells, thoughts—whichever you choose to work with) stay and as the _____ (pictures, sounds, smells, thoughts adjust accordingly to what you choose) all go into containers in the vault. Your brain knows just how to do this. It's like watching a containment channel on TV. Everything that is not now needed just goes in by itself."*

_____

_____

Or fractionate by using just the picture, affect, knowledge, or behavior and containing the rest. The structure of the client's system and memories will determine what fractionations are possible.

Say, "_____ (say star's name), *have you got what you need to feel strong enough to proceed?*"

_____

_____

Affect can be titrated by how the memories are fractionated.

- The therapist will see that the salient part or star is "looking through the eyes" (Paulsen, 1992, 1995, 2008a; Paulsen & Golston, 2005); this means present in the therapy room (not just in the conference room in conscious mind). This author also calls this being "imbued with ego energy" (Paulsen & Watkins, 2003a, 2005; Watkins & Paulsen, 2003; Watkins & Watkins, 1997).
- Other parts might not be present in the therapy room or in the conference room in conscious mind in order to titrate down the intensity of the processing experience.
- Parts may be distanced by imbuing them with object energy (e.g., "that girl over there, not me") whether they are in the conference room or at greater distance, outside of the conference room in the conscious mind.
- For some, it will be enough titration to invite a single alter to be present by looking through the eyes while others are not present in the therapy room but are in the conference room in the conscious mind.
- For others, having one alter present and no others in the conference room in conscious mind will still be too much. For such a case, it will be necessary to titrate down the intensity further for the one that is present by using, for example, containers to hold the behavior, affect, and cognitive aspects, and processing only the somatosensory channel. These several maneuvers are the essence of fractionation and titration.

Usually, it will not be possible until the later phases of therapy with DID clients to fully articulate a target image workup, with negative and positive cognitions, subjective units of disturbance (SUD) and validity of cognition (VoC) levels. This is because the task is less of activating the neural net (accelerator) and more of distancing (braking) to modulate the intensity of experience during the processing. Additionally, the parts of the client engaged in the processing are typically young child alters in intense emotion and so less formal and more child appropriate methods are better suited earlier in trauma work.

E—EMDR and Bilateral Stimulation (BLS)

With all fractionation or titration methods in place, the therapist can initiate bilateral stimulation in this step. Eye movements are more actively engaging than the more passive auditory or tactile forms of BLS. Clients are better able to manage their experience by dissociating using the passive methods. Therapists are, however, unable to observe dissociation as well with the passive methods as with eye movements in which the eyes fixate in dissociation.

Examples of problem solving include the following.

Eyes Fixate

If using eye movements for BLS and eyes fixate, say the following:

Say, *"What just happened there?"*

_____

_____

Process Stuck—Check With Alter or Part

If the answer indicates processing is hung up, say the following:

Say, *"Hi, whatever is right there, welcome. Is it okay with you that we are doing this?"*

_____

_____

If so, say the following:

Say, *"Notice that."*

_____

_____

Continue BLS.
If not, interview, orient, and appreciate the part, such as in the following:

Say, *"What is your job?"*

_____

_____

Say, *"How old were you when you started doing this job?"*

_____

_____

Whatever the answers are, incorporate that information into an appreciative statement, such as the following:

Say, *"Thanks for _____ (state the job function) all these years. That's a difficult job for such a little _____ (say boy or girl)."*

_____

_____

Say, *"By the way, did you know you are in the body with _____ (state her or him)?"*

_____

_____

Say, *"____ (state she's or he's) _____ (state the age of the part) years old and we are in _____ (state the name of where you are)?"*

_____

_____

Whatever the answer, say the following:

Say, *"Notice that."*

_____

_____

If the following is true, say the following:

Say, *"Did you know it isn't happening anymore? That this is a memory?"*

_____

_____

Say, *"Do you have a concern about our helping with this burden of pain?"*

_____

_____

If so, problem solving or shutting down processing until the part's concern can be resolved is helpful. It will be necessary to engage in a range of problem-solving methods, such as the following: titrating affect downward, stopping and negotiating with emerging alters, mediating internal dynamics if needed, offering reframes appropriate to the age of parts of self, and much more. Especially important is to maintain dual attention awareness, which will require more active intervention, than for nondissociative clients. Sessions longer than 2 hours are likely to be counterproductive and destabilizing.

Perpetrator Introjects

Most incidents of looping (stuck processing) and spontaneous headaches will be related to unworked perpetrator introjects or double binds related to competing viewpoints of the perpetrator and the child. This can be understood as an approach avoidance conflict or simply as accelerating while applying the brakes.

Say, *"I'd like to speak directly now to whatever comes up next. Whatever comes up next, do you have a concern?"*

_____

_____

As described in the Trauma Accessing phase of therapy, above, it may be necessary to remind the perpetrator introject of present person, place, and time, appreciate its function, and offer it assistance with its suffering. In particular, it may be carrying the actual external perpetrator's shame.

Say, *"*_____ *(say perpetrator's name), thanks for holding the perpetrator energy all these years. That's a thankless job, but someone had to do it. I'll help the others to understand what a burden you have had. Did you know that you aren't the external* _____ *(say perpetrator's name) but an internal likeness of* (him or her)*?"*

_____

_____

Say, *"Thank you for being loyal to _____ (say perpetrator's name); as that was completely necessary back than. You kept _____ (her or him) silent (or under your thumb) and that's just what was needed for survival back then (if that is true), so thank you. Thank you for seeing it through _____ (say perpetrator's name's) eyes, so at least one part of you knows what power feels like instead of just helplessness. Go with that."* (See Paulsen, 2004, 2008a, 2009 for more discussion of this strategy.)

_____

_____

Titrating Affect Downward

Overwhelm

If the client is experiencing too much material, stop and say the following:

Say, *"Notice there is a dimmer switch under your hand and you can turn it down, turning it down until it's manageable. And your brain knows just how to do this, so just let me know when it is turned down to a manageable level, not completely off, just manageable."*

_____

_____

Confusion

If the client appears confused about where (he or she) is, say the following:

Say, *"Hi, there, welcome. Do you know who I am? I'm _____ (say your name) and I've been helping ___ (her or him) with the pain. Have you been here before?"*

_____

_____

Say, *"Take a look around the office. Did you know it is _____ (say year) and we are in ____ (say town) and ____ (she or he) is ____ (say his or her present age)? This is a lousy old memory I'm helping ____ (her or him) with. It's a memory and it's not happening now. Is it okay with you if we continue?"*

_____

_____

Emerging Alters

If the processing is stuck because one part of the self has a harsh belief about the patient's defectiveness or culpability as a child victim of trauma such as, "She deserved it, the little slut."

Say, *"Do you see how big _____ (her or his) shoulders are?"*

_____

_____

Say, *"Do they put children that age in charge of running corporations?"*

_____

_____

Say, *"Why not?"*

_____

_____

Or you can use other age-appropriate reframes until the client's certainty in defectiveness begins to falter.
Resume BLS.

Say, *"_____ (say star's name), looking through the eyes, as we begin."*

_____

_____

Problems or Shifts Observed

Add bilateral stimulation, a relatively long set, stopping if problems or other shifts are observed.

Say, *"That's it, it is old stuff, I'm right here with you."*

_____

_____

Dual Attention Failing

It is especially important to maintain dual attention awareness, which will require more active intervention than for nondissociative clients. It is usually necessary to maintain almost continuous empathic patter (as in light comments, not glib) as appropriate to the client. If verbal contact is not enough to maintain dual attention awareness, consider touch if it is appropriate and welcome for this client.

Switch to Tapping

Say, *"And what are you aware of?"*

_____

_____

If the client is silent, ask the following:

Say, *"Are you free to speak? Continuing, just notice."*

_____

_____

Client Is Mute

Proceed without client words, if necessary, or ask blended part to give a voice to the inner experience.

Say, *"Can you tell me what _____ (she or he) is experiencing?"*

_____

_____

Orienting With Voice

If the client is obviously losing dual attention awareness, use more voice contact:

Say, *"Here I am, feel the floor beneath you, feel the chair."*

_____

_____

Use Surprise or Interruption

This author, if traditional grounding methods fail, brings out a trained professional, a toy poodle, which has 100% success rate in pulling a client back into the present moment.

As one client said, "It must be now; Michelle (the poodle) isn't old enough to be there then."

If no poodle is available, another bold measure is to say, "How do you like my new hat." If the therapist is wearing no hat, this is likely to snap the client back into the present moment to say, "What hat?" although conceivably with some irritation.

If client looks confused, say the following:

Say, *"That's it, you're here with me in _____ (state the year you are in)."*

_____

_____

Or ask for clarification by saying the following:

Say, *"What year do you think it is?"*

_____

_____

If the therapist cannot tell what's going on:

Say, *"_____ (say the name of the helper part), can someone tell me what's happening? At least whether the processing is continuing? Or is it stuck?"*

_____

_____

Confusion About Present and Past

Sometimes looping results from the client being concerned about something that appears to be in present time, but is actually likely to be a reenactment and as such is part of the memory. Examples of patient utterances of this kind include, "I can't stand it," "You hate me, don't you?" "He's going to get me," "I'm afraid I'll have to kill myself if this doesn't work," "I'm dead meat if I tell what happened." In any such case of language that emerges suddenly during EMDR processing:

Say, *"Is it possible that is part of the memory?"*

_____

_____

Say, *"Notice that possibility."*

_____

_____

Do BLS.

Processing Resolves Extremely Quickly

If processing seems to complete very quickly, it is likely the end of a channel, in EMDR parlance. In DID, that channel may be a single alter or portion of the memory. The next alter in the sequence may not know she or he is up. So, as in the Standard EMDR Protocol, we return to target to evoke the next channel (if session time permits).

Say, *"I'd like to speak to whatever part comes up next, or has a concern. Helper? Anyone? Can you tell me what's next?"*

_____

_____

New Alter or Part

If a part emerges that doesn't know the therapist or know EMDR, stop the EMDR until client readiness is again in place.

Say, *"So sorry, Part, I would never have done this without your permission. I didn't know you were there. I'm _____ (say your name) and I've been working with them for a long time to lift the burden of pain, and today we are using EMDR. Is that okay with you?"*

_____

_____

Say, *"Are you willing to look through the eyes so I can help you too?"*

_____

_____

Continue processing if part is willing. If the part is unwilling, don't resume EMDR yet.

Say, *"So, Part, what do you do?"*

_____

_____

Say, *"Do you know the others?"*

_____

_____

Say, *"Did you know it is _____ (say the current year) and we are in _____ (say the current location) and ____ (she or he) is _____ (say patient's age or) 'about half a century old'?"*

_____

_____

If part denies or is shocked, say the following:

Say, *"Don't take my word for it, but maybe we could check it out together."*

_____

_____

Use a mirror and a town newspaper, magazine, or calendar to orient to person, place, and time, backing off if the client is very resistive to the facts. If other parts are reacting to disown this part, say the following:

Say, *"It's hard for them to understand how you helped. How old was ____ (say she or he) when you started holding _____ (say perpetrator's name) energy? Oh, that means when you got your job, you were very little too. What a hard job for such a little ___ (state girl or boy). By the way, _____ (say perpetrator part of the self's name) did you know that the shame belongs to the external _____ (say actual external perpetrator's name), not to you?"*

_____

_____

Say, *"I'll help the others understand. Is there any part of the self that can see that underneath that perpetrator costume ____ (state she or he) is just a child part too?"*

_____

_____

Say, *"If so, can you welcome this part to the work? _____ (She's or He's) had a hard job too. If you like, _____ (say perpetrator part of the self's name) you can take off your costume and leave it over there on that hook in the conference room. You can always put it back on if you need to. Thank you. Are you willing to look through the eyes so we can help you with your burden too?"*

_____

_____

Say, *"Good. Looking through the eyes."*

_____

_____

Say, *"Go with that."*

_____

_____

Processing Too Intense

If processing is too intense, say the following:

Say, *"If there is a helper part or resource who will step forward to help _____ (state her or him), this would be a good time. And little one, there is a dimmer switch, you can use that to turn down the intensity. I'll help. That's it. And everyone, this time you are not alone. I'm right here with you."*

_____

_____

Processing Blocked

If processing is blocked and no part is evident on inquiry, say the following:

Say, *"Is there someone under the table or in the corner?"*

_____

_____

Say, *"If they are hiding, they must have a good reason. Either they feel afraid or ashamed. But I'm happy to hear their story."*

_____

_____

Continued Blocking

If the process is blocked and the star of EMDR has apparently consented but processing is blocked.

Say, *"Little one, are you looking through the eyes?"*

_____

_____

Say, *"It only works if you are looking through the eyes. Do you want to stop? Okay."*

_____

_____

Determine reason for stopping and problem solve for it if possible.

Say, *"May I know the concern?"*

_____

_____

If the concern is readily addressed, do so and provide reassurance.

Say, *"With that in mind, would you like to continue or stop? Your choice."*

_____

_____

C—Closure

Say star's name or other part that may have emerged in the processing sequence.

> Say, *"We are almost out of time and we'll need to continue this when the time is right. How are you feeling?"*

_____

_____

If Part A or another part reports relief on behalf of one or more parts, as is likely the case, say the following:

> Say, *"Good! Today we took another step toward healing and wholeness, and over time we'll get further and further down that path. For now, it is enough to know _____ (say names of parts that are beginning to feel relief) are beginning to feel relief and we know that the others will too when the time is right."*

_____

_____

For Containment Step 1

> Say, *"Let's begin to wrap up, by gathering up any fragments of memory that are laying around in the conference room. Gathering them up together, putting them in the container, I'll help putting it in the container, putting the lid on the container, and putting the container in the vault, sending the vault down the elevator, and pulling a heavy velvet curtain in front of the elevator. Good. And how does the conference room look now?"*

_____

_____

For Containment Step 2

Do problem solving for any residual memory fragments.

> Say, *"And now, with appreciation to all the parts of the self that have helped today by talking, listening, or allowing the work. Is there anything that simply must be said before we stop?"*

_____

_____

If yes, reassure or engage in problem solving for the problem or issue.

> Say, *"Thanks for reminding us about that concern. I've made a note of it for next time."*

Or you can supply a needed resource in the mind's eye, such as the following:

Say, *"We can put a timer on that issue in the mind's eye, and have the alarm go off 10 minutes before the next appointment, so we can be sure to address it when the time is right."*

_____

_____

If no, say the following:

Say, *"There are* _____ (beautiful fluffy white clouds or whatever other conveyance) *waiting for all the parts of the self, and some can go together and some can go separately . . . . climbing on board . . . Does* _____ (say names of part(s) that processed) *need anything?"*

_____

_____

If so, provide in the mind's eye as in the following:

Say, *"Then I'll wave goodbye as* _____ (the clouds pull away or whatever other conveyance) *and go deep inside for a deep, healing sleep. Deeper and deeper still.* _____ (say name of helper part), *is that you? How do you feel?"*

_____

_____

If protective parts won't go, don't get in a contest, stay neutral and say the following:

Say, *"Well, I know better than to get into a struggle with you, because I know who would win that contest!* _____ (say name of protective part(s)), *there is a ranger station on the horizon with a tower, and if you get tired you can go there because there is a hammock and binoculars so you can keep an eye on things while you get a much needed rest. Thanks,* _____ (say protective part's name, as they go) *and* _____ (say helper part's name). *Thanks for your help. So long* _____ (say front part's name, the part that will need to be executive and grounded to drive home safely)."

_____

_____

Say, *"Coming back from your canoe trip* _____ (or whatever metaphor was used), *coming back, coming all the way back. Are you here? Try pushing your heels into the floor. That will pull you back."*

_____

_____

Using the idea of the grounding poodle is useful here.

T—Tranquility Technology

Say, "_____ (front part's name), *how do you feel?"*

_____

_____

If present and grounded, provide normal EMDR debriefing.

Say, *"Things may come up or they may not. If they do, great, write it down and it can be a target for next time. If you get any new memories, dreams, or situations that disturb you, just take a good snapshot. It isn't necessary to give a lot of detail. Just put down enough to remind you so we can target it next time. The same thing goes for any positive dreams or situations. If negative feelings do come up, try not to make them significant. Remember, it's still just the old stuff. Just write it down for next time. Then use the tape or the Safe Place exercise to let as much of the disturbance go as possible. Even if nothing comes up, make sure to use the tape everyday and give me a call if you need to. You've got the _____ (state tape or say other self-soothing strategy) we made for you, and you know the emergency procedure. If you have a very hard time, you call me okay?"*

_____

_____

S—Stabilize, Synthesize, Soothe

Based upon the client's state at next visit, the therapist will suggest either continued processing, or a period of synthesis or consolidation of gains via talking, imagery, or bilateral stimulation in some cases.

Say, "_____ (say client's name), *how did you do after the EMDR session?"*

_____

_____

Say, *"And how do you feel as we sit here now?"*

_____

_____

Note: If the client feels raw, EMDR is contraindicated until the patient has digested the processing of the last session.

If the client is destabilized, the therapist should emphasize soothing, intervening in dynamics, and slowing of the pace of abreactive work as much as needed.

Say, *"Well, let's just talk today. How is your life going this week?"*

_____

_____

Say, *"Do we need to add any insulation to the vault?"*

_____

_____

Say, *"Is everything still in the containers?"*

_____

_____

Say, *"Who's having a hard time?"*

_____

_____

Say, *"What's going on with them?"*

_____

_____

Note: If the client is not feeling raw, and her or his system wishes to continue processing, clinical judgment should be used to determine the wisdom of that move. If it seems appropriate, the piece or work in the sequence should be targeted with EMDR. That piece may be the same alter as last time or the next alter in the sequence. It may be that the next information channel needs targeting, whether behavior, affect, sensation, cognition or whether organized in another way. In any case, the work should be collaborative and should pace the work to maintain patient's self-efficacy and stabilization.

Say, *"So, I'm hearing that parts of you experienced considerable relief, and you are willing to do another piece of processing today. Who is up next?"*

_____

_____

Repeat sending front part off in canoe or whatever other conveyance the client chooses, utilizing a helper part to identify and communicate with the next part, if next part doesn't come forward and so on. It may require many segments of processing to completely resolve the various alters, time segments, and channels of a traumatic memory in a DID client. The memory is clear, of course, when SUD = 0 and VoC = 7. Although it may not have been possible at the beginning of processing a given memory to identify negative and positive cognitions, or take VoC or SUD ratings, as work proceeds the relevant cognitions will become evident. They can be suggested by the therapist or captured when the client utters them spontaneously. They can be posted in the conference room in the mind's eye. As an example, if in the course of the EMDR one of the parts says he wishes he could feel loved by God, but another part says that God hates him and wants him to die, the therapist can suggest those be used as positive and negative cognitions, respectively.

Say, *"I'm hearing you say that _____ (say negative cognition) and I wonder if you wished you believed _____ (say possible positive cognition). How about if we nominated those to be negative and positive cognitions? In fact, let's post them prominently in the conference room. The negative cognition can be in some hideous old frame on the wall. And the positive cognition can be in a beautiful frame right next to it. Is that okay with you all? Who wants to say something about that?"*

_____

_____

This effort may require some discussion and introspection, or the patient may be ready to resume processing the next piece of the memory.

This completes the ARCHITECTS approach to an EMDR intervention for a DID client. This process will be repeated many times in the abreactive association phase of treatment. The work of trauma processing will be interspersed with other emphases as well; not all is trauma work even in this phase. Trust and the therapeutic relationship will continue to develop over this phase as the client's capacities for relationship functioning are restored. The remainder of this chapter will focus on the final phases of the ACT-AS-IF phases of therapy for DID, namely, skills building, integration, and final or follow-up.

Skills Building (Future Template)

The process of skill building does not begin after trauma work is complete, in fact it will have begun before trauma work is initiated, starting with the containment and stabilization phase. However, in this phase of work, attention is on insuring that the client has the skills in place to function well in the world without relying on dissociation. The performance enhancement protocol is a useful approach (Foster, Lendl, & Paulsen-Inobe, 2000).

Say, *"So let's decide what skills you need to have going forward so you aren't stuck having to just dissociate again."*

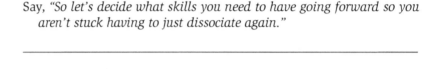

Once needed skills have been identified, determine whether this is a skill set this therapist can help provide, such as assertion training, problem solving, communications skills, and so forth, and refer to a skilled coach or course of training if it is outside the therapist's expertise. If it is within the therapist's knowledge base, identify the specific component steps involved in the skill. Vivify each step in the client's imagination and then link the steps together into a smooth process. For any interference, determine if the interference is a residual traumatic disturbance or a skills deficit and resolve accordingly. See Lendl and Foster (1997) for more information on using performance enhancement EMDR.

Integration (Future Template)

EMDR is always associative, and what it associates is always that which had been dissociated, or not integrated, even in clients who do not have a dissociative disorder per se. Therefore, integration will have been occurring spontaneously over the course of therapy, with every untangled double bind and every cleared and integrated trauma. In this phase, however, the ego investment of any remaining separate ego states can be addressed.

Say, *"You have been feeling better and better and the numbers of you have reduced way down. Let's check, how many of you are left, by a show of hands."*

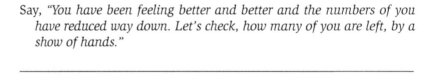

After hearing the count, say the following:

Say, *"And, of course, every person has ego states, that's all right, it's the walls between that can be a problem. How many of you need to*

stay separate in order to keep pain aside, or for some other reason, or
have concerns about being in the same body at this point?"

_____

_____

Address any concerns. For example, if an alter is concerned about either dying or being alone if others are gone, say the following:

Say. *"Sometimes, there is the feeling that separate people would disap-*
pear if you integrated, but the functions you do will remain. The
essence of each of you remains in the one real estate, the one person,
and the walls that divide you would disappear."

_____

_____

The following should not be attempted prematurely; namely, as long as amnesia barriers are needed to hold traumatic material that remains to be processed. Add brief sets of bilateral stimulation and say the following:

Say, *"If all parts are willing to integrate, a brief ritual may be beneficial*
with bilateral stimulation saying, 'Parts holding hands, saying we
are one, we are one, walls falling away, as we becomes I.'"

_____

_____

Stop and check to make sure there are no interferences, and problem solve any interference. Remaining unworked trauma may become evident at this point. Note these so that they can be used as targets in subsequent sessions.

Say, *"How would that be for all of you? Do you have any concerns?"*

_____

_____

More likely, the client may express concern about being lonely without the others. This is a sign that unworked loneliness related to early abandonment and attachment injury will still need to be processed.

Say, *"Is that loneliness a new feeling? Or an old . . . . familiar . . . .*
feeling (pause) *and just notice what it is reminding you of and let*
yourself float back to that time. And what are you finding?"

_____

_____

It is also likely that grief about lost years will need to be processed at this time.

Say, *"Yes, your losses have been very, very great. I'm so sorry about your*
losses."

Those subjects make excellent EMDR targets for subsequent sessions using the Standard EMDR Protocol now that the client is integrating.

Future Template and Follow-Up (Reevaluation and Future Template)

Say, "_____ (state client's name), *we've been working on _____ (name one or more recent therapeutic emphases) for some time. Let's check our work, by seeing what, if anything, is in the way as you imagine your life in the future. What is it you want to be able to do regarding _____ (name a therapeutic emphasis) in the future?*"

_____

_____

When the client identifies the future goal:

Say, *"How would it be to imagine engaging in _____ (state specific behaviors) in the future, having it go the way you want it to go? And, let's notice what, if anything, seems to interfere."*

_____

_____

Add bilateral stimulation.

Say, *"Go with that."*

_____

_____

Say, *"And was there any interference?"*

_____

_____

If there is interference, determine whether they are skills deficits or trauma related fears, avoidances, or other disturbances. If there are skill deficits, use an appropriate skills training approach, augmented by bilateral stimulation. If there are residual traumatic disturbances, process those as usual.

This completes the description of the ACT-AS-IF phases of therapy of a DID client for highly dissociative clients, and the ARCHITECTS description of the steps in an EMDR intervention for DID clients.

In summary, the assessment, containment and trauma accessing phases of ACT-AS-IF therapy prepare clients for trauma work. The middle A in ACT-AS-IF is the actual trauma work of therapy, as expressed in ARCHITECTS. The ARCHITECTS method accesses, refines, obtains consent, and mobilizes resources hypnotically or with imagery and selects the piece or fraction to be processed. It adds bilateral stimulation for the portion that fits in the available time and then closes the session, allowing time and means for self-soothing and synthesis. After the trauma work is completed for clients, the final phases of therapy in ACT-AS-IF are the skills strengthening, integration, and follow-up that prepare clients for life without dissociation and without (or with less) therapy. Although complicated, the methods are also intuitive and allow a tremendous gift of healing to occur in clients' lives.

31

An EMDR Protocol for Dissociative Identity Disorder (DID)

Don Beere

This author conducted—as yet unpublished—research (Beere, 2009a, 2009b) on successful and unsuccessful EMDR with his DID clients. The following protocol is based on this work and is also applicable for complex post-traumatic stress disorder (C-PTSD) clients in which traumas are amnestic and intrude into present functioning. The approach is based on the following specific clinical conclusions:

1. Every effective EMDR intervention allowed the client to process a single traumatic incident from start to finish. This was the case if the incident was targeted with a distressing intrusion or a specific traumatic memory.
2. In every situation, significant aspects of the memory had been amnestic and recall returned during the processing.
3. Every processing involved significant distress always associated with the aspects of memory that had been amnestic and disequilibrated the client between sessions.
4. During EMDR, different alters almost always processed the trauma. Finally, if there were different alters, they integrated during or postprocessing.

EMDR Protocol for Dissociative Identity Disorder Script Notes

The above observations help us to understand how aspects of the Standard EMDR Protocol need to be adapted to work well with DID clients during the Assessment, Desensitization, and Installation Phases, in particular how to set up the Standard Protocol, establish the subjective units of disturbance (SUD) level, and acquire the negative cognition (NC), positive cognition (PC), and validity of cognition (VoC). An amnestic trauma is by definition a trauma that, when activated, is experienced as happening now. In other words, an amnestic trauma is not over but continues in the present when recalled. As a result, the Standard EMDR Protocol is addressed in the following manner:

1. *Positive cognition.* This implicitly specifies a PC for working on DID traumas: "It is over. It is finished. It is past," although during the EMDR processing there might be other PCs that emerge. This also clarifies why it is almost impossible, during these early stages of treatment, to elicit NCs and PCs.
2. *Negative cognition.* In contrast, the most basic NC is "It is not over. It is still happening." Given the difficulty of accessing the full trauma, a transitional NC can be obtained by having clients label what is rolling around in their minds such as "I'm going to die."
3. *Subjective units of disturbance.* Since the trauma is amnestic, assume it is the worst it could be, overwhelming and unmanageable in other words, a SUD of 10. Clients cannot report this directly due to the amnesia. Therefore skip getting a SUD rating. At the end of processing, however, once the trauma has been remembered, obtaining a SUD rating is crucial to be sure that the incident has been fully resolved.

Shapiro's Recent Trauma Protocol Script

Beere's research also establishes that unworked DID traumas resemble experientially not only a recent traumatic event but an ongoing traumatic event. The Recent Traumatic Events Protocol has the client proceed through the trauma as if it were a video, from start to finish, addressing whatever arises moment by moment. The video is replayed until the event no longer evokes distress. Shapiro (2001) defines 7 steps for the Recent Traumatic Events Protocol, however, this too, needs to be modified for the DID client.

Step 1. Obtain a narrative history of the event. This clearly cannot be done in every situation since significant aspects of the event are amnestic.
Step 2. Target the most disturbing aspect of the memory (if necessary). This also cannot be done since it will be amnestic.
Step 3. Target the remainder of the narrative in chronological order. This is accomplished by engaging internal resources of the DID client.
Step 4. Have client visualize the entire sequence of the event with eyes closed and reprocess it as disturbances arise. Repeat until the entire event can be visualized from start to finish without distress. As stated earlier, this is the essential activity in processing the trauma. Since the event is amnestic, hypnotic resources must be engaged to do this processing. A SUD rating is obtained at this point in the protocol with the expectation that it will be 0.
Step 5. Have client visualize the event from start to finish with eyes open and install positive cognition.
Step 6. Conclude with body scan.
Step 7. Process present stimuli, if necessary.

Of particular note is that Shapiro suggests the following positive cognitions, "It's over; I'm safe now." As discussed earlier, these are precisely the cognitions that logically follow from the trauma being amnestic.

The inability to fully access the trauma, as well as the overwhelming distress, creates a potential therapeutic impasse. In these situations, the author has engaged the client's hypnotic capacities in order to do the following:

- Select an appropriate trauma on which to do EMDR.
- To provide containment and distress management before, during, and after processing.

In this regard, this approach is similar to the Wreathing Protocol (Fine & Berkowitz, 2001; Fine, chapter 28) except that a complete trauma is processed from start to finish. The initial structuring does not necessarily involve fractionating the traumatic event, attempting to engage alters that experienced the event, or having other alters go to some internal safe place. In the event of difficulties that arise later with the EMDR, such fractionation or other intervention might troubleshoot those problems. Initially, however, the focus is on the trauma solely. As the trauma is processed chronologically, whichever alters experienced what occurred become active during the appropriate part of the processing. About 60% of the clients seem to need this kind of hypnotic structuring.

A critical aspect of successful resolution of traumatic events, with or without EMDR, is for the client to remain aware of the present. Most—but not all—alters seem to be caught in the past. As Kluft (1993b) has said, DID is "a multiple reality disorder," and those realities are past realities. Helping the client remain present in the office despite distress and helping various alters be present in the office are critical parts of this preparatory process. When alters can truly experience being in the office, discovering over a number of sessions (usually at least five times) that the office and therapist are not hurtful but benign, then that alter can know there is another possibility, which is in the present nothing negative is happening and that the world the alter is trapped in is not actually happening now.

Teaching hypnotic interventions, especially the "Screen," often begin with the stabilization phase of trauma treatment and usually follows the introduction to EMDR. It is distinct from locating alters in the office. This particular hypnotic procedure is one of many the author has used, but this seems to have good generalizable utility. One can understand the Screen, as a method to access unconscious processes. To be effective, the therapist must believe this is possible—otherwise this will be subtly communicated to the client and the depth of the intervention will be ineffective. Often, the client's unconscious tests the therapist and over time, after passing those tests, allows deeper access. For example, information that might have disastrous consequences has been withheld from this author until other issues have been resolved. Over time, the Screen will become a tool for helping clients do the following:

1. Reduce distress.
2. Decrease intrusions.
3. Help alters manage between sessions.
4. Provide guidance during sessions.

The language is important. It is helpful when first using this script to read it aloud to hear and get used to the word usage. For example, Screen is dissociated or made into an entity called Screen. The word use implies and supports autonomous action on the part of the Screen, action independent of the host or any other alter. The words suggest this.

The Desensitization Phase can extend over months and involve intermittent day-to-day difficulties and occasional phone calls. One must be prepared for these eventualities. At some point, the therapist might become aware that the client is functioning well, that alters have been grounded in the office, that distress and symptoms have been contained, and that it might be time to begin EMDR. This is the time to ask Screen if there is a specific trauma that it is possible to work through from start to finish such that it is over, and that every alter who was involved could actually go through knowing it, remembering it, have the emotions associated with it, and possibly have the sensations again. If Screen agrees, then make plans to have a longer session the next time in order to begin EMDR on the selected memory.

The Standard EMDR Protocol

Given the context previously described, the Recent Trauma Protocol has been modified as follows:

1. Client goes through the trauma from start to finish, repeatedly until the SUD is 0.
2. VoC is not initially obtained for the PC, "It is over. It is no longer happening."
3. When VoC = 7, Body Scan is obtained.
4. Residual reactions are processed.
5. Present or future triggers are processed.

Phase 1 (Client History and Treatment Planning) and Phase 2 (Preparation)

Phases 1 and 2 are folded together. Shapiro (2001) considers history taking and treatment planning linked to eventually doing EMDR. The following are the elements of Phase 1:

1. Good working alliance between therapist and client.
2. History taking establishes that there are appropriate targets to be treated with EMDR.
3. Client suitability and readiness is considered. This involves life constraints (e.g., emotional support or work demands) and personal capacities (e.g., the ability to tolerate intense distress). Stabilization and symptom reduction are both necessary to establish the ability to tolerate intense distress.
4. In the context of DID, a focal treatment goal is the resolution of traumas. This goal, then, is implicit as soon as a diagnosis of DID has been made.

The basic elements of Phase 2 are as follows:

1. Introduction to EMDR
   a. Preparation for EMDR.
   b. Education about not reliving trauma.
   c. Education about remaining aware of the present while processing the past.
   d. Education about going through the trauma from start to finish.
2. Hypnotic preparation that includes the following:
   a. Establish the hypnotic tool, Screen.
   b. Develop communication with Screen.
   c. Increase depth of Screen.
   d. Connect Screen to the deepest levels.

Phase 3: Assessment

This phase is significantly truncated as explained previously. It involves using Screen to select the trauma.

Phase 4: Desensitization

Desensitization proceeds over many sessions and includes the following steps:

Step 1. Have Screen begin EMDR from the start of the traumatic incident and proceed through the event until it is over. This phase is almost finished when Screen reports a SUD of 0.

Step 2. Visualize the incident from start to finish with eyes closed.

Step 3. Open eyes if any distress arises and process that distress to a 0.

Step 4. Close the eyes and proceed further through the incident, again stopping by opening the eyes if distress arises and processing that to a 0.

Step 5. This phase is finished when the client can visualize the incident from start to finish without distress.

Step 6. Specific alters are not engaged since they will, if still present, become active during their particular part of the incident. Frequently, alters have integrated during the processing of the incident.

Phase 5: Installation

Installation involves installing the PC "It is over" along with recall of the incident.

Phase 6: Body Scan

Steps for the Body Scan are as follows:

Step 1. Client recalls the incident.

Step 2. Scans the body.

Step 3. If anything arises, process the material until relaxation occurs or it is neutral.

Present and future triggers are elicited and whatever they activate is processed to neutral or relaxation.

EMDR Protocol for Dissociative Identity Disorder Script

Phase 1 and Phase 2: Client History and Treatment Planning and Preparation

The initial history taking that this author uses is the global interview most clinicians would obtain with any client. Most clients with dissociative identity disorders (DID) present initially in turmoil and often the initial therapeutic task becomes crisis management and eventually stabilization. Frequently, this author's clinical experience is being frustrated in trying to obtain a clear developmental history, in particular, isolating problematic and traumatic events. At some point in this process, it becomes clear that the client is dissociative and then possibly DID. This diagnostic conclusion informs the clinician of a history of preadolescent trauma. Usually then, the author attempts to gather information about what those traumas might be. Although this provides some information about trauma history, until resolved those incidents cannot be fully recalled. As a working alliance develops and the client is educated (as presented in the following sections), it then becomes possible to invite Screen (a hypnotic tool) to select the trauma on which to do EMDR. In this regard, there is no EMDR history taking because the details one would obtain with a nondissociative client cannot be obtained from the dissociative one.

Introduction to EMDR

This introduction involves an explanation of EMDR and an explanation of three issues critical for successful EMDR processing: not reliving trauma, remaining aware of the present while processing the past, and going through a trauma from start to finish.

Preparation for EMDR

This step educates the client about EMDR as a treatment and clarifies what will be needed for successful processing. This frequently occurs 1 or 2 years before doing EMDR. Begin with the usual introduction and overview of EMDR as an intervention—as done with a non-DID client. Understanding nondissociative processing first helps. As with any EMDR, the client must feel in control—both in electing to do EMDR and in stopping at any time. This author has had a client say, after this introduction, that there is no way he would do EMDR and then a year later say without prompting, "Okay, let's do EMDR."

> Say, *"Often when something traumatic happens, it seems to get locked in the nervous system with the original picture, sounds, thoughts, feelings, and so on. Since the experience is locked there, it continues to be triggered whenever a reminder comes up. It can be the basis for a lot of discomfort and sometimes a lot of negative emotions, such as fear and helplessness that we can't seem to control. These are really the emotions connected with the old experience that are being triggered.*
> *The eye movements we use in EMDR seem to unlock the nervous system and allow your brain to process the experience. That may be what is happening in REM, or dream sleep: The eye movements may be involved in processing the unconscious material. The important thing to remember is that it is your own brain that will be doing the healing and you are the one in control (Shapiro, 2001, pp. 123–124)."*

———————————————————————————

———————————————————————————

Not Reliving Trauma

This is important to explain and to prepare the client for stabilization, distress management, and eventually staying in the present.

> Say, *"I'm going to explain something that I think you already know in various ways. It will give us a tool later. When an overwhelming trauma happens, sometimes that trauma is not remembered. The technical term is 'amnestic' or having amnesia. Obviously the trauma happened, and even though the person can't remember it, it is filed away somewhere in memory. Sometimes pieces of that trauma surface in our experience such as flashbacks, body memories, emotions that come out of nowhere and don't seem linked realistically to what's going on now, and reactions or thinking that won't stop but don't make sense.*
>
> *Our first step is to help you manage the pieces of the trauma that surface. One way to do that is to really know that the reason they are distressing is that it seems real. In other words, when a trauma that is amnestic begins to surface, it feels real and this is very distressing. Of course, it isn't real. It is a memory. So knowing it is a memory, and that it isn't happening right now is critically important.*
>
> *When we eventually do EMDR that is if you choose to do it, this will be important since to process it fully you will need to remember the incident from start to finish while staying here.*
>
> *There is a metaphor for what happens when an amnestic trauma begins to enter conscious memory. And I want to be sure you don't do this right now. Okay?"*

_____

_____

> Say, *"When folks start to remember or to talk about the things that happened they often get upset, they sort of imagine themselves back in the situation and begin to see or hear what happened. With an amnestic trauma, folks have little bits of it. So when folks start to get closer and closer to it, when they begin to think about it or talk about it or describe specific details, they get pulled into it. It's like swimming closer and closer to a whirlpool. If the swimmer stays far enough away, things are alright. If the swimmer gets too close, he or she gets pulled into the experience. This is what happens when people relive a trauma. We want to avoid this happening to you if possible. One thing we need to do is to have you learn how to get out of that pull. Each time you get yourself out, you develop a little more strength, ability, and knowledge of how to do it. Do you have any questions?"*

_____

_____

Remaining Aware of the Present While Processing the Past

It is crucial that clients continue to remain aware of the present. The client needs to understand the importance of dual attention for effective EMDR and to realize that developing this ability will be helpful not only with EMDR but also with general management of day-to-day difficulties. This enhances stabilization and symptom reduction.

Say, *"I would like everyone to listen; of course, I know they are always listening, but I would like to let everyone know what will make the EMDR processing work. What I am going to say will also help everyone be less distressed in the long run too. So this can be a very useful tool for our work together. Does anyone inside have difficulty in listening right now?"*

_____

_____

Say, *"If so, would someone else be willing to share this conversation with the others inside?"*

_____

_____

Say, *"Thanks. For most folks who are DID, the parts, alters, or ones inside are usually in their own worlds and that world doesn't really change much and very often the same kinds of things seem to happen over and over. The way I understand this is you are actually trapped in the past, in worlds or experiences that you managed by becoming who you are now. So when you can be here in this office and discover that this office is an alright place to be and find that out over and over again, you will finally have some other possibility, and you will now have the option of getting free of what was happening then. So when you are ready, we will slowly help each of you come in here—look around, feel the furniture, move around the office, and get a sense of what the present is like. Sometimes parts will let someone else do the looking at first and check it out from behind. That is fine. Any questions? If you listen inside, are there any questions? Is anyone (part, alter, state) unwilling to do this?"*

_____

_____

If there are questions, concerns, or an unwillingness to come into the office, a quite usual situation, accept whatever is shared and empathize with what you hear as the issue.

Say, *"I understand, ____ (state name of part with concerns) that you are concerned about ____ (state concerns). Am I understanding you correctly?"*

_____

_____

One can anticipate that fear, vulnerability, and loss of control or choice are likely the underlying issues. As well, and not discrete from the prior issues, trust of the therapist would probably be an issue. Often just listening and understanding the concerns will lead to spontaneous willingness to come into the present.

Say, *"Please go on and tell me all that I need to understand about ___ (state the concern)."*

_____

_____

Should that not be the case say the following:

Say, *"What might make a difference so that you could come into the office?"*

_____

_____

Or say, *"What could I do that would make it possible for you?"*

_____

_____

Or say, *"Have I done something that gets in the way of your coming into the office?"*

_____

_____

When all questions and concerns have been addressed, continue with the following:

Say, *"There is another important reason for being here. When we do EMDR, when and only when you decide to do EMDR, then we will work on a trauma. In order to do that you will need to be able to know you are here while you remember what happened. So the first step in helping you do this is to have you come here quite a few times before we do any trauma work. That would be something you need to be able to do whether we end up doing EMDR or not."*

_____

_____

Going Through the Trauma From Start to Finish

Say, *"A trauma is like a wave—before it begins, it is quiet and smooth, then the water starts to rise, to get worse, then it's at the peak, at its worst, the wave crashes, there is tumbling froth, and then it is smooth and quiet again."*

_____

_____

You can draw a graph with the wave representing intensity over time.

Say, *"For many people, when the trauma is too much, they get stuck."*

_____

_____

You can draw a circle on the graph below the peak with an arrow, representing the same stuff going around and around.

Say, *"This is what happens when folks have flashbacks or body memories. It is like it's happening now but it never finishes. And it is like you're caught in it. So our job with the EMDR is to help you go over the top safely and finish the memory so it's over. We'll start at the beginning and go through the trauma until it is finally over. Then we'll do it again and again until there's no more distress. Any questions?"*

_____

_____

Say, *"There was some research done on EMDR with clients who dissociate looking at what happened when EMDR helped DID folks fully resolve these traumas, they went through them from start to finish, over and over, until there weren't any additional distressing reactions (Beere, 2009). That meant they had to be able to know what they were remembering or processing while at the same time know that they were here in the office and nothing was happening to them. In addition, they needed to be able to tolerate the distress of what they were going though. This didn't happen in one session; usually it took weeks and sometimes months to process one of these traumas. And it took time, months or years, until they were ready and able to do it.*

We aren't going to do the EMDR until you're ready. We need to be sure you are doing well—that you are stable and not having lots of symptoms. When you know that deep inside, then some part of you will let us know you're ready. And then we'll begin to set up the EMDR. Do you have any questions?"

_____

_____

Use your clinical judgment to ascertain when someone is ready to begin EMDR. This always follows, at minimum, several months of stabilization and smooth functioning. Sometimes, this has lasted 2 years. The readiness has been signaled by a dream or nightmare, body memory symptoms, or the intrusion of previously inactive alters. Always check with clients whether they are ready to begin EMDR or not. One way to check is to ask Screen (see following section).

Hypnotic Preparation

Warning: It is essential that practioners be trained in hypnosis for psychotherapy before using the following hypnotic tool.

This step hypnotically prepares the DID client's system to do the following:

1. To select a trauma to process from start to finish.
2. To develop containment mechanisms that reduce or eliminate distress, intrusions, or body memories.

Establishing the Hypnotic Tool, Screen

Say, *"I don't know if you are aware yet of being able to see a screen—sort of like a movie screen, a television screen, or a computer monitor. It could be like the screen you project slides on. And it could be inside your mind or outside. The screen could be on the wall like a blank picture with a frame, and, actually, it is important that when you see it, it has a frame around it. It could be black and thick or silver and slim—but whatever its color and thickness the frame will be there, containing the screen, putting a boundary around it. Would you be willing to let me know when you see it?"*

_____

_____

Respond to any questions the client has. Sometimes it is disbelief. DID clients are highly suggestible so this is well within their repertoire.

Say, *"There is no need to work at this. Let's just keep talking and would you let me know when Screen decides to appear?"*

_____

_____

Say, *"Great, thanks."*

_____

_____

Developing Communication With the Hypnotic Tool, Screen, Once Screen Has Been Reported

Say, *"Screen, I'd like to thank you for being willing to appear and to communicate. Would you be willing to communicate with words?"*

_____

_____

Say, *"Screen could write the word 'Yes' on the screen. And would you* (addressing the client) *be willing to let me know what appears on the screen?"*

_____

_____

Say, "Great, has Screen responded?"

_____

_____

After the host has indicated that Screen has responded, it is important to acknowledge the response.

Say, *"Screen, thank you for responding."*

_____

_____

The host will learn how to read the screen. It is not uncommon for the host to have occasional difficulty letting the screen speak or to impose his or her wishes. If the host has difficulty with the concept of Screen you can say the following:

Say, *"I'm quite certain that you have thoughts or pictures that just come to mind. Right? Well, Screen is sort of like that. It just comes to mind,*

except sometimes it is like seeing something that is here but not here,
like a dream picture that can be inside or outside. Does that help?"

_____

_____

Most often, clients have no problem with the idea of the screen, but more with whether it will actually appear; so far this author's clients have had no problem.

Sometimes, Screen makes words unreadable and sometimes the host, for various psychological reasons such as fear, is unable to make sense of the words on the screen. In the event that the client cannot read at all, one can develop pictorial or symbolic language via the screen. One can do so using a variety of options. One could ask Screen the following:

Say, *"And Screen, what picture or shape will mean 'Yes'?"*

_____

_____

Test this out by asking the following:

Say, *"Screen does this mean that* (state the picture or shape just reported) *means 'Yes'?"*

_____

_____

Then follow up with the question:

Say, *"Screen would you also be willing to communicate what picture or*
   shape will mean 'No'?"

_____

_____

Screen will need to respond with the "Yes" picture or shape. Then ask the following:

Say, *"Screen what picture or shape will mean 'No'?"*

_____

_____

Later, if more complicated situations need to be described, one could ask the following:

Say, *"Screen would you display a scene the host could describe that will*
   capture whatever _____ (he or she) *is struggling with right now?"*

_____

_____

The therapist now needs to develop a pattern of communication with Screen over many sessions. This can be helpful in asking for inner help with reducing distress, decreasing intrusions, fostering sleep, gathering information about what might be happening, and so on. In relation to the prior sentence, one can ask the following questions to elicit help from the screen.

Say, *"Screen would you help reduce her distress?"*

_____

_____

Or say, *"Screen would you help reduce the number of memory intrusions?"*

_____

_____

Say, *"Screen would you help her sleep tonight?"*

_____

_____

Say, *"Screen, _____ (she or he) has been bothered recently about something. Would you be willing to indicate what that bother is about?"*

_____

_____

If a client is panicky at the end of a session yet must leave, say the following:

Say, *"Screen would you be willing to help with ___ (his or her) panic?"*

_____

_____

Assuming Screen answers "Yes," ask the following:

Say, *"Screen will you reduce or get rid of the panic?"*

_____

_____

Again, assuming there is a "Yes," say the following:

Say, *"And Screen can that panic be totally gone until it is time to work on it here in session?"*

_____

_____

Once again, let us assume the screen answers "Yes."
Sometimes Screen either does not answer or answers "No."
In those situations, clinical creativity and problem solving are required. If we consider the very first question, "Screen would you be willing to help with her panic?" the therapist can ask a number of follow-up questions.

Say, *"Screen does something else need to happen before panic can be helped?"*

_____

_____

Or say, *"Is there something in fact happening in her life that triggers this panic?"*

_____

_____

Or say, *"Is this a present, a past, or a mixed panic?"*

_____

_____

Let us consider that Screen answers "Yes" to the first question, "Screen is there a need for panic right now?" This could be followed up by these kinds of questions. Once again, this is a list of suggestions. Clinical problem solving and creativity is usually required.

Say, *"Is panic in response to what we have been doing in session?"*

_____

_____

Say, *"Is panic in response to what we had been talking about?"*

_____

_____

Say, *"Is panic in response to specific memories?"*

_____

_____

Say, *"Is panic in response to something I have done or said?"*

_____

_____

Say, *"Since there is a need for panic right now, can that need change so sometime in the future panic can lessen?"*

_____

_____

Say, *"Does panic help _____ (him or her) protect ___ (him or herself)? If so, are there other ways to protect her?"*

_____

_____

Similar kinds of questions could be asked whenever Screen is not willing to answer or says, "No." Usually there is some kind of inner process interfering with utilizing Screen's resources.

Sometimes there is no need to develop more depth in order to do EMDR. In other words, simply having access to Screen is adequate to develop the controls and choices necessary for EMDR. However, some DID clients need deeper communication.

Increasing Depth

Say, *"I am going to tell Screen a story and it is fine if the unconscious of everyone else listens as well, but there is really no need to listen consciously. Can I tell this story?"*

_____

_____

Wait for agreement.

Say, *"Thanks, is there anyone who doesn't want to listen or does not want me to tell the story?"*

_____

_____

Wait for an answer and respond.
If they say "No," use Screen to figure out why.

Say, *"Screen, can you tell us who does not want to listen or does not want me to tell the story."*

_____

_____

Is it lack of trust? Is the system currently overwhelmed and unable to listen? Or is it that, when other people have told stories, bad things happened?

Say, *"Would it be alright for everyone else to listen while _____ (state who does or does not want to listen) drifts off into a deep dreamless sleep?"*

_____

_____

If they say "Yes," say the following:

Say, *"Here is the story. Once upon a time, in a magical land that is so far away it is as close as the next breath, the mind was like an infinite ocean—going out as far as the eye can see or the mind can know in every direction. And the people in the mind floated on the surface or went below the surface when they weren't aware—and of course they could breathe easily no matter how deep they went. Every day problems stir the surface and make it rough, but below the surface there are currents and deeper still those currents lessen and lessen until right at the bottom there is no movement at all and when everyone settles gently on the bottom they come to a deep rest and settle down inside. This is the edge of the mind, the deepest level of the mind—what is amazing and almost like magic, it is possible to gently drift through into open space. A space that has nothing in it and goes as far as the mind can know. Gentle light. Calm. Comfortably and effortlessly dissolving into this space and not knowing in from out, up from down, right from left, just being there and being everywhere and being nowhere and there is no smell, no taste, no hearing, no seeing, no sensing, no feeling, no thinking. And in a moment I'm going to ask Screen if it has understood the story and quite effortlessly let the words appear from that deep down nowhere everywhere inside. If it happens, a finger can raise or the head can nod, when words have appeared on Screen."*

_____

_____

Usually it is helpful to develop this induction to stabilize the depth so it is reliable and deals with whatever arises. This means, for example, that if you ask to communicate with Screen it fairly reliably appears and provides a response. So far in this author's clinical experience, Screen has never been 100% consistent, but has been about 95% responsive. Usually, nonresponse has occurred at times of significant distress and, often with creativity, it is possible to facilitate some kind of response. For example, you might say the following:

Say, *"Screen, is there some difficulty answering because any answer might increase distress, which is overwhelming right now?"*

_____

_____

If the therapist has empathized accurately with the person's internal state that will often allow Screen to respond. An additional way to adjudge how Screen is functioning is the speed of response (though this is situational, for example, intense distress requires more effort, and thus time to respond more so than mild distress). If a client has made an emergency phone call because of distress, impulses to self-mutilate, struggling with suicide, or terrified to sleep because of nightmares, it is helpful to ask the following:

Say, *"Is Screen there?"*

_____

_____

After you have gotten acknowledgement that Screen is there, ask the following:

Say, *"Screen would you be willing to help?"*

_____

_____

Usually you get a "Yes," and then say the following:

Say, *"Could you help turn off _____ (state the appropriate issue, e.g., stop, calm, repress, and so on) what is creating this situation?"*

_____

_____

Clearly, in the event of an ambiguous or negative response from Screen, follow-up exploration about why the person needs to experience this now, what function the problem might be serving, or some other issue, can help begin to handle the emergency.

Say, *"How is it that you need to experience this now?"*

_____

_____

Say, *"Could it be that that problem is helping you in some way?"*

_____

_____

Say, *"Do you have an idea about what is going on?"*

_____

_____

One stopgap measure is to not stop the whole experience, but to simply reduce its intensity or to have it stop periodically to give the person a break.

Say, *"What if we simply reduced the intensity of the experience or gave you more breaks. Would that help with this situation?"*

_____

_____

Connecting Screen to the Deepest Levels

When this kind of depth can be replicated reliably, then hypnotically connect the Waking Screen (the Screen the host sees in the everyday state) with this deep level.

Say, *"And I would like to ask Screen a question. Is Screen willing to answer?"*

_____

_____

Wait for an answer.

Say, *"And Screen, I would like to find out, if as I believe is the case that though you are a Screen you are also an inner window that opens into that infinite, open, light space in which there is nothing and everything and out of which everyone arises inside. Is this correct?"*

_____

_____

When the answer is "Yes," then Screen can access this deepest level and can help in very deep control, distress management, and can select the trauma to be worked as well as the time it can be started. This is set out in the following section.

After Screen has been established and is reliable, you can ask Screen to communicate in some way that the whole system is ready to begin processing a trauma from start to finish so that it is over. You can ask Screen the following kind of questions:

Say, *"Screen, as you have heard EMDR is a method to help process a trauma from start to finish so that it is over, would you be willing to communicate to me when the whole system is ready to begin to do that?"*

_____

_____

If Screen says "No" or does not respond, there are various options. Ask the following:

Say, *"Screen would it help to give you more time to figure out the answer?"*

_____

_____

Or say, *"Screen is there something right now that might interfere with working any trauma through until it is over?"*

_____

_____

When Screen has agreed to let the therapist know when the system is ready, reiterate some of the crucial issues in successful resolution by saying the following.

Say, *"Screen, I would like to remind you and the system what successful EMDR processing needs. Whoever is remembering the trauma must be able to know that he or she is here, in the present, in my office, remembering the incident. Also, the alter who is going through it needs eventually to be able to feel the emotions and possibly the sensations of what has so far not been remembered and processed. So the system will need to be able to tolerate extreme distress, to feel possibly awful sensations and to know what has been too much to know. This does not all have to done at once. It can be done a little bit at a time. But eventually this is what is needed for a full resolution. Screen have you understood this?"*

_____

_____

Wait for an answer.

Say, *"And, Screen, these then must be the conditions when it is time to do EMDR. Will you let me know when this is the situation?"*

_____

_____

Notice that the request unambiguously states what the internal situation must be to successfully do EMDR. Some months later when the client's functioning has stabilized, it is possible to ask the following:

Say, *"Screen is ____ (he or she) ready to begin doing EMDR?"*

_____

_____

Usually, however, it is preferable to not push the issue and ask this question only after there is some kind of clinical hint (such as distress suddenly happening, pain that is a body memory, a dream that symbolically indicates readiness, for example, a group beginning a new journey, or some other kind of life event).

At this point, most of the work has been done to establish EMDR: the client has been introduced to EMDR; its procedures have been described, and the choice of ABS (Alternating Bilateral Stimulation) has been decided. The following is the approach that this author uses for the first time with most DID clients stopping for questions when they are asked.

Say, *"Screen indicates that we can now do EMDR and even though we have discussed it, describing again what we will be doing can be useful. For one thing, you might be able to hear it in a new way. And it could be that others inside also need to hear it and might have questions."*

_____

_____

Say, *"With EMDR, we are going to process a trauma from start to finish. Because you all don't remember all of it, we know that it is stuck or that it is unfinished. For that reason, it comes up as flashbacks, body memories, emotions out of nowhere, and confusing thoughts. I have shown you my drawing of a trauma that looks like a wave; distress starts off low, gets stronger and stronger until it peaks, and then settles back down to low again. Usually folks are stuck before the worst. That's what keeps coming up as flashbacks. With EMDR, we want to help you reprocess the whole experience from start to finish, to go through the worst of it, and to know that it is over. We will go at your pace. And any time you want to stop, you can stop. How would you like to do that? Would holding up your hand like this work for you? Or if your eyes are closed, do you want to open your eyes?"*

_____

_____

Say, *"We will probably go through the incident a little bit at a time until it is over. Then we will go through it again and again until there is no more distress. This means that you will probably feel increasing distress as we go through the experience but remember it is not really happening. It's all a memory. It's all old stuff. Staying aware that you are here in this office with me can help you know that.*
Now let's select the kind of bilateral stimulus you prefer. Remember that you can always change your mind later if you want to switch to a

different modality. We have eye movements, auditory tones, and tactile stimuli. Let's go through each one.

To do the EM, I'll ask you to follow these fingers or my hand with your eyes. How will you do following the fingers? How is that?"

_____

_____

Wait for an answer. Often clients with DID react negatively to a raised hand. If the client has difficulty with the raised hand, develop some other kinds of workable visual focus, for example, a pop can holder, a coaster, a spoon, or a box of tissue.

Move your chair closer so that you would do "ships in the night" if you were to sit down. Before you sit down, say the following:

Say, *"In addition, I will need to be a little closer to you. How do you think that will be for me to be this close? How far away would allow you to feel comfortable?"*

_____

_____

Don't feel constrained by needing to be physically close to your client; it is possible to help clients do effective EMs from across the room, say 6 to 9 feet away.

Once distance and visual focus have been decided, do some trial movements VERY cautiously. Given how quickly some DID folks process, even without activating a specific target, EMs can initiate processing. In the following, move slowly and make at most two round-trips in any direction.

Say, *"I might move the fingers* (or whatever focus you are using) *side to side . . . or diagonally this way . . . or diagonally the other way . . . or up and down. Sometimes I might do figure eights . . . or even circles. Any reactions? What seems best to you?"*

_____

_____

Say, *"We might also use auditory tones."*

_____

_____

Give the client the earphones attached to the Tac or AudioScan (this is a device to create bilateral stimulation through auditory or tactile stimulation, available at www.neurotekcorp.com).

Say, *"I am setting it to the slowest and softest setting. I'm going to start now. And now I am increasing the speed to maximum. And now I'm increasing the volume to maximum. Okay?"*

_____

_____

Turn off the Tac or AudioScan.

Say, *"Any reactions?"*

_____

_____

Disconnect the Audio lead and connect the Tac lead.

Say, *"Next is the TacScan, little taps that you can feel while holding the ends of the device. Take one in each hand. This does not hurt in any way. Okay? I'm going to start it at the slowest speed and then increase it. Okay, I'm turning it on now. Now I'm turning it to the fastest. Okay?"*

_____

_____

Turn off the TacScan.

Say, *"Any reactions?"*

_____

_____

Reconnect the Audio lead to the Tac or AudioScan.

Say, *"If you would like, we can do both the Tac and AudioScan together. So, if you want to see what that would be like, put on the earphones. Okay, now I'm going to start the machine very slowly. Match up the sounds and sensations, or ears and hands, so that the right and left sides are together."*

_____

_____

After a short while, once the sides are lined up, turn off the Tac or AudioScan.

Say, *"Any reactions?"*

_____

_____

Say, *"Do you have a preference for which we should use? Remember, you can change your mind at any time."*

_____

_____

Say, *"If you listen inside, does anybody* (use language appropriate to your client like part, alter, person, or whatever term you are using) *have negative reactions or concerns about doing EMDR?"*

_____

_____

Note: Even though this author has so far relied exclusively on Screen for guiding us to begin EMDR, alters might well have reactions, concerns, and attempts to sabotage (due to fear or anxiety). Alters may be particularly active about this point in the preparation phase since EMDR is now about to occur. This, then, would be a time to help deal with these issues, before EMDR actually starts as in the following questions.

Ask about clients' reactions, concerns, or any other issues concerning beginning EMDR.

Say, *"Could you tell me your concerns about doing EMDR?"*

_____

_____

Communicate that you genuinely and empathically hear the concern.

Say, *"I am hearing that you are feeling _____ (state feelings) about _____ (state the concern)."*

_____

_____

Check that you have heard accurately.

Say, *"Am I hearing correctly what you are telling me?"*

_____

_____

If you have, then ask what options or solutions there might be to reduce the concern or anxiety.

Say, *"What options or solutions might help reduce _____ (state the concern or feeling)?"*

_____

_____

Sometimes, the concerns or anxiety come from misinformation that can be clarified. For example, an alter might believe she will have no choice or cannot stop despite earlier reassurances. The issue, in this situation, is what has prevented the alter from believing what has previously been said.

One could ask, *"Do you have evidence that you can't believe what I say?"*

_____

_____

Phase 3: Assessment

Crystallizing the Target

There are three possible ways to crystallize the target based on how available the material is to conscious memory, in other words, how much dissociative amnesia is linked to the memory.

Apparent Full Recall

This is similar to EMDR on traumatic targets with non-DID clients. In the context of C-PTSD and DID, there is always the possibility that the trauma is more severe than reported. As well, there are probably amnestic blanks, especially since the trauma remains unresolved. If this is the clinical situation, approach this trauma with regular EMDR. In this regard, the scripts of Francine Shapiro apply in this situation. In general, this kind of target is usually not what DID clients report. All of the previous preparation, especially the hypnotic preparation, would not necessarily be pertinent in this context.

Partial Recall

In this situation, often, the client is beset by memory fragments: flashbacks, body memories, emotions, thoughts, sounds, tastes, or smells. In the context of DID, the host (the presenting identity) might recall only parts of the incident. Notice that the target will not be as clear or as explicit as a traditional EMDR target. There are two ways to do the assessment phase.

Use Screen to Connect the Current Symptoms With a Specific Incident

The first way to do the assessment is more explicitly described in the following section on a fully amnestic trauma.

> Say, *"Screen, _____* (state the host's name) *is currently experiencing _____* (name the current symptoms, like emotions, body memories, nightmares and so on). *Are these experiences parts of what happened during _____* (state specific incidents)*?"*

> _____

> _____

> Say, *"Is there a single incident?"*

> _____

> _____

> Say, *"Would it be best to focus on the earliest or the worst?"*

> _____

> _____

> Say, *"And can we now begin EMDR on that incident, proceeding from start to finish, from the beginning to when the incident is over?"*

> _____

> _____

Develop Various Aspects or Sensory Data of the Current Symptoms

If it is possible, get as many different senses as the client can access involved in the description of the target. Approach this situation as follows:

> Say, *"Would you describe exactly what it is that happens?"*

> _____

> _____

Responses might be: "I see a dark shape," "I hear a raspy whisper," "Suddenly I smell mint," "There's an itchy feeling on my leg," "I suddenly get a sense of impending doom," "I see people yelling at each other but I can't hear anything," and so forth.

Try to get more specifics, being careful not to dig too deeply and being careful not to activate the trauma so that it is relived.

Questions to access this kind of detail for sensory fragments might be as follows:

Say, *"Where exactly is it?"*

_____

_____

Say, *"How large is it?"*

_____

_____

Say, *"Does it have a shape?"*

_____

_____

Say, *"Does it have a color?"*

_____

_____

Say, *"Is there anything else about it that seems important?"*

_____

_____

Questions about a partial scene might be as follows:

Say, *"As you think about what you do remember, what seems to be the worst moment?"*

_____

_____

Say, *"What seems to be happening?"*

_____

_____

Say, *"Where are you when this is happening?"*

_____

_____

Say, *"Are there sounds, smells, or tastes?"*

_____

_____

Say, *"Do any sensations arise when you think about this?"*

_____

_____

Say, *"What picture best captures what you remember?"*

_____

_____

Negative Cognition (NC)

Say, *"When you remember this, what does it mean to you that is negative about you?"*

_____

_____

Or say, *"What does this _____* (memory fragment) *mean about you as a person?"*

_____

_____

Or say, *"What does this mean about you as a person that this experience happens to you?"*

_____

_____

Positive Cognition (PC)

Say, *"What would you prefer to say about yourself?"*

_____

_____

Or say, *"If you said something positive instead, what would it be?"*

_____

_____

Validity of Cognition (VoC)

Say, *"When you think of the incident* (or picture) *how true do those words ____* (clinician repeats the positive cognition) *feel to you now on a scale of 1 to 7, where 1 feels completely false and 7 feels completely true?"*

1   2   3   4   5   6   7
(completely false)   (completely true)

Emotions

Say, *"When you bring up the picture* (or incident) *and those words ____* (clinician states the negative cognition), *what emotion do you feel now?"*

_____

_____

Subjective Units of Disturbance (SUD)

Say, *"On a scale of 0 to 10, where 0 is no disturbance or neutral and 10 is the highest disturbance you can imagine, how disturbing does it feel now?"*

0	1	2	3	4	5	6	7	8	9	10
(no disturbance)								(highest disturbance)		

Location of Body Sensation

Say, *"Where do you feel it* (the disturbance) *in your body?"*

_____

_____

You are now ready to begin EMDR. Obviously this approach does not use Screen as a tool.

Fully Amnestic or No Recall

Since there is no recall, indirect means of accessing the memory must be used. In many clinical situations, clients have had a little recall (as in the previous section) but overall do not have full recall. It is helpful to use the screen as a hypnotic adjunct. Most of this has already been established in the earlier phases of treatment.

Nonetheless, always check with Screen that EMDR is currently suitable and that the memory can be accessed.

Say, *"Screen, we have talked about using EMDR with* _____ (state the memory). *Is EMDR currently suitable to do with this memory? Will it be able to be accessed?"*

_____

_____

Keep the following in mind:

1. Never discuss with specific alters their presence or absence during the processing of the incident, usually whoever went through specific parts of the trauma will be activated when the processing gets there.
2. Since the trauma is amnestic, accessing information about the event (pictures, cognitions whether negative or positive, emotions, or sensations) cannot readily be done. Assume, however, that the NC is "It's not over," and the PC is, "It's over." Assume that the SUD is 10 and that the VoC for "It's over" is a 1 is not true.

Note: You can do a complete assessment on whatever memory fragment comes to the client's awareness (and obtain a different NC, PC, SUD, and VoC than those just detailed). This is often a waste of effort because, as explained in the previous paragraph, the NC, PC, SUD, and VoC are implicitly related to the trauma's *not* being over.

Although this author would not, one might elect to do this for various reasons.

For those who elect to assess the fragment, say the following as you talk to the host:

Say, *"Before we ask for Screen's help in beginning EMDR, we know that we are going to be working on something that leads you to have _____* (fill this in with whatever has been surfacing in the client's experience that you know links to this trauma—body memories, flashbacks, nightmares, and so on). *Are there any thoughts about this that you find running around in your mind?"*

_____

_____

Elicit the NC.

Say, *"And what do these thoughts mean to you about you?"*

_____

_____

Elicit the PC.

Say, *"What would you prefer to say about yourself?"*

_____

_____

Elicit the VoC.

Say, *"When you think of the incident* (or picture) *how true do those words _____* (clinician repeats the positive cognition) *feel to you now on a scale of 1 to 7, where 1 feels completely false and 7 feels completely true?"*

1	2	3	4	5	6	7
(completely false)				(completely true)		

Elicit the emotions.

Say, *"When you bring up the picture* (or incident) *and those words _____* (clinician states the negative cognition), *what emotion do you feel now?"*

_____

_____

Elicit the SUD.

Say, *"On a scale of 0 to 10, where 0 is no disturbance or neutral and 10 is the highest disturbance you can imagine, how disturbing does it feel now?"*

0	1	2	3	4	5	6	7	8	9	10
(no disturbance)							(highest disturbance)			

Elicit the sensation and body location.

Say, *"Where do you feel it* (the disturbance) *in your body?"*

_____

_____

You are now ready to begin EMDR processing.

Phase 4: Desensitization Phase

Before beginning processing, it is important to check whether it is appropriate or not to begin. The particular ways it is possible to ask Screen questions about these issues follow.

Say, *"Screen, is it possible now to process a specific trauma from start to finish with EMDR?"*

_____

_____

Say, *"And Screen, I want to be sure that every alter who was involved can actually go through the processing while remaining aware of being here in the office?"*

_____

_____

Be aware of the following:

- *Notice your language.* It is not helpful to ask if it is *possible* because the word possible implies it might not happen.
- *Assurance to start.* Get assurance from Screen that it will happen, otherwise, do not do EMDR!
- *Ask Screen.* Do not ask alters; they do not know, but Screen does. Screen, remember, has been helping throughout all the preparation and can reduce distress, shut off memories, help them sleep, and so on. Screen can respond in ways alters cannot.

Say, *"And Screen I want to be sure that every alter who was involved can actually manage the distress, the sensations, the knowing, the remembering what happened. Screen would you be willing to go to the start of the trauma and then begin going through the trauma from the beginning, at whatever pace is necessary and workable?"*

_____

_____

Say, *"And would you let me know when it is time to stop for the day or when they need a break?"*

_____

_____

Say, *"And Screen, after we have finished today, would you be willing to let everyone go to a quiet, comfortable place inside and go into a deep dreamless, thoughtless, empty state of mind until we meet again?"*

_____

_____

Say, *"And Screen, whatever we process needs to be the right amount so the host can still do all the things _____ (he or she) needs to do every day like go to work, drive safely, take care of _____ (him or herself) and _____ (his or her) family at home, and so on. As you consider the whole experience from start to finish, how much of that incident seems workable today? Five%? A quarter? Half? The whole thing?"*

_____

_____

You might want to follow up with questions about intensity if Screen has some difficulty giving a clear answer to the first question. In this event, say the following:

Say, *"Screen is there an issue about the intensity of the distress during this incident?"*

_____

_____

If Screen responds with "Yes," ask the following:

Say, *"Screen what level of distress on a scale of 0 to 10 would be workable today?"*

0	1	2	3	4	5	6	7	8	9	10
(no disturbance)							(highest disturbance)			

After Screen has provided a number, say the following:

Say, *"Screen will you limit the distress to that level?"*

_____

_____

After Screen responds with "Yes," say the following:

Say, *"Thank you, Screen. And is it possible for us to begin EMDR now?"*

_____

_____

Say, *"Okay, go to the beginning of the incident and go through it from start to finish until the incident is over, being sure that whoever is going through the memory also knows he or she is here in this office where nothing bad is happening. Can we start now?"*

_____

_____

After Screen agrees, it is time to begin. Have the client put on the earphones or take the tactile probes, if you are using the Audio or TacScan. If you are using EM, bring the visual focus to the client. Say the following:

Say, *"Remember, you can stop at any time. Let me know when Screen says we should begin."*

_____

_____

Wait until the client indicates Screen says to start and then begin the BLS.

Keeping Clients in Their "Window of Tolerance" or in Present Time

Be very attentive to how the client is managing during the first few sets.

Track the client closely and if there is a sense of losing contact with being present, say something like the following:

Say, *"Remember, you are in my office and this is old stuff, a memory."*

_____

_____

Stop the first set after a short while (say 20 round-trips for the EM) to find out how the client is doing. For instance, does material seem to be processing? is the distress manageable? is it coming up too fast, and so on?

Say, *"Okay, let's stop this set. Take a deep breath."*

_____

_____

After a short period of time, say 15 to 60 seconds, if the client has not spontaneously begun to talk, say the following:

Say, *"What was that like?"*

_____

_____

Or say, *"What seemed to be happening?"*

_____

_____

Or say, *"Did things continue to change?"*

_____

_____

By the fourth or fifth set, you can leave it to the client to end the set.

Say, *"Okay, I think that you really have a sense of how things are going inside and how the processing is going, what about your being in*

charge of when to stop the set? Would you feel comfortable trying
that out?"

Often clients will simply continue processing for several minutes, sometimes
as long as 10 to 15.

During the EMDR processing, remember the following:

- Be very active in reminding clients that they are in your office, that this is old
  stuff, and that it is a memory.
- Increase the volume of your voice if you get a sense clients are drifting into
  dissociation or are beginning to get lost in the past.
- Use Screen frequently between sets to ask if you should keep going or stop
  and rely on that input.
- Remember that effective reprocessing requires being in the here and now
  while processing the past.
- If clients seem to get lost, almost trapped, in the memory, ask them to come
  back and ask what seems to be going on. To do this, ask the following:

Say, *"Okay, come on back. Look around. Take a deep breath. Move*
around a little to get a sense of your body. Good. What was going on?
What was happening inside?"

The significant issue is how quickly the client reorients to the here and now.
When clients are still caught up in the past or are dissociated, they tend to be spacey
or have difficulty interacting in everyday ways. Taking a minute to make this transition is not unusual, but extended difficulty indicates a need to ground the client more
firmly in the present and probably do shorter sets. Do not do another set until the
client is fully in the present. Regardless of the client's overt state, ask the following:

Say, *"Screen can we do more EMDR?"*

If Screen answers with a "No," close down the session.

If Screen answers with a "Yes," do more EMDR.

On the other hand, you might find that the next set still leads to the client having
difficulty coming back. This is not prognostic of effective reprocessing, although this
author, on occasion, had clients successfully work through traumas from this state.
Take this as a cue to stop EMDR and enhance grounding, reduce set length even
more to reduce internal drifting, or increase external demands from you with your
voice level, word choice, word pace, and so forth, to keep the client in the present.

Phase 6: Closure

For the first few EMDR sessions, it is helpful to do 15 to 20 minutes of reorientation
time before ending the session. In doing this kind of work, it is important to be as-
sured that the client will be able to function effectively, and, in particular, make a
transition back into the everyday world safely such as being sure that the client is

oriented in present time to be able to drive. A way to do this is to provide regular time markers for the client as the session unfolds.

Say, *"We have 20 minutes until we need to stop EMDR."*

_____

_____

Say, *"We have 10 minutes until we need to stop EMDR."*

_____

_____

Say, *"We have 5 minutes until we need to stop EMDR."*

_____

_____

If within these last 5 minutes the client is in an okay state, stop early rather than beginning another set. There will inevitably be material stirred up later. The more settled, grounded, and together the client, the better able that client will be to manage what will probably pop up later.

When a client is experienced with EMDR, a 5- to 10- minute end-of-session transition can work. Use your clinical judgment; the criterion is that the client should be able to function effectively. It is also helpful to ask Screen about stopping if you are getting a sense that the client is getting overwhelmed or having difficulties.

Always get assurance from Screen that the material and distress will be contained between sessions and that the client will be able to function adequately.

Say, *"Screen, will the material and distress be contained until the next session so that _____ (state the host's name) will be able to function adequately."*

_____

_____

In this author's clinical experience, despite assurances, complete containment is seldom the case. Distress that lasts 1 or 2 days and then remits seems to be more usual. Usually the difficulties postsession relate to what we have been processing.

Say, *"Often, after EMDR, the material may keep moving even though it has been 'contained' at the end of the session. This is not unusual. If stuff comes up, just notice it and jot it down. However, if you find that your day-to-day living is becoming too disrupted so that you are unable to go to work, are acting out, you are losing more time, you are having severe body pain, or can't sleep, please be sure to call. If you need to, we can make arrangements for you to come in earlier to help calm things down."*

_____

_____

If the distress lasts more than two days or if clients are so disrupted they cannot function (e.g., doesn't go to work; acts out at school and gets kicked out; loses time; the body feels excruciating pain leading to a hospital visit) that means that the pace is too fast and Screen is not currently a reliable informant or there are other processes impacting containment. This requires more communication with Screen to figure out what is going wrong. One can understand the situation in two ways leading to three main kinds of interventions:

1. The sensations and emotions linked to the event are coming into awareness and generate distress. Interventions for this point of view:
   - Shutting off the sensations or emotions.
   - Reducing their intensity can reduce the distress.

Say, *"Screen, are sensations and emotions related to the event we have been working on presently active?"*

_____

_____

If Screen answers "No," ask the following:

Say, *"Screen, what is the origin of the current distress?"*

_____

_____

Then problem solve to help deal with what is happening now.

Intervention 1: Shutting off sensations or emotions.

If Screen answers "Yes," say the following:

Say, *"Screen will you shut off or stop those sensations and emotions?"*

_____

_____

If Screen answers "No," say the following:

Say, *"Screen, is there something in the way of shutting them off?"*

_____

_____

Intervention 2: Reducing the intensity.

Continue in this way to help Screen "forget what has now been remembered." If this does not work, follow up with reducing the intensity.

Say, *"Screen, since the emotions and sensations cannot be shut off right now, can the intensity be reduced?"*

_____

_____

It is helpful to change the language to asking "can" rather than "will" because so far shutting off the memories has failed and it is more effective to approach this more tentatively. The distress is clearly difficult to control. With a "Yes," simply ask Screen to do so.

Say, *"Screen, would you reduce the intensity to a tolerable level?"*

_____

_____

With a "No," say the following:

Say, *"Screen, what level of intensity is distress now on a scale where 10 is the maximum possible and 0 is no distress at all?"*

0	1	2	3	4	5	6	7	8	9	10
(no disturbance)								(highest disturbance)		

Whatever the number (sometimes greater than 10), say the following:

Say, *"Screen, over several hours does the intensity ever increase or decrease from that number?"*

_____

_____

Intensity always rises and falls. A "No" is a suspicious answer; expect a "Yes." With a "Yes," say the following:

Say, *"Screen, since the intensity changes, a change in intensity is possible, is that right?"*

_____

_____

Once Screen says "Yes," say the following:

Say, *"Screen by how much will it be possible to reduce the intensity? What is the lowest number intensity could go to right now?"* (Negotiate with Screen the reduced intensity and how long that will last.)

0	1	2	3	4	5	6	7	8	9	10
(no disturbance)								(highest disturbance)		

2. An alter, involved in the event, might remain active and be responding as if the event were currently happening. That activated alter is caught in the past.

> Intervention 3: Helping that alter be in the present can diminish the "caught in the past" intrusions.

Say, *"Screen, is there a part of the mind* (an alter or another part) *that is caught in the past?"*

_____

_____

If "No," say the following:

Say, *"Screen, can you tell us what is happening either with words or with pictures?"*

_____

_____

If "Yes," say the following:

Say, *"And has this part ever been in this office?"*

_____

_____

Whether a "Yes" or a "No," say the following:

Say, *"Screen would you be willing to help this part come into the office right now?"*

_____

_____

With a "Yes," begin to actively locate the alter in the office, having the alter stand, move around, look at items in the office, look at the therapist, and so on to fully ground in the present.

_____

_____

Say, *"_____* (name of alter), *if you would like, you can walk around the office and explore the office. You might want to look at me and notice some of the items that are here in the office. (If appropriate) What are you noticing?"*

_____

_____

In the author's clinical experience, such full grounding or orienting always reduces the distress. The distress requires the alter to be in the past. When the alter is in the present, there is nothing to be distressed about and distress reduces.

If Screen says it cannot help bring the alter into the office, ask questions to figure out why this is so. Such questions might be:

Say, *"Screen, why isn't the alter coming into the office?"*

_____

_____

Say, *"Screen what is stopping the alter from coming into the office?"*

_____

_____

Say, *"Screen, what needs to happen so the alter can come into the office?"*

_____

_____

Phase 8: Reevaluation

The Next Session

If you received phone calls, you already know that too much material was processed. What is crucial at the beginning of every post-EMDR session is evaluating how the client is doing. In particular, try to gather information about how the client has functioned, specifically listening and looking for cues that indicate difficulties in functioning and also how the client managed those difficulties.

Say, *"How have you been doing since our last session when we worked on ____ (state what worked on)?"*

_____

_____

Say, *"If you had some difficulties, how did you manage them?"*

_____

_____

Often, the difficulties most clients report are directly linked to the incident we have been processing. As a result, in contrast to regular EMDR, don't target those difficulties. The critical issue is how the client is managing. If the client is too disrupted, then developing tools to manage that disruption precedes continuing with EMDR. On the other hand, if the client has been distressed but has managed, then with Screen's agreement, continue with EMDR.

Continuing Over Many Sessions

Most of this author's DID clients have processed for a minimum of 3 clinical sessions and often 10 to 20 or more. It has been helpful to ask Screen at various points to estimate how much of the incident has been processed as it provides a benchmark for how we are proceeding.

Say, *"Screen, how much of the incident have we processed so far?"*

_____

_____

Generally the most distressing parts of the incident are chronologically between 50% and 90% through the event. Sometimes it is the last part.

After Screen has indicated the whole incident has been processed from start to finish, ask Screen to estimate the SUD level.

Say, *"Screen, considering this incident, on a scale of 0 to 10, where 0 is no disturbance or neutral and 10 is the highest disturbance you can imagine, how disturbing does it feel now?"*

0	1	2	3	4	5	6	7	8	9	10
(no disturbance)										(highest disturbance)

Generally, a client needs to go through an incident a minimum of three times before the SUD reaches 0.

Say, *"Thank you, Screen. And would it be possible to begin going through the incident again from start to finish?"*

_____

_____

If Screen agrees, then resume doing EMDR. Once again, when the incident has been processed a second time, obtain a SUD. Often, when clients process an incident again and again, new and more distressing parts of the incident arise. Do not be surprised to find even more distress in later passes through the incident. Continue going through the incident until Screen reports a SUD of 0. The following context is important in getting a timely SUD rating.

Say, *"Screen, based on the reactions of the host and all of the alters, what is the level of distress associated with this incident on a scale of 0 to 10, where 0 is no disturbance or neutral and 10 is the highest disturbance you can imagine, how disturbing does it feel now?"*

0   1   2   3   4   5   6   7   8   9   10
(no disturbance)   (highest disturbance)

Going Through the Incident Consciously

Once the incident has been fully processed, the client is asked to imagine the whole incident and notice any reactions. They are then processed.

Say, *"Now visualize the whole incident from start to finish with your eyes closed. If any discomfort comes up, open your eyes and we will process that discomfort with EMs. When it is gone, close your eyes and continue visualizing the whole incident until it is over. Then open your eyes and let me know it is over. We will talk about what that was like. Okay?"*

_____

_____

No discomfort should arise as the client imagines the incident. Even if clients have not opened their eyes, if, during the discussion afterward, you have a sense that something has arisen, have clients go through the incident again. Often this takes three or four passes, until no discomfort arises.

Obtaining the VoC

Say, *"Screen, in relation to this incident, how true are the words 'It is over,' on a scale of 1 to 7 where 1 is not true at all and 7 is completely true?"*

1   2   3   4   5   6   7
(completely false)   (completely true)

Sometimes it is important to cross-check this rating in the following way:

Say, *"Screen, for the alters that went through this incident, how true are the words 'It is over,' where 1 is not true at all and 7 is completely true?"*

1	2	3	4	5	6	7
(completely false)				(completely true)		

At this point in the EMDR, if the VoC is less than 7, process what is in the way as you would with a regular EMDR client. Since the SUD is 0, there should now be good recall of the incident and there will be no need to dissociate. However, given the PC "It is over," doubt that it is over suggests that some alter might still be caught in the past. In any event, the clearest way to process this is to say the following:

Say, *"Screen, bring up what is in the way of 'It is over' being totally true. Let me know when that is there."*

_____

_____

Say, *"Good."*

_____

_____

Begin the BLS to process this.
Continue processing until the VoC is 7.

Phase 5: Installation

Often with DID clients, the installation is done after several sessions; this is the reason this phase appears out of order.

Say, *"Screen, bring up that incident and the words 'It is over.'"*

_____

_____

Do slow EMs, about six round-trips. Check in with client after each set.

Say, *"What do you notice?"*

_____

_____

Continue going as long as positive change follows. Now say the following:

Say, *"Would everyone who went through this incident think about it and the words 'It is over.'"*

_____

_____

Wait until you get some indication that has happened.

Say, *"Okay, everyone follow my fingers just being aware of what ever comes to mind."*

_____

_____

Again do very slow EMs, about six round-trips a set. Continue until there is no more positive change.

Phase 6: Body Scan

Again, often with DID clients, the Body Scan is done after several sessions: this is the reason this phase is out of order.

Say, *"Would everybody who went through that incident think about it? Now scan the body and let me know if you notice any tension, distress, or simply anything that comes to your attention."*

_____

_____

Or say, *"Close your eyes and keep in mind the original memory and the positive cognition. Then bring your attention to the different parts of your body, starting with your head and working downward. Any place you find any tension, tightness, or unusual sensation, tell me."*

_____

_____

Wait until the client indicates some completion of the Body Scan.

Say, *"What did you notice?"*

_____

_____

If the client notices anything other than relaxation or ease, process what has been noticed with BLS.

Work with Phase 7 as above.

Although the protocol is long, and when considered piecemeal or seemingly complicated, an overview reveals its simplicity. The protocol takes the DID client through a trauma from start to finish, as one would with a recent traumatic event. The protocol then adds two additional components: stabilization or distress management and accessing amnestic trauma. The methodology to accomplish both is via a hypnotic tool, here called Screen. An additional component of the protocol pertains to the NC, PC, VoC, and SUD. Since the trauma experienced by DID individuals is amnestic, we can assume the NC is "It is not over," the PC is "It is over," the VoC is 1, and the SUD is 10. This solves a difficulty many therapists have in obtaining these with DID clients. Distinct from some approaches with DID, one finds that the alters involved in the trauma naturally get activated at appropriate times during the processing. Finally, helping a DID client process the trauma again and again until there is no distress almost always requires many sessions and involves taking breaks in EMDR processing to help restabilize the client before proceeding.

Protocol for Releasing Stuck Negative Cognitions in Childhood-Onset Complex Post-Traumatic Stress Disorder (C-PTSD)

Denise Gelinas

This protocol was developed to help clients with childhood-onset complex PTSD who have difficulty moving from the Negative Cognition (NC) to the Positive Cognition (PC) and instead, experience persistent looping. This is most likely to occur with adults repeatedly traumatized within their families of origin and when the target memories are taken from that time and milieu. The target memories may be of major traumas or of the small t or developmentally disruptive type (Kitchur, 2000, 2005).

Releasing Stuck Negative Script Notes

What This Looks Like During Desensitization

What happens is that the client can proceed with the Assessment of the target memory and *can* successfully desensitize most of the disturbing material. However, the NC becomes stuck and will not move. Although the client may have processed a considerable portion of the disturbing material and reported a decreased SUDs (subjective units of disturbance) level, the resulting shift of the NC to a PC that is a hallmark of EMDR does not follow. Instead, looping and confusion set in.

The usual interventions for blocked processing do not help. This includes: trying longer sets, changing the direction of the eye movements, working with any identified blocking beliefs, and offering cognitive interweaves (CIs) about responsibility. In these situations, clients exhibit these types of behaviors:

427

1. Clients cannot accept the CIs.
2. Clients may avoid, contradict, or ignore the CI, but at bottom cannot accept or go with it.
3. Clients say often that they know they are not responsible, but they are unable to relinquish their felt responsibility for the disturbing experience and so the NC does not change.
4. Attempts to continue with the desensitization usually result in more looping and a lowering of self-esteem.

What Is Going On: The Packed Dilemma

The intractability of the distorted self-representations (i.e., NCs) in childhood-onset C-PTSD comes as no surprise to clinicians experienced in treating that disorder. A client's processing cannot move an NC to a PC if distortions remain about the client's responsibility in the old experience. As a result, the client is faced with a packed dilemma (see below). The difficulties posed by issues of responsibility, safety, and new choices during processing were a crucial impetus for Shapiro's development of cognitive interweaves (Shapiro, 2001). However, with childhood-onset C-PTSD, the client's processing may not be able to comb spontaneously through issues about responsibility—or even accept CIs about responsibility because of the following issues:

- *Responsibility and family of origin.* Responsibility issues are highly influenced by and entangled with their family of origin relational patterns and attachment considerations.
- *Packed dilemma.* Impeding family of origin patterns involve issues of entitlement, obligation, loyalty, and especially attachment (hence the term "packed dilemma").
- *Client accountability versus parental responsibility.* Clients may show confusion about what, in their families of origin, they were legitimately accountable for and entitled to, but also what holding a dysfunctional (or neglectful or abusive) parent responsible might *mean* about what the nature of that relationship had really been.
- *Idealization of the family.* Additionally, they may have reservations about how allowing shifts in responsibility could affect their idealized view of the family, current attachment relationships, or what might be possible in the future. The fears of losing attachment relationships, or their idealized view of the family (or family member), can feel so unacceptable to some patients that they will essentially forego fully processing a target memory rather than risk such losses.

Disrupted early attachment relationships appear to be an integral part of childhood-onset C-PTSD, and so we are likely to encounter the stuck NC situation when desensitizing these early disturbing memories. In fact, the relational aspects are often found to be what made the old experience so disturbing in the first place. Without having a way to deal with attachment issues, at some point during the desensitization phase, the client's processing will persistently loop. When this occurs, we need to "unpack" the different elements of the dilemma so that shifts in responsibility for the target memory do not result inevitably in further relational loss. With the dilemma unpacked, desensitization can proceed to an adaptive resolution, including the NC shifting to an appropriate PC. The protocol to do this comprises several small steps and it is rather painstaking. The energy and time required to unlock these old conundrums about the self are well worth it and we can then see the deep changes customary to EMDR.

How to Unpack These Dilemmas

Packed dilemmas usually require and respond to a protocol comprising a particular sequence of Socratic CIs, which disentangles two clusters of confusion in turn: first, responsibility and entitlement, and then responsibility and loyalty. Ordinarily, as EMDR therapists, we attempt to stay out of the way of the client's processing, and since CIs can influence processing, we use them sparingly. In a packed dilemma, however, we may *need* to influence the processing because the family attachment patterns are woven into issues of responsibility, which contribute to the embedded immobility of the NC. When these complications are addressed and processed, the NC is freed up to move. Socratic CIs help with this, by moving the client in small steps through "a series of easily answered questions . . . to lead a person to a logical conclusion" (Shapiro, 2001, p. 266).

The initial questions in the protocol are designed to pop the client *out* of the groove they are looping in and these CIs need to have considerable emotional impact. This looping is so powerfully driven by anxiety and avoidance that clients can appear to be essentially oblivious to their present surroundings. Cognitive interweaves based on introducing new perspectives or other rational considerations are usually not effective here because the affect they generate is not nearly as strong as the affect that is looping. To pop the client's processing out of the looping, the clinician needs to grab the client's attention with a simple and obvious question and then elicit a different strong emotion (than the ones that are looping), but one that is moving the processing into a more adaptive direction. Usually what works best for this are CIs designed to elicit the client's protectiveness toward their own children (especially when they were young).

Note: For clients with no children of their own, the clinician can inquire about any children that they know and care about, whether nieces and nephews, or children with whom they may work (e.g., for teachers, nurses, police officers, etc.), or children in their neighborhood, and so forth. The disentangling of the issues occurs in very small steps and as frequently as is possible, by using CI questions rather than statements. It is important throughout the protocol to keep in mind the following:

- Use short sets.
- Use several sets after each CI.
- Reiterate some portion of a CI to assist the client to make a next step.
- Solidly establish each step before proceeding to the next.

Structure of the Protocol for Releasing Stuck Negative Cognitions

The signal that Cluster 1 of this protocol is needed is when the clinician has offered CIs about responsibility, but the client cannot accept them and the processing continues to loop. The clinician can then step back and use Socratic CIs to help the client disentangle the issues a small step at a time. The following points are established in sequence. In the sessions, they are provided as CIs and so are framed as questions. The structure of the sequence is given here first, for clarity, and then the types of questions related to each step in the sequence are provided.

Releasing Stuck Negative Cognitions Protocol Script

Cluster 1: Structure and Questions to Address Issues of Responsibility and Entitlement

Step 1. Age of Client

Ask about the age of the client at the time of the target experience.

Say, *"How old were you when this experience happened?"*

_____

_____

Say, *"Go with that."*

_____

_____

Do short sets of bilateral stimulation (BLS) to install the CI. Check to see if the CI holds.
If so, move on to the next point in the sequence.
If not, work with this material further.

Step 2. Same Age Child Significant to Client

Ask the client if he remembers his daughter, son, or other significant child at that same age

Say, *"Do you remember when _____ (state name of son, daughter, or significant child in client's life) was _____ (at the same age)?"*

_____

_____

Say, *"Go with that."*

_____

_____

Do short sets of BLS to install the CI. Check to see if the CI holds.
If so, move on to the next point in the sequence.
If not, work with this material further.

Step 3. Children's Need and Entitlement for Caretaking

Elicit the need and entitlement of the client's daughter, son, or other significant child in the client's life at that age to receive caretaking.

Say, *"Did ____ (state name of son, daughter or important child in client's life) need to have parents?"*

_____

_____

Or say, *"Did* ___ (state name of son, daughter, or significant child in client's life) *deserve and need caretaking at this age?"*

_____

_____

Say, *"Go with that."*

_____

_____

Do short sets of BLS to install the CI. Check to see if the CI holds.
If so, move on to the next point in the sequence.
If not, work with this material further.

Step 4. Helplessness of Children and Need or Entitlement for Caretaking

Remind clients about the inherent helplessness of their daughter, son, or other significant children in clients' lives and of *all* children at that age; and, therefore, their need and entitlement to receive caretaking.

Say, *"Do you remember how helpless* ____ (state name of son, daughter, or significant child in client's life) *was at that age and how much he or she needed and was entitled to being cared for?"*

_____

_____

Say, *"Sure, and why did* _____ (he or she) *need parents and caretaking back then? Because* _____ (he or she) *was so young and needed parents to keep* _____ (him or her) *safe, to deal with and learn about the world, and help* _____ (him or her) *develop and grow.* _____ (He or she) *needed to be what* _____ (he or she) *was, a child, and to be able to lean on and depend on* _____ (his or her) *parents. Isn't that what all children need and are entitled to when they are* _____ (age at the time of target memory) *years old?"*

_____

_____

Say, *"Go with that."*

_____

_____

Do short sets of BLS to install the CI. Check to see if the CI holds.
If so, move on to the next point in the sequence.
If not, work with this material further.

Step 5. Legitimacy of Client's Need and Deserving Caretaking

Begin to gradually move the processing from all children needing and thus deserving caretaking to the legitimacy of the client at that age needing and deserving caretaking.

Note: Clients with childhood-onset C-PTSD often have little sense of entitlement about themselves. So, during processing, attempting to shift the client's understanding about the entitlement of *all* children to be taken care of directly to understanding their *own* entitlement is too abrupt and is usually rejected by the client. Instead, clients can usually accept this sensitive transition when a transitional figure of "that little 'X'-year-old back then" is used as a bridge. This refers only obliquely to the client in this step, with subsequent steps moving the entitlement closer to the client.

Here the adult perspective is introduced to contrast the position of the child back then, versus the adult vantage point now. This is because later in the protocol, the therapist will be contrasting them and drawing attention to the far greater resources of the current adult.

> Say, *"Looked at from this vantage point as an adult* (adult perspective CI), *wouldn't we say that when that little _____-year-old* (age of child) *back then needed and wanted to be able to rely on and lean on a parent, wasn't that just a normal thing for an ____-year-old* (age of child)*?"*

> _____

> _____

> Say, *"Go with that."*

> _____

> _____

Do short sets of BLS to install the CI. Check to see if the CI holds.
If so, move on to the next point in the sequence.
If not, work with this material further.

Step 6. Normalization of Current Client's Need and Entitlement Back Then

Establish the need and entitlement for caretaking for the client back then at that age—and normalize this for that client.

> Say, *"Are you beginning to see that you were just basically a normal _____-year-old* (age at the time of the trauma), *looking for what all children need and are entitled to, a parent who will try to help them?"*

> _____

> _____

> Say, *"Go with that."*

> _____

> _____

Do short sets of BLS to install the CI. Check to see if the CI holds.
If so, move on to the next point in the sequence.
If not, work with this material further.

Step 7. Client's Need and Entitlement for Caretaking Versus Unresponsive Adults

The client had both the need and entitlement for caretaking back then, but the adults did not respond to the child and they did not fulfill their obligation to provide that caretaking.

> Say, *"That young child both needed and was entitled to being cared for back then, but it was the adults who did not respond to _____* (him

or her) *nor did they fulfill their obligation to provide that caretaking for* _____ *(him or her)."*

_____

_____

Transition from Cluster 1 to Cluster 2

The signal that the second cluster is ready to be disentangled is when the client can now acknowledge and feel that the adults responsible to provide caretaking did not do so but that they should have. This is an important transition point in the transfer of responsibility. Usually the client will show confusion or mixed emotions and, after a couple of BLS sets, comment how dysfunctional or disabled the adults were.

Note: This is not a good point at which to end a session. It is better to stop after Step 5 in the first cluster, and in the following session review the sequence of Steps 1 through 5, including the client's own responses, finish Steps 6 and 7 in Cluster 1, then proceed to the six steps of Cluster 2.

When the client begins to comment about how disabled the adults were, this is usually the old relational pattern emerging; this will hold the NC in its stuck position. So, this is the point at which to begin disentangling the second cluster. Without the use of CIs here, these clients tend to slide back into loyalty and sympathy for the adults' dysfunctional behaviors and resume looping. The following sequence of CIs shunts the processing away from that old pattern in a way that most clients can accept and so can continue processing.

Cluster 2: Structure and Types of Questions for the Issue of Disentangling the Old Relational Pattern

Step 1. Identify Divergent or Complicated Feelings

Identify that it is feeling complicated right now and name the two (or more) sets of feelings.

> Say, *"It sounds like it's feeling complicated. Is it that on the one hand you're feeling* _____ (name one of the feelings the client is having that is sympathetic to the adult responsible for the abuse or the characteristic of the adult at the time of the target memory) *and yet on the other hand you're feeling* _____ (name the other feeling the client is having that demonstrates the client's beginning ability to acknowledge the abusing adult's responsibility for the abuse or the characteristic of the adult back then)*?"*

_____

_____

Say, *"Go with that."*

Do short sets of BLS to install the CI. Check to see if the CI holds.
If so, move on to the next point in the sequence.
If not, work with this material further.

Step 2. Dilemma: Holding Good Feelings and Bad Feelings Even When the Situation is Complicated

There is a dilemma: the feelings are complicated because the situation (or the adult in the target memory) was complicated: acknowledge the two elements or sides of the situation or adult. But note that one side does not erase nor cancel out the other side; both sides remain true.

> Say, *"Sure, that makes sense doesn't it? It is complicated because on the one hand, there are _____ (name one of the feelings back then or the characteristics of the adult back then) feelings, but on the other hand there are _____ (name the other feeling or characteristic of the adult back then) feelings. The thing is, one side doesn't erase the other side or cancel it out. They're both true, aren't they?"*

> _____

> _____

> Say, *"Go with that."*

> _____

> _____

> Do short sets of BLS to install the CI. Check to see if the CI holds.
> If so, move on to the next point in the sequence.
> If not, work with this material further.

Step 3. Adult: Feelings Complicated Not Confusing

For the adult, the feelings are complicated but not confusing.

> Say, *"So, the feelings* (or the two sides of the adult in the traumatic memory) *will probably remain complicated, but not confusing, to you as an adult now. Back then, it was too much to figure out, but now with the experience and perspective of a _____-year-old* (client's current age), *do you have the resources to begin to sort it out?"*

> _____

> _____

> Say, *"Go with that."*
> Do short sets of BLS to install the CI. Check to see if the CI holds.

> _____

> _____

> If so, move on to the next point in the sequence.
> If not, work with this material further.

Step 4. Adults Have Greater Resources Than Children

The adult has more resources. If needed, use CIs to establish an awareness of the client's greater resources as an adult.

> Say, *"Can you think of a resource that you already have that would be helpful for you to use in this situation?"*

> _____

> _____

Or say, *"Remember that time that you were able to* _____ (state the resource)*? Wasn't it a good resource for you?"*

_____

_____

Say, *"Go with that."*
Do short sets of BLS to install the CI. Check to see if the CI holds.
If so, move on to the next point in the sequence.
If not, work with this material further.

Step 5. Adults Can Hold Different Feelings

As an adult, the client can recognize and hold both sets of feelings (or realizations), and can encompass them at the same time in a way that is not possible as a child.

Say, *"So, given all this, can you now recognize and hold both sets of feelings* (or both sets of realizations)*, at the same time, in a way you couldn't back then as a child?"*

_____

_____

Say, *"Go with that."*
Do short sets of BLS to install the CI. Check to see if the CI holds.

_____

_____

If so, move on to the next point in the sequence.
If not, work with this material further.

Step 6. New Perspectives: New PC

The client is beginning to understand the old experience in a different way and beginning to see himself in a different way, too. Develop the client's new PC with several short sets of BLS.

Say, *"So, for you now, can you begin to understand that old experience in a new way and see yourself somewhat differently at this point in time?"*

_____

_____

Say, *"Go with that."*
Do short sets of BLS to install the CI. Check to see if the CI holds.

_____

_____

Check in for a Positive Cognition.

Say, *"When you think of the event* (or incident)*, do the words* _____ (repeat the PC) *still fit, or is there another positive statement you feel would be more suitable?"*

_____

_____

Or say, *"What did you learn today?"*

_____

_____

Say, *"Go with that."*

_____

_____

Clinical Example

Presenting Problem

The following is a partial transcript of using the scripted protocol during EMDR with a woman who was sexually abused by her father as a child. The target memory is her initial memory of when the abuse became much more serious when she was an 8-year-old. At this point in the desensitization of the target memory, the client has been processing different aspects of the traumatic experience and is talking about how she feels:

Client:	*"Panic, from seeing things from* (the memory)*."*
Therapist:	*"It's old stuff, just notice it."*
Client:	*"Stop it. Stop it."* (She is very tearful now and speaking to the father.)
Therapist:	*"It's old stuff and just notice it."*
Client:	*"Even if I'd yelled that, he'd of done it."*

We do two sets of BLS but the client begins to loop around her feelings that she should have yelled anyway.

Therapist uses a CI for responsibility:

Therapist:	*"So, who had all the power?"*
Client:	*"He did."*
Therapist:	*"Go with that."*

Uses a short set. She seems to accept it but it does not go anywhere. Rather than progressing, even a little, about the theme of her having no power back then—and therefore no responsibility—she switches the topic.

Client:	*"She never helped. My mother never helped. She heard what he was doing."*

Uses a short set of BLS.

Client:	*"I'd always pretended that she didn't know, that she'd have saved me if she knew. How stupid is that? What a*

little wimp. Why was I such a wimp? Why didn't I do something?"

The client begins to loop again about being a wimp and that she should have done something. I offer another CI around responsibility invoking her two sisters as well as herself.

Therapist: *"Back then, as an 8-year-old, would either of them* (i.e., the parents) *listen to any of you?"*
Client: *"No."*

She resumes looping. This is the signal to begin Step 1 of the protocol. The client has desensitized considerable disturbance but is persistently looping and the usual interventions have not helped. The clinician has offered CIs about responsibility but the client cannot accept them. The clinician steps back from the unsuccessful attempts at processing the distorted NCs the client is generating around the issues of responsibility and begins to unpack the first cluster using Socratic CIs. The initial questions are designed to first get the looping to stop by grabbing the client's attention and eliciting a different strong emotion than the one she is currently looping about. After each CI and client response, very short sets of BLS are provided as long as the client's responses are developing in an adaptive direction. At times, the clinician repeats some aspect of a CI if the client has become confused. All this is to solidly establish each step before proceeding to the next.

Cluster 1—The Confusion of Responsibility With Entitlement

Step 1. Age of Client

Ask age of client at the time of the target experience.

Therapist: *"Unh-huh, and how old were you when that happened?"*
Client: *"Eight."*
Therapist: *"Go with that."*

Provide a very short set to install the new response.

Client: *"Yep, I was eight."*
Therapist: *"Unh-huh."*

Therapist moves on to next question of the protocol. If the client's response was not well established, the therapist would work to solidify it before going on to the next step of the protocol. However, here the client's response is very definite, so the therapist can see that her response is holding and the therapist can move to the next question.

Note: It is important here not to ask "What do you notice?" because the idea is not to have them noticing all kinds of things; in this kind of situation what the client will notice is a compulsive repeat of the old affective and relational patterns—the looping is almost like a tic! The therapist is trying hard

(continued)

to nudge them away from looping. So here, when the client said "Eight (years old)" and the therapist said, " Great—go with that," use a very short set, just to set it in a bit. This is just a little step in a Socratic sequence, so you are moving her along in the direction toward a more adaptive perspective. Later, the therapist needs to follow up on some of the client's responses with BLS to help either process disturbance or to install a positive shift, however at this point be careful to not open anything up. Just steer!

Step 2. Same Age Child, Significant to Client

Ask client if she remembers her daughter or son at that same age.

Therapist:	*"Do you remember when your daughter was 8 years old?"*
Client:	*"Well, yes."*

Client looks a bit confused.

Therapist:	*"Go with that."*

Do short sets of BLS to install the CI. Check to see if the CI holds. If so, move on to the next point in the sequence. If not, work with this material further.

Therapist:	*"What's coming up about that?"*
Client:	*"Well, sure I remember when she was eight."*

CI is holding, so move on to the next point in the sequence.

Step 3. Child's Need and Entitlement for Caretaking

Establish the need and entitlement of the client's daughter or son at that age to receive caretaking.

Therapist:	*"Did she need to have parents?"*
Client:	*"What do you mean?"*

Client looks confused, but it is the kind of confusion we sometimes see when a person has been jogged out of their usual thought patterns.

Therapist:	*"Would you have wanted her orphaned, to have to meet the world alone?"*
Client:	*"Of course not."*

Client responds with considerable asperity here. This strong protective feeling is what we are looking for in this protocol and it is worth building up.

Therapist:	*"Sure and why not?"*
Client:	*"Because she was too young, an 8-year-old can't handle that."*

Build on this and then move to the next step.

(continued)

Therapist: *"Go with that."*

Do short sets of BLS to install the CI. Check to see if the CI holds.

Therapist: *"What's coming up about that?"*
Client: *"8-year-olds can't do it all by themselves."*

The client's response is holding (i.e., solidly accepting the CI and reinforcing her first response to the CI), so I move on to the next point in the sequence. If not, work with this material further.

Step 4. Helplessness of Children and Need or Entitlement for Caretaking

Establish the inherent helplessness of their daughter or son and of all children at that age and therefore their need and entitlement to receive caretaking.

Therapist: *"Unh-huh, of course she couldn't, she was still too young yet. She needed parents to keep her safe, to deal with and learn about the world, and to help her develop and grow. She needed to be able to be what she was, a child, and to be able to lean on and depend on her parents. Isn't that what all children need and are entitled to when they are 8 years old?"*
Client: *"Yes."*

Client is weeping openly now.

Therapist: *"Go with that."*

Do short sets of BLS to install the CI. Check to see if the CI holds.

Therapist: *"What's coming up about that?"*
Client: *"Well, sure."*

The therapist moves on to the next step in the sequence. If not, work with this material further.

Step 5. Legitimacy of Client's Need and Deserving Caretaking

Shift the focus to a transitional figure of "that little 'X-year-old' back then (the client) and establish that child's need for and entitlement (like all children) to receive caretaking.

Therapist: *"Looked at from this vantage point as an adult* (CI: adult perspective), *wouldn't we say that when that little 8-year-old girl back then needed and wanted to be able to rely on and lean on a parent, wasn't that just a normal thing for an 8-year-old?"*

(continued)

Client:	*"Well, yes, I guess it was."*
Therapist:	*"Go with that."*

Do short sets of BLS to install the CI. Check to see if the CI holds.

Therapist:	*"What's coming up about that?"*
Client:	*"Well it was—an 8-year-old wants to be able to lean on an adult."*

Therapist can move on to the next step in the sequence because the CI is holding. If not, work with this material further.

Step 6. Normalization of Current Client's Need and Entitlement Back Then

Bring it closer to the client back then at that age and establish his or her need and entitlement for caretaking in a way that normalizes it, given the above progression.

Therapist:	*"Are you beginning to see that you were just basically a normal 8-year-old, looking for what all children need and are entitled to, a parent who will try to help them?"*
Client:	*"Yes."*

Client is showing considerable affect and open weeping.

Therapist:	*"Go with that."*

Do short sets of BLS to install the CI. Check to see if the CI holds.

Therapist:	*"What do you notice now?"*
Client:	*"I'm really sad, I just wanted a parent, a real parent."*
Therapist:	*"Go with that."*

Because the client is experiencing disturbance, the therapist provides a longer, desensitizing set of BLS.

Therapist:	*"And what do you notice now?"*
Client:	*"What was going on anyway?"*

Because the client has processed her disturbance and is showing an openness to looking at the old situation differently, the therapist can move on to the next point in the sequence. If not, work with this material further.

Step 7. Client's Need and Entitlement for Caretaking Versus Unresponsive Adults

The client had both the need and entitlement for caretaking back then, but the adults did not respond to it or fulfill their obligation to provide that caretaking.

(continued)

Therapist: *"So, looked at again from the perspective of an adult, should she have tried to help you even if she couldn't always succeed, should she have tried to help you?"*

Client: *"Yes, they were both just so fucked up. They were miserable with each other and hateful to each other and put us in the middle. They used us to meet their needs, they came first."*

Therapist: *"Go with that."*

Do short sets of BLS to install the CI. Check to see if the CI holds.

Therapist: *"What do you notice?"*

Client: *"He was out of control, he couldn't manage himself."*

The old attachment pattern of caretaking toward this parent is beginning to emerge.

Therapist: *"Just notice that."*

Therapist provides short set of BLS.

Therapist: *"And what are you noticing about that now?"*

Client: *"I have both feelings on right now—angry, hating, and love."*

Therapist: *"Go with that."*

Do short sets of BLS to install the CI. Check to see if the CI holds.

Therapist: *"What do you notice about that?"*

Client: *"Same."*

Cluster 2—Separating Responsibility From Loyalty

The signal that the second cluster is ready to be disentangled is when the client can now acknowledge and feel that the adults responsible to provide caretaking did not do so, but that they *should* have (the transition point in the transfer of responsibility). She is showing mixed emotions and is commenting about how dysfunctional the adults were, but in a manner that can swiftly relieve the adults of their responsibility. The old relational pattern is emerging and this is what will hold the NC in its stuck position. This is the point at which to begin disentangling the second cluster. Without the provision of CIs here, this client was heading back into her old loyalty and sympathy position toward the adults' dysfunctional behaviors and, presumably, would resume looping. The

(continued)

following sequence of CIs shunts the processing away from that old pattern in a way that most clients can accept and so can continue processing.

Step 1. Identify Divergent or Complicated Feelings

Inquire whether this feeling is complicated right now, and identify the two (or more) sets of feelings.

Therapist: *"It sounds like it's feeling complicated? That you feel some sympathy for your father but that you can also see more clearly how he was responsible for the sexual abuse?"*
Client: *"Yes."*

The client is nodding.

Therapist: *"Go with that."*

Do short sets of BLS to install the CI. Check to see if the CI holds.

Therapist: *"What do you notice?"*
Client: *"There's a lot, but it's everywhere."*

If so, move on to the next step in the sequence. If not, work with this material further.

Step 2. Dilemma: Holding Good Feelings and Bad Feelings Even When the Situation is Complicated

There is a dilemma: the feelings are complicated because the situation or the adult in the target memory was complicated; here is an acknowledgement of the two elements or sides of the situation or adult. But note that one side does not erase nor cancel the other side out, both sides remain true.

Therapist: *"Sure, that's okay. It is complicated. He was the one that you could sometimes get taken care of by, but he was also responsible for the abuse. The thing is, one side does not erase the other side or cancel it out. They are both true, aren't they?"*
Client: *"Yeeessss."*

Client is nodding head slowly and looking very intent.

Therapist: *"Go with that."*

Do short sets of BLS to install the CI. Check to see if the CI holds.

Therapist: *"What do you notice about that?"*
Client: *"Yes, I guess they are, both of them."*

If so, move on to the next step in the sequence. If not, work with this material further.

(continued)

Step 3. Adult: Feelings Complicated Not Confusing

For the adult, the feelings are complicated but not confusing.

> Therapist: *"So, the feelings will probably remain complicated, but not confusing, to you as an adult now. Back then, it was too much to figure out, but now with the experience and perspective of a _____ (state the age) year-old, do you have the resources to begin to sort it all out?"*
>
> Client: *"Oh yes."*

The client is still looking very intent but nodding vigorously at this point.

> Therapist: *"Go with that."*

Therapist provides short BLS set, to strengthen the client's new learning.

> Therapist: *"And what are you noticing about that?"*
>
> Client: *"Oh, Unh-huh, sure. They don't have to blend. That's just the way things are."*

Step 4. Adults Have Greater Resources Than Children

The adult has more resources than a child. If the client cannot quite make that jump, use CIs to establish awareness of greater resources as an adult.

Examples of Socratic CI Resources series are the following: If the situation is especially stuck, the clinician may even want to begin with Socratic CIs that are almost ridiculously incontrovertible as adult resources. For example, one might ask in a series of questions and responses from a client. This is an example but you could use anything comparable and relevant to your client.

> Therapist: *"Oh, well, let me ask, do you drive a car now?"*
>
> Client: *"Well, yeesss."*
>
> Therapist: *"Go with that."*

Do short sets of BLS to install the CI. Check to see if the CI holds.

> Therapist: *"What do you notice about that?"*
>
> Client: *"Well, sure I drive a car, everyday."*

If so, move on to the next step in the sequence. If not, work with this material further.

> Therapist: *"Unh-huh, and so you have a license to operate a vehicle now?"*
>
> Client: *"Duh! Of course!"*
>
> Therapist: *"Go with that."*

Do short sets of BLS to install the CI. Check to see if the CI holds.

(continued)

Therapist: *"What do you notice about that?"*
Client: *"Just the same."*

If so, move on to the next point in the sequence. If not, work with this material further.

Therapist: *"Unh-huh, and let me ask, aren't you holding down a full-time job right now?"*
Client: *"Yeah, yeah. You know, I can see where you're going with that!"*
Therapist: *"Well sure. It's okay, just go with that, okay?"*

Do short sets of BLS to install the CI. Check to see if the CI holds.

Therapist: *"What do you notice?"*
Client: *"Yes, I do work full time now."*

If so, move on to the next step in the sequence. If not, work with this material further.

Therapist: *"And so, unlike back then, you can support your-self financially* (or contribute to the family income, etc.)*?"*
Client: *"Yes."*
Therapist: *"Go with that."*

Do short sets of BLS to install the CI. Check to see if the CI holds.

Therapist: *"What do you notice?"*
Client: *"I can support myself by myself if I need to."*

If so, move on to the next step in the sequence. If not, work with this material further.

Therapist: *"So, in fact, can you see that now you can do things that back then, no child, no matter how bright or motivated, could have possibly managed?"*
Client: *"Absolutely."*
Therapist: *"Go with that."*

Do short sets of BLS to install the CI. Check to see if the CI holds.

Therapist: *"What do you notice about that now?"*
Client: *"Well, sure. Things are different now."*

If it is moving, go on to the next step in the sequence.
If not, work with this material further.

When the client's realization of having greater resources is well established, the clinician can return to the CIs about whether the client can now manage to hold both sets of realizations and both sets of feelings together, at the same time. It might look something like:

(continued)

Therapist: *"So, in view of all the above resources you now have as an adult and are now so much more aware of, can you begin to hold both sets of realizations and feelings at the same time?"*

Client: *"Oh yes* (looking very intent but nodding vigorously)*."*

Reinforce with several short sets the client's new ability to simultaneously hold complicated feelings without becoming confused.

Therapist: *"Go with that."*

Use BLS.

Therapist: *"What do you get now?"*
Client: *"It's just true. Isn't it? All the realizations are true. It's weird but it's just what is."*

Step 5. Adults Can Hold Different Feelings

As an adult, the client can recognize and hold both sets of feelings or realizations and encompass them, at the same time in a way not possible as a child.

Therapist: *"So, given all this, can you now recognize and hold both sets of feelings* (or both sets of realizations)*, at the same time, in a way you couldn't back then, as a child?"*

Client: *"Oh yes, they are both true, both sides."*

Step 6. New Perspectives: New PC

Beginning to understand the old experience in a different way and beginning to see herself in a different way, too. Develop the client's new PC with short sets of BLS.

Therapist: *"Now, can you begin to understand that old experience in a new way and see yourself somewhat differently now?"*

Client: *"Oh yeah, I didn't do anything wrong back then, I didn't do too bad, I wasn't fucked up then, and I'm not ways fucked up now. I'm going to be fine now. Can you believe all what went on back then?"*

She is shaking her head with occasional small bursts of tearfulness.

Therapist: *"Yes I can, can you?"*
Client: *"Oh yes, I can. Oh yes."*
Therapist: *"Go with that."*

Use a short set of BLS.

(continued)

Therapist: *"What do you get now?"*
Client: *"I was reacting naturally back then. I was okay. I'm fine."*

We had used up our time, but at this point the client's SUD level was down to a 1. If she had had a higher level, we might have used Calming Place for a few minutes, or she might have taken a seat in the waiting room to do her calming routine. However, after this session, we talked for a couple of minutes about returning to this target memory the next week and reviewed her plans for after the session. Because she had desensitized several target memories before this one, she was familiar with the procedures of giving herself some time before getting into her car to drive; her usual routine was to go to a local café and have something hot to drink while she just sat there quietly, and then she would go on to do a couple of errands in town before returning to work. So we talked about which café she'd go to and this author reminded her of the usual auto caution and we scheduled our next appointment. She knew she could call me if need be and already knew my availability structure.

After the reevaluation the following week, she reported that the SUD = 5 (and did not become a total 0 because of ecological validity).

Reevaluation

Client: *"Now, for the first time, I feel bad about some of the things I did to my parents when I was younger. I was just so mad, so frozen in my anger. It's so much easier just despising them for the horrible things they did to me and my sisters. But, I was so stuck and it all kept going in my head. Now, I'm out of it."*

Acknowledgments

The issues around accountability, the inherent entitlement of children to receive care, obligation, and loyalty are based on "contextual therapy," the work of Ivan Boszormenyi-Nagy and his colleagues, including Barbara Krasner, Margaret Cotroneo, David Ulrich, and Geraldine Spark (1986).

PART IV

EMDR and Clients With Addictive Behaviors

Early work with addictive behaviors and EMDR first came in the form of A. J. Popky's Smoking Cessation Protocol. In the December *Network Newsletter*, Ron Martinez (1992) referenced it in his "EMDR: Innovative Uses" column and noted that it was available from Dr. Popky by request. By 1993, Vogelmann-Sine and Sine (1993a) wrote about "EMDR With Clients in Recovery From Chemical Dependency" in the winter newsletter of that year. They posited five important steps to address while working with this population: arriving at an accurate diagnosis, developing a treatment program, educating clients about EMDR, timing the use of EMDR, and increasing clients' readiness to benefit from EMDR. They go on to address unresolved issues and questions in their article. All three explained their work at the second and third annual EMDR conferences in California those years (Popky, 1993, 1994; Vogelmann-Sine, & Sine, 1993b; 1994).

In 1995, Dr. Popky began to give his specialty program on the Addiction Protocol, as it was then known, during the EMDR Level II trainings (1995b). He also reported on an addictions research project in the newsletter (1995c) and presented it at the EMDR Networker meeting in Sunnyvale, California (1995a), that he was developing in conjunction with Drs. Vogelmann-Sine and Sine. This group—adding Lazrove, Speare, Wade, and Wade—presented "Symposium: Advanced Clinical Applications of EMDR to Addictive Behaviors" (Vogelmann-Sine et al., 1995) at the EMDR International Association Conference in Santa Monica, California.

Drs. Popky, Vogelmann-Sine, Carlson, and Sine reported on their project at the EMDR International Association Conference in Denver, Colorado, on "Addictions: An Integrative Approach and Research Design" (1996). Vogelmann-Sine, Sine, and Popky followed this up with their presentation "EMDR Treatment for Chemical Dependency: Training for Participation in a Multisite Study" (1997).

Drs. Vogelmann-Sine, Sine, Smyth, and Popky created a comprehensive and flexible treatment manual (1998) that incorporated EMDR into a recovery program for clients with chemical dependency. Their text included assessment and clinical applications for the particular protocols that they used for this population. Drs. Smyth, Vogelmann-Sine, and Sine (1998) went on to present this at the EMDR International Association Conference in Baltimore, Maryland. In 1998, Dr. Smyth pursued her interest in EMDR and addictions by presenting at the Arbour Health Conference in Buffalo, New York on "Eye Movement Desensitization and Reprocessing: Research and Clinical Applications: Linking Theory with Practice."

Dr. Popky (1999) continued to develop his protocol as his database grew and he changed its name to DeTUR, which stands for the desensitization of triggers and urge reprocessing. He presented on this protocol at several EMDR conferences (2002, 2003) and then wrote a chapter in Robin Shapiro's *EMDR Solutions* (2005) on the same subject.

Michael Hase, an EMDR Europe Trainer in Germany, began his work in the area of addictions by looking at the idea of the addiction memory; these are memories of clients' experiences of drug consumption, relapse, and of intense cravings. He found that when he had his clients process these memories, they showed a significant reduction in craving 1 month out of treatment and less relapse 6 months later. Dr. Hase (2005, 2006) began preliminary research and reported on his results at the EMDR European Association Annual Conference (2005) and in the following year at the EMDR International Association Conference (2006). His article on this subject appeared in the *Journal of EMDR Practice and Research* (Hase, Schallmayer, & Sack, 2008). Dr. Hase's work inspired two other colleagues who have written (Earley, 2007) and presented on this topic (Rougemont-Buecking, 2007).

There have been several other articles written about addictive behaviors and EMDR. Cox and Howard (2007) wrote on the "Utilization of EMDR in the Treatment of Sexual Addiction: A Case Study for the journal *Sexual Addiction & Compulsivity*" by exploring the connection between trauma in the etiology and treatment of sexual addiction. Zweben and Yeary (2006) wrote about "EMDR in the Treatment of Addiction" in the *Journal of Chemical Dependency Treatment* emphasizing the importance of safety while using this with a vulnerable population. Brown, Gilman, and Kelso (2008) presented their "Integrated Trauma Treatment Program: A Novel EMDR Approach for PTSD and Substance Abuse," a 4–year pilot program using EMDR and Seeking Safety© an integrated trauma treatment program in a Drug Court. At the 20th EMDR: A Conference Susan Brown, Sara Gilman, and A. J. Popky (2009) presented on "using the DeTur™ Model and EMDR to Treat Addictions and Impulse Control Disorders while Jamie March (2009) presented the results of her dissertation and suggested a series of general guidelines for using EMDR with recovering alcoholics.

In 1995, Jim Knipe addressed other types of addictive behaviors when he looked in depth at the concept of how to address defensive avoidance. He wrote about it in the *EMDR Network Newsletter* (1995) and later went on to pursue the topic more thoroughly in his chapter, "It was a Golden Time . . . Treating Narcissistic Vulnerability" in Phillip Manfield's edited book, *Extending EMDR: A Casebook of Innovative Applications* (1998). His question was how to address the embedded strong positive affect that was compelling his clients to engage in this behavior. The same year, he presented on this topic at the EMDR International Conference (Manfield, Knipe, & Snyker, 1998) and continued to write about his findings in the *EMDRIA Newsletter* (Knipe, 1999). Knipe wrote another chapter expanding this subject, "Targeting Positive Affect to Clear the Pain of Unrequited Love, Codependence, Avoidance, and Procrastination" in Robin Shapiro's, *EMDR Solutions* (2005). Dr. Knipe presented "EMDR Toolbox" around the world (2006, 2007, 2008) as he continued to develop his expertise and share it with other clinicians.

The chapters 33 to 36 in this section on addictive behaviors begin with Knipe targeting dysfunctional positive affect. By working with a topic that many practitioners encounter on a regular basis, Dr. Knipe opens up a whole new realm of dealing with stuck processing. His chapters on working with clients with unwanted avoidance defenses, procrastination, the pain of unrequited love, and codependence or obsession with self-defeating behavior are fascinating as he takes us through how to address these issues and move into further trauma processing.

Hase's work (chapter 37) is on extinguished cravings or CravEx and his protocol follows the idea of addressing the addictive memory mentioned above as the core approach to treating addictions. Popky's exposition of his DeTUR protocol (chapter 38) steps us through the facets of his treatment with ways to address this complex topic. All of these chapters shed some light on different ways to address the difficulty of addictive behaviors.

33

Dysfunctional Positive Affects: To Assist Clients With Unwanted Avoidance Defenses

Jim Knipe

Unwanted Avoidance Defenses Script Notes

When working with ambivalence, it is helpful to identify the two or more sides of the ambivalence, such as the client who wants to work on a disturbing memory but is too afraid, or the client who wants to have an important conversation with someone but says, "I never get around to it," and so forth. Sometimes, if the client impulsively uses avoidance and is frustrated with her ambivalence, the most accessible point of entry into effectively using EMDR to process a problem may be to target the feeling of relief associated with avoiding that problem.

Do not use this with a client who truly does not wish to work with a disturbing thought or memory, but only with clients who have unwanted (and perhaps very strong) avoidance impulses.

These procedures were partially derived from Popky's Desensitization of Triggers and Urge Reprocessing (DeTUR) Protocol for using EMDR to treat addictive behaviors. Popky's approach (Popky, 1994) fits into the model described here, in that, generally, addictive behaviors tend to be maintained and reinforced by the stress relief associated with using. The level of urge to avoid (LoUA) method is simply extending Popky's approach to those individuals who habitually use mental, not substance-assisted, avoidance to contain disturbing material (Shapiro, 2005).

This procedure may be used when the issue or memory that is being avoided has already been identified by the client. The method can even be used in situations where the therapist does not know the specifics of the avoided material. For example, the client might say, "There is something (memory or issue) I want to get over, but I don't want to tell you what it is." All that is required is that the client can identify the issue or memory, and be able to tell the therapist if changes in the avoidance urge are occurring during processing.

To Assist Clients With Unwanted Avoidance Defenses Script

Say, *"Can you make an image of what you want to avoid?"*

_____

_____

Say, *"When you realize that we have the whole session in front of us and plenty of time to work on ___ (state the issue), how much on the 0 to 10 scale do you not want to think of it (or 'are not able to tell me about it')? I know that intellectually you really wish to do this work, because you know that it will help. But what I am asking is, how much is your gut-level urge to think or talk about something else, to get away from it?"*

_____

_____

0	1	2	3	4	5	6	7	8	9	10
(no urge to avoid)								(most urge to avoid)		

Say, *"Where is that _____ (state number) in your body right now?"*

_____

_____

Say, *"Would you be willing to stay with that feeling? That feeling of not wanting to talk or think of it, while you _____ (state type of BLS). Just stay with the feeling of how much you don't want to ____ (think of that)."*

_____

_____

Use bilateral stimulation (BLS).

Say, *"When you realize we now have ___ (state the minutes left in the session), and we could use that remaining time working with this old memory or issue, how much on our 0 to 10 scale do you not want to right now?"*

_____

_____

0	1	2	3	4	5	6	7	8	9	10
(no urge to avoid)								(most urge to avoid)		

Usually, when this procedure is used, the LoUA scores will go down with continuing sets of BLS, until the client spontaneously begins direct targeting of the memory or issue. Then, use the Standard EMDR Protocol to directly target the incident. Often, during this processing, clients will make connections between avoidance urges and difficult childhood events in which avoidance was the only available option. If, during processing, the avoidance urge remains strong, there may be hidden traumatic material (e.g., a perpetrator who threatened harm if the child ever told of abuse). If the client is able to identify this trauma, even in their unspoken thoughts, this method is a useful option to facilitate processing.

34

Dysfunctional Positive Affect: Procrastination

Jim Knipe

Procrastination Script Notes

One way of thinking about procrastination is to regard it as a form of addiction; an addiction to putting things off. As with other addictive patterns, the client will choose a short-term gratification (i.e., of delay and avoidance) instead of going for a long-term result that might, in the end, be more satisfying or empowering. As with other addictions, a procrastinating client often suffers ongoing erosion of her self-esteem. Quite often, procrastination may function as a defense—as a way to avoid other life issues that are disturbing.

With this type of problem, we can use a variation of Popky's (1994) addiction protocol, and the level of urge to avoid (LoUA) procedure. In order to begin this procedure, it is necessary for the therapist to know the specific times when the client has a problem with procrastination. It is also important to use resource installation procedures to help the client develop an image of the benefits (including more comfortable physical sensations) that would come with being free of this problem.

Procrastination Script

Say, *"Tell me about your problem with procrastination."*

_____

_____

Say, *"Would you like it if you could get over procrastinating, so that it is no longer a problem in your life?"*

_____

_____

Installation of a Positive Resource of a Procrastination-Free Day in the Future

Say, *"Think of a day in the future when you no longer have this problem with procrastination. On that day, what 'positives' would you have in your life? How would your life be different or what goodies would you have in your life that you do not have now, while you still have this procrastination problem?"*

_____

_____

Say, *"So get a picture in your mind that really represents that day in the future when you really no longer have any problem with procrastination."*

_____

_____

At this point, the therapist can help the client create a positive visual image that incorporates all of the positive elements that have been identified by the client. The client may be able to access a positive image easily, or, if not, the therapist can put all of the elements together in a representative positive image and offer it to the client.

For example, say, *"The space has opened up, you feel good about yourself. You feel relaxed and comfortable. You have a nice feeling of trust in yourself that you can easily focus on doing all the things that need to be done. Just think of this day in the future. Get a picture of it. What are you doing on this day in the future to enjoy your time? Make it really positive."*

_____

_____

Say, *"Is this a nice image for you to think of?"*

_____

_____

Say, *"Just hold that picture in your mind and make it bright and clear with colors, get an image of it. It really feels good. Add in anything else that makes it feel even more positive. Just notice how good that feels."*

_____

_____

Give the client time to access and develop the positive image.

Then say, *"Does that feel good right now?"*

_____

_____

Say, *"Notice where that good feeling is in your body. Now just continue thinking of that and enjoying that and ___ (state type of bilateral stimulation [BLS])."*

_____

_____

As the client is processing, say words such as the following:

Say, *"That's right. Just enjoy that. Just enjoy being there and now step into the picture. That's right."*

_____

_____

Stop BLS.

Say, *"How is that?"*

_____

_____

Then say, *"Just continue to think of that."*

_____

_____

To create an association with the positive physical sensations, the client may be asked to use BLS with the Butterfly Hug (crossing arms over chest and using the tips of your fingers from each hand to touch the area under the connection between the clavicle and shoulder then alternate self-tap or see chapter 1 in this book).

Say, *"And while you are enjoying that, take your hands like this (thera-pist demonstrates) and tap your own chest, noticing those feelings in your body, the nice feelings of enjoyment, while you think of _____ (state the nice feelings in the client's body)."*

_____

_____

Directly Target the Procrastination Urge

Now say, *"Okay, now let's shift gears a little bit. You said you have a problem with procrastination. Now, bring to mind a really clear example—a representative example of what is really problematic to you—about procrastinating."*

_____

_____

Say, *"Can you get a representative image of that, of your problem with procrastinating?"*

_____

_____

Say, *"If you were to simply solve the _____ (state the major problem) when you go home today, what if you really got it in your head with a sense of determination, today is the day I am going to solve this problem of ____ (state the problem), what would you do?"*

_____

_____

Say, *"Okay, so here's a question. Think of _____ (describe the visual image that represents the problem of procrastination), and when you think of that right now and that work that needs to be done, how much on a scale of 0 to 10 where 0 is hardly any urge and 10 is the most urge, do you want to just go do something else?"*

0	1	2	3	4	5	6	7	8	9	10
(no urge)										(most urge)

Say, *"And where is that ___ (state number) in your body right now?"*

_____

_____

Say, *"Can you hold in your mind right now—that urge to do something else? Make it as if you were right there. You haven't decided yet, maybe you are going to do something about _____ (state the problem) or maybe you are going to do something else. Just be aware of that urge to go do something else. Go with that."*

_____

_____

Do BLS. As the client is processing the material, say the following:

Say, *"Just be aware of how strong the urge is to do something else. That's good. Just go with that."*

_____

_____

Say, *"Okay, now take a deep breath and go back to the situation we started with. You could do _____ (describe the work behavior) or you could do something else, what do you get right now?"*

_____

_____

Say, *"Go with that."*

_____

_____

Then say, *"Go back again. You are* _____ (state the behavior that is a problem). *How strong is the urge right now to go do something else on the 0 to 10 scale, where 0 is hardly any urge and 10 is the most urge to do something else? It might not change or maybe it has changed. Okay, what do you get now when you think of procrastinating about* _____ (state the problem)?*"*

0	1	2	3	4	5	6	7	8	9	10
(no urge)									(most urge)	

If it is still an issue, do what follows:

Say, *"Go back again to* _____ (state the problem). *How strong is the urge right now to do something else on our 0 to 10 scale? Again, it might not change or maybe it has changed?"*

0	1	2	3	4	5	6	7	8	9	10
(no urge)									(most urge)	

If it is 1 or higher, say the following:

Say, *"Okay, let's talk about that* ____ (state number). *What's that about?"*

_____

_____

Whatever the client's answer, say the following

Say, *"Stay with that* (do another set of BLS).*"*

_____

_____

Say, *"Go back again to it and see if there's any urge left, even a trace, any urge to do something else instead of* _____ (state the problem).*"*

_____

_____

When it is still 1 or higher, do the following:

Say, *"Here is another question. 'Would you like it to be a 0'?"*

_____

_____

Or, *"What prevents it from being a 0?"*

_____

_____

Say, *"Okay, now go back and look at* _____ (state the problem) *and what do you get?"*

_____

_____

Whatever the client's answer, continue the processing:

Say, *"Stay with that."*

_____

_____

Do another set of BLS.

If the client has had an insight into the connection between the behavior and procrastination, say the following:

Say, *"We have been working on the issue of* _____ (state the insight the client has had). *Can you see the connection with procrastination? Does it help you see that connection?"*

_____

_____

Say, *"So is there any trace of urge, while you are* _____ (state the problem), *to go and do something else?"*

_____

_____

If it is a 0, say the following:

Say, *"Think again of that situation and do this tapping again* (self-tapping of hand or butterfly hug), *noticing those feelings in your body, the nice feelings of enjoyment, while you think of* _____ (the initial problematic situation)."

_____

_____

Future Template for Action

Say, *"Okay, with all this in mind, go back to the situation we started with* _____ (state the problem), *the way it is now, right at this moment as we are talking, and how it will be when you go home today. What do you get now when you think of that?"*

_____

_____

If any additional procrastination urges arise at this point, continue to process in the same manner as described above, until a LoUA score of 0 is attained.

If there is still a problem, check to see if there is an earlier incident or blocking belief that would be helped by using the EMDR Standard Protocol.

Note: These methods are best used in the later stages of therapy when there is a solid therapeutic relationship, since letting go of an overly idealized image or defense may be a very vulnerable act for the client.

35

Dysfunctional Positive Affect: To Clear the Pain of Unrequited Love

Jim Knipe

To Clear the Pain of Unrequited Love Script Notes

Feeling the pain of rejection by someone you love is one of the most difficult experiences that we can have as human beings. Often, this terrible feeling is, in part, based on an unrealistic idealization of the lost lover. This protocol assists your client in focusing on those aspects of the remembered love relationship that retain the intense positive affect, so that a disinvestment process can occur, and the client can come to see the former relationship more realistically, with all its good and bad aspects. Clients in this situation will generally feel some relief from their previous obsessive thought pattern (i.e., pleasant memories of the ex-lover, quickly followed by feelings of intense loss and grief). Freed from this pattern, the client is more easily able to accurately access their options and move on.

The level of positive affect or (LoPA) score is a scale of 0 to 10 that is used instead of the SUD scale for this protocol. When setting up this protocol, the positive representative image, the LoPA for the positively felt emotion, and the location of that number in positive body sensations, are elicited.

Note: The self-referencing cognition is not actively elicited, as this may often bring up feelings of shame or inadequacy.

To Clear the Pain of Unrequited Love Script

Say, *"After everything that has happened, would you like it if there were a way for you to _____ ("no longer love," "really let go of," or "no longer be longing for") _____(state his or her name)?"*

_____

_____

Say, *"Does it go like this? You start to think of the good times and then it turns to a painful sadness?"*

_____

_____

Say, *"Would it be okay if we worked on this today?"*

_____

_____

Say, *"Right now can you get a mental image, a picture of the nicest time with _____ (state his or her name)? A time that really represents the loving feeling, the positive feeling you still have for _____ (state his or her name)?"*

_____

_____

Say, *"You do not have to tell me what it is but just hold that image in mind right now. Is there a positive feeling connected with that?"*

_____

_____

Say, *"When you hold that picture in mind right now, here is a question. When you hold that picture in mind of that loving time, how much right at this moment do you _____ ("still love" or "want to hang onto") ____ (state his or her name), using the 0 to 10 scale where 10 is the most positive urge and 0 is the least urge?"*

0   1   2   3   4   5   6   7   8   9   10
(no positive affect or urge)   (most positive affect or urge)

Say, *"So, just hold in mind that picture and those feelings in your _____ (heart, abdomen, chest, wherever the client reports feeling the sensations) and _____ (state BLS)."*

_____

_____

Use bilateral stimulation (BLS).

Say, *"And what do you get now?"*

_____

_____

Work with the material until you reach the end of a channel of information and then suggest the following:

Say, *"Please go back to that picture we started with, the one that repre-sents all of your positive feelings. When you think of that right now, using the numbers 0 to 10, how strong is that positive feeling now, that feeling of _____ (loving or wanting to hang onto) _____ (state his or her name)?"*

0	1	2	3	4	5	6	7	8	9	10

(no positive affect or urge)   (most positive affect)

If it is not a 0, say the following:

Say, *"Does it feel better now that it is a ____ (state LoPA), and not a 10?"*

_____

_____

Whatever the client's answer, say the following:

Say, *"Stay with that* (do another set of BLS)."

_____

_____

Say, *"Where is it now on the 0 to 10 scale?"*

0	1	2	3	4	5	6	7	8	9	10

(no positive affect or urge)   (most positive affect)

Say, *"Okay, it is a _____ (state LoPA). So what makes it a _____ (state LoPA)? Please talk about that."*

_____

_____

Say, *"Go with that."* Do BLS.

_____

_____

Say, *"Go back again and think of that picture that represents your love and good times together, on the 0 to 10 scale, what number do you get now?"*

0	1	2	3	4	5	6	7	8	9	10

(no positive affect or urge)   (most positive affect or urge)

Say, *"Go with that."*

_____

_____

Do BLS until it comes down to 0 and the client can let it go or it brings up a blocking belief or issue that would be a target to use with the EMDR Standard Protocol. Some clients may prefer to retain part of their positive feeling for the former lover, and this is a good outcome if it is not problematic and not disturbing for the client. When the protocol is complete, be sure to check your work at the beginning of the next session.

36

Dysfunctional Positive Affect: Codependence or Obsession With Self-Defeating Behavior

Jim Knipe

When there is a repetitive interaction pattern in a client's life that is difficult to resolve because the codependent behavior in question has become part of the client's identity or a lifetime way of connecting, it can be helpful to use a protocol that targets this positive affective urge. Examples would be clients who obsessively say, "I'm sorry" whenever there is a trace of conflict or tension with another person, or clients who are compelled to take responsibility for another person's problems in an attempt to insure the continuation of that relationship.

Codependence or Obsession With Self-Defeating Behavior Script

Say, *"Can you get a picture of a time when you _____ (describe the repeating interaction pattern with the significant person in the client's life)? A time that really represents your intense need to (describe the repeating interaction pattern) with _____ (state the name of the significant person)."*

_____

_____

Say, *"When you think of _____ (The visual image that represents the intense need to repeat the unwanted codependent behavior. This is usually some provocative behavior on the part of the other person.), how strong is the urge right now on a scale of 0 to 10, where 0 has no positive urge and 10 is the highest urge, to once again _____ (describe the behavior)?"*

0	1	2	3	4	5	6	7	8	9	10

(no positive affect or urge)   (most positive affect or urge)

Say, *"Where do you notice that urge in your body?"*

_____

_____

Say, *"Just hold that picture in mind and where you notice that in your body and go with that."*

_____

_____

Do bilateral stimulation (BLS).

Say, *"And what do you get now?"*

_____

_____

Work with the material until you reach the end of a channel of information and then say the following:

Say, *"Please go back to that picture we started with, the one that represents the positive felt urge you have to engage in _____ (state the behavior). When you think of that right now, using the scale of 0 to 10, how strong is that urge now?"*

0	1	2	3	4	5	6	7	8	9	10

(no positive affect or urge)   (most positive affect or urge)

If it is not a 0, say the following:

Say, *"Does it feel better now that it is a _____ (state LoPA), and not a 10?"*

_____

_____

Whatever the client's answer, say the following:

Say, *"Stay with that."*

_____

_____

Do another set of BLS.

Say, *"But it is not a 0 so what makes it a _____ (state level of positive affect [LoPA])?"*

_____

_____

Say, *"Go with that."*

_____

_____

Do BLS.

Say, *"Go back again and think of that picture that represents your positive urge to _____ (state the repeating interaction), on the 0 to 10 scale, what number do you get now?"*

0   1   2   3   4   5   6   7   8   9   10
(no positive affect or urge)   (most positive affect or urge)

Say, *"Go with that."*

_____

_____

Do sets of BLS until it comes down to 0 and the client can let it go or it brings up a blocking belief or issue that would be a target to use with the Standard EMDR Protocol. Again, with this protocol, some clients may reach a preferred ecological resolution with the LoPA score more than 0.

When the protocol is complete, be sure to check your work at the beginning of the next session.

CravEx: An EMDR Approach to Treat Substance Abuse and Addiction

Michael Hase

CravEx Script Notes

The comorbidity of post-traumatic stress disorder (PTSD) and substance abuse gives sufficient reason to treat patients who are addicted with EMDR. However, there are several pathways leading to addiction and PTSD is only one of them. Thirty years of addiction research have provided sufficient evidence for the crucial role of memory in drug dependency. The addiction memory (AM) serves as a useful concept for obsessive-compulsive craving to be seen in drug addicted patients (Boening, 2001). The concept of AM and its importance in relapse occurrence and maintenance of learned addictive behavior has gained growing acceptance in the field of addiction research and treatment. The characteristics of the addiction memory are as follows:

- An *individual-acquired memory following drug consumption* in some individuals.
- Based on *normal memory systems* and systems of neuronal information processing.
- Can be *activated at any time* by relapse-endangering complex, internal, or external situations thus experiencing cue-stimulated craving.
- Becomes *part of the personality*, especially in the episodic memory (also known as the "one shot" learning mechanism).
- This neurobiological-based, imprinted, addictive behavior seems to *resist change* under normal circumstances.

The implicit nature of the addiction memory seems to qualify it as a target for EMDR treatment. There are two types of targets for EMDR concerning addiction memories:

- *Memories of drug consumption or relapse.* As an activated addiction memory would initiate a chain of rather subconscious processes leading into

467

drug consumption, these memories of drug consumption—against willful intention—should qualify as targets for EMDR reprocessing.

- *Memories of intense cravings.* As craving seems to be the conscious representation of these processes, memories of intense craving should also qualify as targets for EMDR reprocessing.

The AM develops on the basis of experiencing drug use and drug effects. The AM includes a compulsive urge or craving for the drug and a loss of control in limiting or ceasing drug consumption and will more likely be an episodic type of memory. There are strong indicators that the AM consists of two components: a drug-independent memory of loss of control and a drug-specific memory of the addictive drug. Without adequate therapeutic interventions, it is hardly extinguishable (Wolffgramm & Heyne, 1995) as shown in the animal model where a remodeling of the AM facilitated by steroids extinguished craving in opiate-addicted rats (Wolffgramm, Galli, Timm, & Heyene, 2000), and just to underline the findings—deleting the addiction memory cured 100% of the animals of their addiction. Thus, altering or extinguishing the AM in human addicts could add an important component to well-established treatment modalities.

Reprocessing of the Addiction Memory

The presumably episodic type of AM, its cue reactivity and power resembles the maladaptive traumatic memory forming the core of PTSD (van der Kolk, Burbridge, & Suzuki, 1997). There are two major hypotheses:

- Thus the reprocessing of the AM with EMDR should lead to measurable changes of addiction symptoms, if the AM qualifies for maladaptive memory within the adaptive information processing (AIP) model.
- As the AM includes the urge to consume the drug of abuse, more aptly named craving, reprocessing of the AM should lead to a reduction in craving. Thus, in alcohol-dependent patients, the reprocessing of the AM should lead to a reduction of the craving measurable by the obsessive-compulsive drinking scale (OCDS), an instrument to measure alcohol-related craving (Mann & Ackermann, 2000).

Thirty-four patients with chronic alcohol dependency, in an inpatient detoxification facility, were randomly assigned to one of two treatment conditions during a pilot study: treatment as usual (TAU) or TAU + EMDR. In the TAU + EMDR group, patients received two sessions of EMDR in order to activate and reprocess the addiction memory, they focused on the following targets:

- Memories of intense craving
- Memories of relapse

The craving for alcohol was measured by the OCDS pre, post, and 1 month after treatment. The TAU + EMDR group showed a significant reduction in craving posttreatment and 1 month after treatment whereas TAU did not. The TAU + EMDR group showed less relapse at the 6-month follow-up. The results indicate that EMDR might be a useful approach for the treatment of addiction memory and associated symptoms of craving (Hase, Schallmayer, & Sack, 2008).

Craving Extinguished (CravEx)—The Manual

The name CravEx was given to this EMDR strategy because craving seemed to vanish during EMDR reprocessing of the addiction memory in some of the patients. It is important when treating comorbid addicted and traumatized patients to take into account the severity of PTSD and the addiction simultaneously. Several strategies such as extensive stabilization—resource development and installation (Korn & Leeds, 2002) or the inverted standard protocol for unstable complex PTSD (Hofmann & Sack, 2006) address this problem.

Note: In comorbid clients, the addiction has to be treated first, as ongoing drug consumption is a clear no go for trauma therapy.

CravEx, as part of a treatment for comorbid addictive clients, focuses on reprocessing of the addiction memory thus leading to stabilization in the addiction. The client should be able to stay sober for a sufficient period of time around a scheduled treatment session. Achieving even short time sobriety has to be planned according to the drug of abuse. Chronic alcohol-addicted patients, for example, would need medical detoxification treatment in a specialized in- or outpatient unit to achieve sobriety without endangering their lives. Reduction of acute craving is reported for various drugs of abuse, such as nicotine, alcohol, and heroin.

During EMDR reprocessing, it is essential to monitor craving. Therefore, the subjective units of disturbance scale (SUDs) measure has been replaced by the level of urge (LoU), initiated by A. J. Popky in his DeTUR Protocol for Addictions (2005) and see chapter 38 in this book. This is an appropriate but small modification of the EMDR 8-phases procedure and with minimal modification in EMDR procedures, the EMDR therapist can easily adapt to this approach. The Standard EMDR Protocol remains the guideline for treatment planning, thus addressing past, present, and future. Addressing the past means targeting memories of past cravings and relapse(s), thus leading to the reprocessing of the addiction memory, or rather memories in the addiction memory network. Focusing on the present means targeting current problems or triggers. Work in the future includes the future template to facilitate adaptive behavior in order to maintain abstinence.

CravEx Script: EMDR 8 Phases

Phase 1: History Taking

During, the history-taking phase, the standard history is taken. It is essential to use standard diagnostic procedures to screen for dissociative disorders and post-traumatic stress disorder. Make sure to incorporate the rules of treatment planning for complex PTSD while working with this population. The therapist should take a history of the addictive behavior and a trauma history. The therapist should pay attention to the interaction of trauma and addictive behavior:

Say, *"When did you lose control over your addictive behavior?"*

_____

_____

_____

_____

Say, *"What was happening in your life when your drug consumption increased?"*

_____

_____

_____

_____

Also the therapist should search for access to the memory of addiction, asking for recent relapse and intense craving as well as associated cues.

Say, *"When did you relapse recently?"*

_____

_____

Say, *"When did you experience intense craving for your drug, even if you just managed to stay sober?"*

_____

_____

Say, *"Is there anything you see, hear, smell, taste, or feel able to evoke craving?"*

_____

_____

The therapist should also ask for current stressors and about the fear of failing to sustain sobriety in order to elicit targets for the present part of the Standard EMDR Protocol and the future template.

Say, *"Are there any current problems that could disturb you and endanger your ability to stay sober?"*

_____

_____

———————————————————————————

———————————————————————————

Say, *"What are your fears about future dangers that may cause you to relapse?"*

———————————————————————————

———————————————————————————

———————————————————————————

———————————————————————————

For example, a client may discuss her spouse's ongoing skepticism to her sobriety as a current stressor and her fear of meeting old friends trying to persuade her to go drinking in the future. It is helpful to write down the traumatic material and addiction memories according to the 3-Pronged Protocol.

Addiction Memories and Traumatic Material Worksheet

Addiction Memories

Past

Memories of relapse(s)

Most recent _____

First _____

Worst _____

Memories of intense craving

Most recent _____

First _____

Worst _____

Other memories related to addictive behaviors _____

Present

Cues for craving

_____

_____

Current stressors resulting in addictive behaviors

_____

_____

Future

Future fears concerning addiction and addictive behaviors

_____

_____

Related Traumatic Material

Past traumas

_____

_____

Present trauma triggers

_____

_____

Future fears concerning trauma and addictive behaviors

_____

_____

Resources

_____

_____

Resources needed

_____

_____

The therapist assesses the areas in need of treatment and decides where to begin. In addition, the worksheet helps to address the question of past, present, and future targets for addiction or PTSD. The addiction is targeted first via reprocessing the addiction memory. Memories of relapse or intense craving form the targets in the past, while cues for craving as well as current stressors are reprocessed in the present part of the Standard EMDR Protocol. The fears of the patient form the basis of building a future template and are reprocessed accordingly. This is standard EMDR therapy. Major traumas also can impact on addictive behaviors and are important to include in treatment planning.

Phase 2: Preparation

The basic preparation in Phase 2 is essential to work in this model. This includes establishing a Safe Place, introducing the basic mechanics of EMDR, and rationale and what to expect during the processing. It is helpful to prepare the client for the experience of drug effects.

> Say, *"When we are working on a memory of craving or relapse, you may experience the need to take the drug. This is not a problem and will decrease as the therapy continues. You can seek appropriate support between sessions if you experience craving for the drug. In the session, you may experience a milder form of drug effect, like feeling relaxed or aroused according to the property of your drug of abuse."*

Prepare the client for the possibility of experiencing associated memories.

> Say, *"Sometimes, though not very often, associated memories of some incident or problem may arise when we are working on a memory of craving. I'd like to suggest that we just continue with our work if that happens. These memories can be reprocessed in our work or we will address them in a separate session. We will just stay with the memory of relapse or craving with which we began."*

If a patient reports craving in the session, the modified Absorption Technique offers an approach to tackle acute craving. It can also be used when the patient seems unstable and may not be able to target a memory of craving or relapse. Therefore, it is appropriate to set up this resource before beginning reprocessing. When working with bilateral stimulation (BLS) make sure to work with care. Slow eye movements (EMs), for instance 3 to 12 EMs per set, and for tones, often 1/4 Hz and short sets seem effective to install a resource. The Butterfly Hug (see chapter 1) is helpful for severely traumatized patients.

CravEx Resource for Acute Craving Script (Silvia Franke, Personal Communication)

The goal here is to reduce the craving. Start with evaluating the Level of Urge (LoU).

LoU

> Say, *"Please evaluate the intensity of your craving for _____ (state substance) on a scale of 0 to 10, where 0 is no craving or neutral and 10 is the most craving you can imagine, how strong does your craving feel now?"*

0	1	2	3	4	5	6	7	8	9	10
(no craving)								(most craving)		

Say, *"How would you feel if you had taken your drug of abuse? Please describe up to three states of mind and body."*

1. _____

2. _____

3. _____

Often the answer will be relaxed, calm, and so forth.

Resources

Ask for any memory—except using a drug—containing at least parts of these states of mind and body as a resource, such as memories of exercising, success, good relationships, therapy, and so forth. Find one memory for resources one through three.

Say, *"Has there been a moment or situation in your life when you experienced a bit of this resource or quality?"*

_____

_____

Say, *"What was the moment or situation in your life when you experienced a bit of the body experience or state of mind of experience 1?"*

_____

_____

Say, *"Good. Now, what was the moment or situation in your life when you experienced a bit of the body experience or state of mind of Experience 2?"*

_____

_____

Say, *"Okay, now what was the moment or situation in your life when you experienced a bit of the body experience or state of mind of Experience 3?"*

_____

_____

Installation

Assist the client in focusing on the resource memory (questions, vividness), using approximately 3 to 10 sets. Should the patient feel uncomfortable with the therapist-conducted stimulation, the therapist can instruct the client how to work with self-stimulation, such as the Butterfly Hug."

Say, *"The next step is to just focus on the memory, the image, and these pleasant sensations and then just follow my fingers. Does that feel comfortable for you?"*

_____

_____

If not, say the following:

Say, *"Cross your arms over your chest so that the tip of your fingers from each hand can touch the area that is located under the connection between the clavicle and the shoulder. Your eyes can be closed or partially closed looking toward the tip of your nose. Next, you alternate the movement of your hands, like the flapping wings of a butterfly. You breathe slowly and deeply (abdominal breathing), while you observe what is going through your mind and body such as thoughts, images, sounds, odors, feelings, and physical sensation without changing, pushing your thoughts away, or judging. You can pretend as though what you are observing are like clouds passing by. How is that for you?"*

_____

_____

Repeat the stimulation when the resource becomes stronger.

Say, *"What do you get now?"*

_____

_____

Say, *"Does it feel more positive?"*

_____

_____

Say, *"Just stay with that and follow my fingers!"* (or have the client use the Butterfly hug)

_____

_____

Interrupt the client when any association into traumatic memory networks occurs.

Positive Cognition (PC)

Assist the client to find a PC. Connect the three resources and the PC and strengthen with BLS.

Say, *"When you bring up that picture or incident, what would you like to believe about yourself now?"*

_____

_____

Say, *"Think of your resources of _____* (remind client of the three resource states) *and _____* (state the PC). *Go with that."*

_____

_____

Use 4 to 6 slow BLS, or the Butterfly Hug

Say, *"What do you get now?"*

_____

_____

Cue Word

Say, *"Think of a word that represents your strength or skill and feel those positive feelings and sensations as you _____ (state BLS)."*

_____

_____

Reevaluation

Now take another look on the craving.

Say, *"Please evaluate the intensity of your craving for _____ (state substance) on a scale of 0 to 10 (LoU), where 0 is no craving or neutral and 10 is the most craving you can imagine, how strong does your craving feel now?"*

0	1	2	3	4	5	6	7	8	9	10
(no craving)										(maximum craving)

If the LoU has decreased and the client feels as if she can handle the remaining craving, continue with the assessment.

If the LoU has not decreased at all, check for a Touchstone Event concerning the issue, using the Float-Back Technique or Affect Scan (Shapiro, 2001, see Appendix); install resources appropriate to the issue, or reprocess the memory that may have been triggered before you continue with the assessment. Also, check further for complex PTSD or dissociative disorder not otherwise specified (DDNOS).

Phase 3: Assessment

An essential part of therapy is the reprocessing of memories in the addiction memory network. The CravEx Worksheet provides instruction—according to the EMDR Standard procedures—with just one slight modification: the nodes to target are memories of intense craving or relapse in abstinence-motivated clients.

Target Selection and Evaluation

Important guidelines for target selection, evaluation, and EMDR reprocessing:

1. *Relapse and intense craving.* Evaluate and reprocess two essential memories: a memory of relapse and a memory of intense craving.
2. *Recent first.* Target recent memories first, as these are easier to access and evaluate.
3. *First and worst.* The first and worst memory of each category should be targeted and at least evaluated in the course of therapy.
4. *LoU scale.* It is essential to monitor craving by using the level of urge scale while reprocessing.
5. *LoU = 0.* Reprocessing should lead to maximum reduction of the LoU, preferably to zero, before switching to installation of a positive cognition.
6. *VoC and body scan.* A validity of cognition (VoC) of 6—7 is better—and a clear body scan indicate successful reprocessing.
7. *NC and PC.* Clinical observation indicates the necessity to elicit negative and positive cognitions. The experience of craving and relapse alter the patient's concept of self. The cognitions address this material and facilitate the generalization of treatment effects.

Directions

Choose which memory to start with, either the memory of a relapse or an intense craving. Start the reprocessing with the most recent, then go to the first memory and then the worst memory. After these are completed, and, if necessary, use the same script to work with the memory of relapse or intense craving that was not chosen at first and reprocess these memories.

Incident—Most Recent

Say, *"The memory that we will start with today is _____ (select the memory of a relapse or an intense craving). What was the most recent one that you remember?"*

_____

_____

_____

_____

Say, *"What happens when you think of the incident?"*

_____

_____

Picture

Say, *"What picture represents the entire incident?"*

_____

_____

If there are many choices or if the client becomes confused, the clinician assists by asking the following:

Say, *"What picture represents the most intense part of the incident?"*

_____

_____

When a picture is unavailable, the clinician merely invites the client to say the following:

Say, *"Think of the incident."*

_____

_____

Negative Cognition (NC)

Say, *"What words best go with the picture that express your negative belief about yourself now?"*

_____

_____

Positive Cognition (PC)

Say, *"When you bring up that picture or incident, what would you like to believe about yourself now?"*

_____

_____

Validity of Cognition (VoC)

Say, *"When you think of the incident* (or picture) *how true do those words* _____ (clinician repeats the positive cognition) *feel to you now on a scale of 1 to 7, where 1 feels completely false and 7 feels completely true?"*

   1   2   3   4   5   6   7
(completely false)   (completely true)

Emotions

Say, *"When you bring up the picture* (or incident) *and those words* _____ (clinician states the negative cognition), *what emotion do you feel now?"*

_____

_____

Level of Urge (LoU)

Say, *"Please evaluate the intensity of your craving for* ____ (state substance) *on a scale of 0 to 10, where 0 is no craving or neutral and 10 is the most craving you can imagine, how strong does your craving feel now?"*

  0   1   2   3   4   5   6   7   8   9   10
(no craving)   (maximum craving)

Location of Body Sensation

Say, *"Where do you feel it* (the disturbance) *in your body?"*

_____

_____

Process this memory completely before moving to the next target.

Incident—First Memory (if Necessary)

Say, *"The memory that we will start with today is* _____ (select the memory of a relapse or an intense craving). *What was the first one that you remember?"*

_____

_____

_____

_____

Say, *"What happens when you think of the incident?"*

_____

_____

Picture

Say, *"What picture represents the entire incident?"*

_____

_____

If there are many choices or if the client becomes confused, the clinician assists by asking the following:

Say, *"What picture represents the most intense part of the incident?"*

_____

_____

When a picture is unavailable, the clinician merely invites the client to say the following:

Say, *"Think of the incident."*

_____

_____

Negative Cognition (NC)

Say, *"What words best go with the picture that express your negative belief about yourself now?"*

_____

_____

Positive Cognition (PC)

Say, *"When you bring up that picture or incident, what would you like to believe about yourself now?"*

_____

_____

Validity of Cognition (VoC)

Say, *"When you think of the incident* (or picture) *how true do those words _____* (clinician repeats the positive cognition) *feel to you now on a scale of 1 to 7, where 1 feels completely false and 7 feels completely true?"*

    1   2   3   4   5   6   7
    (completely false)   (completely true)

Emotions

Say, *"When you bring up the picture* (or incident) *and those words* _____ (clinician states the negative cognition)*, what emotion do you feel now?"*

_____

_____

Level of Urge (LoU)

Say, *"Please evaluate the intensity of your craving for* _____ (state substance) *on a scale of 0 to 10, where 0 is no craving or neutral and 10 is the most craving you can imagine, how strong does your craving feel now?"*

0	1	2	3	4	5	6	7	8	9	10
(no craving)										(maximum craving)

Location of Body Sensation

Say, *"Where do you feel it* (the disturbance) *in your body?"*

_____

_____

Whichever the client chooses—either the relapse memory or memory of intense craving—be sure to process the other.

Incident—Worst Memory (if Necessary)

Say, *"The memory that we will start with today is* _____ (select the other memory—either of a relapse or an intense craving). *What was the worst memory that you remember related to that?"*

_____

_____

_____

_____

Say, *"What happens when you think of the incident?"*

_____

_____

Picture

Say, *"What picture represents the entire incident?"*

_____

_____

If there are many choices or if the client becomes confused, the clinician assists by asking the following:

Say, *"What picture represents the most intense part of the incident?"*

_____

_____

When a picture is unavailable, the clinician merely invites the client to say the following:

Say, *"Think of the incident."*

_____

_____

Negative Cognition (PC)

Say, *"What words best go with the picture that express your negative belief about yourself now?"*

_____

_____

Positive Cognition (PC)

Say, *"When you bring up that picture or incident, what would you like to believe about yourself now?"*

_____

_____

Validity of Cognition (VoC)

Say, *"When you think of the incident* (or picture) *how true do those words _____* (clinician repeats the positive cognition) *feel to you now on a scale of 1 to 7, where 1 feels completely false and 7 feels completely true?"*

1	2	3	4	5	6	7
(completely false)				(completely true)		

Emotions

Say, *"When you bring up the picture* (or incident) *and those words _____* (clinician states the negative cognition), *what emotion do you feel now?"*

_____

_____

Level of Urge (LoU)

Say, *"Please evaluate the intensity of your craving for _____* (state substance) *on a scale of 0 to 10, where 0 is no craving or neutral and 10 is the most craving you can imagine, how strong does your craving feel now?"*

0	1	2	3	4	5	6	7	8	9	10
(no craving)							(maximum craving)			

Location of Body Sensation

Say, *"Where do you feel it* (the disturbance) *in your body?"*

_____

_____

Process this memory completely before moving on to the next target.

Now, go back and work with the type of memory that you did not choose first, for instance, if you started memories of relapse, now go back and use the script to work with memories of intense craving.

Make sure all memories of relapse or intense cravings are processed before moving forward to any of the traumatic material elicited or that came up while reprocessing. Check to see if they need to be reprocessed first. If so, use the script above.

Phase 4: Desensitization

The work in Phase 4 follows the Standard EMDR Protocol.
To begin, say the following:

Say, *"Now, remember, it is your own brain that is doing the healing and you are the one in control. I will ask you to mentally focus on the target and to* _____ (state BLS you are using). *Just let whatever happens, happen, and we will talk at the end of the set. Just tell me what comes up, and don't discard anything as unimportant. Any new information that comes to mind is connected in some way. If you want to stop, just raise your hand."*

Then say, *"Bring up the picture and the words* _____ (clinician repeats the NC) *and notice where you feel it in your body. Now follow* _____ (state BLS)."*

_____

_____

This procedure is to be repeated until the SUDs = 0. Then the positive cognition is installed. Each traumatic event associated with the addictive problem that is not reprocessed during the normal course of the first target needs to be processed using the above protocol until the SUDs reaches an ecological 1 or 0 and the positive cognition is installed.

Note: According to experience from several sessions, feelings of well-being, happiness, mild drowsiness, for example, surfacing early in Phase 4 indicate the processing of addiction memory components (e.g., drug effects). This material should be kept in the process (say, "Stay with that") and does not indicate the end of a channel or of Phase 4. After the processing of this material, other components or negative affect may surface to be processed thus leading to complete solution.

Phase 5: Installation

Say, *"How does* _____ (repeat the PC) *sound?"*

_____

_____

Say, *"Do the words* _____ (repeat the PC) *still fit or is there another positive statement that feels better?"*

_____

_____

If the client accepts the original positive cognition, the clinician should ask for a VoC rating to see if it has improved.

Say, *"As you think of the incident, how do the words feel to you now on a scale of 1 to 7, where 1 feels completely false and 7 feels completely true?"*

1   2   3   4   5   6   7
(completely false)   (completely true)

Say, *"Think of the event and hold it together with the words* _____ (repeat the PC)."

_____

_____

Do a long set of BLS to see if there is more processing to be done.

Phase 6: Body Scan

Say, *"Close your eyes and keep in mind the original memory and the positive cognition. Then bring your attention to the different parts of your body, starting with your head and working downward. Any place you find any tension, tightness, or unusual sensation, tell me."*

_____

_____

Phase 7: Closure

Say, *"Things may come up or they may not. If they do, great, write it down and it can be a target for next time. If you get any new memories, dreams, or situations that disturb you, just take a good snapshot. It isn't necessary to give a lot of detail. Just put down enough to remind you so we can target it next time. The same thing goes for any positive dreams or situations. If negative feelings do come up, try not to make them significant. Remember, it's still just the old stuff. Just write it down for next time. Then use the tape or the Safe Place exercise to let as much of the disturbance go as possible. Even if nothing comes up, make sure to use the tape everyday and give me a call if you need to."*

_____

_____

Phase 8: Reevaluation

Follow the EMDR Standard 8 Phase procedure (Shapiro, 2001). Look at the treatment plan: further addiction memory, cues, and so forth. After the processing of memories of relapse or intense craving triggers for substance abuse and current problems (e.g., quarrelling with spouse) should be targeted and reprocessed.

Present Triggers

Say, *"We have some of the situations, events, and stimuli that trigger your addictive behaviors from when we first started. They were _____ (read the list from the worksheet). Are they still issues for you? Are there any other ones that you have thought of since then or that you have noticed? Let's process these situations, events or stimuli triggers one by one."*

_____

_____

If the client has a hard time coming up with the situations, events, or stimuli that are triggers, standard EMDR methods to elicit related memories such as the Float-Back Technique or Affect Scan may be used (Shapiro, 2001).

Situations, Events, or Stimuli Trigger List

T1:

_____

_____

T2:

_____

_____

T3:

_____

_____

T4:

_____

_____

Say, *"What situation, event, or stimulus that triggers you would you like to use as a target today?"*

_____

_____

Picture

Say, *"What picture represents the _____ (state the situation, event, or stimulus) that triggers you?"*

_____

_____

Negative Cognition (NC)

Say, *"What words best go with the picture that express your negative belief about yourself now?"*

_____

_____

Positive Cognition (PC)

Say, *"When you bring up that picture or _____* (state the situation, event, or stimulus) *that triggers you, what would you like to believe about yourself now?"*

_____

_____

Validity of Cognition (VoC)

Say, *"When you think of the incident _____* (state the situation, event, or stimulus) *that triggers you, how true do those words ____* (clinician repeats the positive cognition) *feel to you now on a scale of 1 to 7, where 1 feels completely false and 7 feels completely true?"*

1   2   3   4   5   6   7
(completely false)   (completely true)

Emotions

Say, *"When you bring up the picture or _____* (state the situation, event, or stimulus) *that triggers you, and those words ____* (clinician states the negative cognition), *what emotion do you feel now?"*

_____

_____

Level of Urge (LoU)

Say, *"On a scale of 0 to 10, where 0 is no urge to take the drug or neutral and 10 is the highest urge you can imagine, how do you feel it now?"*

0   1   2   3   4   5   6   7   8   9   10
(no urge)   (highest urge)

Location of Body Sensation

Say, *"Where do you feel it* (the disturbance) *in your body?"*

_____

_____

Work with each trigger until each one is fully processed.

Future Template (Shapiro, 2006, pp. 51–53)

A future template as in Standard EMDR Protocols and procedures (e.g., difficulties in imagining saying no to a friend who wants to go out for a drink) is essential for stable treatment effects.

Image as Future Template

Say, *"I would like you to imagine yourself coping effectively with _____ (state the goal) in the future. With the positive belief _____ (state the positive belief) and your new sense of _____ (state the quality, i.e., strength, clarity, confidence, calm), imagine stepping into this scene."*

_____

_____

Say, *"Notice what you see and how you are handling the situation. Notice what you are thinking, feeling, and experiencing in your body."*

_____

_____

Say, *"Are there any blocks, anxieties, urges, or fears that arise as you think about this future scene?"*

_____

_____

If yes, say the following:

Say, *"Then focus on these issues or urge and follow my fingers (or any other BLS)."*

_____

_____

If the issues, especially the urge, do not resolve quickly, evaluate if the client needs any new information, resources, or skills to be able to comfortably visualize the future coping scene. Introduce needed information or skills.

Say, *"What would you need to feel confident in handling the situation?"*

_____

_____

Or say, *"What is missing from your handling of this situation?"*

_____

_____

If the block still does not resolve and the client is unable to visualize the future scene with confidence and clarity, use direct questions, the Affect Scan, or the Float-Back Technique to identify old targets related to blocks, anxieties, or fears. Use the Standard EMDR Protocol to address these targets before proceeding with the template (see Worksheets in the Appendix).

If there are no apparent blocks and the client is able to visualize the future scene with confidence and clarity as in the following:

Say, *"Please focus on the image, the positive belief, and the sensations associated with this future scene and follow my fingers* (or any other BLS).*"*

_____

_____

Process and reinforce the positive associations with BLS. Do several sets until the future template is sufficiently strengthened.

Say, *"Go with that."*

_____

_____

Then say, *"Close your eyes and keep in mind the experience that you will have in the future. Then bring your attention to the different parts of your body, starting with your head and working downward. Any place you find any tension, tightness, or unusual sensation, tell me."*

_____

_____

If any sensation is reported, do BLS.

If it is a positive or comfortable sensation, do BLS to strengthen the positive feelings.

If a sensation of discomfort is reported, reprocess until the discomfort subsides. Check the VoC.

Say, *"When you think of the incident* (or picture) *how true do those words _____* (clinician repeats the positive cognition) *feel to you now on a scale of 1 to 7, where 1 feels completely false and 7 feels completely true?"*

1   2   3   4   5   6   7
(completely false)   (completely true)

Continue to use BLS until reaching the VoC = 7 or there is an ecological resolution. When the image as future template is clear and the PC true, move on to the movie as future template.

Movie as Future Template

During this next level of future template, clients are asked to move from imagining this one scene or snapshot to imagining a movie about coping in the future, with a beginning, middle, and end. Encourage clients to imagine themselves coping effectively in the face of specific challenges, triggers, or snafus. Therapists can make some suggestions of things in order to help inoculate them with future problems. It is helpful to use this type of future template after clients have received needed education concerning social skills and customs, assertiveness, and any other newly learned skills.

Say, *"This time, I'd like you to close your eyes and play a movie, imagining yourself coping effectively with _____* (state where client will be) *in the future. With the new positive belief* ___ (state positive belief) *and your new sense of* ___ (strength, clarity, confidence, calm), *imagine stepping into the future. Imagine yourself coping with ANY challenges that come your way. Make sure that this movie has a beginning, middle, and end. Notice what you are seeing, thinking, feeling, and experiencing in your body. Let me know if you hit any blocks. If you do, just open your eyes and let me know. If you don't hit any blocks, let me know when you have viewed the whole movie."*

_____

_____

· If the client hits blocks, address as above with BLS, interweaves, new skills, information or resources, direct questions, Affect Scan, or Float-Back, and so forth.

If the client is able to play the movie from start to finish with a sense of confidence and satisfaction, ask the client to play the movie one more time from beginning to end and introduce BLS. In a sense, you are installing this movie as a future template.

Say, *"Okay, play the movie one more time from beginning to end. Go with that."*

Use BLS.

Anecdotal reports from clinicians indicate an effect of the reprocessing of the addiction memory in patients addicted to heroin or psychostimulants. According to research in the animal model, the same principles should apply. Clinical observation shows specific drug effects surfacing in the processing of the addiction memory; therefore, with an amphetamine-addicted patient, arousal will show and should be held in processing the material. It could well be that the power of the drug in the central nervous system has implications on the dose of EMDR. A cocaine addict may need more sessions than a patient addicted to alcohol to reduce craving. Further research is absolutely necessary.

The Desensitization of Triggers and Urge Reprocessing (DeTUR) Protocol

Arnold J. Popky

DeTUR Script Notes

The DeTUR method is an urge reduction protocol used as the center of an overall methodology for the treatment of a wide range of chemical addictions and dysfunctional behaviors. This method was developed and refined by the author through client interaction and feedback from other EMDR-trained therapists using the same protocol. It was initially introduced as a stop smoking protocol at the first EMDR conference (Popky, 1993). This eclectic addiction treatment method is trauma based, combining client internal resources with external support including the 12-step model and other known and proven treatment methods such as Cognitive Behavioral Therapy, Solution-Focused, Erickson, Thought Field Therapy, Satir, Neuro Linguistic Programming, and so forth. The basis or foundation is the adaptive information processing (AIP) using bilateral stimulation (BLS) as outlined in EMDR to uncover and process the base trauma(s) or core issues as the underlying cause behind the addiction.

This protocol represents a small part of a complete treatment model that includes a treatment team approach. Practitioners can fulfill these functions depending on their areas of expertise and personnel available:

- *Case manager.* To manage clients and their resources in the service of adaptive functioning and coping.
- *Diagnostician.* To evaluate clients to assess for comorbidity with other disorders and subsequent referrals to psychiatrists for medication; appropriate medical personnel to check for any physiological or neurological difficulties; and mental health practitioners for individual, couples, or family therapy.
- *Addiction expert.* To assess the severity of addiction(s) and the need for a detoxification program.
- *Social worker.* To assess the need for other types of resources such as 12-step groups and other types of support networks, groups, or associations.

- *Skills support.* To assess what skills clients need and either refer or provide clients with the learning needed.

Note: Most clients presenting with addiction will need access to the wide range of services as frequently there are comorbidity issues, day-to-day stressors, and survival issues that need to be addressed along with other problems such as the need for food and shelter.

DeTUR and EMDR

This author has used the structure of the EMDR methodology to inform the creation of the DeTUR Protocol. The similarities between EMDR and DeTUR are as follows:

- Require a thorough history taking, assessment, and diagnosis for insuring client safety before starting treatment.
- Use bilateral stimulation (BLS).
- Installation of the positive.

The differences between EMDR and DeTUR are as follows:

- *Present versus past.* DeTUR targets the situations, events, or stimuli that bring up the uncomfortable feelings leading to the urges at the outset, then future issues, and works with the past as it opens up, while EMDR starts with past issues and then goes to present triggers and future issues. With the desensitization of each trigger and the installation of the positive treatment goal, the client's ego strength seems to grow to a point where threads open leading back to core issues (if they arise) but only after sufficient ego strength is built. Once desensitized triggers are no longer the stimuli for using. Instead the triggers are connected to the new response that of the treatment goal.
- *Sensation versus affect and cognitions.* DeTUR accesses positive experience through positive body states while the EMDR protocol addresses positive experience through affect and positive and negative cognitions.
- *LoU versus SUD and VoC.* DeTUR measures the Level of Urge (LoU) while EMDR measurements are the subjective units of disturbance (SUD) and validity of cognition (VoC) scales.
- *Early processing versus later processing.* Initially, it was not considered advisable to use EMDR or any type of therapy on addicts early in recovery. Work on any traumatic issues was not done until they were stable and had a long period of abstinence. The concern was that an emerging traumatic event might be too overwhelming for the client to handle and cause the client to relapse, binge, or overindulge. However, using DeTUR, it is possible to work with addicts early in treatment.

Other important components of DeTUR:

- DeTUR protocol is flexible in order to be tailored to each individual client's needs, goals, and values.
- The therapeutic process is necessary in order to address client core traumatic events or issues underlying their psychological addiction.
- Therapeutic interweaves and interventions utilize the therapist's training and style, evolving continual client feedback, thus aiding clients in the processing of each step through completion of any or all core and causal issues.

- Bilateral stimulation in the AIP model is the catalyst and accelerator for uncovering and processing of core events or issues through to completion in order to prevent relapse.
- Client empowerment through resource accessing, identification and installation of positive treatment goals, identification and desensitization of triggers, and techniques of relapse prevention.

It is also helpful to address the significant differences in this treatment approach versus the prevalent 12-step method advocated by Alcoholics Anonymous (AA), Narcotics Anonymous (NA), and the other treatment approaches for addictions.

- Client's attention is directed toward a positive, attractive, achievable, compelling goal of coping and functioning, NOT away from a negative behavior. The reason for this is that as soon as you are told not to think about something the result is to think of it.
- Abstinence, though highly recommended, is not required in the definition of the treatment goal; coping and functioning in a positive manner as described by the client is the treatment goal. It is their therapy.
- Relapse is reframed from failure to new targets of opportunity to be addressed in following sessions.
- Chemical withdrawal and anxiety appear to be addressed since the process seems to take place out of the client's conscious level of awareness, not requiring constant attention on the part of the client. Clients often report surprise that at the end of the day they had not engaged in the negative behavior, or that they had but not as often, or had noticed urges to engage and could put them aside.
- Targeting the individual triggers for desensitization allows this model to be used with clients early in recovery.

The purpose of the protocol is to uncover the core traumas and reprocess them through to completion. In achieving reprocessing, the triggers no longer stimulate the need to use or act out and the new response becomes the positive treatment goal of coping and functioning successfully in life as determined by the client. Successful results have been reported by clinicians across the spectrum of addictions and dysfunctional behaviors: chemical substances (nicotine, marijuana, alcohol, methamphetamine, cocaine, crack, heroin, methadone, etc.), eating disorders such as compulsive overeating, anorexia and bulimia, along with other behaviors such as sex, gambling, shoplifting, anger outbursts, and trichotillomania, and so forth. As new information becomes available, it is incorporated into the protocol.

The Steps of DeTUR

Step 1: Rapport

The basis of any good psychotherapy is gaining rapport with your client.

Step 2: History, Assessment, Diagnosis

Due to the long history of difficulties of addicted clients, it is mandatory to take a detailed history. Testing for dissociative disorders and or any other *DSM-IV* disorders insures that the therapists know what problems might arise and have the necessary skills, competencies, or referral base to handle situations that might arise. This author has clients complete the dissociative experience scale (Carlson & Putnam, 1992), Beck depression inventory (Beck, Steer & Brown, 1996), and the Lazarus multimodal forms (Lazarus & Lazarus, 1991) and review them before the history taking session. The genogram is a useful visual reminder to detail information about family of origin, relationships issues, their present status, previous problems, previous therapeutic relationships, state of health, medications, and then their drug or addiction history. As in any therapeutic process, all standard client cautions and safety issues should be addressed. Most, if not all, of the clients in the addictive population have dual diagnoses.

It is important that clients be committed to complete the therapy. They should be made aware that rapid improvements, though satisfying, do not mean that the treatment is complete. These fast results sometime lead clients to believe they have been cured and prematurely drop out of treatment. For treatment to be successful, triggers that bring up urges must be desensitized and core events or trauma reprocessed to completion. Consider the stories of individuals diagnosed with bipolar disorders, when feeling good decide that they no longer need medication and discontinue using it thus obstructing their progress.

Step 3: Support Resources

Clients need a safe environment to express their thoughts, feelings, fears, and so forth; a place where they can openly and freely speak their mind, be heard, and get feedback that is honest, supportive, nonjudgmental, and not critical. When things get tough, as before relapsing, they need someone to talk to or even to be able to hear themselves speak their thoughts out loud. Groups such as 12-step groups, AA, NA, CA, RR (Rational Recovery), MM (Managed Moderation), religious organizations, fraternal organizations, women's or men's groups, family, or friends should be supportive, nonjudgmental, and flexible to clients' needs, not just the group process.

Step 4: Accessing Internal Resource State

It is customary to ask clients about their problems when they come for treatment. Based on Robbie Dunton's work with children (personal communication, 1990), this author began sessions using her question, "What do you like and do best?" followed by eye movements. This intervention allows clients to access positive internal states and sets a positive tone for the work to follow.

Step 5: Positive Treatment Goal

The positive treatment goal is central to the client's treatment plan and should have the following attributes:

- Uses only positive language.
- Occurs within the near future.
- Achievable by the client.
- Uses client's language about what it means to cope and function successfully.
- It is attractive, magnetic, and compelling.

It is important that the treatment goal be defined and owned by the client; it is their therapy, therefore their goal. Abstinence, though highly desirable, is not required as a necessity in the definition of the treatment goal; it will be implied.

Note: Although abstinence may be requested, it should not be part of the goal. It is very difficult concentrating on NOT doing something without focusing on the thing that you do not want to do.

Step 6: Associated Positive State

The next step is to have clients associate with their goal. Give them the experience of how it would feel to achieve their goal successfully, and then using associative representation anchor the experience into their physiology. Physical anchoring or conditioned response are processes of being able to replicate the physiological experience associated with an emotion or state by linking it to a physical experience such as slight finger pressure on a part of the body. After obtaining permission, the idea is to exert slight pressure on, for example, a knuckle; this anchor becomes the concrete symbol of the experience. Often, this author chooses the knuckle of the little finger, since it seems to be the least intrusive.

Step 7: Identify Urge Triggers

This step is to figure out the situations, events, and stimuli such as emotions, smells, tastes, objects, or actions that trigger the urge to use. The idea is to help them recognize how they know when to use and to help them understand that they learned this behavior as a way to reduce the negative affect that was connected with early traumatic events. Using helped them cope with the symptoms of the trauma such as the negative feelings, sensations, and thoughts associated with the experiences.

Help clients create a list that specifies the details of the situations, events, and stimuli that trigger them and can be used as targets for processing. For example, if smoking clients report that they get the urge with morning coffee, after meals, and with drinks mark them with $t_{morning\ coffee}$ t_{meals} and t_{drinks}. For those with weight problems, the triggers can represent those times when they eat larger portions, wrong type of foods, unnecessary snacks, and so forth. After compiling the list of known triggers, prioritize them in the order of what seems to be important, weakest to strongest. Often, it is helpful to begin the desensitization with the weakest trigger while installing the positive state and then desensitize each of the following triggers until they end up with the most distressing trigger. This allows clients—at the same time—to build up their ego strength.

Step 8: Desensitize Triggers

It is during this desensitization process, where the therapists' individual style and skills are required, when clients get stuck, loops, abreacts, or other nodes open up. The cognitive or therapeutic interweave as taught in the EMDR Institute basic training is the therapist's best tool to aid clients during this desensitization or reprocessing phase. This author finds it to be more powerful when using it during processing.

Step 9: Install Positive State

As with the Installation Phase of EMDR, this step connects the positive state with the situation, event, or stimuli that triggered the urge. The idea is that whenever one of these triggering situations occur, the using response is replaced with the positive state that the client has anchored. The effect is that after the reprocessing occurs, clients do not have to think about the process as it takes place outside their conscious experience and the new response begins to occur automatically. Ask the client to access the previous triggering event, apply pressure to the anchor, and then use BLS. Reinforce positive affect or thoughts with another set of BLS. When a negative response occurs, more dysfunctional material has been unearthed and can be addressed.

Step 10: Test and Future Check

This step tests the strength of the work by asking clients to bring up their triggers, asking for their LoU and seeing if there is any remaining urge. If there is, go back to Step 8. If not, reinforce the client's success.

Step 11: Closure and Self-Work

End the session by reminding clients that the process may continue to move and teach them how to do self-soothing with BLS.

Step 12: Follow-Up Sessions

Follow-up sessions are for reinforcing the gains clients have made and targeting any new situations, events, or stimuli that have triggered them between sessions, or teaching new skills or information as needed.

DeTUR Protocol Script

Step 1: Rapport

The foundation for trust in any relationship is rapport. One of the most important characteristics of a therapist is the ability to gain the trust rapidly with the client and to maintain it throughout the therapeutic process. Rapport allows the therapist the right to ask questions and to elicit appropriate answers. This is crucial for the following steps in this model.

Step 2: History, Assessment, Diagnosis

Specific questions to delve into the addiction history are the following:

Say, *"What is the problem that you want to address?"*

_____

_____

_____

_____

Say, *"How long have you been using each substance?"*

_____

_____

Say, *"When did you start?"*

_____

_____

Say, *"Why did you start or what made you start?"*

_____

_____

_____

_____

Say, *"How did the use of the substance proceed?"*

_____

_____

_____

_____

Say, *"Was there a particular time that you noticed an acceleration of your use?"*

_____

_____

_____

_____

Say, *"What do you get out of it?"*

_____

_____

Say, *"Do you use just one substance or is there multiple use?"*

_____

_____

Say, *"Did you notice any problems that it causes?"*

_____

_____

_____

_____

Say, *"What are your reasons for quitting?"*

_____

_____

Say, *"How motivated are you to quit?"*

_____

_____

Say, *"What will it get you if you quit?"*

_____

_____

Say, *"Is there any other way to get the same results?"*

_____

_____

Say, *"How many times have you quit?"*

_____

_____

Say, *"What worked and what didn't?"*

_____

_____

Look for possible secondary gain issues that might have to be addressed.

Say, *"Is there anything that you will lose if you quit?"*

_____

_____

Say, *"What are the types of thoughts that go on in your head about this issue or use?"*

_____

_____

Say, *"Are there particular ways you think of yourself because of it?"*

_____

_____

In addition to standard history and cautions, asking open-ended questions such as many of those above will reveal client patterns, communication styles, and decision-making criteria. Listening for key words, phrases, patterns, and belief systems reveals useful insight for metaphors, reframes, and so forth for use in interventions in the therapeutic interweave be it narrative, cognitive, psychodynamic, whatever the therapist's style; this information is useful in maintaining client rapport and for individual therapeutic interventions when nodes open to emerging events relating to core issues.

Step 3: External Support Resources

Say, *"What are the support systems that you have in place?"*

_____

_____

_____

_____

Tailor your suggestions to the needs of your clients.

Step 4: Accessing Internal Resource State

Remembering a positive experience supports clients in accessing their strengths and creating a positive forward movement for the rest of your work.

Say, *"Recall a time when you felt resourceful, powerful, in control and focus on those experiences and feelings."*

_____

_____

_____

_____

Say, *"It is helpful to notice the things that you see, hear, smell, taste, and anything else that you were noticing while you were having those experiences. What did you notice while you were in that state?"*

_____

_____

_____

_____

Relate back to clients what they have told you that they see, hear, smell, taste, and so forth, while doing BLS, keeping clients in the positive feelings.

Use bilateral stimulation (at least 24 rapid BLS) to empower clients and allow the process to move faster.

> Say, *"So focus on that time when you were seeing* _____ (state what client is seeing), *hearing* _____ (state what the client is hearing), *feeling* _____ (state what the client is feeling), *smelling* _____ (state what the client is smelling), *and tasting* _____ (state what the client is tasting) *and follow my fingers* (or whatever BLS you are using)*."*

> _____

> _____

Do BLS.

> Say, *"Now notice all* _____ (repeat their description of what they were seeing, hearing, and feeling) *and think of a word that goes with this. What would that be?"*

> _____

> _____

Repeat again asking them to assign a word (auditory anchor) to that experience and repeat the word while experiencing that moment. This is an auditory anchor that they can use to bring back those positive feelings.

> Say, *"Now repeat that word as you are experiencing that moment."*

> _____

> _____

This appears to empower clients and allows the process to move faster.

Test the resource anchor by asking the client to think of a small disturbing experience, notice the emotions, and then speak their resource word and notice the shift to positive feelings.

> Say, *"Now think of a small disturbing experience, notice the emotions, and then say your resource word* _____ (state the resource word)*. What do you notice?"*

> _____

> _____

If clients are only able to momentarily bring up something positive and then immediately the scene shifts to a negative component, have them freeze the experience and only focus on the positive element before doing eye movements.

> Say, *"Okay, let's freeze the experience to right before it became negative. Now focus on that positive element. Go with that."*

> _____

> _____

Do BLS.

If clients are not able to think of anything positive in their life to concentrate on, say the following:

Say, *"If it is hard for you to come up with something positive right now, sometimes it helps to think of times when you were involved in sports, or any time you accomplished something no matter how big or small, even times like when you finished washing and shining your car or the feelings you had when your favorite team won an event. Does anything like come to mind for you now?"*

_____

_____

Creativity and flexibility are the keys in these difficult situations.

Step 5: Positive Treatment Goal (PG)

A well-formed positive treatment goal uses positive language, occurs in the near future, is achievable, uses the client's own language concerning coping and functioning successfully, and is attractive, magnetic, and compelling. Guide them through the specifics until they can create a clear image of how they would look being successful, fully functional, and having attained their goal.

Say, *"Imagine seeing a picture of yourself already achieving your goal. Think about what your life would be like after all this is over, without _____ (list the addiction, or dysfunctional behavior the client would like to be rid of)."*

_____

_____

_____

_____

Say, *"What will you be doing instead?"*

_____

_____

_____

_____

Say, *"What do you want?"*

_____

_____

_____

_____

Say, *"What will it get you?"*

_____

_____

_____

_____

Say, *"How will you know when you have gotten it?"*

_____

_____

_____

_____

Say, *"What would you be seeing?"*

_____

_____

_____

_____

If the response is negative, say the following:

Say, *"If you won't be _____ (state what the client will not be doing), or won't have to . . . . (state what they are moving away from), what will you be doing instead?"*

_____

_____

The challenge is to guide them to describe their goals in positive, concrete, sensory-based terms. After they have built the picture, check to see if this is really what they want.

Say, *"Is this what you really want?"*

_____

_____

Say, *"Is it desirable? Does it have a strong attraction or pull to it?"*

_____

_____

Make any adjustments to make it more appealing, does it feel better if they make the picture bigger, clearer, brighter, bring it closer, and add sounds?

Say, *"Does it feel better if you make the picture bigger, clearer, brighter, bring it in closer, or add sounds?"*

_____

_____

Say, *"Go with that."*

_____

_____

Help them make any adjustments to make it more appealing. For example, if the client is a smoker worried about gaining weight, be sure they see themselves looking the way they want to look, perhaps in a special outfit (the same for weight loss clients, inches are more important than pounds). When the picture has the strongest attraction and feels best to them use BLS to make the goal more compelling and attractive.

> Say, *"Are there any other adjustments that you would like to make so that it is even more appealing?"*

_____

_____

Then do BLS.

Step 6: Associated Positive State

Fully associate a positive state with the positive goal by anchoring and strengthening them.

> Say, *"You can build your positive treatment goal. Bring up a clear picture of it. What are the kinds of things that you will be able to do when you have it?"*

_____

_____

_____

_____

> Say, *"Step into your picture of your positive treatment goal, into that body posture* (as if state). *Notice and experience the positive feelings, breathe into these feelings, move around in them, experience being successful. Notice what you see, hear, feel, smell, and taste. Notice what it's like to function successfully. As you notice and experience those positive feelings, touch your knuckle in this positive state until your positive state is the most desirable. Increase pressure slightly to that same place on your knuckle as your positive feelings peak, strengthening the mind–body link."*

_____

_____

As you or the client touch the anchor, do BLS.

> Say, *"As you make these visual adjustments, notice how you feel inside. You can change the brightness, the focus, the contrast, the tint, the size, the distance, whatever feels right for you. And as you notice the changes that you feel inside, increase the pressure slightly on your knuckle while I do _____ (state BLS) with you."*

_____

_____

This strengthens the mind–body link through touch and the BLS. Repeat the same process using sounds.

Say, *"As you listen to the positive words or sounds that you are saying to yourself and the positive words that others would be saying, adjust the auditory components: the volume, the tone, the tempo, the balance, and so forth and as the positive experience peaks, please touch your anchor and follow my fingers."*

_____

_____

Apply the anchor touch and the simultaneous BLS to further anchor the feelings of success into their physiology as the association with success peaks. Do BLS.

Test the positive state by having the client touch the knuckle and notice the results. They should report a positive experience. It is important for the client to have a strong, positive, sensory-based experience of having successfully achieved their goal anchored into their physiology.

Say, *"Now touch your knuckle. What do you feel?"*

_____

_____

Step 7: Identify the Urge Triggers

Identify and make a list of the situations, events, and stimuli that stimulate clients' urges.

Say, *"How do you know when to _____ (use or do the activity to which you are addicted)? What prevents you from being in your positive state? These triggers can be a place, person, time, emotion, smell, taste, event, action, or object. Make a list below of all the triggers for use, indicating the level of urge (LoU) on the 0 to 10 scale with 10 being the strongest urge. Then rank them based on intensity on the chart below from weakest (0) to strongest (10) by level of urge."* (Use Trigger List Worksheet below.)

_____

_____

_____

_____

_____

_____

Say, *"Bring up the picture, along with any words, tastes, or smells that go with it. How strong is the level of urge (LoU), right now, from 0 to 10, where 0 is the lowest and 10 is the strongest?"* (Use Trigger List Worksheet below).

Trigger List Worksheet

	Beginning	**Ending**

t_1: _____

_____ LoU =   LoU =

_____

t_2: _____

_____ LoU =   LoU =

_____

t_3: _____

_____ LoU =   LoU =

_____

t_4: _____

_____ LoU =   LoU =

_____

t_5: _____

_____ LoU =   LoU =

_____

t_6: _____

_____ LoU =   LoU =

_____

t_7: _____

_____ LoU =   LoU =

_____

t_8: _____

_____ LoU =   LoU =

_____

t_9: _____

_____ LoU =   LoU =

_____

t_{10}: _____

_____ LoU =   LoU =

_____

Step 8: Desensitizing Each Trigger

Often, it is helpful to give them a metaphor to help explain the process.

> Say, *"If strong emotions come up we will keep going. You know how it is when we are driving up a hill, if we take our foot off the accelerator we end up back at the bottom of the hill, but if we keep our foot on the gas we can get to the top and momentum will carry us forward. Processing is sort of like that."*

Beginning with t_1 (weakest) and proceeding through the final trigger (strongest), repeat the following procedure:

> Say, *"Bring up the picture of that trigger along with any words, tastes, smells, or sounds that go with it. How strong is the level of urge (LoU) right now, from 0 to 10 where 0 is no urge and 10 is the strongest?"*

0	1	2	3	4	5	6	7	8	9	10
(no urge)										(strongest urge)

> Say, *"Where are you feeling that number in your body?"*

_____

_____

> Say, *"Hold the picture along with all the associated words, tastes, and smells. Notice what and where you are feeling the urges in your body."*

_____

_____

Begin using BLS, Use at least 24 passes and watch for changes in the client physiology. As you notice changes:

> Say, *"Good"* or *"That's right."*

_____

_____

After each set of BLS:

> Say, *"What are you getting now?"*

_____

_____

> Or say, *"What is coming up now?"*

_____

_____

> Or say, *"What are you noticing now?"*

_____

_____

Say, *"Go with that."*

_____

_____

Or say, *"Concentrate on that."*

_____

_____

Or say, *"Think about that."*

_____

_____

Resume BLS.
Repeat until the desire drops to 0 (LoU = 0).
When the client reports a LoU of 0:

Say, *"Go with that."*

_____

_____

Do another set of BLS.

Troubleshooting

1. If the client is looping or getting off track, do the following:

   Say, *"Return to the target trigger and what is the LoU? Focus on the body location and go with that."*

   _____

   _____

2. If clients report no change, increase the width, distance, speed, number, or direction of the passes.
3. If clients intellectualize, increase the speed.
4. If clients abreact, continue the BLS until they calm down and say the following:

   Say, *"It's in the past, a long time ago . . . it's old stuff, let it go where old stuff belongs."*

   _____

   _____

5. If clients dissociate, keep them in their body:

   Say, *"Notice you are feeling it in your body. Notice any change, even the smallest change."*

   _____

   _____

Another way to keep clients in their bodies and in present time is to have them process while balancing on a balance or Pilates ball. It is difficult to dissociate while trying to balance yourself on the ball or do the BLS while the client is on a Pilates ball. It is difficult to dissociate while balancing on the ball (Lanius, 2003).

6. If traumatic material or core issues emerge as you address a trigger, you can continue and do another set to see if it processes through or switch to the Standard EMDR Protocol and process that material until the SUD is reduced to zero.

Say, *"Go with that."*

_____

_____

Always go back to the target triggers after long conversations with the client, when lost or confused, or when you feel that the LoU = 0 or is close to 0.

Step 9: Link and Install Positive State

After the LoU for a specific trigger reduces to 0 with BLS, anchor and install.

Say, *"Bring up the triggering incident again and apply slight pressure to your knuckle."*

Do BLS.

Say, *"What do you notice now?"*

_____

_____

Whatever positive feelings or statement the client reports after the set:

Say, *"Hold that* (and do another set of BLS)*."*

Say, *"What do you notice now?"*

_____

_____

If the client's report is negative, usually another channel has opened up and needs to be addressed.

Step 10: Test and Future Check

In this step, it is important to test installations and future check after each trigger is desensitized.

Say, *"Imagine a time in the future when _____* (state the event that triggered the client), *what is the level of urge, with 0 being little or no urge and 10 being the highest?"*

0	1	2	3	4	5	6	7	8	9	10
(no urge)										(highest urge)

Say, *"Where do you feel that in your body?"*

_____

_____

Do another set of BLS along with the anchoring pressure to the knuckle.

Say, *"Go with that as you use your knuckle anchor."*

_____

_____

If there is any remaining urge, work with each trigger until each one is reprocessed. Use Steps 8 through 10.

Step 11: Closure and Self-Work

Remind the client that the process continues after the session is over and that they may or may not experience new thoughts, memories, or experiences, and that they can contact you if necessary. If they notice anything unusual to make a note of it for the next session.

Say, *"The process continues after the session is over and you may or may not experience new thoughts, memories, or experiences. Please make note of them for the next session. If you have any major concerns or questions, please call me."*

_____

_____

To give them more resources, say the following:

Say, *"If you feel any urges, notice what and where you are feeling it or them. If any uncomfortable urges arise, pick a spot on the wall and move your eyes rapidly back and forth until the urge or desire fades and then touch your knuckle* (i.e., anchor the positive state). *If the urge remains, call your sponsor or support group person. If you are unable to prevent the urge and indulge in the dysfunctional behavior, remember that this is new information emerging and make a note of it so we can work on it during your next visit. It is like peeling away the leaves of an artichoke to get to the heart of the matter."*

Step 12: Follow-Up Sessions or Reevaluation

At the beginning of each session, check for the following: new targets or relapse triggers, new information, previously desensitized triggers, or relapse. Do BLS on all successes to build ego strength. This helps build ego strength on the successes noticed to date. If client reports relapse, begin working on the triggers causing the relapse.

Say, *"Okay, let's go over what happened since our last session and if you have learned any new information concerning your urges. What is happening concerning the triggers that we have worked on?"*

_____

_____

_____

_____

If the client is successful, say the following:

Say, *"Think about the success that you have accomplished and _____ (state the BLS)."*

_____

_____

If client reports relapse, work on the newly emerging triggers that brought up the urge to use. See Steps 8 through 10.

Desensitizing Trigger Worksheet

Note: Please refer to troubleshooting tips on main worksheet if urge is not reducing as planned.

Say, *"What trigger are we working on today?"*

_____

_____

$t_{\#}$___: _____

Say, *"What is the picture?"*

_____

_____

To desensitize say the following:

Say, *"Bring up the picture, along with any words, tastes, or smells that go with it. How strong is the LoU right now, from 0 to 10, where 0 is the lowest urge and 10 is the highest?"*

Starting LoU = 0   1   2   3   4   5   6   7   8   9   10
              (no urge)   (highest urge)

Say, *"Where are you feeling that number in your body? Hold the picture along with all the associated words, tastes, and smells. Notice what and where you are feeling the urges in your body."*

_____

_____

Begin using BLS. Use about 24 passes and watch for changes in the client's physiology. After each set, ask one of the following:

Say, *"What are you getting now?"*

_____

_____

Or say, *"What's coming up now?"*

_____

_____

Or say, *"What are you noticing now?"*

_____

_____

After the client responds, say the following

Say, *"Go with that."*

_____

_____

Or say, *"Concentrate on that."*

_____

_____

Or say, *"Think about that (and resume BLS)."*

_____

_____

Repeat until the desire drops to 0 (LoU = 0). Use the space below to record what the client says between sets.

When LoU = 0: Say, *"Go with that."*

Do another set of BLS.

Install the Positive Internal State With the Triggering Incident

Say, *"Bring up that triggering incident again and apply slight pressure to the knuckle."*

_____

_____

Do a set of BLS.

Whatever positive feelings or statements the client reports after the set:

Say, *"Notice those positive feelings and go with that (Do BLS)."*

_____

_____

If the client's reports are negative, another channel has likely opened up and needs to be addressed.

Test and Future Check

To test the installations:

Say, *"Bring the trigger up again. What is the LoU right now, from 0 to 10, where 0 is the lowest urge and 10 is the highest?"*

0	1	2	3	4	5	6	7	8	9	10
(no urge)										(highest urge)

If the LoU is above 0, say the following:

Say, *"Where are you feeling that in your body? Concentrate on that."*

_____

_____

Do BLS.

If the LoU = 0, do another set of BLS.

Say, *"Imagine a time in the future when you experience the trigger. What is the LoU right now, from 0 to 10, where 0 is the lowest urge and 10 is the highest?"*

0   1   2   3   4   5   6   7   8   9   10
(no urge)   (highest urge)

If the LoU = 0:

Say, *"Think about it and press your knuckle and follow my fingers (or other BLS)."*

_____

_____

Refer to main worksheet for session closure and relapse prevention instructions.

EMDR and Clients With Pain

Pain and how to treat it with EMDR has been of interest to the EMDR community from the very beginning. In the December 1991 *Network Newsletter*, Blanford and Blanford (1991) reported some success when using EMDR with 10 subjects who had chronic pain, while in the following year, McCann (1992) wrote in the *Journal of Behavior Therapy and Experimental Psychiatry* about his success in treating a burn patient in one session using EMDR.

Bruce Eimer—who had been working in the area of pain management prior to learning EMDR—was the inspiration for some of the protocols that follow in this book (see chapters 39–40). Dr. Eimer (1993a, 1993b) created an in-depth treatment he called the Chronic Pain Protocol that he explained in the *EMDR Network Newsletters* in the winter and spring of 1993. His first protocol included 13 steps while his spring version consisted of 21 steps. Basically, he assessed the "pain complex" of the client based on Cheek and LeCron's work (1968) and the "coping complex" that the client was using.

Dr. Eimer's major focus at first was on the pain itself, having the patient target the actual physical attributes of the pain. He then introduced the idea of "antidote images" to help with negative images that the patient used to represent pain; his protocol was formulated around the basic structure of the Standard EMDR Protocol and went on to incorporate the types of information important to working with patients with chronic pain. Although he had not yet done research, Dr. Eimer (1994, 1995) noted that he was getting excellent results with those pain patients with whom he had worked. He presented his findings at several EMDR International Association conferences.

A single case history by Hassard (1993) was published in the journal *Behavioural Psychotherapy* on treating a patient who had anxieties and body image issues resulting from operation scars and some physical disability; the procedure was effective within one session. In 1995, Hassard wrote "Investigation of Eye Movement Desensitization in Pain Clinic Patients" for the *Behavioral and Cognitive Psychotherapy* journal. He worked with 27 pain patients referred for EMD; 19 finished treatment (12 were successful and 7 were clear failures) and 7 dropped out before completing treatment. For the most part, there was an overall decrease with some return of symptoms at the 3 month follow-up.

Rost (2003) published an article addressing the need for understanding the significance of trauma in the chronic pain patient's treatment and how EMDR can support recovery. Her review appeared in the journal, *Zeitschrift fur Psychotraumatologie und Psychologische Medizin* on "EMDR in the Treatment of Chronic Pain."

The earliest recounting of work with EMDR and phantom limb pain was in the *Network Newsletter* when Levin (1992) worked with a man who had lost his finger in an industrial accident; he noted that the issue was addressed in one session. In 1996, Francine Shapiro conducted an EMDR training in Bogota, Columbia, for an organization called Forjar that works with children who have AIDS or cancer and have been abandoned. At the time, Vanderlaan (2000) used EMDR with a young girl who just had her leg amputated and was experiencing phantom limb pain; afterward, the child no longer had phantom limb pain. The report of this experience at the 1996 Denver conference inspired Tinker, Wilson, and Becker to do a pilot study using the case series approach with seven amputees. They reported on their success in San Francisco at the EMDRIA conference (1997). For most patients, the phantom limb pain disappeared within three sessions of treatment. Later, they went to work in Germany and used brain imaging to see the pre- and post-EMDR conditions of patients with phantom limb pain (Wilson, Tinker, Becker, Hofmann, & Cole, 2000). In 2005, Tinker and Wilson's chapter on "The Phantom Limb Pain Protocol" was published in *EMDR Solutions* (2005). In general, they reported that the protocol for phantom limb pain (PLP) consisted of three parts: history taking and relationship building, targeting the trauma of the experience, and fully targeting the pain itself. This was quite successful in treating their patients who had experienced phantom limb pain.

Since then, Wilensky reported on his work with phantom limb pain and EMDR in the *EMDRAC Newsletter* (2000) and the *Journal of Brief Therapy* (2006) where he reported on the treatment of six case studies. De Roos, Veenstra, and Van Rood reported on their work with phantom limb pain and whiplash at the EMDR European conference (2005). Recently, Schneider, Hofmann, Rost, and Shapiro wrote an article on "EMDR and Phantom Limb Pain" for the *Journal of EMDR Practice and Research* (2007) and on "EMDR in the Treatment of Chronic Phantom Limb Pain" in the journal, *Pain Medicine* (2008). Using a case series of five phantom limb patients, they described that EMDR resulted in significant decrease or elimination of phantom limb pain, reduction in depressive and post-traumatic stress disorder (PTSD) symptomatology, and significant decrease in medications. The authors agreed that EMDR was successful in the treatment of the phantom limb pain and the psychological consequences of amputation and that further research is needed.

Navy Commander Russell saw the importance of this work to the United States Armed Forces, given that since September 2006 more than 725 service members have experienced and survived combat-related traumatic amputations that often resulted in phantom limb pain. As a doctoral level psychologist, Russell documented his work with an active duty patient who suffered a traumatic leg amputation due to a noncombat-related motor vehicle accident. After four sessions of EMDR, the patient's PLP was eliminated and there was a reduction in his PTSD and depression symptomatology. He noted that the results were promising and more research is needed (2008).

Mark Grant has been talking, writing, and creating audiotapes or CDs concerning pain treatment and management since 1997. He began at the EMDRIA conference and spoke on "EMDR in a Multi-Modal Approach to Chronic Pain" (1997). Grant then created a manual to assist other clinicians, "Pain Control Based on EMDR" (1997, 2001). He reported on his work in the *EMDRIA Newsletter* (1999, 2000) and by 2000, he had created Mark Grant's Chronic Pain Pages (now www.overcomingpain.com). His Web site is a source of information on issues concerning EMDR and issues related to chronic pain. He also wrote an article for the journal, *Complementary Therapies in Nursing and Midwifery* (2000), discussing EMDR and the treatment of chronic pain. With A. Just, Grant published "EMDR and Compassionate Psychotherapy: A New Treatment for Chronic Pain" for the *EMDRIA Newsletter* (Grant & Just, 2000). In 2001, he wrote "Pain Control With EMDR" including theory, assessment, and specialized protocols for pain patients. Grant and Threlfo's report for three cases (2002), "EMDR in the Treatment of Chronic Pain," was published in the *Journal of Clinical Psychology*; Grant and Threlfo noted that all their subjects reported substantially decreased pain levels, lowering of negative affect, and were able to control their pain subsequent to treatment; they concluded that the results indicated EMDR may be efficacious and called for more research. Recently, Grant completed a new report, *Pain and Stress: Why You Hurt More Than You Should and How You Can Feel Better* (2008) and has self-published *Change Your Brain, Change Your Pain, Based on EMDR* (Grant, 2009).

The authors in Part V of this book have been working on their material over a period of time. Grant's protocol on "Pain Control With EMDR" (chapter 39) reflects the evolution of his work over the past decade. He uses the eight phases of EMDR treatment to discuss the ways that differ and what is consistent with the Standard EMDR Protocol. He assesses and educates clients about pain, prepares them for EMDR, targets the pain by eliciting a description of physical sensations, reprocesses, installs either the PC or antidote imagery to build a resource out of the change, introduces a future template to manage future pain episodes, and follows the rest of the phases.

De Roos and Veenstra's chapter 40 also targets current pain. They distinguish between three types of EMDR targets and have created a protocol for current pain. They, too, follow the eight phases including giving clear details concerning the component parts of the protocol that are pertinent for pain patients. De Roos and Veenstra describe some of the issues that occur in processing such as when clients are unable to focus on the processing or unable to perceive or describe change. They give suggestions on how to address the difficulties and different types of interweaves to target stuck processing. They discuss the virtues of installing a positive cognition versus antidote imagery for pain patients and how to close down the session. Reevaluation is an important part of the process.

In chapter 41, Wilson and Tinker describe the process they used in their study on PLP. As in most special populations, they address the need for a particular type of history taking to acquire all of the necessary information for solid treatment planning. Part of Wilson and Tinker's preparation is to create a Safe Place and then they move on to the Assessment Phase addressing the trauma that caused the phantom pain. They also have created a phantom pain scale (PPS) to measure the range of pain on a 0 to 10 scale, similar to the subjective units of disturbance (SUDs). The work is complete when all aspects of the emotional trauma associated with the loss is reprocessed.

These three chapters can give the clinician who is schooled in working with pain patients more resources to use when thinking about their clients' treatment plans.

Pain Control With EMDR

Mark Grant

The treatment of chronic pain is a new and growing application of EMDR. The suitability of EMDR for chronic pain stems from a number of sources. There are similarities and overlaps between traumatic stress and physical pain that would suggest EMDR as an appropriate addition to working with chronic pain. Also, the method's ability to change physical and neurological aspects of trauma (van der Kolk, 2002) bodes well for pain patients. Although it is too early from a research point of view, this application of EMDR has attracted a lot of interest with a growing number of studies indicating that EMDR can be effective in the treatment of chronic pain (Grant & Threlfo, 2002; Schneider et al., 2007, 2008; Tinker, Wilson, & Becker, 1997). Pain experts are excited by the promise of EMDR as a treatment method for chronic pain (Ray & Zbik, 2001, Scaer, 2008, personal communication).

Pain Control With EMDR Script Notes

Phase 1: History Taking

The history taking starts out with the presenting problem and then broadens to assess other relevant circumstances and issues. Given the amount of research documenting the relationship between stress and pain, it is particularly important to assess the pain client's stress history and the presence of comorbid stressors and psychological problems. Chronic pain is rarely an isolated problem, as anxiety, depression, PTSD, and emotional regulation problems are frequently associated with this issue. Prior to attempting the Desensitization Phase, the therapist must assess what the primary presenting problem is. Given EMDR's origins as a treatment for traumatic stress, the first thing to consider is whether the client's physical pain is associated with a trauma.

1. *Pain associated with a traumatic event.* If the client's pain is associated with traumatic stress, the Assessment Phase involves identifying the trigger memory associated with the client's physical pain. The types of trauma most commonly associated with chronic pain include accidents, assaults, combat service, medical mishaps, chronic medical conditions, and so forth. Chronic pain itself can be a trauma because of the discomfort it involves

and its negative effects on life functioning. Where pain is associated with a traumatic event, it can be incorporated into the target as part of the affect instead of emotion. For example, a phantom limb pain sufferer might have as their target an image of the accident in which they lost their leg, a negative cognition and either an emotion or physical pain as the affect.

2. *Pain not associated with a traumatic event.* If the pain is not associated with a traumatic event, there may be no single trigger memory. In this case, the therapist may need to construct a target based on the client's pain. A pain-based target can be created by simply asking the client to describe their pain in terms of a size, shape, color, and so forth (see scripts below). It is not always necessary or desirable to obtain a negative and positive cognition when processing this type of chronic pain. For one thing, if the pain is associated with a medical condition, clients may not necessarily have a negative cognition. It is also easier and more efficient to perform the bilateral stimulation (BLS) on the client's imaginal view of their pain without the addition of a cognitive element.

Phase 2: Preparation Phase

The Preparation Phase involves engaging the client in the treatment process.

Pain is rarely just pain so before trying to construct a target for EMDR treatment, the therapist should first conduct a thorough assessment of the client's life circumstances and concerns. It is helpful, in particular, to assess and support for the following three issues:

1. *Seeds of hope.* Many chronic pain sufferers feel helpless and hopeless as a result of failed treatment, dashed hopes, and the seemingly interminable reality of their pain. Therapeutic engagement and motivation may need to be stimulated. One way to do this is to demonstrate to the client early in therapy that they can feel different; this sows seeds of hope. Offer some quick strategies for relieving pain, such as learning to focus on something soothing when in pain, changing their sleep routine (which relieves fatigue—a major exacerbating factor), teaching them how to pace themselves better, or just highlighting everyday activities that they are maintaining despite their pain and all its limitations. For example, reminding a parent, "Even though you can't pick up your children, you can still tell them you love them."

2. *Safety.* Where physical pain is associated with psychological trauma (such as child physical or sexual abuse, combat-related injuries, industrial accidents, etc.), clients may have safety issues. This may require establishment of a Safe Place and possibly ego-strengthening work to enable them to participate in what can be a lengthy treatment course. Safety issues with chronic pain sufferers may include inadequate pain control, diagnostic uncertainty, loss of control associated with decreased physical functioning, insurance issues, and so forth.

3. *Case management.* Occasionally, the therapist may need to get involved in case management, including talking to the client's physician about their medication (if inadequate or being misused), family members about support, and so on. Not every case will need this, but for a variety of reasons, pain is often mismanaged and therapy will get nowhere so long as the client feels vulnerable as a result of unmanaged external stressors.

Phase 3: Assessment

There are four important issues to keep in mind when working on the Assessment Phase:

1. *Detachment.* As in the treatment of post-traumatic stress, clients need to be introduced to the concept of thinking about their pain from a detached

awareness standpoint. For example, one of the first questions of the treatment phase is "When you bring up the picture (or incident) and those words _____ (clinician states the negative cognition), what emotion do you feel now?" or "When you think of the incident what do you get?" Notice how this question sets up a mental separation between the problem and the emotional response associated with the problem. Because of the involvement of emotion in pain, it is helpful to use this phraseology when talking about physical pain. For example, instead of asking, "How do you feel?" the therapist might ask, "How does the pain make you feel?" This wording sets up a separation between the client and the problem and elicits a less emotionally loaded description of the problem. There is, however, no need to seek a description of the pain until you get to the treatment phase.

2. *Target.* The next step is to develop a target for reprocessing. The best way to do this is to ask clients to describe their pain in sensory–emotional terms. For example, "What size or shape is the pain?" "Is it hard or soft," and so forth (see scripts below). The result should be a fairly accurate description of how the pain is felt in the body. Many clients have never really verbalized their pain and simply getting them to describe it can be a powerful intervention. Bringing the pain into consciousness is also an essential precondition for EMDR treatment.

3. *Negative cognition (NC).* Once a description and an image of the pain have been obtained, a negative cognition needs to be created. As indicated above, this is optional where the pain is not associated with a trauma. This will involve clients' attitudes or beliefs about themselves around their pain. For example, "I can't control it," "I'm helpless," "There's something wrong with me," and so forth. While most people can more or less identify how their trauma or pain makes them feel, they are rarely conscious of its effects on their identity or self-esteem. This question helps bring that self-referential material to the surface where it can be addressed.

4. *Measurement.* It is helpful to quantify the pain so that a baseline measure can be established by using the SUD scale (Wolpe, 1958), for instance, "How bad is the pain on a scale of 0 to 10, where 0 is no pain or neutral and 10 is the most pain you can imagine?" If clients have multiple pain sites, simply ask them "Which site is the worst?" or "Which one they would like to work on first?"

Phase 4: Desensitization

Attend to three important aspects of the Desensitization Phase:

1. *Dual attention stimulation (DAS).* The treatment phase is when the client is asked to focus on their pain while attending to DAS. In this unique treatment element of EMDR, the client is subjected to a titrated exposure to their pain, mediated by the influence of DAS. Research on DAS finds that it stimulates physiological changes consistent with relaxation, including decreased respiration rate, decreased systolic blood pressure, and a decrease in galvanic skin response (Elofsson, von Schèele, Theorell, & Sondergaard, 2008). It seems reasonable to surmise that these effects are behind the pain relief that EMDR produces.

2. *End of set.* After each set of DAS, clients are instructed to take a breath and notice what they feel in their body. At this point, many clients will report their pain feels duller, softer, further away, or just less distressing. This sense of relief or distance from the pain is maintained by repeated instructions to just notice during additional sets of DAS.

3. *Measurement and positive cognition (PC).* Once a relatively low, stable level of distress has been achieved, clients are asked to review the negative

"I statement" they made at the beginning of treatment (if a negative cognition was obtained). As a result of feeling less distressed or more relaxed, clients generally find that this has changed and the positive cognition can be tested. Where a negative cognition was not initially obtained, the therapist can invite a positive cognition by simply asking the client how they feel about their ability to cope with their pain now.

Phase 5: Installation

In EMDR treatment of chronic pain, the Installation Phase can mean either installing a positive cognition or installing imaginal resources for controlling the pain.

1. *Positive cognition.* Since complete pain relief is relatively rare in chronic pain sufferers, in most cases installation of the positive cognition (where used) will need to be coupled with antidote or pain-relieving imagery.
2. *Antidote or pain-relieving imagery.* Drawing on Ericksonian methods, the therapist should utilize the clients' responses to EMDR to create healing imagery. For example, when clients report feeling more relaxed or less pain following a set of DAS but the pain is not completely resolved and the therapist needs to bring the session to a close, the therapist should ask clients to think of something that reminds them of "that feeling of relaxation or pain relief." Clients typically report things like a sponge, a wet towel, a small spot, like a coin, and so forth. The point is simply to get an image that resonates with the feelings of relief and install that. It can also be helpful to pair the antidote imagery with an anchor word by asking, "Is there a word or phrase that goes with that image?" This can be used as part of a future template (see scripts below).

Phase 6: Body Scan

Issues to keep in mind concerning the Body Scan Phase and sensation.

1. *Body scan and desensitization.* The therapist should continuously check in with clients regarding their physical experience after each set of DAS ("What do you notice now?"), in other words, for chronic pain sufferers, the body scan is addressed during the course of desensitization and not only at the end of the treatment. The aim is to keep processing until the client's pain reduces to as low a level as possible.
2. *Assist clients to identify change.* Because clients sometimes fail to notice changes in how they feel, the therapist may need to help them identify and report on changes. For example, if the client says they feel better ask, "What are you feeling that is different (e.g., is the pain softer, smaller, moved, etc.)?" The Body Scan thus becomes part of helping clients to crystallize changes following EMDR.
3. *Clarify responses.* The therapist also needs to clarify the client's responses, for example, a "Nothing" response to "What do you notice now?" may mean that nothing has changed, or that the client feels no pain—the therapist should ask rather than assume.

Phase 7: Closure

The following issues should be considered during the Closure Phase:

1. *Better place.* Each session should end with the client in a stable better place, even if their pain is not completely reprocessed.

2. *Mastery.* Each session should end with the client having an increased sense of mastery over their pain or at least a new tool to try. This will have been facilitated by questioning the client about changes in their pain experience during the sets of DAS and the development of resource imagery.
3. *Affect management strategies.* While Safe Places and resource installations are often reviewed at this stage of trauma treatment, unless the chronic pain is part of a traumatic stress reaction, it is more likely that affect-management strategies such as antidote imagery and pain-control strategies will be the focus.
4. *Review.* The closure section of each session can also be a time to review any other advice the client may need for understanding, coping with their pain, and its effects upon their life. As mentioned, pain is rarely an isolated problem and EMDR treatment of chronic pain will usually be conducted in conjunction with other inputs.

Phase 8: Reevaluation

Each session should begin by reviewing clients' experience of their pain and related stress or trauma over the period since the last session, making sure to ask for specific changes, otherwise clients may forget to report them. Use this information as the basis for the current session's reprocessing.

The following protocol is based on the author's clinical experience and research, based on over 10 years working with this client population. This protocol should nevertheless be considered a work in progress, to be used in conjunction with the clinician's own skills, preferences, and experience. Try to balance your need for information against the client's needs for relief and hope and be prepared to intersperse your information gathering with treatment. As with any complex presenting problem this protocol and EMDR should be incorporated into a multimodal therapeutic approach incorporating psychoeducation, supportive psychotherapy, pain-management skills training (e.g., hypnosis, visualization, meditation), case management, and so on.

Note: The questions below are offered as guidelines, please feel free to skip some questions if you do not feel they are necessary. Please also feel free to modify the wording if you are not comfortable with the phraseology.

Pain Control and EMDR Script

Phase 1: History Taking

The purpose of the history taking is to define and understand the presenting problem in the context of the client's life.

Say, *"What is the purpose of your coming in for treatment?"*

_____

_____

_____

_____

Say, *"When did the pain begin?"*

_____

_____

_____

_____

Say, *"How long have you had problems with pain?"*

_____

_____

_____

_____

Say, *"How did the pain begin?"*

_____

_____

_____

_____

Say, *"What is your medical diagnosis?"*

_____

_____

_____

_____

Clients may not know their diagnosis or they may not accept it. If the client does not know the diagnosis, say the following:

Say, *"What is your understanding of the problem?"*

_____

_____

_____

_____

If the client does not accept the diagnosis, you will need to review the client's medical investigations and discuss their options regarding further investigations.

Say, _"Please tell me what you have done so far to understand what is going on with you concerning your pain."_

_____

_____

_____

_____

Say, _"What do you see your options are concerning any further medical investigations?"_

_____

_____

_____

_____

Say, _"Did you have any health problems prior to the injury?"_

_____

_____

_____

_____

Say, _"What treatment have you had?"_

_____

_____

_____

_____

Say, _"How effective was it?"_

_____

_____

_____

_____

Say, _"What else do you do to cope with your pain?"_

_____

_____

_____

_____

Say, *"Tell me about your family. What sort of a family was or is it?"*

_____

_____

_____

_____

Say, *"Tell me about how you grew up. How was your birth? Walking? Talking? Did you have any problems with growing up?"*

_____

_____

_____

_____

Say, *"How would you describe your relationship with your family? How close do you feel you are to your spouse, parents, brothers, and sisters?"*

_____

_____

_____

_____

Say, *"Apart from the accident or illness that triggered your pain, have you had to deal with any other major stressors in your life?"*

_____

_____

_____

_____

Say, *"How do you feel about yourself?"*

_____

_____

_____

_____

Say, *"How well do you think you are able to look after your self in the areas of personal health, social contacts, and rest and relaxation?"*

_____

_____

_____

_____

Say, *"What type of supports do you have in the form of family or friends?"*

_____

_____

_____

_____

Say, *"Are there any other stressful circumstances in your life?"*

_____

_____

_____

_____

Say, *"How do you cope with stress?"*

_____

_____

_____

_____

Say, *"How do you cope with the emotional aspects of your ordeal, for example, do you get angry, depressed, and so forth?"*

_____

_____

_____

_____

Say, *"Are you still able to feel positive about life and how do you do that?"*

_____

_____

_____

_____

Fill in this history with any other normal history-taking information that you think is important for you to have or is mandated. The need to take a complete history may also need to be balanced against the need to engage the client and generate relief, particularly if the client presents in crisis. History taking is thus a process that can continue throughout therapy rather than something that is necessarily completed in a single session.

Phase 2: Preparation

Clients also need to be educated about the nature of chronic pain, the relationship between stress and pain, normal emotional aspects of pain, and the possibility that they can learn to feel different.

Say, *"Chronic pain is stressful and it is normal to feel anxious, angry, or depressed—these feelings are an understandable response to a problem like this. However, if not understood and managed, they can also make things worse. If you can learn how to manage these feelings, it can help you cope better and even have less pain."*

At the same time, it's important not to overlook the reality of pain, the contribution of physical injury, and the possibility that the client may have undiagnosed physical pathology. Even where there are many stress risk factors, one should not rule out the possibility that there is undiagnosed organic pathology.

Say, *"Accepting that stress might be contributing to your pain doesn't mean it is not real and you should always ensure you have had all reasonable investigations and treatment."*

As with treating trauma, clients need to be introduced to the concept of thinking about their pain from a detached awareness standpoint. Instead of asking how the client feels:

Say, *"What does the pain feel like?"*

_____

_____

During the Preparation Phase, it is important to sow seeds of hope.

Say, *"Even though it can feel like the pain is never ending, there is always hope, things change, nothing lasts forever."*

Say, *"It is often helpful to have some of what I call quick strategies to help manage your pain more effectively. For example, many chronic pain sufferers find it hard to sleep normally. This is a normal consequence of chronic pain. Although traditional approaches to insomnia emphasize trying to maintain a normal sleep routine, this may be unrealistic when you are struggling with a problem like chronic pain. Therefore, instead of trying to sleep normally, a more effective approach is to simply sleep whenever your body will let you. This may sound crazy but it actually makes a lot of sense; the reality is that your pain and stress is going to affect your circadian rhythms and it is better to work with how you feel rather than trying to act normal. At least this way even if you are awake in the middle of the night, you know that you can get some rest later when your body feels ready."*

Clients need to accept that they need to pace themselves differently.

Say, *"When you have chronic pain, it is important that you learn how to pace yourself so that you're not constantly aggravating your pain. Pacing yourself means stopping whatever you're doing when the pain starts to come on. It may mean changing your expectations; instead of finishing tasks in one go, they may need to be broken down and completed in bite-sized chunks."*

Also, point out the things that they are still doing despite their pain and all its limitations.

Say, *"It is also important for you to think about _____ (state what they can do despite their pain). You know that is really impressive that even though you have all of this pain, you can succeed at _____ (state their success)."*

Where the pain is associated with trauma (such as child physical or sexual abuse, combat-related injuries, industrial accidents etc.), clients may have safety issues.

Say, *"Is there anywhere you can go or anything you can do where you feel safe from the trauma or pain? Some people feel better when they are doing something they enjoy that takes their mind off the pain; some people like listening to the soothing sounds of nature, such as the ocean, or rain on a roof; some people feel better when they can talk to someone who understands. What do you do that makes you feel safe?"*

_____

_____

_____

_____

Pain and the Adaptive Information Processing Model

Prior to commencing reprocessing, it can be helpful to explain chronic pain in terms of the Adaptive Information Processing (AIP) model. The following is an example of how to present these concepts:

Say, *"Pain can occur for many reasons. We generally understand pain as a signal that something is wrong physically. However, sometimes pain can continue longer than expected despite medical treatment. Pain can persist because of fatigue, stress, and biochemical and neurological changes. As a result of these changes, the pain becomes locked in the nervous system. EMDR is a way of stimulating the nervous system to facilitate healing. Even though we might not be able to completely eliminate your pain, EMDR often stimulates feelings of relaxation, which always reduces pain.*

We can't predict how your nervous system will respond to the EMDR stimulation, so try and adopt an open mind and just notice the sensations of your pain as best you can. Initially, the intensity of the pain may not seem to change or it may even increase, this is just the pain response shifting in response to the stimulation. In the unlikely event that the pain increases to an intolerable level, just raise your hand like this (show stop signal). Remember your nervous system knows what to do, so there's no need to try and make it happen, just notice and just let whatever happens happen.

What we will be doing often is a simple check on what you are experiencing. I need to know from you exactly what is going on, with as clear feedback as possible. Sometimes things will change and sometimes they won't. There are no supposed tos. Just notice and just let whatever happens happen."

Phase 3: Assessment

There are two types of pain that come up in clinical work. This protocol focuses primarily on the pain as the target.

Pain Primarily Related to Trauma

If the pain is a result of a trauma, follow the targeting as described in the Standard EMDR Protocol, with the exception that you can substitute the pain for the trauma-related emotion.

Emotions or Pain

Say, *"When you bring up the picture* (or incident) *and those words* _____ (clinician states the negative cognition), *what is the pain that you feel now?"*

_____

_____

Subjective Unit of Pain (SUP)

Say, *"On a scale of 0 to 10, where 0 is no pain or neutral and 10 is the most pain you can imagine, how disturbing does it feel now?"*

0   1   2   3   4   5   6   7   8   9   10
(no pain)   (most pain)

EMDR Pain Target

The target for the assessment is for the pain itself. Vague descriptions (e.g., a dull ache) are generally not adequate as targets for reprocessing. By eliciting a clear, more specific description of the pain, you are helping clients develop a meaningful cognitive representation of it. The therapist can suggest possibilities, if careful not to influence clients to adopt material that is not their own.

Say, *"Can you describe the pain in terms of the physical sensations you feel in your body?"*

_____

_____

_____

_____

If the client is unable to describe their pain, say the following:

Say, *"If your pain had a size how big would it be?"*

_____

_____

Say, *"If your pain had a shape what shape would it be?"*

_____

_____

Say, *"If your pain had a color what color would it be?"*

_____

_____

Say, *"Does your pain feel like it is hot or cold? How hot or cold?"*

Where clients are unable to find words or images to describe their pain, ask them to draw a picture of their pain. Do not be put off by clients' objections that they are not artists as even a dark angry line can be a helpful tool in focusing the client and concretizing the pain.

Say, *"Some people find it helpful to draw their pain. You do not have to be an artist to draw the feeling behind the pain. What does the pain look like to you? Here are paper and pencil."*

Negative Cognition (NC)

This is optional when the pain is not related to trauma. If possible, the NC will elicit clients' attitudes or beliefs about themselves around their pain.

Say, *"What words best go with the pain that express your negative belief about yourself now?"*

Or say, *"What does it feel like your pain is telling you about yourself?"*

Positive Cognition (PC)

The next step in the assessment is to obtain a positive cognition. This is a statement about how clients would like to feel about themselves in relation to their pain (e.g., "I can cope," "I'm alright," etc.).

Say, *"When you bring up that picture or incident, what would you like to believe about yourself now?"*

Validity of Cognition (VoC)

Elicit a VoC.

Then say, *"When you think of the pain, how true do those words ____ (clinician repeats the positive cognition) feel to you now on a scale of 1 to 7, where 1 feels completely false and 7 feels completely true?"*

1	2	3	4	5	6	7
(completely false)				(completely true)		

Emotions

Elicit the emotions.

> Say, *"When you think of the pain and those words _____* (clinician states the negative cognition), *what emotion* (or feeing) *do you feel now?"*

_____

_____

Subjective Units of Disturbance (SUD)

Elicit the SUD.

> Say, *"On a scale of 0 to 10, where 0 is no disturbance or neutral and 10 is the highest disturbance you can imagine, how disturbing does it feel now?"*

> 0   1   2   3   4   5   6   7   8   9   10
> (no disturbance)   (highest disturbance)

Location of Body Sensation

Elicit the sensation or location.

> Say, *"Where do you feel it* (the disturbance) *in your body?"*

_____

_____

Phase 4: Desensitization

> Say, *"Now I'd like you to focus on the pain the way you've just described it to me, at the same time _____* (state whatever form of DAS the client prefers) *and just let whatever happens happen. Just notice."*

_____

_____

Commence DAS.

> Say, *"What do you notice now?"*

_____

_____

> Say, *"That's fine, just go with that."*

_____

_____

If client reports a difference, elicit details and restimulate using what they reported as a target. Responses like "It feels better," are okay, but asking for more details, such as when you get a response that is something concrete, such as, "softer, smaller," helps you get a better target with which to continue processing as in the following:

Say, *"But how does it feel better? What feels different about it?"*
Then say, *"Notice that."*

_____

_____

Commence DAS.

Never accept responses like "Nothing" or "It's the same." These are analyses rather than direct reports and give you nothing to reprocess.

Say, *"Yes, okay, but I need to know exactly what you are experiencing,*
like when you described it before we started."

_____

_____

Note: Stop the DAS if it is making the pain worse, use other methods (e.g., hypnosis, imagery, pacing, emotional containment techniques, support, etc.) to manage the pain.

If the pain is changing, say, *"Notice that."*

Continue DAS and reviewing the client's responses until the SUD has decreased to an acceptable level before proceeding to the Installation Phase. An acceptable level of pain may be anywhere between 0 and a 4 or 5. The best way to determine this is to ask clients whether they think they can achieve any further improvement or not and whether they feel like continuing.

Say, *"On a scale of 0 to 10, where 0 is no pain or neutral and 10 is the*
highest pain you can imagine, how disturbing does it feel now?"

0   1   2   3   4   5   6   7   8   9   10
(no pain)   (highest pain)

Say, *"Does it feel like you can achieve any further improvement?"*

_____

_____

However, it is always important when the number is higher than 0 to ask the following:

Say, *"What prevents the number from being a 0?"*

_____

_____

Or say, *"If you focus on the number _____ (state the number given),*
what is behind it?"

_____

_____

Say, *"Go with that."*

_____

_____

Do DAS.

Say, *"Do you want to continue?"*

_____

_____

Also look for physical signs of progress such as changes in posture, facial expression, and so forth. If you are in tune with your client you should be able to sense their energy levels and capacity for further work versus needing to finish.

Phase 5: Installation

When working with pain control, depending on whether the pain is trauma-related or not, positive cognitions or antidote imagery are installed to assist in controlling pain.

> Say, *"Think of something that reminds you of that feeling of relaxation or pain relief."*

_____

_____

> Say, *"What is it?"*

_____

_____

The idea is to link the feeling of relief to a memory association. Clients will say things like "a wet blanket," "a pac-man," "an absorbent sponge." Once clients have identified a healing image, ask them to think of a word that goes with that image and install it by pairing it with DAS.

> Say, *"Now think of a word that goes with that image and go with that."*

_____

_____

Do DAS.
If clients have a cessation of pain with SUD = 0 and VoC = 7, follow the normal installation directions.

> Say, *"How does _____ (repeat the PC) sound?"*

_____

_____

> Say, *"Do the words _____ (repeat the PC) still fit or is there another positive statement that feels better?"*

_____

_____

If clients accept the original positive cognition, the clinician should ask for a VoC rating to see if it has improved.

Say, *"As you think of the incident, how do the words feel, from 1 being completely false to 7 being completely true?"*

1   2   3   4   5   6   7
(completely false)   (completely true)

Say, *"Think of the event and hold it together with the words _____ (repeat the PC)."*

_____

_____

Do a long set of BLS to see if there is more processing to be done.

Antidote Imagery

When clients report differences in pain or changes in the way it is perceived, ask questions to build a resource out of the change.

Say, *"So what's come in the pain's place? What's there now where the pain was before?"*

_____

_____

Sometimes, when the pain doesn't change of its own accord, it may be necessary to instruct clients to do the following:

Say, *"Think of something that could take the pain away or make it better, don't worry about whether it seems realistic or not, just let your imagination run wild."*

_____

_____

Once you obtain something concrete (e.g., smooth, softer, smaller, etc.), restimulate.

If change continues after a couple more sets, ask the following:

Say, *"What's that like? What does it remind you of?"*

_____

_____

Future Template

Once clients can describe a stable image that is linked to pain relief, this can be used as a basis for managing future pain episodes.

Say, *"Now think of your pain again and _____ (antidote imagery) and notice what happens."*

_____

_____

Assuming clients report feeling relief, say the following:

Say, *"Is there a word or phrase that goes with that feeling?"*

_____

_____

Note: You are not looking for a positive cognition here, just a catch or cue word that gives clients a cognitive anchor or trigger for their antidote imagery.

Say, *"So the next time you need pain relief, you can stop, close your eyes, and think of that _____ (say trigger word and antidote imagery)."*

Say, *"Practice thinking of your trigger word and antidote imagery. The more often you do that, the more you will be able to control your pain."*

_____

_____

Positive Cognition (PC)

Pair a word with the metaphor and install.

Say, *"Is there a word or phrase that goes with how you feel when you think of that image?"*

_____

_____

Resume DAS until clients report the stable presence of the positive cognition.

Note: The positive cognition can be skipped when using DAS for pain relief in conjunction with antidote imagery and future template. However, once clients report feeling more in control of their pain, it should be evoked and installed in the usual way.

Validity of Cognition (VoC)

Say, *"When you think of pain now, how true do those words _____ (clinician repeats the positive cognition) feel to you now on a scale of 1 to 7, where 1 feels completely false and 7 feels completely true?"*

1	2	3	4	5	6	7
(completely false)				(completely true)		

Say, *"Is there another positive statement or cognition that fits better now? If so, what would it be?"*

_____

_____

Phase 6: Body Scan

If clients report "No change" following the DAS, use a cognitive interweave as in the following:

Say, *"Are you sure it is really no different?"*

_____

_____

If clients answer "Yes," say the following:

Say, *"Okay, do you have any idea about what's stopping the pain from changing?"*

_____

_____

When clients report no pain or it is apparent that clients cannot improve any further, say the following:

Say, *"Close your eyes and keep in mind the original memory or image and the positive cognition. Then bring your attention to the different parts of your body, starting with your head and working downward. Any place you find any tension, tightness, or unusual sensation, tell me."*

_____

_____

Phase 7: Closure

If the pain is part of a traumatic reaction say the following:

Say, *"Things may come up or they may not. If they do, write them down, and they can be a target for next time. If you get any new memories, dreams, or situations that disturb you, just take a good snapshot. It isn't necessary to give a lot of detail. Just put down enough to remind you so we can target it next time. The same thing goes for any positive dreams or situations. If negative feelings do come up, try not to make them significant. Remember, it's still just the old stuff. Just write it down for next time. Then use the tape or the Safe Place exercise to let as much of the disturbance go as possible. Even if nothing comes up, make sure to use the tape everyday and give me a call if you need to."*

If the pain is not part of a traumatic reaction, say the following:

Say, *"The changes you have experienced today may lead to permanent change in how you experience your pain. It is important to notice any changes in your pain experience. Whatever happens, just notice what happens with your pain between now and the next session and it is helpful to take notes so that we can work on that next time."*

Phase 8: Reevaluation

Each session should begin by reviewing the client's experience of their pain and related stress or trauma over the period since the last session. Changes in sleeping patterns, physiological arousal, and activity levels need to be screened for, identified and feedback to clients to avoid a false perception that nothing has changed.

Say, *"So what have you noticed about your trauma or pain since our last session?"*

_____

_____

_____

_____

Say, *"Have you noticed any changes in your sleeping pattern?"*

_____

_____

Say, *"Have you noticed any changes in your activity levels since last time?"*

_____

_____

Say, *"Have you noticed any changes in your mood since last time?"*

_____

_____

Inquire about specific areas of the client's life that they have identified as problematical or affected by their stress, trauma, or pain, such as sleep, relationships, activity levels, etc.

Say, *"Tell me about _____ (state problem areas) since the last session. What have you noticed?"*

_____

_____

_____

_____

The therapist needs to check with clients for any changes in how they have been feeling in terms of the material that was processed at the previous session and use this as a basis for constructing new targets for EMDR reprocessing. It is not uncommon for the image of the pain to change between sessions, as the clients experience changes, particularly if progress is being made.

Acknowledgments

I thank Francine Shapiro, PhD, and Bruce Eimer, PhD.

40

EMDR Pain Protocol for Current Pain

Carlijn de Roos and Sandra Veenstra

In the search for effective treatment for patients suffering from chronic pain, EMDR is being added to the store of possible treatment methods. Evidence from case reports of a limited number of patients suggests that EMDR can also be effective in the long-term resolution of chronic pain and phantom limb pain (De Roos et al., 2009; Grant & Threlfo, 2002; Russell, 2008; Schneider, Hofmann, Rost, & Shapiro, 2007, 2008; Tinker & Wilson, 2005; Wilensky, 2006). Although the effectiveness of EMDR with post-traumatic stress disorder (PTSD) has indeed been established, with regard to the treatment of pain, its application is still experimental.

There are three types of EMDR targets that can be distinguished in the treatment of patients with chronic pain:

1. *Traumatic memory.* A classic trauma or trauma-related memory, such as having experienced a serious accident, amputation, or operation.
2. *Pain-related memory.* A current emotionally disturbing memory that is related to traumatic pain experiences or the traumatic consequences of the pain. Several examples are: having a pain attack, being abandoned by friends and family, or losing one's job.
3. *Current pain.* As a target does not in fact involve a memory, but the pain as it is now and as it is now experienced.

EMDR Pain Protocol for Current Pain Script Notes

When identifying suitable targets for EMDR in the treatment of pain, every event from the pain history that is still emotionally disturbing is, in principle, suitable. One important question to ask is which strategy will lead to the most efficient target selection, and, subsequently, the quickest and most thorough decrease in pain. In patients suffering pain, often, all three types of targets are present. Should treatment commence with addressing trauma targets or is a direct focus on the current pain indicated? At the moment, no definitive guidelines exist in this regard. The intake data can assist the therapist in hypothesizing the etiology of the pain and what is maintaining the pain symptoms. This hypothesis gives direction to the target selection and the order in which the targets can be desensitized.

Traumatic Memory

If the chronic pain of a patient is associated with traumatic memories—such as an accident or amputation—the logical move is to commence with these targets using the Standard EMDR Protocol. The application of this protocol has been proven effective for PTSD and yields relatively rapid results. As the post-traumatic stress decreases, one can expect a favorable effect on overall functioning. This is motivating both to the patient and the therapist. Furthermore, if chronic pain is the result of the dysfunctional storage of a somatosensory memory as part of a traumatic memory, this somatosensory memory will be functionally (re)stored through the reprocessing of the information, with a reduction in the pain as a consequence.

Pain-Related Memory

Pain-related memories are also desensitized using the Standard EMDR Protocol. These are focused on by the patient after the processing of the traumatic memory(ies) or in the absence of presently highly disturbing classic traumatic memories. Pain-related memories concern current emotionally disturbing memories related to traumatic pain experiences or the traumatic consequences of the pain. The hypothesis is that these memories intensify the emotional experience of the pain or are the impetus for, or help maintain, the dysfunctional significance attached to the pain. The goal of the application of the EMDR procedure to these memories is the normalization of the emotional component of chronic pain, which will hopefully lead to more effective, functional cognition, coping strategies, and behavior. As a result, the feeling of being in control of the pain will increase, while the current pain level may decrease as well (Grant & Threlfo, 2002).

Activation of Somatosensory Memories With the Standard EMDR Protocol

During the desensitization of the trauma and pain-related targets with the Standard EMDR Protocol, it is important that patients specifically be asked to report physical perceptions or that the therapist pay extra attention to these perceptions. This increases the likelihood that somatosensory memories will be activated and integrated during the processing; in fact, patients report that talking about what bodily sensations are occurring helps them maintain their concentration on physical sensations for a longer period of time. Another possible tool could be an extensive Body Scan (Tinker & Wilson, 2005).

Current Pain

If the above-mentioned targets cannot be pinpointed, or if the targets have no effect on the pain, the therapist focuses the patient's attention on the current pain. For this target, the EMDR Pain Protocol for Current Pain is used (see script below).

In this chapter, the EMDR Pain Protocol for Current Pain is scripted; it is based on a pilot study for phantom limb pain (De Roos et al., 2009) and uses current pain as a target for patients with chronic pain. The pilot study required a structured protocol so the authors constructed one based upon the Standard EMDR Protocol of Shapiro (2001), the Pain Protocol of Grant (1999), and the Dutch Standard EMDR Protocol (De Jongh & Ten Broeke, 2003). The goal of the EMDR Pain Protocol for Current Pain is to decrease current pain.

Note: It is important that therapists working with EMDR and chronic pain, have knowledge about EMDR as well as about chronic pain. Both are necessary to offer an adequate treatment because EMDR for these patients is often embedded in a broader treatment plan.

EMDR Pain Protocol For Current Pain Script

Phase 1: Client History

Take a full pain history (see U.S. Department of Health and Human Services, 1994). For the purpose of this chapter, the most essential questions about pain and its association with traumatic events are selected. General questions common for every intake are left out and should be included by therapists according to their own needs.

Pain Assessment

Description

1. Say, *"How does the pain feel exactly?"*

   _____

   _____

2. Say, *"What words would you use to describe your pain? Is it sharp, burning, shooting, hot, cold, electrical, whining, etc."*

   _____

   _____

Help the patient describe the pain with concrete examples to clarify how it feels (e.g., "It feels like there is a knife cutting in my foot.").

Location

3. Say, *"Where is the pain exactly?"*

   _____

   _____

4. Say, *"Draw a picture of the pain at this moment. Draw the whole body if necessary, from the front and from the back, and draw the pain in the body with another color* (or colors).*"*

   _____

   _____

Assess Pain Intensity: Onset and Temporal Pattern

5. Say, *"When did your pain start?"*

   _____

   _____

6. Say, *"How often does it occur?"*

   _____

   _____

7. Say, *"Has its intensity changed since the beginning?"*

   _____

   _____

8. Say, *"Does the pain intensity change during the day?"*

_____

_____

Intensity

9. Say, *"On a scale of 0 to 10 where 0 is no pain to 10 is the worst pain imaginable, choose the number that fits the pain at this moment during the intake."*

0	1	2	3	4	5	6	7	8	9	10
(no pain)										(worst pain)

10. Say, *"Choose the number that fits the worst amount of pain during the last week?"*

0	1	2	3	4	5	6	7	8	9	10
(no pain)										(worst pain)

11. Say, *"Choose the number that fits the lowest amount of pain during the last week?"*

0	1	2	3	4	5	6	7	8	9	10
(no pain)										(worst pain)

12. Say, *"Let's draw a time line of the course of your pain from when it started until now. The horizontal line represents the time and the vertical line represents the pain from 0 to 10."*

_____

_____

Help the patient draw the time line on a piece of paper.

Aggravating and Relieving Factors

13. Say, *"What helps the pain to decrease?"*

_____

_____

14. Say, *"What can make the pain worse?"*

_____

_____

15. Say, *"How does the pain react to warmth, moving, walking, distraction, rest, and so forth?"*

_____

_____

Diagnoses and Previous Treatments

16. Say, *"What diagnoses were made by the physicians that you have seen so far?"*

_____

_____

17. Say, *"Do you know if you have any damaged nerves?"*

_____

_____

18. Say, *"What type of treatments have you tried to relieve your pain?"*

_____

_____

19. Say, *"Were they effective or are they still effective?"*

_____

_____

20. Say, *"What medications do you use and what is the dosage that you take for each of your medications?"*

_____

_____

Addictive Behaviors

21. Say, *"Do you feel that you cannot stop using a medicine?"*

_____

_____

If using opiates or benzodiazepines, say the following:

22. Say, *"Would you be willing to stop using this or to decrease the use of your medicine before trying EMDR?"*

_____

_____

Effects on Functioning

23. Say, *"How does the pain affect your physical functioning?"*

_____

_____

_____

_____

24. Say, *"How does the pain affect your social functioning?"*

_____

_____

_____

_____

25. Say, *"How does the pain affect your mood and your ability to pay attention or concentrate (emotional and cognitive functioning)?"*

_____

_____

_____

_____

26. Say, *"What do you do to reduce the pain to make it bearable (behavioral functioning)?"*

_____

_____

_____

_____

History of Trauma and Pain-Related Incidents

27. Say, *"Did the pain start with a traumatic event?"*

_____

_____

_____

_____

28. Say, *"Does the pain remind you of another specific event?"*

_____

_____

_____

_____

29. Say, *"Did you have any traumatic experiences before the start of the pain?"*

_____

_____

_____

_____

30. Say, *"Did you have any traumatic medical experiences?"*

_____

_____

31. Say, *"Please make a drawing of the time line of the course of your pain* (see question 12). *Let's put in the major issues or events related to your pain."*

32. Say, *"Have you noticed any post-traumatic stress related symptoms such as flashbacks, hyper vigilance, and so forth?"*

Phase 2: Preparation Phase

After the therapist and patient have identified the EMDR targets in the Client History Phase, the order in which targets will be desensitized is chosen, based on the hypothesis concerning the etiology and maintenance of the pain symptoms.

Explanation to the Patient

A clear rationale for treatment contributes both to the degree of cooperation of the patient and the effect of treatment. A simple text with which the rationale of treatment can be explained is the following:

> Say, *"Pain is a normal signal that something is wrong. Sometimes the pain remains present even though the cause of the problem has long been gone. Long-term pain changes the nervous system and influences the experience of pain. The pain remains enclosed, as it were, in the nervous system. The goal of EMDR is to stimulate the nervous system to, in effect, transform the experience of the pain."*

An extended text, used for patients who are interested in a detailed neurobiological explanation is the following:

> Say, *"Normally, pain is a signal that something is going wrong in the body. Sometimes the cause of the pain is gone but the pain remains, or the pain is worse than the nature of the injury would lead you to expect.*
>
> *We experience pain with our brains, where several brain areas work together in a network. It has been shown that intense, threatening, and chronic pain causes changes in the nervous system. In chronic pain patients, some brain areas become hypersensitive or overly active, while activity in other areas decreases. In chronic pain, it's as if the brain is off balance. Another potential cause for this unbalancing of the brain—signaled by pain—is the loss of nerve pathways, for example, due to amputations as in phantom pain or nerve damage.*
>
> *Scientific research has shown that EMDR normalizes brain activity in post-traumatic stress disorder. EMDR may also be able to influence brain patterns in certain types of chronic pain, but research has not yet been conducted on the subject."*

Teach Patients How to Use Language to Describe Pain

There are not that many words available with regard to pain, and as a rule, patients are not accustomed to speak about their pain in these words. In those patients with a moderate or minimal capacity for verbalization and visualization, it is more difficult to monitor the EMDR process during the Desensitization Phase and continue to keep the process in motion. Therefore, it is important, in the Preparation Phase, for the therapist to teach patients how to use language to describe pain. For example, it is possible to suggest words that describe the quality or intensity of the pain by giving examples of visualized pain.

> Say, *"Not many words are available to describe pain and most patients are not accustomed to talk about their pain. However, finding words to communicate about your pain helps you to concentrate on your pain during the EMDR procedure and helps me* (the therapist) *to follow the course of the information you are processing. You can describe the quality or intensity of your pain in words, images, or a combination of both."*

From the intake, the therapist knows if the patient is able to find words or imagines describing the pain. If so, continue the protocol. If not, it is important to take extra time here to teach the patient how to use language to describe pain. For example,

> *"Some patients describe their pain as scale of flames, a buckle around the foot, or an apple with spikes. How would you describe your pain?"*

_____

_____

_____

_____

The pain descriptors of the McGill Pain Questionnaire (Melzack, 2005) can be very helpful for this purpose.

Choice of Bilateral Stimulation (Visual, Auditory, or Tactile)

Visual, auditory, or tactile stimuli can be used for processing. Thus far, there is no scientific support for the hypothesis that one of the three types of stimuli has a greater affect than the others so patients can choose the one that fits for them.

Stop Signal

The more intense the pain becomes, the more difficult it is for patients to concentrate on the pain for a long period of time; in this case, the patient's attention shifts to dealing with the pain or even to surviving. If the pain becomes too intense, patients are instructed to use a stop signal and it is determined whether continuing the EMDR session is feasible and bearable.

> Say, *"Although the unpleasant pictures, sensations, or emotions may come up as we do the _____* (state BLS using), *you can stop the process whenever you want simply by raising your hand like this* (therapist demonstrates movement)."

Phase 3: Assessment Phase

Most elements of the Assessment Phase in the EMDR Pain Protocol for Current Pain are the same as in the EMDR Standard Protocol. The differences concern the target and the subjective units of disturbance (SUD). In this EMDR Pain Protocol, the target is not a memory but always the current pain. The SUD is replaced by the SUP (Subjective Units of Pain). This fits the goal of this protocol more, which is decrease of the pain.

Identification of the Target

The target in the pain protocol is the current pain and not the memory of the pain; the pain is usually already present. In the Assessment Phase, the goal is to fine-tune the pain and optimally activate the network of pain memories. Here the term fine-tuning means that patients focus all their attention on the pain, thus activating the area of the brain that is involved in the relevant pain network.

First of all the therapist asks the patient to describe the pain in comparison to the Standard EMDR Protocol questions: "What happens when you think of the incident?" or "When you think of the incident what do you get?"

Say, *"Please describe how your pain feels now."*

_____

_____

Subsequently the patient is asked to make a drawing of the pain.

Say, *"Draw the pain as you feel it right now."*

_____

_____

The patient can apply nuances in pain intensity or location of the painful body part by using colors. Some people prefer showing the pain symbolically, for example as a bowl of flames or a sharp piece of glass. If the description of the pain is general or the drawing shows few details, helpful questions can be asked such as:

Say, *"If the pain had a color, what color would it be?"*

_____

_____

Say, *"If the pain had a shape, what shape would it be?"*

_____

_____

Say, *"If the pain had a temperature, what temperature would it be such as hot or cold?"*

_____

_____

Say, *"Does the pain feel hard or soft?"*

_____

_____

Visualizing the pain with questions concerning the shape and color of the pain can help increase concentration on the pain. A visual image is apparently easier to hold onto or recall than a physical sensation. Questions about the temperature of the pain and the structure are more related to the quality of the pain. These questions broaden the vocabulary and simplify communication about the pain.

Absence of Pain

If a patient's pain occurs in the form of attacks, it is possible that the pain may not be present at the beginning of a session. The challenge for the person treating the patient is to activate the pain memory network in such a way that pain is actually experienced. The first question that arises is:

Say, *"Think back to the first time you experienced pain."*

_____

_____

Or if that memory concerns mild pain:

Say, *"Think back to the time the pain was the most intense."*

_____

_____

As patients describe how their pain felt, often the pain reoccurs. Visualization of this pain is particularly important in order for patients to keep their concentration optimal, and to allow therapists to give patients support as they bring back the old pain. When the pain is activated, you can start the Assessment Phase of this Pain Protocol.

Negative Cognition (NC)

Look out for the following when identifying NC and Emotion:

- The lower the pain level, the more difficult it becomes to identify current negative cognitions as they are less dysfunctional and not always strongly affectively laden.
- Since patients have habituated to their affect related to pain, they often do not pay attention to them.
- Sometimes dysfunctional cognitions and emotions related to the pain have already faded during the sessions focused on trauma- and pain-related targets.
- To establish the cognitions, the known cognitive domains are used: responsibility and guilt, control, self-esteem, vulnerability and safety. However, cognitions related to the pain are mostly in the domain of control and self-esteem. Frequently mentioned negative cognitions are: "I am powerless," "I am a wreck," and "I am worthless."

Say, *"What words best go with the pain that express your negative belief about yourself or the pain now?"*

_____

_____

Check if these words are evocative of the pain for the patient.

Say, *"What does this pain say about you as a person?"* or *"What would you call such a person?"* or *"What is this sort of person often called?"*

_____

_____

Preferred Positive Cognition (PPC)

Say, *"When you concentrate on the pain, what would you prefer or like to believe about yourself now?"*

_____

_____

Validity of Cognition (VoC)

Say, *"When you concentrate on the pain, how true do those words _____ (clinician repeats the positive cognition) feel to you now on a scale of 1 to 7, where 1 feels completely false and 7 feels completely true?"*

1   2   3   4   5   6   7
(completely false)   (completely true)

Emotion(s)

As far as the emotions that are named, sorrow and anger are heard most frequently.

Say, *"When you concentrate on the pain and those words_____ (clinician states the negative cognition), what emotion do you feel now?"*

_____

_____

Pain Score: Subjective Units of Pain (SUP)

The SUP is a way for patients to communicate their intensity of pain.

Say, *"If you concentrate on the pain and at the same time you say _____ (state the negative cognition), how strong does the pain feel on a scale of 0 to 10, where 0 is no pain or neutral and 10 is the highest pain you can imagine."*

0   1   2   3   4   5   6   7   8   9   10
(no pain)   (worst pain)

Location of the Pain

The question: "Where in your body do you feel the pain the strongest?" is easy to answer, and is often already clear from the first interview. By asking about this, the attention is explicitly focused on the relevant part of the body, which leads to the activation of the relevant region of the brain. It is not about disturbance here but really about the pain. This is a crucial difference with the Standard EMDR Protocol.

When the authors have tested it out, patients said that asking about disturbance here is irrelevant.

Say, *"Where do you feel the pain in your body?"*

_____

_____

Phase 4: Desensitization

In the Desensitization Phase, patients focus their attention on the current pain in combination with the bilateral stimulation (BLS).

Say, *"Concentrate on the pain and say to yourself _____ (state the NC). Feel the pain in _____ (state the location of the pain) and _____ (state the BLS the patient chose)."*

_____

_____

Allow the client to concentrate and say the following:

Say, *"Okay, have you got it? Go with that."*

_____

_____

Do BLS.

Say, *"What are you noticing now?"* or *"What do you get now?"*

_____

_____

Say, *"Go with that."* or *"Concentrate on that."*

_____

_____

Do BLS.
Continue until there are no new changes (chain of associations).
When the processing stops and there is no longer any change, the end of the association channel has been reached. Then, there is a return to the original target (current pain) to assess if there has been any change in the pain.

Say, *"If you concentrate on the pain, how strong does the pain feel on a scale of 0 to 10, where 0 is no pain or neutral and 10 is the worst pain you can imagine."*

0	1	2	3	4	5	6	7	8	9	10
(no pain)										(worst pain)

If the SUP is greater than 0, say the following:

Say, *"What is there in the pain that is causing the _____ (state the SUP) or what aspect of the pain is causing the _____ (state the SUP)?"*

_____

_____

Say, *"Go with that"* or *"Concentrate on that."*

_____

_____

Do BLS.

Repeat the procedure until the SUP = 0. When the SUP = 0, go to Phase 5 the Installation Phase.

Note: If the SUP > 0 at the end of the session, go to the installation and use the Antidote Imagery or go to Phase 7: Positive Closure.

Say, *"If you concentrate on the pain, how strong does the pain feel on a scale of 0 to 10, where 0 is no pain or neutral and 10 is the worst pain you can imagine."*

Final SUP = 0   1   2   3   4   5   6   7   8   9   10
        (no pain)   (worst pain)

The following types of reactions for patients are frequently seen using the EMDR Pain Protocol for Current Pain.

1. Less diversity in associations (compared with the Standard EMDR Protocol) because associations are mainly physical.
2. Change in the quality and intensity of the pain; pain is more muted, seems further away, becomes more vague or outside the body.
3. Reports of relaxation or tiredness and frequent yawning.

Issues in Processing

Unable to Focus on the Processing

When it occurs that there is no change in associations, it is possible that the chronic pain patients are unable to follow the instructions. Sometimes they do not realize that it is necessary to focus on the internal process to activate and change the pain. This can occur when patients have tried many ways to address their pain with little or no result and feel that there is little hope for change.

Say, *"It is important that you allow yourself to concentrate on the pain and focus all your attention on the pain and notice what happens. Without this focus, change is not possible. Go ahead and do that now. What do you notice?"*

_____

_____

Unable to Perceive or Describe Change

Sometimes, there is insufficient capacity to perceive change, or that patients do not (yet) have sufficient access to the words needed to describe changes and movement. Once again, activating all aspects of the pain or offering new sets of eye movements, possibly longer sets, often helps the patient to concentrate on the internal process once more.

Use the questions here about color, shape, temperature, and so forth, if appropriate.

Say, *"Please describe again how your pain feels now. Check in with the color, shape, temperature, or any other descriptive word that makes sense to you. What do you notice?"*

_____

_____

Do BLS.

Say, *"What do you notice?"*

_____

_____

Lack of Associations

If no associations arise after repeated application of the back to target procedure, or if the patient always reports the same association, there are various options (choice in focus) for keeping the process active. In case there is pain in different locations, say the following:

Say, *"Please focus on the pain that is most intensely present now. Go with that."*

_____

_____

Do BLS.

Say, *"What do you notice?"*

_____

_____

Say, *"Or you can focus on a different area where you do not feel your pain as intensely. Now go with that."*

_____

_____

Do BLS.

Say, *"What do you notice?"*

_____

_____

Warm or Tingling Sensations Instead of Pain

During decreasing pain, patients often report a warm or tingling sensation at the place where the pain used to live. This, usually, concerns a pain intensity (SUP) of 3 or lower. Focusing attention on the warmth and tingling intensifies these feelings, or results in expanding the warm or tingling area. Often, this helps to decrease the pain intensity.

Say, *"Focus now on that _____ (state the positive sensations) where the pain used to live and go with that."*

_____

_____

Do BLS.

Say, *"What do you notice?"*

_____

_____

Excessive Pain Intensity

The more intense the pain becomes, the more difficult it is for patients to concentrate on it for a long period of time. In this case, dosing the pain is helpful by limiting the duration of the EMDR session in order to avoid exhausting the patient. The duration of the pain session can vary from 5 minutes to 90 minutes; this is decided in conjunction with patients. This collaboration increases patients' abilities to monitor and control their pain.

Say, *"It seems that your pain has really increased a great deal. Is it okay for you to continue or do you want to stop now?"*

_____

_____

Interweaves When Processing Blocks

Because patients report mainly physical associations, processing can block sooner and calls for a more active role on the part of the therapist. Other types of interweaves can be helpful in moving or reengaging the processing.

Technical Interweaves

Use another type of BLS, for example, if you are using eye movement, switching to hand taps or auditory stimuli is often helpful to unblock the process.

Say, *"Let's try another form of BLS. What do you think would be helpful?"*

_____

_____

Switch Modalities

Ask about thoughts as in the following:

Say, *"While you concentrate on the pain, what are you thinking?"*

_____

_____

Or ask about images such as the following:

Say, *"While you concentrate on the pain, what do you see before you or what image do you see?"*

_____

_____

Questions about feelings related to the pain often do not result in extra associations.

Somatic Interweaves

For pain patients, somatic interweaves especially focused on the pain can be important supplements.

Say, *"What would your body like to do?"*

_____

_____

Say, *"What would you need in order to let go of the pain?"*

_____

_____

Say, *"If your pain had a voice, what would it say?"*

_____

_____

Antidote Imagery

Use the antidote imagery as an interweave (see Installation Phase); however, results are variable, especially when patients are unable to use fantasy in general.

Say, *"Concentrate on the picture that represents what has come in place of the pain* (for example, an ice cube). *Go with that."*

_____

_____

Do BLS.

Say, *"What do you notice?"*

_____

_____

Phase 5: Installation

Patients' pain rarely decreases to a SUP of 0 and there is often a certain amount of residual pain (SUP = 2, 3, or 4), resulting in more incomplete sessions.

When SUP > 0 there are several options at the end of the session.

1. Use the PC as a coping statement rather than the more standard installation of a positive self-perception.
2. Install antidote imagery.
3. Go to Phase 7: Positive Closure.

Use the PC as a Coping Statement

Say, *"Concentrate on the pain as you feel it now and say to yourself 'I can deal with this.' Go with that."*

_____

_____

Do BLS.

Check VoC level after each set and continue until VoC does not increase anymore.

Say, *"When you think of the pain how true do those words 'I can deal with this' feel to you now on a scale of 1 to 7, where 1 feels completely false and 7 feels completely true?"*

1	2	3	4	5	6	7
(completely false)				(completely true)		

If SUP = 0, install PC (see your assessment phase) and test VoC.

Say, *"How does _____ (repeat the PC) sound?"*

_____

_____

Say, *"Do the words _____ (repeat the PC) still fit, or is there another positive statement that feels better?"*

_____

_____

If the client accepts the original positive cognition, the clinician should ask for a VoC rating to see if it has improved.

Say, *"As you concentrate on the pain, how do the words feel from 1 being completely false to 7 being completely true?"*

1	2	3	4	5	6	7
(completely false)				(completely true)		

Say, *"Concentrate on the pain and hold it together with the words _____ (repeat the PC)."*

_____

_____

Do BLS.
Test VoC.

Say, *"As you concentrate on the pain, how do the words feel from 1 being completely false to 7 being completely true?"*

1	2	3	4	5	6	7
(completely false)				(completely true)		

Check VoC level after each set and continue until VoC = 7.
Note: If VoC < 6 or 7 at the end of the session: go to Phase 7: Positive Closure.

Installation of Antidote Imagery

Another possibility with regard to pain is to install antidote imagery (Grant, 1999).
When there is change in the pain, say the following:

Say, *"What has come in place of the pain?"*

_____

_____

If the pain does not change, say the following:

Say, *"What can you think of that would make the pain better or make it go away?"*

_____

_____

Patients often say that there is relaxation or peace.
The therapist invites the patient to make a visual representation of this.

Say, *"Go ahead and make a picture in your mind about this."*

_____

_____

If the patient has no response, say the following:

Say, *"When you make a picture in your mind about this it can be in fantasy or reality based. Some people have thought about feeling a cool mist or ice cubes while others think about an airplane that takes the pain up in the air. Do any of those work for you or do you have one that comes to mind now that fits you better?"*

_____

_____

Say, *"Go with that."*

_____

_____

Do BLS.

Say, *"What do you notice?"*

_____

_____

When positive associations occur, do a new set to reinforce it.

Say, *"Go with that."*

_____

_____

Do BLS.
Continue with BLS until no more change occurs.
Link a word to the feeling that fits the image in order to ensure that the positive feeling becomes more easily accessible and easier to call up.

Say, *"Now think of a word that fits the feeling and image that you have. Do you have it?"*

_____

_____

Say, *"Okay, now think of the word as you feel the positive feeling and go with that."*

_____

_____

Do BLS.
Continue with BLS until no more change occurs.

Phase 6: Body Scan

Use the Body Scan after the installation of the PC, if SUP = 0.

Since the purpose of this Pain Protocol for Current Pain is expressly to focus on the pain in the body, the goal of this Body Scan is another chance to see if there is residual tension in some other part(s) of the patient's body as in the Standard EMDR Protocol.

Say, *"If you think of the pain and say to yourself _____ (repeat the PC), scan your entire body from top to toe and notice if you feel any other tension in your body. Is there any tension?"*

_____

_____

If there is tension, do sets of BLS and say the following:

Say, *"What comes up? What do you notice now?"*

_____

_____

Continue until the tension is gone and/or there are no more new associations.

Phase 7: Positive Closure

Positive closure is particularly important, because at the end of the session the intensity of the pain (SUP) is often greater than 0. As a result, the installation of the PC and Body Scan is not helpful. Nonetheless, the therapist wants to send the patient home in a positive state of mind at the end of the EMDR session. The point is to cash in on an observed change and consolidate it. This is the third way to end the session as mentioned above.

Say, *"What is the most positive thing you have learned about yourself during the session regarding the pain?"*

_____

_____

If the patient mentions something negative, the therapist continues to elicit a positive statement about what happened during the session or related to other areas of a patient's functioning.

If necessary say, *"What does this say about yourself as a person?"*

_____

_____

Install with BLS until there are no further (positive) changes.
After the incomplete session and the complete session, say the following:

Say, *"The pain intensity can temporarily increase. Sometimes this is the case but not always. Also images, thoughts, feelings, or sensations related to the pain may come up or they may not. If they do, write them down so we can see together next time what happened with the pain or what you experienced. Just write it down for next time and give me a call if you need to."*

Phase 8: Reevaluation

During the Evaluation Phase, the therapist looks back with patients at the period since the last session.

Say, *"Let's look back over the period of time since our last session. What have you noticed?"*

_____

_____

It is important to ask for the log and review the contents for any EMDR session but, because of the experimental nature of the treatment, evaluation is of extra significance.

Say, *"Let's look at your log and see what you have written down since the last session."*

Log results can be used to add to issues that need to be reprocessed or resources that need to be developed.

Termination of EMDR Treatment

In the Standard EMDR Protocol, the criteria for ending processing is clear: SUD = 0 and VoC = 7. In this Pain Protocol, the end point is not always as clear; therefore the question "How long should the pain protocol continue to be applied?" is relevant. It is, after all, not certain that the score of the pain intensity (SUP) can become 0. In a pilot study (De Roos et al., 2009), based on the observation of 10 patients, the authors set the criterion of completing the EMDR Pain Protocol for Current Pain as the consecutive achievement of the same SUP score three times (at the end of the session). The results of other EMDR pain treatments in our clinical practice show there is no evidence to assume that more processing would result in a further decrease in the pain.

When working with any new application, it is possible to overestimate its usefulness or efficacy, especially when the need for effective methods for treating chronic pain is so great. The EMDR Pain Protocol for Current Pain represents a combination of clinical experience with the preliminary observations of a pilot study to demonstrate that EMDR is effective for certain subgroups of chronic pain patients.

Acknowledgments

The authors would like to acknowledge Yanda van Rood for her useful comments on this chapter.

41

EMDR and Phantom Pain Research Protocol

Sandra A. Wilson and Robert Tinker

EMDR and Phantom Pain Research Protocol Script Notes

The important elements of the EMDR and Phantom Pain Research Protocol are the following:

- Client history taking and relationship building
- Targeting the trauma of the experience
- Targeting the pain

This protocol is set up to follow the eight phases of the 11-Step Standard Procedure.

While the authors have not undertaken formal research, they have been doing a case series with phantom limb patients since 1996. As part of the case series, they have obtained a few before and after EMDR magnetoencephalograms (MEGs) at the University of Tübingen, Germany on arm amputees that show the presence of phantom limb pain (PLP) in the brain images before EMDR and the absence of it after EMDR. In these case series, they have found that PLP in leg amputations is much easier to treat than arm amputations, likely due to the much more extensive and complex arm and hand representation in the sensory-motor cortex compared to the leg and foot representation. While leg amputees can often lose their phantom limb pain in two or three sessions of EMDR, PLP from arm amputations often require more sessions and different forms and locations for bilateral stimulation (BLS). For example, one client minimized his PLP only after bilateral stimulation of his upper lip with buzzers. The lip representation is next to the thumb representation in the sensory-motor cortex. This stimulation of the lip presumably inhibits the thumb neurons from the absent thumb from responding as lip neurons, which has been found to be associated with phantom pain. Since 1996, they have also assisted a good number of EMDR therapists in elimination of PLP in their clients, most often successfully.

EMDR and Phantom Pain Research Protocol Script

Phase 1: Client History Taking

First Hour

The goal is to find out what happened.

> Say, *"It is important for you to know that I am serious about treating your phantom pain that technically doesn't exist. In fact, phantom limb pain is a normal experience for most people who have had a part of their body amputated. Some of the research that has been done on this subject reports that between 60% to 70% of amputees suffer pain in their phantom limbs. I am going to enlist you to help me understand what your experience is and has been with your amputation."*

Say, *"Please tell me when your amputation occurred."*

_____

_____

_____

_____

_____

_____

Say, *"What happened?"*

_____

_____

_____

_____

_____

_____

Say, *"What kind of injuries did you have?"*

_____

_____

_____

_____

Say, *"How did you feel about it then?"*

_____

_____

_____

_____

Say, *"How do you feel about it now?"*

_____

_____

_____

_____

Say, *"What have you tried to handle it so far?"*

_____

_____

_____

_____

Say, *"What have your physicians told you about it?"*

_____

_____

_____

_____

Say, *"What is your mental picture of your injury?"*

_____

_____

_____

_____

Say, *"What image do you have of the position your* _____ (state part amputated) *was in when it was amputated?"*

_____

_____

_____

_____

Say, *"Tell me about your experience getting your prosthesis?"*

_____

_____

_____

_____

Say, *"What was it like for you when you first saw your stump?"*

_____

_____

_____

_____

Say, *"What was it like when a family member first saw you without your* _____ (state body part)*?"*

_____

_____

_____

_____

Say, *"What can you do with and without your prosthesis?"*

_____

_____

_____

_____

Second Hour

Discuss the changes in lifestyle, self-esteem, and the amount of therapy and medication they have had.

Say, *"Tell me about changes in your lifestyle. What has changed socially?"*

_____

_____

_____

_____

Say, *"What has changed occupationally?"*

_____

_____

_____

_____

Say, *"What has changed recreationally?"*

_____

_____

_____

_____

Say, *"How has the amputation affected your sexual life?"*

_____

_____

_____

_____

Say, *"How has the amputation affected your quality of life?"*

_____

_____

_____

_____

Say, *"How has it impacted your family?"*

_____

_____

_____

_____

Say, *"How has it impacted your usual activities in general?"*

_____

_____

_____

_____

Say, *"What do you miss most about the loss of your _____ (state the body part)?"*

_____

_____

_____

_____

Say, *"How are you feeling about yourself since the loss of your _____ (state the body part)?"*

_____

_____

_____

_____

Say, *"Have you ever had prior injuries to the _____ (state the body part)?"*

_____

_____

_____

_____

Say, *"Have other family members had parts of their body amputated? If so, does this have any special meaning for you?"*

_____

_____

_____

_____

Third Hour

Do a detailed analysis on every single part of the limb that hurts and how it hurts. Also, include the McGill Pain Scale (Melzack, 2005) here.

> Say, *"Let's do a detailed analysis on every single part of that _____ (state body part lost) that hurts and how it hurts. On a scale of 0 to 10 where 0 is no pain to 10 is the worst pain imaginable, choose the number that fits the pain at this moment."*
>
> 0   1   2   3   4   5   6   7   8   9   10
> (no pain)   (worst pain)

Only ask about the phantom pain next.

> Say, *"Tell me every detail about your phantom pain."*
>
> _____
>
> _____
>
> _____
>
> _____
>
> _____
>
> _____

Phantom Pain Scale (PPS)

> Say, *"On a scale of 0 to 10, where 0 is no pain or neutral and 10 is the worst pain you can imagine, how painful does it feel now?"*
>
> 0   1   2   3   4   5   6   7   8   9   10
> (no pain)   (worst pain)
>
> Say, *"What is your daytime average over the past 7 days on a scale of 0 to 10, where 0 is no pain or neutral and 10 is the worst pain you can imagine?"*
>
> 0   1   2   3   4   5   6   7   8   9   10
> (no pain)   (worst pain)
>
> Say, *"What is your nighttime average within the past 7 days on a scale of 0 to 10, where 0 is no pain or neutral and 10 is the worst pain you can imagine?"*
>
> 0   1   2   3   4   5   6   7   8   9   10
> (no pain)   (worst pain)

Fourth Hour

In this hour, conduct an EMDR session on the worst traumatic aspect of this amputation. For some clients, it might be the accident itself; for others, waking after the surgery; for others yet, seeing the stump for the first time. Targets here are chosen in the same way as for any other trauma in EMDR; that is, for the client to tell you what the worst part of their experience was.

Phase 2: Preparation

Construct a Safe Place

Say, *"First, we'll set up a Safe Place. What for you is a place where you feel a sense of peace, well being, relaxed, and happy from your present or past?"*

_____

_____

_____

_____

Say, *"Can you see a picture of that in your mind? Briefly tell me about that picture."*

_____

_____

Say, *"As you hold that picture, what feelings come up for you?"*

_____

_____

Say, *"Where do you feel these feelings in your body?"*

_____

_____

Say, *"I'm going to move closer so you can follow my fingers with your eyes. Is that okay?"*

_____

_____

Arrange best positions; check distance.

Say, *"Now hold all three—the picture, the feelings, and the body sensations—in your mind and follow my fingers."*

_____

_____

Do several sets of BLS. While the authors have not used the enhanced model of the Safe Place (they were doing PLP sessions before the longer Safe Place Protocol was adopted), they see no problem with using the longer protocol with challenges and a cue word associated with it.

Say, *"We will use this safe place in 3 ways: If you feel way too upset by your feelings, give me a hand signal to stop. We will stop and have you bring up your safe place. We'll use it to end our session today and you can use it on your own between sessions."*

Phase 3: Assessment

Process every aspect of the trauma, using as many targets as possible, to ensure that the trauma has been completely desensitized before focusing on the pain itself.

Phantom Limb Trauma

Say, *"What is your worst memory about the trauma that caused the phantom pain?"*

_____

_____

_____

_____

Picture

Say, *"What picture represents the most traumatic part of the incident?"*

_____

_____

Negative Cognition (NC)

Say, *"What words best go with the picture that express your negative belief about yourself now?"*

_____

_____

Positive Cognition (PC)

Say, *"When you bring up that picture or incident, what would you like to believe about yourself now?"*

_____

_____

Say, *"When you think of the incident* (or picture) *how true do those words* _____ (clinician repeats the positive cognition) *feel to you now on a scale of 1 to 7, where 1 feels completely false and 7 feels completely true?"*

1	2	3	4	5	6	7
(completely false)				(completely true)		

Sometimes it is necessary to explain further:

Say, *"Remember, sometimes we know something with our head, but it feels differently in our gut. In this case, what is the gut-level feeling of the truth of* _____ (clinician state the positive cognition), *from 1 being completely false to 7 being completely true?"*

1	2	3	4	5	6	7
(completely false)				(completely true)		

Emotions

Say, "When you bring up the picture (or incident) *and those words* _____ (clinician states the negative cognition), *what emotion do you feel now?"*

_____

_____

Subjective Units of Disturbance (SUDs)

Say, *"On a scale of 0 to 10, where 0 is no disturbance or neutral and 10 is the highest disturbance you can imagine, how disturbing does it feel now?"*

0	1	2	3	4	5	6	7	8	9	10
(no disturbance)							(highest disturbance)			

Location of Body Sensation

Say, *"Where do you feel it* (the disturbance) *in your body?"*

_____

_____

Phase 4: Desensitization

Say, *"Now I'd like you to bring up that picture, those negative words* _____ (repeat the NC), *those feelings* _____ (mention the stated feelings), *and where you feel them in your body. Then, follow my fingers. The main thing though is to let whatever comes up, come up. You don't have to make anything come to mind or keep anything from coming to mind. Just let whatever comes to mind, come to mind."*

_____

_____

Start BLS. Give verbal encouragement if abreaction occurs.

Say, *"That's it."*

_____

_____

Or say, *"That's good."*

_____

_____

Or say, *"Stay with it, it is old stuff."*

_____

_____

Or say, *"You are on a train, it is all scenery, just notice it."*

_____

_____

Or say, *"It's like a movie."*

_____

_____

Check how many BLS sets occurred:

1_ 2_ 3_ 4_ 5_ 6_ 7_ 8_ 9_ 10_ 11_ 12_ 13_ 14_ 15_ 16_ 17_ 18_ 19_ 20_ +

This must be checked.

Phase 5: Installation

When you have an incomplete session, it is important to abide by the following:

1. Do not install the PC with the memory.
2. Get clear SUD and VoC scores.

Skip to closure and use the Safe Place or Vipassana Light Stream Imagery.

When you install the PC, link the PC with the original memory (not the picture as the picture may have changed). This is done after the SUD has been checked and found to be 0 to 1. If the SUD level has a score of 2 or more, continue with BLS to reprocess this information.

Say, *"Do the words* _____ (repeat PC) *still fit or would other words fit better?"*

_____

_____

Say, *"Think about the original memory we started with and those words* _____ (state the PC). *I'd like you to hold them both together in your mind and follow my fingers."*

_____

_____

Do BLS.

Say, *"When you think of the incident* (or picture) *how true do those words* _____ (clinician repeats the positive cognition) *feel to you now on a scale of 1 to 7, where 1 feels completely false and 7 feels completely true?"*

1	2	3	4	5	6	7
(completely false)				(completely true)		

If a person reports a 6 or less, check for appropriateness of the PC and address blocking beliefs, if necessary, with additional reprocessing. Issues that come up more often with PLP clients are frequently associated with being deformed, useless, not competent, ugly, an object of curiosity, different, not-as-good-as, and a failure.

Go on to the Body Scan when the installation is complete.

Phase 6: Body Scan

Say, *"Think about the event and the PC _____ (state the PC) and mentally scan your body, tell me where you feel anything."*

_____

_____

If any sensation is reported, do BLS.
If there is a positive or comfortable sensation, do BLS to strengthen.
If a sensation of discomfort is reported, reprocess until discomfort subsides.

Phase 7: Closure

Say, *"Bring up your Safe Place and go with that."*

_____

_____

Repeat with several sets of BLS.

Say, *"We have started a process today that may continue after you leave,
on both a conscious and an unconscious basis. It may affect your
dreams, your thoughts, your memories, your mental pictures, your
feelings, or your insights* (understandings). *Just notice what it's like
for you. It may be helpful for you to keep a journal of material that
comes up and bring this with you to the next session. If you find
yourself becoming extremely upset or unable to function, please call
the office where someone will be available to assist you.*
When you come back next time we'll start with what you've noticed."

Phase 8: Reevaluation

In the next session be sure to check the VoC and SUD scales on the original event.

Say, *"Okay, let's think about the work we did last time on _____
(state the target worked on)."*

_____

_____

Validity of Cognition (VoC)

Say, *"When you think of the incident* (or picture) *how true do those
words _____* (clinician repeats the positive cognition) *feel to you
now on a scale of 1 to 7, where 1 feels completely false and 7 feels
completely true?"*

1	2	3	4	5	6	7
(completely false)				(completely true)		

Desensitize further, if necessary, before going on to a new image, using the 11-
Step Standard Procedure. After all elements of the trauma (before, during, and after
the trauma) have been desensitized, then, and only then, focus on the phantom
pain itself.

Say, *"Now that we have worked on all of the elements of before, during, and after _____ (state the trauma), please describe the way that your phantom limb pain feels now."*

_____

_____

Phantom Pain Scale (PPS)

Say, *"On a scale of 0 to 10, where 0 is no pain or neutral and 10 is the worst pain you can imagine, how painful does it feel now?"*

0	1	2	3	4	5	6	7	8	9	10
(no pain)										(worst pain)

Say, *"Focus on the pain and let me know when it changes in any way. It may get worse, better, or different. Just say 'Okay' to let me know that it has changed and I'll stop, have you take a deep breath, and tell me what has happened."*

_____

_____

Say, *"Go with that."*

_____

_____

Do BLS.

Say, *"What are you noticing now?"*

_____

_____

Say, *"Go with that."*

_____

_____

Do BLS.

Continue in this fashion until the phantom pain has been eliminated, using standard EMDR closure techniques at the end.

End of Session Summary for Trauma   Clinical Notes

SUDs (0–10):
Beginning: ___/10_____
Ending: ___/10_____
VoC (1–7):
Beginning: ___/7_____
Ending: ___/7_____
Phantom Pain (0–10):
Beginning: ___/10_____
Ending: ___/10_____
Total Session Time: (90 minute maximum)

In summary, the idea behind this PLP Protocol, is to desensitize all of the emotional trauma associated with the loss of limb (or other body parts, where loss has been associated with great pain: e.g., phantom breast pain, phantom gall bladder pain, phantom tooth pain; phantom finger, or hand pain) and after that focus on the pain itself. Outside of EMDR, there is good support for this, as chronic pain has been shown to have a different neural pathway in the brain, in contrast with acute pain (de Charms et al., 2005; Hoffman, Papas, Chatkoff, & Kerns, 2007). This different pathway goes to the areas of the brain that process negative emotions (the insula and the anterior cingulate cortex). This means that chronic pain (including PLP) cannot be treated without accessing the negative emotions associated with it. A recent meta-analysis of 22 different chronic pain studies confirms that psychological interventions are the most effective (more effective than surgery) with chronic pain. This interesting convergence of information, from studies outside of EMDR, gives some validation for the form and sequence of the EMDR PLP Protocol.

EMDR and Specific Fears

There is one person who comes to mind when the subject of EMDR and phobias enters the conversation: Ad de Jongh. Dr. de Jongh is a dentist and clinical psychologist who has integrated his two professions through his understanding of trauma. As a result, he has become one of the world's experts on dental phobia and a leader in the area of psychotraumatology. Since he learned EMDR in 1992, his extensive understanding of research has made him a principal contributor in EMDR research—especially in the treatment of phobias. He is most concerned that practitioners learn how to distinguish between traumatic phobias that have more in common with post-traumatic stress disorder (PTSD) than other phobias that are not trauma-related.

The earliest publications on EMDR treatment of phobias, however, did not come from de Jongh. Sanderson and Carpenter (1992) published the first article on phobias in the *Journal of Behavior Therapy and Experimental Psychiatry*. In the following year and the same journal, Kleinknecht (1993) reported on the rapid treatment of blood and injection phobias with EMDR.

In 1993, Dr. de Jongh began publishing his findings, often with his friend and colleague Erik ten Broeke, and sometimes including colleagues Korrelboom, Renssen, van der Meer, Serra, Wanders, and van den Oord. Their first work appeared in the Dutch journal, *Tijdschrift voor Directieve Therapy and Hypnose* and since then they have published two books (De Jongh & ten Broeke, 2003; ten Broeke & De Jongh, 2008), eight articles in veted journals (De Jongh & ten Broeke, 1993, 1994, 1998, 2007; De Jongh, ten Broeke, & Renssen, 1999; De Jongh, ten Broeke, & Van der Meer, 1995; De Jongh, Van den Oord, & ten Broeke, 2002; ten Broeke & De Jongh, 1995), and two articles in the *EMDRIA Newsletter* (2000a, 2000b). On his own, Dr. de Jongh has written about specific phobias for the EMDR Institute

Listserv (1998); presented at conferences for the EMDR International Association (1999), the EMDR European conferences (2003, 2006), the International Association for Dental Research (2002), and the European Congress of Hypnosis (2008) on the subject. He has presented with Marcia Whisman at an EMDRIA conference (2001), published three articles for the *Journal of EMDR Practice and Research* (De Jongh & ten Broeke, 2007; de Roos & De Jongh, 2008; Wanders, Serra & De Jongh, 2008), and for a wide range of scientific journals in the Dutch language (De Jongh & ten Broeke, 2002a, 2002b; ten Broeke, Korrelboom, & De Jongh, 1998).

Dr. de Jongh's chapter on his phobia protocol integrates his years of experience with his research expertise. During the history-taking phase, he advocates the following:

- Understanding the nature of the interplay of issues.
- Making sure that the diagnosis is of a specific phobia and not something else.
- Finding out exactly what causes the fear and the expected consequences.
- Establishing the goal(s) of treatment.
- Checking for the Touchstone Event, ancillary event, most frightening, and most recent events.

During the Preparation Phase, Dr. de Jongh teaches clients about these aspects of the process:

- Information about EMDR and what to expect.
- Self-control procedures such as distraction.
- The applied tension technique.

He gives particular attention to each element of the Assessment Phase and the types of issues of which to be aware when working with clients with specific fears. Desensitization, Installation, Future Template, and Body Scan follows as in the Standard EMDR Protocol. To check the work, in vivo confrontations are suggested to avoid avoidance and promote mastery. Closure is essential and homework is assigned as a way to maintain the changes experienced in the session. Reevaluation and checking in about homework and responses between sessions is an integral part of the work. Dr. de Jongh also highlights some of the differences when working with patients with blood phobias. An annotated script and script without commentary are provided.

42

EMDR and Specific Fears: The Phobia Protocol Single Traumatic Event

Ad de Jongh

When a person starts to demonstrate an excessive and unreasonable fear of certain objects or situations that in reality are not dangerous, it is likely that the person fulfils the criteria for specific phobia as stated in the *Diagnostic and Statistical Manual of Mental Disorders,* 4th edition, text revision (American Psychiatric Association, 2000). The main features of a specific phobia are that the fear is elicited by a specific and limited set of stimuli (e.g., snakes, dogs, injections, etc.) that confrontation with these stimuli results in intense fear and avoidance behavior, and that the fear is unreasonable and excessive to a degree that interferes with daily life. The *DSM–IV–TR* distinguishes the following five main categories or subtypes of specific phobia:

- Animal type (phobias of spiders, insects, dogs, cats, rodents, snakes, birds, fish, etc.)
- Natural environment type (phobias of heights, water, storms, etc.)
- Situational type (phobias of enclosed spaces, driving, flying, elevators, bridges, etc.)
- Blood, injury, injection type (phobias of getting an injection, seeing blood, watching surgery, etc.)
- Other types (choking, vomiting, contracting an illness, etc.).

With regard to treatment in vivo exposure has proven to be the treatment of choice for a variety of specific phobias (Wolitzky-Taylor, Horowitz, Powers, & Telch, 2008). Results from uncontrolled (e.g., De Jongh & ten Broeke, 1998; Kleinknecht, 1993; Marquis, 1991), and controlled case reports (e.g., De Jongh, Van den Oord, & ten Broeke, 2002; Lohr, Tolin, & Kleinknecht, 1996) show that EMDR can also be effective in clients suffering from fears and phobias, and that significant improvements can be reached within a limited number of sessions (see De Jongh, ten Broeke, & Renssen, 1999 for a review). EMDR may be particularly useful for phobic conditions with high levels of anxiety, with a traumatic origin or with a clear beginning, and for which it is understandable that resolving the memories of the conditioning events would positively influence its severity (see De Jongh, Van den Oord, & ten Broeke, 2002).

The aim of this chapter is to illustrate how EMDR can be applied in the treatment of specific fears and phobic conditions. The script has frequently been applied in both clinical practice and research projects (e.g., De Jongh, Van den Oord, & ten Broeke, 2002). For example, in a series of single case experiments to evaluate the application of EMDR to traumatically induced dental phobia it was found that in two to three sessions of EMDR treatment, three of the four patients demonstrated substantially reduced self-reported and observer-rated anxiety, reduced credibility of dysfunctional beliefs concerning dental treatment, and significant behavior changes. These gains were maintained at the 6 week follow-up. In all four cases, patients actually underwent the dental treatment they feared most within 3 weeks following EMDR treatment.

Treatment of a fear or a phobic condition cannot be started if the therapist is unaware of the factors that cause and maintain the anxiety response. Therefore, one of the first tasks of the therapist is to collect the necessary information. This is usually done by means of a standardized clinical interview, such as the Anxiety Disorder Interview Scale, which is primarily aimed at the diagnosis of anxiety disorders (ADIS-R; DiNardo et al., 1985). There are two important aims of this clinical interview:

- One of the aims of a clinical interview is to gain insight into the interplay of factors on several possible problem areas, including the possibility of secondary gain issues; that is, the extent to which the client derives positive consequences by avoiding anxiety provoking situations, such as losing a job or receiving extra attention and consideration from others.
- Since many clients have several interrelated problems, another important component of the assessment is to establish the relative importance of these problems and how they are related to the diagnosis specific phobia. For example, it may be that a client's claustrophobia is not very specific and occurs in a variety of situations. In this case it may be wise to consider (or to rule out) the possibility of the diagnosis panic disorder as this condition generally needs more elaborate treatment.

In order to further enhance the reliability of the diagnostic process it is often desirable to use valid and standardized diagnostic measures. These can be of help in getting a clear picture of the severity of the anxiety, in detecting other possible problem areas, and to make it possible to evaluate the course of treatment. Many examples of useful self-report questionnaires for fears and specific phobias can be found in Antony, Orsillo, and Roemer's practice book (2001).

Another factor of significance is the motivation of the client. For example, it is important to find out why the client seeks treatment at this particular time. Different issues that affect motivation are as follows:

- *Self versus forced referral.* There may be a marked difference in effectiveness of the treatment depending on whether the client requested referral himself or was forced into it (e.g., "My wife said she would leave me if I did not get my teeth fixed").
- *Past experience with therapy.* Also clients' experiences of therapy in the past may determine their attitudes toward treatment. If, for whatever reason, it did not work in the past, it is useful to find out why and to attempt to discriminate between genuinely fearful reluctance and lack of effort.

- *Comorbid psychiatric issues.* The therapist should remain aware that comorbid psychiatric illness, such as severe depression, might be a contributing factor toward a lack of motivation.
- *Low self-esteem.* If the phobic client suffers from feelings of low self-esteem, which, in the opinion of the therapist, contributes to a large extent in the client's avoidance behavior this may be resolved first and becomes a primary target of processing.

The Phobia Protocol Script Notes

Phase 1: History Taking

Determine the Type of Fear and Its Severity

Say, *"What is the fear or concern that has brought you in today?"*

_____

_____

Say, *"Does this fear or concern seem excessive or unreasonable to you?"*

_____

_____

If so, say, *"Tell me about it."*

_____

_____

Determine to What Extent the Client Fulfills All DSM-IV-TR Criteria of Specific Phobia

- Marked and persistent fear that is excessive or unreasonable, cued by the presence or anticipation of a specific object or situation.
- Exposure to the phobic stimulus almost invariably provokes an immediate anxiety response, which may take the form of situationally bound or situationally predisposed panic attack. Note: In children, the anxiety may be expressed by crying, tantrums, freezing, or clinging.
- The person recognizes that the fear is excessive or unreasonable. Note: In children, this feature may be absent.
- The phobic situation(s) is avoided or else is endured with intense anxiety or distress.
- The avoidance, anxious anticipation, or distress in the feared situation(s) interferes significantly with the person's normal routine, occupation, (academic) functioning, social activities, relationships, or there is marked distress about having the phobia.
- In individuals under 18 years, the duration is at least 6 months.
- The anxiety, panic attacks, or phobic avoidance associated with the specific object or situation are not better accounted for by another mental disorder, such as obsessive-compulsive disorder, post-traumatic stress disorder, social phobia, or panic disorder.

Identify the Stimulus Situation (Conditioned Stimulus [CS])

An important goal of the assessment is to gather information about the current circumstances under which the symptoms manifest, about periods and situations in which the problems worsen or diminish, and about external and concrete (discriminative) anxiety provoking cues or CS. The therapist should also be aware of other types of anxiety producing stimuli, including critical internal cues, for example, particular body sensations (e.g., palpitations), images, and self-statements (e.g., "I can't cope"). To gather information concerning the anxiety provoking stimuli the following questions may be asked:

Say, *"Describe the object or situation that you are afraid of."*

_____

_____

Or say, *"What exactly do you need to see, hear, or feel in order to get an immediate fear response?"*

_____

_____

Say, *"What exactly about _____ (state the object or situation) triggers your fear most?"*

_____

_____

Say, *"Which incident caused your fear of _____ (state the object or situation)?"*

_____

_____

Identify the Expected Consequence or Catastrophe (Unconditioned Stimulus [UCS])

To understand the dynamic of the client's fears or phobia, it is necessary to determine not only the aspects of the phobic object or situation that evokes a fear response (the CS), but also what the client exactly expects to happen when confronted with the CS and then the UCS. For example, a dog phobic may believe that if he gets too close to a dog (CS), it will attack him (UCS), whereas an injection phobic may believe that if he has blood drawn (CS), he will faint or that the needle will break off in his arm (UCS).

The most commonly used method to elicit this type of information is to ask the client a series of open-ended questions that can be framed in the context of hypothetical situations (e.g., "What is the worst thing that might happen, if you were to drive a car?") or actual episodes of anxiety (e.g., "During your recent appointment with the dentist, what did you think might happen?"). If the client remains unspecific about the catastrophe (e.g., "then something bad will happen") it is useful to respond with more specific questions (e.g., "What exactly will happen?" or "What bad things do you mean?") until more specific information is disclosed ("I will faint," "I will die," "I will suffocate," etc.).

Please note that the UCS, being the mental representation of the catastrophe the client fears, should refer to an event that automatically evokes a negative emotional response. It is not always immediately clear where this information might have come from; that is, when and how the client has ever learned that his catastrophe (e.g., fainting, pain, etc.) might happen. The therapist should be aware of the following possible events that may have laid the groundwork for the patient's fear or phobia.

1. A distressing event the client once experienced herself. For example, she might have fainted in relation to an injection (traumatic experience) at an early age.
2. A horrific event the client once witnessed (vicarious learning). For example, witnessing mother's extremely fearful reaction to a needle.

3. An unpleasant or shocking event the client read or heard about that has happened to someone or from learning otherwise that injections or anesthetic fluid can be dangerous (negative information).

Say, *"What are you afraid of that could happen when you are exposed to _____* (state the object or situation: CS)*."*

_____

_____

Say, *"Which incident caused your fear of _____* (state the catastrophe the client expects to happen)*?"*

_____

_____

Assess Validity of Catastrophe

The severity of a client's fear or phobia is reflected in the strength of the relationship between the stimulus and patient's perceived probability that the expected negative consequence would actually occur. This relationship can simply be indexed using a validity of catastrophe rating (in this case the validity of catastrophe that expresses the strength of the relationship between the CS and UCS in a percentage between 0% and 100%, using an IF-THEN formula. For example, IF [. . . "I get an injection," CS], THEN [. . . "I will faint"]. Such a rating could be obtained before and after each EMDR session. The general aim of the EMDR treatment of the phobic condition would then be to continue treatment until the client indicates a validity of catastrophe rating as low as possible.

Say, *"Then you are saying that IF you would be exposed to _____* (state the phobic object or situation) *THEN you would _____* (state the catastrophe the client fears to happen). *Is this true?"*

_____

_____

Say, *"On a scale from 0% to 100% where 0% means this is completely false and 100% means it is completely true, how true does this feel?"*

0% 10% 20% 30% 40% 50% 60% 70% 80% 90% 100%
(completely false)   (completely true)

Provide Information About the Fear or Phobia if Necessary

If adequate information about the dangerousness of the object, the animal, or the situation, is lacking—and the client has irrational and faulty beliefs about it—it is of paramount importance that the practitioner provides appropriate and disconfirming information to the contrary. However, some clients need to be guided past the initial awkwardness or need for such education. For example, if the client's lack of knowledge of the phobic objects (e.g., about airplanes and their safety) is likely to play a part, it may be wise to spend some time on this aspect first and suitable reading material should be provided where appropriate.

Say, *"What do you know about the relative dangerousness of _____* (therapist fills in the information specific to the phobic stimulus with which he or she is dealing)? *Since there are people that are not as fearful as you are of _____ (state the phobic object or situation), wouldn't it be wise to spend some time investigating whether it is really as dangerous as you think it is? Just to be sure that you don't overestimate the probability of the danger or that something bad will happen to you. Even if it appears to be more dangerous to be exposed to _____ (state the phobic object or situation) than you think it is now, it is important to find out, don't you think? Let's look for the information we need. Where shall we start?"*

_____

_____

Determine an Appropriate and Feasible Treatment Goal

There are a wide variety of treatment goals, from simple goals to more global or complex goals. An example of a limited goal for a needle phobic individual might be pricking a finger, while a more global goal might be undergoing injections or blood draws, while remaining confident and relaxed. Generally speaking, treatment is aimed at reducing anxiety and avoidance behavior to an acceptable level and at learning how to cope. Goals can be formulated concerning both what the therapist would like the client to achieve during a single therapy session and what exactly the client should manage to do in natural situations when confronted with the phobic object. Clearly, the treatment aim is set in consultation with the client and will depend both on the client's level of commitment and the clinical judgment of the therapist about what seems realistic or ecologically feasible. However, sometimes clients formulate a treatment goal that is not within their reach, unnecessarily difficult, or simply dangerous, such as a person with a dog phobia who set himself the target of acquiring the ability to spontaneously pet all sorts of dogs. A more appropriate aim of treatment, however, could be the ability to walk outside without having to change direction because of the appearance of a dog. The therapist should be clear about the objectives for each session but also be prepared to adapt to unexpected happenings.

> Say, *"Based on all that we have been talking about, let's discuss our goal(s) for treatment. What is the goal and how will you know when you have reached your goal?"*

_____

_____

Therapist and client come to a mutual, attainable goal based on what is known from the client's history.

Identify the Conditioning Experience

In general, with regard to the procedure, the memories of the meaningful and disturbing past events (i.e., the conditioning event, the worst—or the most representative—event, and the most recent event) are used as a focus for a series of subsequent EMDR (basic protocol) procedures that are applied separately, each involving a distinct target memory. Although the memory of the conditioning event will be the primary target of processing first, all relevant targets need to be identified.

The first target that needs to be identified is the origin; that is, the memory of the event that has caused (or in the patient's perception clearly worsened) the fear (e.g., being bitten by a dog in case of a dog phobia, or having undergone a horrific medical or dental treatment that led to a medical phobia). To identify the first target for processing, one or more of the following strategies could be used.

Say, *"Which incident caused you to be afraid of _____ (state the stimulus or CS)?" Or in other words when did this fear begin?"*

_____

_____

Or say, *"When did you notice this fear for the first time?"*

_____

_____

Or say, *"What incident causes you to be afraid of _____ (state the feared consequence or UCS)?"*

_____

_____

Check for Possible Earlier (Ancillary) Experience

Check whether this is indeed the first event. If not, identify the incident when the fear was felt for the first time.

Say, *"Is this indeed the first incident related to this fear? Are you absolutely sure you did not have this fear or phobia prior to this incident?"*

_____

_____

Identify the Most Representative Experience

Say, *"What is the most extreme or most frightening experience that clearly worsened your fear or phobia?"*

_____

_____

Identify the Most Recent Experience

Say, *"When was the last time you experienced the fear that is still disturbing when you think about it?"*

_____

_____

Identify Other Relevant Experiences

The assessment should not only focus on the experiences pertinent to the development of the phobia per se. The therapist should check for related memories of events or present stimuli, including possible collateral damage. For example, being ridiculed by peers when the patient reacted with extreme fear when confronted with a small dog. These kinds of experiences are likely to have had an effect on an individual's self-image and self-worth in general and therefore may also need to be addressed.

> Say, *"What other past experiences might be important in relation to the acquisition or worsening of your fear or phobia?"*

_____

_____

Phase 2: Preparation

The reprocessing work should not start until rapport and trust have been established and the client has been introduced to EMDR; that is, what is EMDR and what can the client expect to happen? A basic example (Shapiro, 2001) is given below of what therapists can say. Clearly, the explanation could be changed, based on the current state of knowledge on trauma and trauma resolution, as well as certain personality characteristics, such as age and sophistication of the client.

> Say, *"When a trauma occurs it seems to get locked in the nervous system with the original picture, sounds, thoughts, and feelings. The eye movements we use in EMDR seem to unlock the nervous system and allow the brain to process the experience. That may be what is happening in REM or dream sleep—the eye movements may help to process the unconscious material. It is important to remember that it is your own brain that will be doing the healing and that you are the one in control."*

Another well established guideline when using EMDR is the preparation of the client for the EMDR therapy. To this end, it is important to make sure that the client is not afraid of his or her own fear reactions, since many phobias entail a fear of fear. If the client has never been able to deal with fear adequately, these things have to be worked out before targeting any traumatic memory. One helpful way to deal with it is to apply self-control procedures before a confrontational method such as EMDR is used. Particularly, training a client in the use of distraction may be a way of challenging the client's faulty beliefs, for example the perception that he or she can exert no control over her anxiety. Later in therapy, distraction can be used as an immediate anxiety management strategy, for example between sessions. For example,

> Say, *"Please describe out loud the content of the room with as much detail as you can."*

_____

_____

Distraction techniques also include mental exercises such as counting backward from 1,000 in 7s or remembering a favorite walk in detail. For example,

> Say, *"Please count backward from 1,000 by 7s."*

_____

_____

Or say, *"In detail, tell me about a favorite walk that you took."*

_____

_____

In the case of a child distraction can be applied, for instance, by thinking of animals beginning with each letter of the alphabet in turn.

Say, *"Think of an animal that begins with the letter A."*

_____

_____

Say, *"Great, now let's continue finding the names of animals using the rest of the alphabet. What would the name of an animal be for the letter B?"*

_____

_____

One of the benefits of using distraction is that once the client feels confident with its use, these skills are helpful to direct her attention away from thoughts concerned with possible catastrophic happenings or with evaluating his or her own performance.

Say, *"These exercises that we have been practicing may help you distract yourself when you are dealing with anxiety-provoking situations."*

It is essential to explain how important it is to prepare oneself for possible discomfort and any between session disturbance and to practice with what has been learned. This makes it more likely that the client will become proficient and confident in the utilization of such techniques.

Say, *"It is really important for you to prepare yourself for possible discomfort between sessions by practicing these exercises. The more you practice, the better you will get at them."*

There are indications that blood or injury phobics display an atypical symptom pattern in which an initial increase in heart rate and blood pressure is followed by a sudden drop and sometimes fainting. In such cases it may be important to teach clients the applied tension technique, as this procedure takes into account the diphasic response pattern that is considered to be characteristic of this type of phobia (Öst & Sterner, 1987). This tension technique teaches clients to tighten their muscles, which seems to counteract the drop in blood pressure.

For clients with blood or injury phobias, say the following:

Say, *"Please make it comfortable for yourself. Now, tense all of your muscles in your body, including those in your arms, torso, legs, and face. Please increase this tension. Now, hold this tension (for about 15 seconds) until there is a warm feeling in your head. Okay? Release the tension and let your body return to its normal state (for about 30 seconds)."*

_____

_____

This tension–relaxation cycle should be repeated five times within each practice session. If the therapist has access to equipment for measuring blood pressure it may be instructive to demonstrate the effect of the tension technique to the client.

The client should be requested to start practicing the tension technique 1 week prior to the actual beginning of the EMDR treatment. Practicing needs to be done five times throughout the day, practicing five tension–relaxation cycles per time. If the client has a medical condition that could be affected by the procedure, for instance hypertension, he or she should consult a physician prior to practicing this technique. It is important to note that when the client feels headaches during the practices the strength of the tension should be decreased.

> Say, *"You can start practicing the tension technique this week as we will begin our EMDR treatment next time. Practicing means doing the technique five times throughout the day, practicing five tension-relaxation cycles per time. If you have hypertension, it is wise for us to check with our physician before practicing this technique. If you experience any headaches during the practices, decrease the strength of the tension."*

Phase 3: Assessment

Target Selection

Select a target image (stationary picture) of the memory. (See Phase 1: History Taking: Determine an Appropriate and Feasible Treatment Goal for the series of targets that need to be processed.)

> Say, *"What picture represents the most disturbing part of this incident now?"*

_____

_____

Obtaining Negative Cognition (NC) and Positive Cognition (PC)

The selection of cognitions within the EMDR treatment is an idiosyncratic process and will greatly depend on the client and the specific characteristics of the target event. For example, the clinician should be sure that cognitions meet the following criteria:

- Appropriate for the issue.
- Formulated in the here and now.
- Connected to the target image.
- Conveyed the present state about the current belief in relation to the past event such as "I am out of control," not a statement of what was experienced in the past such as "I was out of control."
- Described the actual experience in terms of a belief statement (e.g., NC: "I am a prey") and not the emotional state, (e.g., NC: "I am desperate").
- Found in the control domain (e.g., "I am helpless," "I am powerless," "I am not in control") in the majority of the cases the NC of the memory of the conditioning experience.

Therapists will discover in their work with clients suffering from phobic conditions that certain categories of cognitions pertain to specific types of fears, for example:

Animal Type Phobias

I am weak   I am strong

I am a prey (e.g., dogs and insects)   I am someone like anyone else.

I am Okay

Situational Type and Natural Environment Type Phobias

I am a coward   I am Okay

Blood–Injury–Injection Type Phobias

I am a number, a piece of meat   I am a human being. I am Okay

The main criterion of the PC selection is the following:

- Level of meaning parallels (in the same cognitive domain) the NC.
- Empowerment of the individual (e.g., "I can handle it").
- Ecologically valid or feasible (e.g., PC: "I have control over the spider").

In case it appears necessary to address other relevant memories(see Phase 1: History Taking: Determine an Appropriate and Feasible Treatment Goal), the therapist should take into account that the NC and PC of these targets may have different cognitive domains (e.g., within the self-worth domain rather than within the control domain).

Negative Cognition (NC)

Say, *"What words best go with the picture that express your negative belief about yourself now?"*

_____

_____

Positive Cognition (PC)

Say, *"When you bring up the picture of the incident, what would you like to believe about yourself now?"*

_____

_____

Validity of Cognition (VoC)

Say, *"When you bring up the picture of the incident, how true do those words _____ (clinician repeats the positive cognition) feel to you now on a scale of 1 to 7, where 1 feels completely false and 7 feels completely true?"*

_____

_____

1	2	3	4	5	6	7
(completely false)				(completely true)		

Identify Emotion, SUD Level and Location of the Feeling

Emotions

Say, *"When you bring up the picture* (or incident) *and those words* _____ (clinician states the negative cognition), *what emotion do you feel now?"*

_____

_____

Subjective Units of Disturbance (SUD)

Say, *"On a scale of 0 to 10, where 0 is no disturbance or neutral and 10 is the highest disturbance you can imagine, how disturbing does it feel now?"*

0	1	2	3	4	5	6	7	8	9	10
(no disturbance)							(highest disturbance)			

Location of Body Sensation

Say, *"Where do you feel it* (the disturbance) *in your body?"*

_____

_____

Phase 4: Desensitization

Apply the Standard EMDR Protocol for All Targets

The Standard EMDR Protocol is used to process all targets. There is, however, one difference. To adequately tap into the memory network, it is most useful to have a somewhat different strategy for going back to target than is recommended for using the Standard EMDR procedure. More specifically, after having gone back to target the client is asked to focus on the most salient detail of the target; that is, the aspect that provokes most disturbance. Therefore, the client may need time to connect emotionally with the disturbing material, but as soon as the client has decided what aspect is now perceived as most disturbing, bilateral stimulation (BLS) is introduced. Such a strategy of using a clear focus on the aspects of the target image by which the affect is triggered has proven to be an excellent way to facilitate a connecting of the nodes in the fear network that still need to be processed, often effectively activating a new flow of associations.

Say, *"When you go back to the original incident, on a scale of 0 to 10, where 0 is no disturbance or neutral and 10 is the highest disturbance you can imagine, how disturbing does it feel now?"*

0	1	2	3	4	5	6	7	8	9	10
(no disturbance)							(highest disturbance)			

If the SUD is 1 or higher, options are as follows:

Say, *"Look at the incident as it is now stored in your head. What aspect of it is most disturbing?"*

_____

_____

Or say, *"What is there in the picture that is causing the _____ (state the SUD level)? What do you see?"*

_____

_____

Then say, *"Concentrate on that aspect. Okay, have you got it? Go with that."*

_____

_____

Sets of eye movements (EMs) or other BLS until SUD = 0.

Phase 5: Installation

Install the PC

Say, *"As you think of the incident, how do the words feel from 1 being completely false to 7 being completely true?"*

1   2   3   4   5   6   7
(completely false)   (completely true)

Say, *"Think of the event and hold it together with the words _____ (repeat the PC). Go with that."*

_____

_____

Continue this procedure until the VoC is 7.

Check the Other Targets

See Phase 1: History Taking: Determine an Appropriate and Feasible Treatment Goal and decide whether it is still necessary to reprocess these experiences (SUD when bringing up the memory > 0).

Say, *"Okay, let's check the next target that is on your list _____ (state the next target). On a scale of 0 to 10, where 0 is no disturbance or neutral and 10 is the highest disturbance you can imagine, how disturbing does it feel now?"*

0   1   2   3   4   5   6   7   8   9   10
(no disturbance)   (highest disturbance)

If the SUD is > 0, continue the procedure and start at Phase 8: Reevaluation.

Installation of the Future Template

If all targets (Phase 1: History Taking: Determine an Appropriate and Feasible Treatment Goal) are desensitized, the client may still have to anticipate future situations in which the former phobic stimuli are present (e.g., a dental treatment situation) and in which he or she needs to interact with these stimuli. To prepare for that, the client is asked to mentally progress in time to identify a specific mental image of a typical future situation by which the fear prior to this session certainly would have been triggered. This may be a situation that the client usually avoids because of fear or a situation that he, until now, is not able to enter or to undergo without fear.

> Say, *"Okay, we have reprocessed all of the targets that we needed to that were on your list. Now let's anticipate what will happen when you are faced with _____ (state the fear). Think of a time in the future and identify a mental image or photo of a typical situation that would have triggered your fear prior to our work together. What would that be?"*

_____

_____

For the Future Template it is useful to have the client select a picture of a situation in which he behaves and feels in the way he really wants it to happen. The goal of this procedure is merely to inoculate clients to future relapse triggers by preparing them for future confrontations with the conditioned and fear provoking stimuli, thereby further increasing their feelings of self-confidence. From a practical point of view, clients are requested to hold in mind their picture and to visualize this scene as well as possible, while keeping in mind a standard PC (e.g., "I can cope," or "I can handle it"). Next, the BLS is introduced. This is continued as long as the client reports a strengthening of validity (until VoC = 7). Thus, when this form of installation procedure has succeeded the client fully believes that he or she is able to deal with their mental representation of the experience.

> Say, *"I would like you to imagine yourself coping effectively with or in _____ (state the fear trigger) in the future. Please focus on the image and say to yourself, 'I can handle it,' notice the sensations associated with this future scene and follow my fingers (or any other BLS)."*
> Then say, *"To what extent do you believe you are able to actually handle this situation (VoC) on a scale of 1 to 7, where 1 feels completely false and 7 feels completely true?"*

> 1   2   3   4   5   6   7
> (completely false)   (completely true)

The therapist continues with this procedure (instruction and VoC rating) until the Future Template is sufficiently installed (VoC = 7).

If there is a block, meaning that even after 10 or more installations the VoC is still below 7, there probably are more targets that need to be identified and addressed. The therapist should use the Standard EMDR Protocol to address these targets before proceeding with the template (see Worksheets in Appendix A). Also evaluate whether the client needs any new information, resources, or skills to be able to comfortably visualize the future coping scene. Introduce this needed information or skill.

> Say, *"What would you need to feel confident in handling the situation?"*

_____

_____

> Or say, *"What is missing from your handling of this situation?"*

_____

_____

Phase 6: Body Scan

Say, *"Close your eyes and keep in mind the experience that you will have in the future. Then bring your attention to the different parts of your body, starting with your head and working downward. Any place you find any tension, tightness, or unusual sensation, tell me."*

_____

_____

If any sensation is reported, the therapist introduces BLS.

If it is a positive or comfortable sensation, BLS is used to strengthen the positive feelings.

If a sensation of discomfort is reported, this is reprocessed until the discomfort subsides. Finally, the VoC has to be checked.

Say, *"As you think of the incident, how do the words feel from 1 being completely false to 7 being completely true?"*

1	2	3	4	5	6	7
(completely false)				(completely true)		

Video Check

After the incorporation of a positive template for future action, the clinician asks the client to close his eyes, and to run a mental video. That is, the client imagines himself in the future and mentally runs a videotape of the time between the present session and a next possible (but successful) confrontation with the anxiety-provoking stimulus or situation (e.g., an upcoming dental treatment: waking, going to the dentist, taking a seat in the waiting room, etc.). The client is asked to identify any disturbing aspect in the mental video and is instructed that—as soon as any disturbance arises during the running of the videotape—he stops, opens his eyes, and informs the therapist.

Say, *"This time I'd like you to imagine yourself stepping into the future. Close your eyes and play a movie from the beginning until the end. Imagine yourself coping with any challenges that come your way. Notice what you are seeing, thinking, feeling, and experiencing in your body. While playing this movie, let me know if you hit any blocks. If you do, just open your eyes and let me know. If you don't hit any blocks, let me know when you have viewed the whole movie."*

_____

_____

Next, these disturbing aspects are targeted with BLS where appropriate. This is done by holding in mind the same PC as was used in the previous step ("I can handle it"), while a long set is administered.

The mental videotape is repeated until it can be viewed entirely without distress.

If the client encounters a block and opens her eyes this is a sign for the therapist to instruct the client to say the following:

Say, *"Say to yourself 'I can handle it' and follow my fingers* (or other form of BLS).*"*

_____

_____

To provide the clinician with an indication regarding client's self-efficacy, have her rate her response on a VoC scale from 1 to 7. This procedural step may give the clinician feedback on the extent to which the goals are met.

Say, *"As you think of the incident, how do the words feel, from 1 being completely false to 7 being completely true?"*

1	2	3	4	5	6	7
(completely false)				(completely true)		

If the client is able to play the movie from start to finish with a sense of confidence and satisfaction, the client is asked to play the movie once more from the beginning to the end, BLS is introduced, and the PC "I can handle it" is installed. In a sense, this movie is installed as a Future Template.

Say, *"Okay, play the movie one more time from beginning to end and say to yourself 'I can handle it.' Go with that."*

_____

_____

Prepare the Client for In Vivo Confrontations

It is likely that, through the application of the previous steps of the EMDR procedure, the meaning or severity of the initial event has been effectively reappraised. Yet, it could be that the client is not completely convinced of her ability to cope with a future encounter with the phobic stimulus. Sometimes clients have avoided certain activities for so long that they no longer know how to behave and how to feel secure in their formerly phobic situation. If this is the case, it is important that the therapist identifies and counters existing irrational beliefs that contribute to a sense of threat and anxiety, for instance, by the use of in vivo exposure assignments or behavioral experiments.

If the client is actually confronted with the stimuli that normally would evoke a fear response and the client gains an experience that the catastrophe she fears does not occur, this would help to demonstrate that her fears may be unfounded.

Say, *"Many clients appear to avoid certain activities for so long that they no longer know how to behave or how to feel secure in this situation. To be able to help you alleviate your fears and concerns, it is important that you learn to counter the negative belief that contributes to this sense of threat and anxiety. Therefore, you need to actually test the catastrophic expectations that you have that fuels your anxiety in real life. I would like to ask you to gradually confront the objects or situations that normally would provoke a fear response. It may seem odd, but if you have a positive experience and it appears that the catastrophe you fear does not occur, it helps you to further demonstrate—or to convince yourself—that your fear is unfounded."*

A behavioral experiment is an excellent opportunity to test if the treatment effects are generalized to all associated triggers or aspects of the situation. To this end, real-life exposure to the anxiety provoking stimulus after successful reprocessing of the traumatic memories may further strengthen the believability of the positive cognition as the NC (and other still existing assumptions and beliefs) is contradicted by the consequences of acting in new ways.

As with any of the other steps in the phobia protocol, the in vivo exposure part should be a joint venture of client and therapist. Unforced willingness must be ensured. Some gentle persuasion is certainly permissible, but it must be clear to the client that nothing will happen against his or her will during the confrontation with the phobic stimuli or situation. Also, unexpected introduction of new fearful material is counterproductive as this can both damage confidence and lead to a revision of estimates of the likelihood of threat and increased caution.

Say, *"I want you to understand that nothing will happen against your will during the confrontation with the things that normally would evoke fear. The essence of this confrontation is that it is safe."*

In Vivo Exposure

In vivo exposure is applied to reduce avoidance and promote the opportunity to evoke mastery through observing that no real danger exists. All varying stimulus elements within a situation should be explored. Therefore, the eliciting situation should hold the client's attention. For instance, a person fearful of high places could be encouraged to be on the roof of an apartment building that is not too distressful while paying attention to what is happening on the street or to certain objects such as trees, cars, and people.

It is essential that the therapist helps the client to pay attention to features of the phobic object or situation that are positive or interesting while being exposed to it.

Say, *"Please describe the most notable features of the situation. Are you noticing any interesting elements about _____ (state the phobic object or situation)?"*

_____

_____

To identify negative thought content, say the following:

Say, *"What are you thinking as you pay attention to _____ (state the phobic object or situation)?"*

_____

_____

To cognitively reconstruct the situation, say the following:

Say, *"How would someone else who is not afraid of _____ (state the phobic object/situation) view or evaluate this situation?"*

_____

_____

It is important to anticipate various possibilities regarding elements that can be manipulated to ameliorate or to intensify the impact. It is our experience that it is helpful to make variations with regard to the stimulus dimensions such as action, distance, and time. That is, in a real-life confrontation, for example with an animal, the animal can be induced to be more or less lively, close or more distant, to be positioned with its head to the client or not, and during a long or a more limited period of time. If necessary the therapist can demonstrate to the client how he or she would handle the feared object (e.g., by petting a dog).

> Say, *"Isn't it interesting to notice that now that you are confronted with this* _____ *(state the object or situation),* _____ *(state the catastrophe the client normally would have feared to happen) does not occur?"*

_____

_____

> Say, *"Do you notice that your anxiety is not as physically harmful as you might have expected?"*

_____

_____

> Say, *"These emotional reactions will subside and fade over time. Therefore, it is important that you continue exposing yourself to the feared stimuli as long as you feel that you have achieved a certain degree of self-mastery. Please note that you are gradually learning to feel that you are capable of handling a certain level of anticipatory anxiety with confidence."*

_____

_____

The therapist should make sure that confrontations are repeated so that the reduction in distress is fully consolidated before moving on. Thus, the overall aim is to foster confidence in a general ability to cope despite variations in circumstances.

The therapist should act in such a confident and relaxed manner that the client feels prepared for any eventuality. The results can be checked by assessing the validity of catastrophe.

> Say, *"If you would encounter* _____ *(state the phobic object or situation) again, on a scale from 0% to 100% where 0% means this is completely false and 100% means this is completely true, how true does this feel?"*

0%   10%   20%   30%   40%   50%   60%   70%   80%   90%   100%
(completely false)   (completely true)

Phase 7: Closure

At the end of every session, consolidate the changes and improvement that has occurred.

> Say, *"What is the most positive thing you have learned about yourself in the last hour with regard to* _____ *(state the incident or theme)?"*

_____

_____

If the cognitions are not already on the identity level, say the following:

Say, *"What does this say about yourself as a person?"*

_____

_____

Say, *"Go with that."*

_____

_____

Install with eye movements until there are no further positive changes. Next, check the results by assessing the validity of catastrophe.

Say, *"If you would be exposed to _____* (state the phobic object or situation), *on a scale from 0% to 100% where 0% means this is completely false and 100% means this is completely true, how true does this feel?"*

0%   10%   20%   30%   40%   50%   60%   70%   80%   90%   100%
(completely false)   (completely true)

Next, an explanation is provided about the coming 3 days: agreements, diary, and contact information.

Say, *"Things may come up or they may not. If they do, great. Write it down, and it can be a target for next time. If you get any new memories, dreams, or situations that disturb you, just take a good snapshot. It isn't necessary to give a lot of detail. Just put down enough to remind you so we can target it next time. The same thing goes for any positive dreams or situations. If negative feelings do come up, try not to make them significant. Remember, it's still just the old stuff. Just write it down for next time."*

Planning Self-Managed Homework Assignments

After the therapy has been concluded, the therapist makes it clear that it is important to keep practicing during daily life in order to ensure that the changes are maintained.

Say, *"It is very important to keep practicing with exposing yourself to difficult situations in your daily life in order to maintain the changes that you have experienced."*

The client should be told to stop any current avoidance behavior as much as possible, and to consider each confrontation with the feared stimulus as an opportunity to put the newly acquired skills into practice. By using self-managed assignments the client should be encouraged to incorporate as many critical situations in real life as possible. This allows the client to gain self-confidence through overcoming her fears on her own, to learning of new and more independent and appropriate ways of coping, and to perceiving further progress. Thus, dependence on the therapist should certainly be avoided. Clients are expected to confront situations regularly and alone on the basis of agreed homework tasks. These may include taking a holiday flight, visiting a dentist for a check-up, opening a window of their house on summer days when wasps are flying, using elevators, meeting people with dogs, climbing towers in cases of height phobia, or swallowing solid food in cases of choking phobia.

> Say, *"Each time that you have a chance to see* _____ (state the feared stimulus), *it is an opportunity for you to practice these new skills that you now know how to do. So, the more that you encounter* _____ (state the feared stimulus), *the better you can get at* _____ (state the goal). *Your brain learns new behaviors by practicing."*

With regard to blood phobia, the procedure is different in that the client is instructed to practice the applied tension technique (see Preparation Phase) in real-life situations, while exposing himself to his anxiety provoking stimulus as much as possible, such as watching violent films with bloodshed, paying visits to a blood bank, and talking about blood-related topics.

> Say, *"Please practice the applied tension technique in real-life situations as much as possible, while exposing yourself to* _____ (state anxiety provoking stimulus). *That may, for example, be talking about blood-related topics with friends, watching a medical documentary, a violent film with bloodshed, or paying a visit to a blood bank."*

_____

_____

Phase 8: Reevaluation

The length of the interval between sessions will depend on several factors, including the nature of the problem, the frequency with which significant eliciting situations are encountered, and the availability of the therapist and the client. It is sometimes inevitable that clients experience a relapse. In many cases, this is due to the fact that clients now expose themselves to situations that they avoided for a long period of time. Also, a spontaneous return of fear should be expected to occur during the interval between sessions. This may lead to increased arousal, which in turn could render clients disappointed about the improvements that they expected, thus interpreting this as a signal that their problems will only worsen. It is therefore important to label their behavior in a positive sense and to redefine the relapse as a challenge to put into practice what is learned.

> Say, *"Make sure to write down your responses when you are practicing your new skills. Sometimes, even with the skills, you might find that you reexperience your fear. I want to tell you that this can happen sometimes, and that it is not unusual. What you can do at that time is to note what has led up to the feeling, what is going on around you, and what you did to help yourself handle the situation. Jot down some notes about what happened as soon as you can so that you won't forget what happened and then bring them to the next session so that we can figure it out."*

After the application of the phobia protocol there may still be a need for additional targeting and other strategies necessary to ensure that the treatment goals are met. An evaluation of what still remains to be done should be made at the beginning of the next session. The client is asked about his current symptoms and about his progress in terms of success in carrying out homework tasks. It is advisable to always evaluate in terms of a client's SUD level on the already processed material.

> Say, *"As you think back on the target that we were working on last time, on a scale of 0 to 10, where 0 is no disturbance or neutral and 10 is the highest disturbance you can imagine, how disturbing does it feel now?"*

> 0   1   2   3   4   5   6   7   8   9   10
> (no disturbance)   (highest disturbance)

If the disturbance level has increased, these reverberations need to be targeted or otherwise addressed.

The therapist should assess the necessity of teaching the client additional self-control and perhaps relaxation techniques or other relevant exercises that could further enhance his or her ability to confront the former anxiety-provoking situation in real life.

> Say, *"So what other resources do you think might be helpful in assisting you to deal with this situation?"*

> _____

> _____

Repeated rehearsal and reinforcement for success needs to be emphasized. To encourage hope and foster engagement in treatment, it is crucial that therapy sessions and homework assignments furnish experiences of success that clients can attribute to themselves.

> Say, *"I can see that through all of the work that you did between sessions that you are really working hard _____ (reinforce what the client has done that has been successful)."*

In this respect these successes provide clients with direct experiential evidence that anxiety can, through their own effort, be controlled. Clinically it is often observed that once a client manages to realize even a small achievement, the vicious circle of dependency, low self-esteem, avoidance, and further anxiety is broken. Therefore, it is important to work toward attainable and personally gratifying goals.

The Phobia Protocol Script

Phase 1: History Taking

Determine the Type of Fear and Its Severity

Say, *"What is the fear or concern that has brought you in today?"*

_____

_____

_____

_____

Say, *"Does this fear or concern seem excessive or unreasonable to you?"*

_____

_____

If so, say, *"Tell me about it."*

_____

_____

_____

_____

Determine to What Extent the Client Fulfills All DSM-IV-TR Criteria of Specific Phobia

- Marked and persistent fear that is excessive or unreasonable, cued by the presence or anticipation of a specific object or situation.
- Exposure to the phobic stimulus almost invariably provokes an immediate anxiety response, which may take the form of a situationally bound or a situationally predisposed panic attack. Note: In children, the anxiety may be expressed by crying, tantrums, freezing, or clinging.
- The person recognizes that the fear is excessive or unreasonable. Note: In children, this feature may be absent.
- The phobic situation(s) is avoided or else is endured with intense anxiety or distress.
- The avoidance, anxious anticipation, or distress in the feared situation(s) interferes significantly with the person's normal routine, occupation, (academic) functioning, social activities, relationships, or there is marked distress about having the phobia.
- In individuals under 18 years, the duration is at least 6 months.
- The anxiety, panic attacks, or phobic avoidance associated with the specific object or situation are not better accounted for by another mental disorder, such as obsessive-compulsive disorder, post-traumatic stress disorder, social phobia, or panic disorder.

Identify the Stimulus Situation (Conditioned Stimulus [CS])

Say, *"Describe the object or situation that you are afraid of."*

_____

_____

_____

_____

Or say, *"What exactly do you need to see, hear, or feel in order to get an immediate fear response?"*

_____

_____

_____

_____

Say, *"What exactly about* _____ (state the object or situation) *triggers your fear most?"*

_____

_____

_____

_____

Say, *"Which incident caused your fear of* _____ (state the object or situation)*?"*

_____

_____

_____

_____

Identify the Expected Consequence or Catastrophe (Unconditioned Stimulus [UCS])

Say, *"What are you afraid of that could happen when you are exposed to* _____ (state the object or situation: CS)*?"*

_____

_____

_____

_____

Say, *"Which incident caused your fear of* _____ (state the catastrophe the client expects to happen)*?"*

_____

_____

_____

_____

Assess Validity of Catastrophe

Say, *"Is it true you are saying that IF you would be exposed to _____ (state the phobic object or situation) THEN you would _____ (state the catastrophe the client fears to happen)?"*

_____

_____

Say, *"On a scale from 0% to 100% where 0% means it is completely false and 100% means it is completely true, how true does this feel?"*

0% 10% 20% 30% 40% 50% 60% 70% 80% 90% 100%
(completely false)   (completely true)

Provide Information About the Fear or Phobia if Necessary

Say, *"What do you know about the relative dangerousness of _____ (therapist fills in the information specific to the phobic stimulus with which he or she is dealing)? Since there are other people that are not that fearful as you of _____ (state the phobic object or situation), wouldn't it be wise to spend some time investigating whether it is really as dangerous as you think it is? Just to be sure that you don't overestimate the probability of the danger or that something bad will happen to you. I mean, even if it appears to be more dangerous to be exposed to _____ (state the phobic object or situation) than you think it is now, it is important to find out, don't you think? Thus, let's look for the information we need. Where shall we start?"*

_____

_____

Determine an Appropriate and Feasible Treatment Goal

Say, *"Based on all that we have been talking about, let's discuss our goal(s) for treatment. What is the goal and how will you know when you have reached your goal?"*

_____

_____

Identify the Conditioning Experience

Say, *"Which incident caused you to be afraid of _____ (state the stimulus or CS)?" Or, in other words, when did this fear begin?"*

_____

_____

_____

_____

Or say, *"When did you notice this fear for the first time?"*

_____

_____

Or say, *"What incident causes you to be afraid of _____ (state the feared consequence or UCS)?"*

_____

_____

Check for Possible Earlier Ancillary Experience

Check whether this is indeed the first event. If not, identify the incident when the fear was felt for the first time.

Say, *"Is this indeed the first incident related to this fear? I mean, are you absolutely sure you did not have this fear or phobia prior to this incident?"*

_____

_____

_____

_____

Identify the Most Representative Experience

Say, *"What is the most extreme or most frightening experience that clearly worsened your fear or phobia?"*

_____

_____

_____

_____

Identify the Most Recent Experience

Say, *"What is the most recent time that you experienced the fear that is still disturbing when you think about it?"*

_____

_____

_____

_____

Identify Other Relevant Experiences

Say, *"What other past experiences might be important in relation to the acquisition or worsening of your fear or phobia?"*

_____

_____

_____

_____

Phase 2: Preparation

Explanation of EMDR.

> Say, *"When a trauma occurs it seems to get locked in the nervous system with the original picture, sounds, thoughts, and feelings. The eye movements we use in EMDR seem to unlock the nervous system and allow the brain to process the experience. That may be what is happening in REM or dream sleep—the eye movements may help to process the unconscious material. It is important to remember that it is your own brain that will be doing the healing and that you are the one in control."*

Teach distraction techniques for immediate anxiety management between sessions such as the following:

> Say, *"Please describe out loud the content of the room with as much detail as you can."*

_____

_____

Distraction techniques also include mental exercises such as counting backward from 1,000 in 7s, remembering a favorite walk in detail, etc. For example,

> Say, *"Please count backward from 1,000 by 7s."*

_____

_____

> Or say, *"In detail, tell me about a favorite walk that you took."*

_____

_____

In the case of a child distraction can be applied, for instance, by thinking of animals beginning with each letter of the alphabet in turn.

> Say, *"Think of an animal that begins with the letter A."*

_____

_____

> Say, *"Great, now let's continue finding the names of animals using the rest of the alphabet. What would the name of an animal be for the letter B?"*

_____

_____

Continue education of the process.

> Say, *"These exercises that we have been practicing may help you distract yourself when you are dealing with anxiety-provoking situations."*

Say, *"It is really important for you to prepare yourself for possible discomfort between sessions by practicing these exercises. The more you practice, the better you will get at them."*

Teach the Applied Tension Technique for blood or injury phobics who often have an initial increase in heart rate and blood pressure that is followed by a sudden drop or fainting.

For clients with blood or injury phobias:

Say, *"Please make it comfortable for yourself. Now, tense all of your muscles in your body including those in your arms, torso, legs, and face. Please increase this tension. Now hold this tension (for about 15 seconds) until there is a warm feeling in your head. Okay? If so, release the tension and let your body return to its normal state (for about 30 seconds)."*

_____

_____

This tension–relaxation cycle should be repeated five times within each practice session.

Say, *"You can start practicing the tension technique this week as we will begin our EMDR treatment next time. Practicing means doing the technique five times throughout the day, practicing five tension–relaxation cycles per time. If you have hypertension, it is wise for you to check with your physician before practicing this technique. If you experience any headaches during the practices, decrease the strength of the tension."*

Phase 3: Assessment

Target Selection

Select a target image (stationary picture) of the memory. (See Phase 1: History Taking: Determine an Appropriate and Feasible Treatment Goal for the series of targets that need to be processed.)

Say, *"What picture represents the most disturbing part of this incident now?"*

_____

_____

Obtaining the Negative and Positive Cognitions

Negative Cognition (NC)

Say, *"What words best go with the picture that express your negative belief about yourself now?"*

_____

_____

Positive Cognition (PC)

Say, *"When you bring up the picture of the incident, what would you like to believe about yourself now?"*

_____

_____

Validity of Cognition (VoC)

Say, *"When you bring up the picture of the incident, how true do those words* _____ (clinician repeats the positive cognition) *feel to you now on a scale of 1 to 7, where 1 feels completely false and 7 feels completely true?"*

1   2   3   4   5   6   7
(completely false)   (completely true)

Identify Emotion, SUD Level and Location of the Feeling

Emotions

Say, *"When you bring up the picture* (or incident) *and those words* _____ (clinician states the negative cognition), *what emotion do you feel now?"*

_____

_____

Subjective Units of Disturbance (SUD)

Say, *"On a scale of 0 to 10, where 0 is no disturbance or neutral and 10 is the highest disturbance you can imagine, how disturbing does it feel now?"*

0   1   2   3   4   5   6   7   8   9   10
(no disturbance)   (highest disturbance)

Location of Body Sensation

Say, *"Where do you feel it* (the disturbance) *in your body?"*

_____

_____

Phase 4: Desensitization

Apply the Standard EMDR Protocol for All Targets

This protocol uses a different strategy to go back to target then in the Standard EMDR procedure.

Say, *"When you go back to the original incident, on a scale of 0 to 10, where 0 is no disturbance or neutral and 10 is the highest disturbance you can imagine, how disturbing does it feel now?"*

0   1   2   3   4   5   6   7   8   9   10
(no disturbance)   (highest disturbance)

If the SUD is 1 or higher, options are as follows:

Say, *"Look at the incident as it is now stored in your head. What aspect of it is most disturbing?"*

_____

_____

Or say, *"What is there in the picture that is causing the _____ (state the SUD level)? What do you see?"*

_____

_____

Then say, *"Concentrate on that aspect. Okay, have you got it? Go with that."*

_____

_____

Do sets of eye movements or other BLS until SUD = 0.

Phase 5: Installation

Install the PC

Say, *"As you think of the incident, how do the words feel from 1 being completely false to 7 being completely true?"*

1	2	3	4	5	6	7
(completely false)				(completely true)		

Say, *"Think of the event and hold it together with the words _____ (repeat the PC). Go with that."*

_____

_____

Continue this procedure until the VoC is 7.

Check the Other Targets

See Phase 1: History Taking: Determine an Appropriate and Feasible Treatment Goal and decide whether it is still necessary to reprocess these experiences (SUD when bringing up the memory > 0).

Say, *"Okay, let's check the next target that is in your list _____ (state the next target). On a scale of 0 to 10, where 0 is no disturbance or neutral and 10 is the highest disturbance you can imagine, how disturbing does it feel now?"*

0	1	2	3	4	5	6	7	8	9	10
(no disturbance)										(highest disturbance)

If the SUD is > 0, continue the procedure and start at Phase 8: Reevaluation.

Installation of the Future Template

Say, *"Okay, we have reprocessed all of the targets that we needed to that were on your list. Now let's anticipate what will happen when you are faced with _____ (state the fear). Think of a time in the future and identify a mental image or photo of a typical situation that would have triggered your fear prior to our work together. What would that be?"*

_____

_____

_____

_____

Say, *"I would like you to imagine yourself coping effectively with _____ (state the fear trigger) in the future. Please focus on the image, say to yourself, 'I can handle it,' notice the sensations associated with this future scene, and follow my fingers (or any other BLS)."*

_____

_____

Say, *"To what extent do you believe you are able to actually handle this situation (VoC) on a scale of 1 to 7, where 1 feels completely false and 7 feels completely true?"*

1   2   3   4   5   6   7
(completely false)   (completely true)

The therapist continues with this procedure (instruction and VoC rating) until the future template is sufficiently installed (VoC = 7).

If there is a block, meaning that even after 10 or more installations the VoC is still below 7, there are more targets that need to be identified and addressed. The therapist should use the Standard EMDR Protocol to address these targets before proceeding with the template (see Worksheets in the Appendix). Also evaluate whether the client needs any new information, resources, or skills to be able to comfortably visualize the future coping scene. Introduce this needed information or skill.

Say, *"What would you need to feel confident in handling the situation?"*

_____

_____

Or say, *"What is missing from your handling of this situation?"*

_____

_____

Phase 6: Body Scan

Say, *"Close your eyes and keep in mind the experience that you will have in the future. Then bring your attention to the different parts of your body, starting with your head and working downward. Any place you find any tension, tightness, or unusual sensation, tell me."*

_____

_____

If any sensation is reported, the therapist introduces BLS.

If it is a positive or comfortable sensation, BLS is used to strengthen the positive feelings.

If a sensation of discomfort is reported, this is reprocessed until the discomfort subsides. Finally, the VoC has to be checked.

Say, *"As you think of the incident, how do the words feel from 1 being completely false to 7 being completely true?"*

1	2	3	4	5	6	7
(completely false)				(completely true)		

Video Check

Say, *"This time, I'd like you to imagine yourself stepping into the future. Close your eyes and play a movie from the beginning until the end. Imagine yourself coping with any challenges that come your way. Notice what you are seeing, thinking, feeling, and experiencing in your body. While playing this movie, let me know if you hit any blocks. If you do, just open your eyes and let me know. If you don't hit any blocks, let me know when you have viewed the whole movie."*

_____

_____

If the client encounters a block and opens her eyes this is a sign for the therapist to instruct the client to say the following:

Say, *"Say to yourself 'I can handle it' and follow my fingers (or other form of BLS)."*

To provide the clinician with an indication regarding client's self-efficacy have her rate her response on a VoC scale from 1 to 7. This procedural step may give the clinician feedback on the extent to which the goals are met.

Say, *"As you think of the incident, how do the words feel from 1 being completely false to 7 being completely true?"*

1	2	3	4	5	6	7
(completely false)				(completely true)		

If the client is able to play the movie from start to finish with a sense of confidence and satisfaction, the client is asked to play the movie once more from the beginning to the end, BLS is introduced, and the PC "I can handle it" is installed. In a sense, this movie is installed as a Future Template.

Say, *"Okay, play the movie one more time from beginning to end and say to yourself 'I can handle it.' Go with that."*

_____

_____

Prepare the Client for In Vivo Confrontations

Say, *"Many clients appear to avoid certain activities for so long that they no longer know how to behave and how to feel secure in this situation. To be able to help further alleviate your fears and concerns, it is important that you learn to counter the negative belief that contributes to this sense of threat and anxiety. Therefore, you need to actually test the catastrophic expectations you have that fuels your anxiety in real life. I would like to ask you to gradually confront the objects or situations that normally would provoke a fear response. It may seem odd, but if you have a positive experience and it appears that the catastrophe you fear does not occur, it helps you to further demonstrate—or to convince yourself—that your fear is unfounded."*

Say, *"I want you to understand that nothing will happen against your will during the confrontation with the things that normally would evoke fear. The essence of this confrontation is that it is safe."*

In Vivo Exposure

This is done to reduce avoidance and evoke mastery while observing no real danger exists.

It is essential that the therapist help the client pay attention to features of the phobic object or situation that are positive or interesting while being exposed to it.

Say, *"Please describe the most notable features of the situation. Are you noticing any interesting elements about* _____ (state the phobic object or situation).*"*

_____

_____

To identify negative thought content, say the following:

Say, *"What are you thinking as you pay attention to* _____ (state the phobic object or situation)?*"*

_____

_____

To cognitively reconstruct the situation, say the following:

Say, *"How would someone who is not afraid of* _____ (state the phobic object or situation) *view or evaluate this situation?"*

_____

_____

If needed, give advice to help the client cope with both the situation and their own mental and body sensations.

It is our experience that it is helpful to make variations with regard to the stimulus dimensions such as action, distance, and time.

Say, *"Isn't it interesting to notice that now that you are confronted with this* _____ (state the object or situation) _____ (state the catastrophe the clients normally would have feared to happen) *does not occur?"*

_____

_____

Say, *"Do you notice that your anxiety is not as physically harmful as you might have expected?"*

_____

_____

Say, *"These emotional reactions will subside and fade over time. Therefore, it is important that you continue exposing yourself to the feared stimuli as long as you feel that you have achieved a certain degree of self-mastery. Please note that you are gradually learning to feel that you are capable of handling a certain level of anticipatory anxiety with confidence."*

The therapist should make sure that confrontations are repeated so that the reduction in distress is fully consolidated before moving on.

The results can be checked by assessing the validity of catastrophe.

Say, *"If you would encounter _____ (state the phobic object or situation) again, on a scale from 0% to 100% where 0% means it is completely false and 100% means it is completely true, how true does this feel?"*

0%   10%   20%   30%   40%   50%   60%   70%   80%   90%   100%
(completely false)   (completely true)

Phase 7: Closure

At the end of every session, consolidate the changes and improvement that has occurred.

Say, *"What is the most positive thing you have learned about yourself in the last hour with regard to _____ (state the incident or theme)?"*

_____

_____

If the cognitions are not already on the identity level, say the following:

Say, *"What does this say about yourself as a person?"*
Say, *"Go with that."*

_____

_____

Install with eye movements until there are no further positive changes. Next, check the results by assessing the validity of catastrophe.

Say, *"If you would be exposed to _____ (state the phobic object or situation), on a scale from 0% to 100% where 0% means it is completely false and 100% means it is completely true, how true does this feel?"*

0% 10% 20% 30% 40% 50% 60% 70% 80% 90% 100%
(completely false)   (completely true)

Next, an explanation is provided about the coming 3 days: agreements, diary, and contact information.

Say, *"Things may come up or they may not. If they do, great. Write it down and it can be a target for next time. If you get any new memories, dreams, or situations that disturb you, just take a good snapshot. It isn't necessary to give a lot of detail. Just put down enough to remind you so we can target it next time. The same thing goes for any positive dreams or situations. If negative feelings do come up, try not to make them significant. Remember, it's still just the old stuff. Just write it down for next time."*

Planning Self-Managed Homework Assignments

After the therapy has been concluded, the therapist makes it clear that it is important to keep practicing during daily life in order to ensure that the changes are maintained.

Say, *"It is very important to keep practicing with exposing yourself to difficult situations during your daily life in order to maintain the changes that you have experienced.*
Each time that you have a chance to see _____ (state the feared stimulus), it is an opportunity for you to practice these new skills that you now know how to do. So, the more that you encounter _____ (state the feared stimulus), the better you can get at _____ (state the goal). Your brain learns to do new behaviors by practicing."

For clients with blood phobia say the following:

Say, *"Please practice the applied tension technique in real-life situations as much as possible, while exposing yourself to _____ (state anxiety provoking stimulus). That may, for example, be talking about blood-related topics with friends, watching a medical documentary, a violent film with bloodshed, or paying a visit to a blood bank."*

Phase 8: Reevaluation

Say, *"Make sure to write down your responses when you are practicing your new skills. Sometimes, even with the skills, you might find that you reexperience your fear. I want to tell you that this can happen sometimes, and it is not unusual. What you can do at that time is to note what has led up to the feeling, what is going on around you, and what you did to help yourself handle the situation. Jot down some notes about what happened as soon as you can so that you won't forget what happened and then bring them to the next session so that we can figure it out."*

Evaluate whatever is left to be done.

Say, *"As you think back on the target that we were working on last time, on a scale of 0 to 10, where 0 is no disturbance or neutral and 10 is the highest disturbance you can imagine, how disturbing does it feel now?"*

0	1	2	3	4	5	6	7	8	9	10
(no disturbance)										(highest disturbance)

If the disturbance level has increased, these reverberations need to be targeted or otherwise addressed.

The therapist should assess the necessity of teaching the client additional self-control and perhaps relaxation techniques or other relevant exercises that could further enhance his or her ability to confront the former anxiety-provoking situation in real life.

Say, *"So what other resources do you think might be helpful in assisting you deal with this situation?"*

_____

_____

Repeated rehearsal and reinforcement for success needs to be emphasized. To encourage hope and foster engagement in treatment, it is crucial that therapy sessions and homework assignments furnish experiences of success that clients can attribute to themselves.

Say, *"I can see that through all of the work you did between sessions that you are really working hard _____ (reinforce what the client has done that has been successful)."*

_____

_____

PART VII

EMDR and Clinician Self-Care

Becoming a mental health practitioner is not for the faint of heart. Whereas the rewards are huge, a profession that pulls for all of the negative emotions and behaviors that, often, society prefers to ignore, can take its toll on its practitioners. As a result, clinicians need to make sure that they not only take care of their clients but they also take care of themselves.

As EMDR is known for its impact on trauma, EMDR practitioners, in particular, are amongst those who are called on to deal with the worst of the worst. As seen in this volume, our clients must manage a range of pain, suffering, and the vicissitudes of life. We need to be alert, responsive, empathic, and mindful of ourselves as the instruments through which change can evolve in partnership with our clients.

Indicative of the clinician's focus on other, the EMDR literature and workshops on clinical self-care are sparse. At the 1995 joint conference of the EMDR Institute and the EMDR International Association, David Calof (1995) reported on "The Self of the Therapist: An Experiential Clinic for Clinicians With Abuse Recovery Issues" and at the same conference, Cooper (1995) presented on "EMDR With Victims of Trauma: Protecting Your Client, Protecting Yourself."

Neal Daniels, a psychologist for many of his years, had seen the range of psychology practice from a noncombatant soldier in a medical unit during World War II, to structural family therapist, to chief psychologist on an inpatient unit, and later as head of the post-traumatic stress disorder (PTSD) unit at the Philadelphia Veterans Administration. In this last capacity, Dr. Daniels was the host of a weekly EMDR study group that became a breeding ground for creative ideas and action. Out of this study group's discussion of the ways that members had been utilizing EMDR to help themselves in their own process of self-care and personal growth and discussions with other colleagues, this author put together a presentation on the subject for the EMDR regional network meeting in the Greater Delaware Valley (Philadelphia). In April 1993, this author reported on how she and her fellow EMDR practitioners from the group and colleagues from other parts of the country had been using EMDR for themselves (Luber, 1993). Illustrations of the variety of uses fell into the following seven categories:

1. Clearing the channels or the relaxation response.
   a. To desensitize yourself whenever something is bothering you, think of the negative self-cognition, picture what is bothering you, feel the feelings and then use bilateral stimulation (BLS; Popky, personal communication, March, 1993).
   b. For "the light stuff to take off the rough edges," use BLS in conjunction with Benson's (1975) relaxation response and focus on the word "one." (Puk, personal communication, March, 1993).
   c. Put yourself in a place of calm or safety and from there do EMDR along with a positive cognition(s) (Dunton, personal communication, March, 1993).
   d. Use BLS in the shower in the morning to "clear the channels" and install positive cognitions for the day. This allows for better focus during the day and clears issues that may be of concern or distress (Luber, personal communication, March, 1993).

2. Performance anxiety.
   a. Performance anxiety with symptoms of heart palpitations can respond well to the use of BLS.
   b. Use prior to a presentation to help decrease anxiety (Luber, personal communication, March, 1993).

3. Physical symptoms.
   a. Aches and pains often respond by focusing on the body ache or pain and doing BLS to support the relaxation response (Puk, personal communication, March, 1993).
   b. Chronic itches can decrease—although not entirely diminished—by focusing on the itch and using BLS (DelMaestro, personal communication, March, 1993).
   c. Pain from endometriosis can be addressed by getting on all fours on the floor, concentrating on the pain, and using BLS.
   d. Menopausal symptoms such as the physical heart palpitations and hot flashes; affects such as panic, anger, and distress; and negative cognitions concerning this life shift have responded by focusing on the symptom and using BLS (Luber, personal communication, March, 1993).

4. Occupational stress.
   a. At the end of the a grueling day, use BLS (about 36 sweeps) to get rid of vicarious trauma (Puk, personal communication, March, 1993).
   b. When anxious in the morning, before getting out of bed, focus on the feeling of distress in your stomach (or the location of whatever is prominent), the negative affect that has been triggered, note what you would prefer to feel and would help you be more productive, and install the positive affect, image, and cognition with BLS.
   c. Use EMDR between clients to help you clear your mind and be ready for your next client (Daniels, chapter 43).

5. Optimal performance.
   a. Enhance performance before a presentation by installing a positive cognition (PC) while using BLS (Popky, personal communication, March, 1993).

    b. If you are a martial arts specialist, visualize images of the different martial arts katas and use BLS to help install positive images of good form (Puk, personal communication, March, 1993).

6. Sleep aids.

    a. Use EMDR for sleep by moving your eyes back and forth with your eyes shut while counting backward (Popky, personal communication, 1993).

    b. Other clinicians have focused on moving their eyes by imagining a clock and then moving their eyes back and forth between the opposite numbers, about 10 sets for each, (i.e., from 12 to 6, from 1 to 7, etc.) around the clock until falling asleep.

7. Decision making.

    a. To help make decisions, focus on the issue of conflict inside and use BLS to help process yourself through the conflict (Dunton, personal communication, March, 1993).

Ways to do the actual mechanical aspect of BLS were as varied as the number of clinicians polled: focus on two different points in the room such as the door jamb to a picture on the wall; use two points on a frame of a picture; use even tiles in a bathroom shower; take any two points vertically, horizontally, or diagonally on a wall, ceiling, or floor; use BLS vertically while working; use the ticking of two clocks or metronomes that are a shade off from each other while flicking eyes side to side from these two stationary points; hand tapping, snapping fingers, and pressing bilaterally are ways to work with BLS and heralded the use of sound and touch for BLS. Whatever you do, be careful of flicking your eyes back and forth as you watch your client doing EMDR!

Even though the literature is meager in this area of clinician self-care, there are many of these formal and informal regional groups that meet and provide the support and comfort needed all over the world. It is this element of the EMDR community that has been so supportive and satisfying to this author and the other EMDR practitioners with whom this author has spoken over the years. If you are not a member of one of these groups, it is highly recommended for you to go out and join a study or regional group or start a peer support group. The EMDR associations encourage these groups and have a number of resources that you can access to support the learning environment and success of your group (see Appendix C for EMDR Association information). One of the best ways to take care of yourself is to connect with this type of group.

Neal Daniels was particularly skillful in identifying roadblocks in himself, his staff, and his patients. Understanding the effects of secondary PTSD, Dr. Daniels began to use EMDR on himself on his "peskies" and suggested to his team that they do the same. His chapter on "Self-Care for EMDR Practitioners" is a testimony to his concern about taking care of himself, as well as his staff. If he were here, he would invite you to do the same.

Mark Dworkin, a social worker, with a talent for understanding the importance of interpersonal dynamics has consistently been an advocate of the importance of clinician self-care. He began speaking on this topic with his colleague, Sheila Bender at the EMDR International Association Conference (2000). Since that time, he has presented almost every year at the EMDR International and EMDR European Annual Conferences (2001, 2002, 2003a, 2003b, 2005b, 2005c, 2006, 2008a, 2008b). His book, *EMDR and the Relational Imperative: The Therapeutic Relationship in EMDR Treatment* (2005a) is a thoughtful exploration on how the therapeutic relationship applies to the practitioner and his client in EMDR treatment. In chapter 44 in this volume, he has included the questionnaire he created to assist clinicians to uncover what is triggering them when working with their clients so that they can go about processing this material and can regain their sense of equilibrium or to understand how the effects of their clients' issues could be affecting them. This is a tool that can be used by clinicians themselves or by consultants in their consultancy practice and is updated frequently.

Even though this is an area that is in its nascent stages, the following chapters are helpful additions to any clinician's self-care. In addition, it is important to remember that as helpful as self-care methods are and can be, they are not a substitute for resolving issues or trauma that loom large in the practitioner's psyche. If self-care does not seem adequate, make sure to seek out the help that you need to resolve your problem through psychotherapy or consultation.

43

Self-Care for EMDR Practitioners

Neal Daniels

This protocol was derived from the notes of Neal Daniels, a clinical psychologist who was the director of the PTSD Clinical Team at the Veterans Affairs Medical Center in Philadelphia, Pennsylvania. Always concerned about the welfare of clients and practitioners, he put together a short, simple, and effective protocol for the practitioner on the completion of any session where there was negative affect remaining.

Self-Care Script Notes

In Dr. Daniels's words, "The procedure is short, simple, effective. Right after the session or later on in the day when it is possible, bring up the image of the patient, do 10–15 eye movements (EMs); generate a positive cognition (PC) and install it with the patient's image, and do another 10–15 EMs. Once the negative affects have been reduced, realistic formulations about the patient's future therapy are much easier to develop. Residual feelings of anger, frustration, regret, or hopelessness have been replaced by clearer thoughts about what can or cannot be done. Positive, creative mulling can proceed without the background feelings of unease, weariness, and ineffectiveness. Daily, weekly, or even career-long burnout can be viewed as the accumulated residual of negative feelings that were not dealt with effectively when they occurred."

The idea was to work on the material right after the session or later in the day when time allowed.

Clinician Self-Care Script

Say, *"Bring up the image of the patient."*

_____

_____

Do 10 to 15 eye movements.

Say, *"Notice whatever positive cognition comes to mind."*

_____

_____

Say, *"Now install the positive cognition* _____ (state the positive cognition) *with the patient's image."*

_____

_____

Do 10 to 15 eye movements.

Say, *"What do you notice?"*

_____

_____

Once the negative affects have been reduced, realistic formulations about the patient's future therapy are much easier to develop. Residual feelings of anger, frustration, regret, or hopelessness have been replaced by clearer thoughts about what can or cannot be done. Positive, creative mulling can proceed without the background feelings of unease, weariness, and ineffectiveness.

Daily, weekly, or even career-long burnout can be viewed as the accumulated residual of negative feelings that were not dealt with effectively when they occurred.

44

The Clinician Self-Awareness Questionnaire in EMDR

Mark Dworkin

The Clinician Self-Awareness Questionnaire Script Notes

Whenever an EMDR treatment session becomes problematic, consider this self-administered instrument when reflecting on this session. EMDR consultants can also use this measure in their consulting groups to assist consultees in understanding when work with clients have an impact on the therapist.

The purpose of using the Clinician Self-Awareness Questionnaire includes the following:

- To assist in raising awareness of what may be triggering the therapist.
- To assess what may be coming from the therapist and what may be coming from the client.
- To develop EMDR relational strategies.

Different problems can arise in different phases of the protocol. Sometimes, problems for the therapist may occur in Phase 1 when a client shares information that evokes negative arousal, or Phase 2 when the client has trouble understanding the elements of preparation or wants to get going processing trauma prematurely and the therapist has a negative response, or Phase 3 when there is a problem structuring the assessment piece. Sometimes, client information may not evoke negative arousal in the therapist until Phase 4 when the client is actively processing. Often times, the therapist's triggers are from old memories. These memories may be explicit; at other times, implicit (somatosensory). As therapists begin to notice these moments in themselves, they may aid themselves and their clients in continuing productive processing by using the Clinician Self-Awareness Questionnaire.

Portions of this chapter are modified from *EMDR and the Relational Imperative: The Therapeutic Relationship in EMDR Treatment*, by Mark Dworkin, for The Clinical Awareness Questionnaire (2005a), pp. 247–252, Taylor and Francis Group via the Copyright Clearance Center.

Clinician Self-Awareness Questionnaire Script

Background Information

Say, *"How many times have you seen this client?"*

_____

_____

Say, *"What is the client's gender?"* M ___ F ___

_____

_____

Say, *"What is the marital status?"* M ___ D ___ S ___ W

_____

_____

Say, *"How many children do you have?"*

_____

_____

Say, *"What are their gender and ages?"*

_____

_____

Say, *"What is the occupation of the client?"*

_____

_____

Say, *"What is the religious or spiritual affiliation of the client?"*

_____

_____

Protocol Questions

1. Say, *"Is this the first time you have felt triggered by this client?"* Y ___ N ___

_____

_____

If no, say the following:

2. Say, *"Think back, perhaps there is another time when you were triggered concerning this same issue with this or any other client. When or what might that have been?"* Y ___ N ___

_____

_____

3. Say, *"Do you get triggered by the same issue with other clients?"* Y __ N __

_____

_____

4. Say, *"Have you ever been traumatized?"* Y __ N __

_____

_____

5. Say, "Could your old trauma be triggered?" Y __ N __

_____

_____

6. Say, *"Do you believe that you are struggling with compassion fatigue, vicarious traumatization, or secondary traumatic stress?"* Y __ N __

_____

_____

7. Say, *"Describe the presenting problem* (or Present Day Referents).*"*

_____

_____

8. Say, *"What old trauma(s) are related to question 7?"*

_____

_____

_____

_____

9. Say, *"Describe what is triggering you with this client now. How are you triggered?"*

_____

_____

_____

_____

10. Say, *"Why do you believe that you are being triggered now?"*

_____

_____

_____

_____

11. Say, *"What makes this client unusually challenging for you now?"*

_____

_____

_____

_____

12. Say, *"What is it about this client's style of struggle with their problem _____ (state whatever it is that therapist is having difficulty with, i.e., externalizing, intellectualizing, substance abusing) that may trigger you now. Why now? Please describe it."*

_____

_____

_____

_____

13. Say, *"Describe this client's presentation style. For instance, it could be avoidant, aggressive, straightforward, shameful, guilt ridden, and so forth."*

_____

_____

_____

_____

14. Say, *"What triggers you about their style of struggle and their presentation style?"*

_____

_____

_____

_____

15. Say, *"When you think of the problem you are experiencing with this client what picture comes to your mind now?"*

_____

_____

_____

_____

16. Say, *"When you see this picture in your mind, what negative cognition do you get about yourself now?"*

_____

_____

17. Say, *"When you link the picture with the negative cognition what unpleasant sensations do you experience right now? Where in your body do you experience these sensations?"*

_____

_____

18. Say, *"When you picture the client in your mind's eye, who does this client remind you of? Check as many as fit."*

_____

_____

☐ Mom

☐ Dad

☐ Sibling (which one) _____

☐ Clergy

☐ Teacher

☐ Relative (which one)_____

☐ Other(s) _____

19. Say, *"What old memories emerge?"*

_____

_____

_____

_____

If there is a problem connecting with old memories, use the Float-Back Technique (based on Shapiro, 2006, p. 48).

20. Say, *"Now please bring up that picture of _____ (repeat client's disturbing image) and those negative words _____ (state the negative cognition). Now, notice what feelings are coming up for you and where you are feeling them in your body, and just let your mind float back to an earlier time in your life, don't search for anything, just let your mind float back and tell me the earliest scene that comes to mind where you had similar thoughts of _____ (repeat negative cognition), feelings of _____ (repeat emotions), and where you feel it in your body?"*

_____

_____

21. Say, *"What negative cognitions go along with these old memories? When you link the picture of the most disturbing part of the memory with this negative cognition, what feelings and sensations arise in you right now? Where do you feel these sensations in your body?"*

_____

_____

NC: _____

Picture: _____

Feelings and sensations: _____

SUD: 0   1   2   3   4   5   6   7   8   9   10
     (no disturbance)   (highest disturbance)

Body Location: _____

22. Say, *"Does your client notice your getting triggered?"* Y __ N __

_____

_____

23. Say, *"If yes, how?"*

☐ Ignore: ___

☐ Anxiety: ____

☐ Annoyance: ____

☐ Attack: ____

☐ Guilt: ____

☐ Shame: ____

☐ Curiosity: ____

☐ Suspicion: ____

24. Say, *"What does your client do with their reactions to your reactions? To do this, reconstruct a piece of process that became problematic between the two of you."*

_____

_____

25. Say, *"After examining this piece of process how would you now reconceptualize this treatment problem?"*

_____

_____

_____

_____

_____

_____

26. Say, *"What relational strategy(s) can you develop now to overcome this problem?"*

_____

_____

_____

_____

_____

_____

Practicum Script

Note: When this questionnaire is part of a workshop or study group you may have the option of processing this issue to possible closure, including debriefing. Consider using the Float-Back Technique when stuck in the present without old memories available.

27. Say, *"What is the present day referent* (or presenting problem) *in the treatment moment?"*

_____

_____

Picture

28. Say, *"What picture represents that moment in the treatment room?"*

_____

_____

If there are many choices or if the therapist-as-client becomes confused, the clinician assists by asking the following.

Negative Cognition (NC)

29. Say, *"When you bring up that moment what words best go with the picture that express your negative belief about yourself now?"*

_____

_____

Positive Cognition (PC)

30. Say, *"When you bring up that picture or incident, what would you like to believe about yourself, now?"*

_____

_____

Validity of Cognition (VoC)

31. Say, *"When you think of the incident* (or picture) *how true do those words* _____ (clinician repeats the positive cognition) *feel to you now on a scale of 1 to 7, where 1 feels completely false and 7 feels completely true?"*

1   2   3   4   5   6   7
(completely false)   (completely true)

Emotions

32. Say, *"When you bring up the picture* (or incident) *and those words* _____ (clinician states the negative cognition), *what emotion do you feel now?"*

_____

_____

Subjective Units of Disturbance (SUD)

33. Say, *"On a scale of 0 to 10, where 0 is no disturbance or neutral and 10 is the highest disturbance you can imagine, how disturbing does it feel now?"*

0	1	2	3	4	5	6	7	8	9	10
(no disturbance)										(highest disturbance)

Location of Body Sensation

34. Say, *"Where do you feel it* (the disturbance) *in your body?"*

_____

_____

If there is a problem connecting with old memories, use the Float-Back Technique (based on Shapiro, 2006, p. 48).

35. Say, *"Now please bring up that picture of* _____ (repeat client's disturbing image) *and those negative words* _____ (state the negative cognition). *Now notice what feelings are coming up for you and where you are feeling them in your body, and just let your mind float back to an earlier time in your life, don't search for anything, just let your mind float back and tell me the earliest scene that comes to mind where you had similar thoughts of* _____ (repeat negative cognition), *and feelings of* _____ (repeat emotions), *and where you feel it in your body?"*

_____

_____

_____

_____

36. Say, *"Based on your experiential work, how do you now reconceptualize this problem? How does this answer differ from question #25?"*

_____

_____

_____

_____

37. Say, *"What relational strategy might you consider now to help work this problem out?"*

_____

_____

_____

_____

Past Memory Worksheet Script (Shapiro, 2001, 2006)

Incident

Say, *"The memory that we will start with today is _____ (select the incident to be targeted)."*

_____

_____

Say, *"What happens when you think of the _____ (state the issue)?"*

_____

_____

Or say, *"When you think of _____ (state the issue), what do you get?"*

_____

_____

Picture

Say, *"What picture represents the entire _____ (state the issue)?"*

_____

_____

If there are many choices or if the client becomes confused, the clinician assists by asking the following:

Say, *"What picture represents the most traumatic part of _____ (state the issue)?"*

_____

_____

Negative Cognition (NC)

Say, *"What words best go with the picture that express your negative belief about yourself now?"*

_____

_____

Positive Cognition (PC)

Say, *"When you bring up that picture or* _____ (state the issue), *what would you like to believe about yourself now?"*

_____

_____

Validity of Cognition (VoC)

Say, *"When you think of the incident* (or picture) *how true do those words* _____ (clinician repeats the positive cognition) *feel to you now on a scale of 1 to 7, where 1 feels completely false and 7 feels completely true?"*

1   2   3   4   5   6   7
(completely false)   (completely true)

Emotions

Say, *"When you bring up the picture or* _____(state the issue) *and those words* _____ (clinician states the negative cognition), *what emotion do you feel now?"*

_____

_____

Subjective Units of Disturbance (SUD)

Say, *"On a scale of 0 to 10, where 0 is no disturbance or neutral and 10 is the highest disturbance you can imagine, how disturbing does it feel now?"*

0   1   2   3   4   5   6   7   8   9   10
(no disturbance)   (highest disturbance)

Location of Body Sensation

Say, *"Where do you feel it* (the disturbance) *in your body?"*

_____

_____

Phase 4: Desensitization

To begin, say the following:

Say, *"Now, remember, it is your own brain that is doing the healing and you are the one in control. I will ask you to mentally focus on the target and to follow my fingers* (or any other bilateral stimulation [BLS] you are using). *Just let whatever happens, happen, and we will talk at the end of the set. Just tell me what comes up, and don't discard anything as unimportant. Any new information that comes to mind is connected in some way. If you want to stop, just raise your hand."*

_____

_____

Then say, *"Bring up the picture and the words _____* (clinician repeats the negative cognition [NC]) *and notice where you feel it in your body. Now follow my fingers with your eyes* (or other BLS)."

_____

_____

Phase 5: Installation

Say, *"How does _____* (repeat the PC) *sound?"*

_____

_____

Say, *"Do the words _____* (repeat the PC) *still fit or is there another positive statement that feels better?"*

_____

_____

If the client accepts the original positive cognition (PC), the clinician should ask for a VoC rating to see if it has improved.

Say, *"As you think of the incident, how do the words feel, from 1 being completely false to 7 being completely true?"*

1	2	3	4	5	6	7
(completely false)				(completely true)		

Say, *"Think of the event and hold it together with the words _____* (repeat the PC)."

_____

_____

Do a long set of bilateral stimulation (BLS) to see if there is more processing to be done.

Phase 6: Body Scan

Say, *"Close your eyes and keep in mind the original memory and the positive cognition. Then bring your attention to the different parts of your body, starting with your head and working downward. Any place you find any tension, tightness, or unusual sensation, tell me."*

_____

_____

Phase 7: Closure

Say, *"Things may come up or they may not. If they do, great. Write it down and it can be a target for next time. You can use a log to write down triggers, images, thoughts, cognitions, emotions, and sensations; you can rate them on our 0 to 10 scale where 0 is no disturbance or neutral and 10 is the worst disturbance. Please write down the positive experiences, too."*

"If you get any new memories, dreams, or situations that disturb you, just take a good snapshot. It isn't necessary to give a lot of detail. Just put down enough to remind you so we can target it next time. The same thing goes for any positive dreams or situations. If negative feelings do come up, try not to make them significant. Remember, it's still just the old stuff. Just write it down for next time. Then use the tape or the Safe Place exercise to let as much of the disturbance go as possible. Even if nothing comes up, make sure to use the tape every day and give me a call if you need to."

_____

_____

Phase 8: Reevaluation

There are four ways to reevaluate our work with clients.

1. Reevaluate Since the Last Session

Reevaluate what has come up in the client's life since the last session.

Say, *"Okay, let's look at your log. I am interested in what has happened since the last session. What have you noticed since our last session?"*

_____

_____

Say, *"What has changed?"*

_____

_____

If the client has nothing to say or does not say much, say the following:

Say, *"Have you had any dreams or nightmares?"*

_____

_____

Say, *"What about _____ (state symptoms you and client have been working on) we have been working on, have you noticed any changes in them? Have they increased or decreased?"*

_____

_____

Say, *"Have you noticed any other changes, new responses, or insights in your images, thoughts, emotions, sensations, and behaviors?"*

_____

_____

Say, *"Have you found new resources?"*

_____

_____

Say, *"Have any situations, events, or other stimuli triggered you?"*

_____

_____

Use the material from your reevaluation to feed back into your case conceptualization and help decide what to do next concerning the larger treatment plan.

2. Reevaluate the Previous Target

Reevaluate the target worked on in the previous session. Has the individual target been resolved? Whether the previous processing session was complete or incomplete, use the following instructions to access the memory and determine the need for further processing.

Say, *"Bring up the memory or trigger of _____ (state the memory or trigger) that we worked on last session. What image comes up?"*

_____

_____

Say, *"What thoughts about it come up?"*

_____

_____

Say, *"What thoughts about yourself come up?"*

_____

_____

Say, *"What emotions did you notice?"*

_____

_____

Say, *"What sensations do you notice?"*

_____

_____

Say, *"On a scale of 0 to 10, where 0 is no disturbance or neutral and 10 is the highest disturbance you can imagine, how disturbing does it feel now?"*

0   1   2   3   4   5   6   7   8   9   10
(no disturbance)   (highest disturbance)

Evaluate the material to see if there are any indications of dysfunction. Has the primary issue been resolved? Is there ecological validity to the client's resolution of the issue? Is there associated material that has been activated that must be addressed?

If you are observing any resistance to resolving the issue, say the following:

Say, *"What would happen if you are successful?"*

_____

_____

If there are no indications of dysfunction, and SUD is 0, do a set of BLS to be sure that the processing is complete.

Say, *"Go with that."*

_____

_____

Say, *"What do you get now?"*

_____

_____

Check the positive cognition.

Say, *"When you think of the incident* (or picture) *how true do those words* _____ (clinician repeats the positive cognition) *feel to you now on a scale of 1 to 7, where 1 feels completely false and 7 feels completely true?"*

1	2	3	4	5	6	7
(completely false)				(completely true)		

If the VoC is 7, do a set of BLS to be sure that the processing is complete.

Say, *"Go with that."*

_____

_____

Say, *"What do you get now?"*

_____

_____

If there are any signs of dysfunction such as a new negative perspective(s), new facets of the event, or the SUD is higher than 0, say the following:

Say, *"Okay, now please pay attention to the image, thoughts, and sensations associated with* _____ (state the memory or trigger) *and just go with that."*

_____

_____

Continue with the Standard EMDR Protocol until processing is complete. If the VoC is less than 7, say the following:

Say, *"What is keeping it from being a 7?"*

_____

_____

Note the associated feelings and sensations and resume processing.

Say, *"Go with that."*

_____

_____

Continue with the Standard EMDR Protocol through the Body Scan until processing is complete.

If a completely new incident or target emerges, say the following:

Say, *"Are there any feeder memories contributing to this problem?"*

_____

_____

Do the Assessment Phase on the appropriate target and fully process it. It is not unusual for another aspect of the memory to emerge that needs to be processed.

If the client claims that nothing or no disturbance is coming up (or he can't remember what was worked on in the previous session) and the therapist thinks that the work is probably still incomplete and that the client is simply not able to access the memory, say the following:

Say, *"When you think of* _____ (state the incident that was worked on) *and the image* _____ (state the image) *and* _____ (state the NC), *what body sensations do you feel now?"*

_____

_____

Say, *"Go with that?"*

_____

_____

Continue processing with the Standard EMDR Protocol.

If the client wants to work on a charged trigger that came up since the last session instead of the target from the previous session, say the following:

Say, *"Yes, this is important information. Tell me about what came up for you."*

_____

_____

Then assess the magnitude of the trigger. If it is indeed a severe critical incident, then proceed accordingly using the Assessment Phase to target the new material and return to the original target when possible.

If it is not, then say the following:

Say, *"Yes this is important, however, it is important that we finish our work on* _____ (state what you are working on) *before moving to another target. It is like what happens when you have too many files open on your computer and it slows down, or finishing the course of antibiotics even if you feel okay* (or any other appropriate metaphor for your client)."

_____

_____

Fully reprocess each target through the Body Scan and reevaluation before moving on to the next in order to ensure optimal results.

3. Reevaluate at Critical Points

At various critical points in treatment (before moving on to the next symptom, theme, goal, etc.), reevaluate what has been effectively targeted and resolved and what still needs to be addressed.

Say, *"Now that we have finished this work, let's reevaluate our work so far. Remember _____ (state the work you have done). On a scale of 0 to 10, where 0 is no disturbance or neutral and 10 is the highest disturbance you can imagine, how disturbing does it feel now?"*

0	1	2	3	4	5	6	7	8	9	10
(no disturbance)								(highest disturbance)		

If the SUD is higher than 0, evaluate what else needs to be done by continuing to work with the disturbance in the framework of the Standard EMDR Protocol.

Also evaluate whether the client has been able to achieve cognitive, behavioral, and emotional goals in his life.

Say, *"Have you accomplished all of the goals that we had contracted to work on such as _____ (read the list of agreed upon goals)?"*

_____

_____

If not, evaluate what still needs to be targeted such as feeder memories.

Say, *"Please scan for an earlier memory that incorporates _____ (state the negative cognition). What do you get?"*

_____

_____

Use the Standard EMDR Protocol to process any feeder memories.
Check if previously identified clusters of memories remain charged.

Say, *"Are there any memories left concerning _____ (state the cluster of memories previously worked on)?"*

_____

_____

If so, work on the memory(ies), using the Standard EMDR Protocol. Make sure to incorporate the positive templates for all previously disturbing situations and projected future goals. See the Future Template Worksheet Script.

4. Reevaluate Before Termination

Before termination, reevaluate targets worked on over the course of therapy and goals addressed during treatment.

Say, *"Before we end our treatment, let's reevaluate our work to make sure that all of the targets are resolved and goals are ad-*

dressed. Are there any past targets that remain unresolved for you?"

_____

_____

Or say, *"These are the past targets with which we worked, do any of them remain unresolved? What about the memories that we listed during our history taking and over the course of treatment."*

_____

_____

Check with the SUDs for any disturbance.

Say, *"On a scale of 0 to 10, where 0 is no disturbance or neutral and 10 is the highest disturbance you can imagine, how disturbing does it feel now?"*

0   1   2   3   4   5   6   7   8   9   10
(no disturbance)   (highest disturbance)

Check the major negative cognitions to see if there are any unresolved memories still active.

Say, *"These are the main negative cognitions with which we worked. Hold _____ (state one of the cognitions worked with) and scan for any unresolved memories. Does anything surface for you?"*

_____

_____

If there is more unresolved material, check with BLS to see if the charge decreases. If not, use the Standard EMDR Protocol.

Say, *"Now scan chronologically from birth until today to see if there are any other unresolved memories. What do you notice?"*

_____

_____

If there is more unresolved material, check with BLS to see if the charge decreases. If not, use the Standard EMDR Protocol.

Progressions can occur during other events or during the processing of a primary target, use your clinical judgment whether it is important to return and re-evaluate these memories.

Clusters are related memories that were grouped together during treatment planning and can be scanned to identify any memories that were not involved through generalization of treatment effects.

Say, *"Let's check the _____ (state the cluster), we worked on earlier. When you think about it are there any other memories that were not involved that you are aware of now?"*

_____

_____

If there is more unresolved material, check with BLS to see if the charge decreases. If not, use the Standard EMDR Protocol.

Participants are significant individuals in the client's life who should be targeted if memories or issues regarding them remain disturbing.

> Say, *"Let's check if there are any remaining concerns or memories concerning _____ (state whoever the client might be concerned about). Is there anything that still is bothering you about _____ (state the person's name)?"*

_____

_____

If there is more unresolved material, check with BLS to see if the charge decreases. If not, use the Standard EMDR Protocol.

> Say, *"Are there any present or recent triggers that remain potent?"*

_____

_____

> Say, *"Are there any current conditions, situations, or people that make you want to avoid them, act in ways that are not helpful, or cause you emotional distress?"*

_____

_____

If there is more unresolved material, check with BLS to see if the charge decreases. If not, use the Standard EMDR Protocol.

> Say, *"Are there any future goals that have not been addressed and realized?"*

_____

_____

Make sure to use the Future Template for each trigger, new goal(s), new skill(s), issues of memory, or incorporating the client's new sense of himself. See Future Template Worksheet Script in Appendix A.

Present Trigger Worksheet Script

Target and reprocess present triggers identified during history taking, reprocessing, and reevaluation. Steps for working with present triggers are the following.

Step 1. Identify the presenting trigger that is still causing disturbance.

Step 2. Target and activate the presenting trigger using the full assessment procedures (image, negative cognition, positive cognition, VoC, emotions, SUD, sensations).

Step 3. Follow Phases 3 through 8 with each trigger until it is fully reprocessed (SUD = 0, VoC = 7, clear Body Scan) before moving to the next trigger. Note: In some situations a blocking belief may be associated with the present trigger requiring a new targeting sequence plan.

Step 4. Once all present triggers have been reprocessed, proceed to installing Future Templates for each present trigger (e.g., imagining encountering the same situation in the future). (See Future Template Protocols.)

Present Stimuli That Trigger the Disturbing Memory or Reaction

List the situations that elicit the symptom(s). Examples of situations, events, or stimuli that trigger clients could be the following: another trauma, the sound of a car backfiring, or being touched in a certain way.

Say, *"What are the situations, events, or stimuli that trigger your trauma _____ (state the trauma). Let's process these situations, events, or stimuli triggers one by one."*

_____

_____

_____

_____

_____

_____

Situations, Events, or Stimuli Trigger List

Target or Memory

Say, *"What situation, event, or stimulus that triggers you would you like to use as a target today?"*

_____

_____

Picture

Say, *"What picture represents the _____ (state the situation, event, or stimulus) that triggers you?"*

_____

_____

If there are many choices or if the client becomes confused, the clinician assists by asking the following:

Say, *"What picture represents the most traumatic part of the* _____ (state the situation, event, or stimulus) *that triggers you?"*

_____

_____

When a picture is unavailable, the clinician merely invites the client to do the following:

Say, *"Think of the* _____ (state the situation, event, or stimulus) *that triggers you."*

_____

_____

Negative Cognition (NC)

Say, *"What words best go with the picture that express your negative belief about yourself now?"*

_____

_____

Positive Cognition (PC)

Say, *"When you bring up that picture or the* _____ (state the situation, event, or stimulus) *that triggers you, what would you like to believe about yourself now?"*

_____

_____

Validity of Cognition (VoC)

Say, *"When you think of the* _____ (state the situation, event, stimulus, or picture that triggers you), *how true do those words* _____ (clinician repeats the positive cognition) *feel to you now on a scale of 1 to 7, where 1 feels completely false and 7 feels completely true?"*

1	2	3	4	5	6	7
(completely false)				(completely true)		

Sometimes it is necessary to explain further.

Say, *"Remember, sometimes we know something with our head, but it feels differently in our gut. In this case, what is the gut-level feeling of the truth of* _____ (clinician states the positive cognition), *from 1 being completely false to 7 being completely true?"*

1	2	3	4	5	6	7
(completely false)				(completely true)		

Emotions

Say, *"When you bring up the picture* (or state the situation, event, or stimulus) *that triggers you and those words* _____ (clinician states the negative cognition), *what emotion do you feel now?"*

_____

_____

Subjective Units of Disturbance (SUD)

Say, *"On a scale of 0 to 10, where 0 is no disturbance or neutral and 10 is the highest disturbance you can imagine, how disturbing does it feel now?"*

0	1	2	3	4	5	6	7	8	9	10
(no disturbance)							(highest disturbance)			

Location of Body Sensation

Say, *"Where do you feel it* (the disturbance) *in your body?"*

_____

_____

Continue to process the triggers according the Standard EMDR Protocol.

Future Template Worksheet (Shapiro, 2006)

The future template is the third prong in the Standard EMDR Protocol. Work with the Future Template occurs after the earlier memories and present triggers are adequately resolved and the client is ready to make new choices in the future concerning their issue(s). The purpose of it is to address any residual avoidance, to work with further issues of adaptation, to help with incorporating any new information, and to allow for the actualization of client goals. It is another place, in this comprehensive protocol, to catch any fears, negative beliefs, inappropriate responses, and so forth, to reprocess them and to make sure that the new feelings and behavior can generalize into clients' day-to-day lives.

There are two basic future templates:

1. Anticipatory anxiety

    Anticipatory anxiety needs to be addressed with a full assessment (Phase 3) of the future situation.

2. Skills building and imaginal rehearsal

    These do not need a full assessment of target and can begin directly with running a movie.

Future Template Script (Shapiro, 2001, pp. 210–214; 2006, pp. 51–53)

Check the Significant People and Situations of the Presenting Issues for Any Type of Distress

It is helpful to check to see if all the material concerning the issue upon which the client has worked is resolved or if there is more material that has escaped detection so far. The Future Template is another place to find if there is more material that needs reprocessing.

Significant People

When the client's work has focused on a significant person, ask the following:

> Say, *"Imagine yourself encountering that person in the future* _____ (suggest a place that the client might see this person). *What do you notice?"*

_____

_____

Watch the client's reaction to see if more work is necessary. If a client describes a negative feeling in connection with this person, check to see if it is reality based.

> Say, *"Is* _____ (state the person's name) *likely to act* _____ (state the client's concern)*?"*

_____

_____

If the negative feeling is not matching the current reality, say the following:

> Say, *"What do you think makes you have negative feelings toward* _____ (state the person in question)*?"*

_____

_____

If the client is unsure, use the Float-Back Technique or Affect Scan to see what other earlier material may still be active.

If the negative feelings are appropriate, it is important to reevaluate the clusters of events concerning this person and access and reprocess any remaining maladaptive memories. (See Past Memory Worksheet.)

Significant Situations

It is important to have the client imagine being in significant situations in the future; this is another way of accessing material that may not have been processed.

> Say, *"Imagine a videotape or film of how* _____ (state current situation client is working on) *and how it would evolve* _____ (state appropriate time frame) *in the future. When you have done that let me know what you have noticed."*

_____

_____

If there is no disturbance, reinforce the positive experience.

Say, *"Go with that."*

Do BLS.

Reinforce the PC with the future situation using BLS as it continues the positive associations. For further work in the future, see below.

If there is a disturbance, assess what the client needs: more education, modeling of appropriate behavior, or more past memories for reprocessing.

Say, *"On a scale of 0 to 10, where 0 is no disturbance or neutral and 10 is the highest disturbance you can imagine, how disturbing does it feel now?"*

0   1   2   3   4   5   6   7   8   9   10
(no disturbance)   (highest disturbance)

Anticipatory Anxiety

When the SUD is above a 4, or when the Desensitization Phase is not brief, the clinician should look for a present trigger and its associated symptom and develop another Targeting Sequence Plan using the 3-Pronged Protocol. (See worksheets on Past Memories and Present Triggers.)

When there is anticipatory anxiety at a SUD level of no more than 3 to 4 maximum, it is possible to proceed with reprocessing using the Future Template. The Desensitization Phase should be quite brief.

Say, *"What happens when you think of _____ (state the client's anticipatory anxiety or issue)?"*

_____

_____

Or say, *"When you think of _____ (state the client's anticipatory anxiety or issue), what do you get?"*

_____

_____

Picture

Say, *"What picture represents the entire _____ (state the client's anticipatory anxiety or issue)?"*

_____

_____

If there are many choices or if the client becomes confused, the clinician assists by asking the following:

Say, *"What picture represents the most traumatic part of _____ (state the client's anticipatory anxiety or issue)?"*

_____

_____

Negative Cognition (NC)

Say, *"What words best go with the picture that express your negative belief about yourself now?"*

_____

_____

Positive Cognition (PC)

Say, *"When you bring up that picture or _____ (state the client's anticipatory anxiety or issue), what would you like to believe about yourself now?"*

_____

_____

Validity of Cognition (VoC)

Say, *"When you think of _____ (state the client's anticipatory anxiety or issue) or picture, how true do those words _____ (clinician repeats the positive cognition) feel to you now on a scale of 1 to 7, where 1 feels completely false and 7 feels completely true?"*

1   2   3   4   5   6   7
(completely false)   (completely true)

Emotions

Say, *"When you bring up the picture or _____ (state the client's anticipatory anxiety or issue) and those words _____ (clinician states the negative cognition), what emotion do you feel now?"*

_____

_____

Subjective Units of Disturbance (SUD)

Say, *"On a scale of 0 to 10, where 0 is no disturbance or neutral and 10 is the highest disturbance you can imagine, how disturbing does it feel now?"*

0   1   2   3   4   5   6   7   8   9   10
(no disturbance)   (highest disturbance)

Location of Body Sensation

Say, *"Where do you feel it (the disturbance) in your body?"*

_____

_____

Phase 4: Desensitization

To begin, say the following:

Say, *"Now remember, it is your own brain that is doing the healing and you are the one in control. I will ask you to mentally focus on the target and to follow my fingers* (or any other BLS you are using). *Just let whatever happens, happen, and we will talk at the end of the set. Just tell me what comes up, and don't discard anything as unimportant. Any new information that comes to mind is connected in some way. If you want to stop, just raise your hand."*

_____

_____

Then say, *"Bring up the picture and the words* _____ (clinician repeats the NC) *and notice where you feel it in your body. Now, follow my fingers with your eyes* (or other BLS)."

_____

_____

Continue with the Desensitization Phase until the SUD = 0 and the VoC = 7.

Phase 5: Installation

Say, *"How does* _____ (repeat the PC) *sound?"*

_____

_____

Say, *"Do the words* _____ (repeat the PC) *still fit or is there another positive statement that feels better?"*

_____

_____

If the client accepts the original positive cognition, the clinician should ask for a VoC rating to see if it has improved.

Say, *"As you think of the incident, how do the words feel, from 1 being completely false to 7 being completely true)?"*

1	2	3	4	5	6	7
(completely false)				(completely true)		

Say, *"Think of the event and hold it together with the words* _____ (repeat the PC)."

_____

_____

Do a long set of BLS to see if there is more processing to be done.

Phase 6: Body Scan

Say, *"Close your eyes and keep in mind the original memory and the positive cognition. Then bring your attention to the different parts of your body, starting with your head and working downward. Any place you find any tension, tightness, or unusual sensation, tell me."*

_____

_____

Make sure that this anticipatory anxiety is fully processed before returning to the Future Template.

The Future Template for appropriate future interaction is an expansion of the Installation Phase; instead of linking the positive cognition with the past memory or trigger, the PC is linked to the future issues. Once the client's work has been checked and the other known issues in the past and present have been resolved, each client has the choice to do a more formal Future Template installation. The first option is to work with the situation or issue as an image.

Image as Future Template: Imagining Positive Outcomes

Imagining positive outcomes seems to assist the learning process. In this way, clients learn to enhance optimal behaviors, to connect them with a positive cognition, and to support generalization. The assimilation of this new behavior and thought is supported by the use of bilateral stimulation (BLS) into a positive way to act in the future.

Say, *"I would like you to imagine yourself coping effectively with or in* _____ (state the goal) *in the future. With the positive belief* _____ (state the positive belief) *and your new sense of* _____ (state the quality: i.e., strength, clarity, confidence, calm), *imagine stepping into this scene.*

Notice what you see and how you are handling the situation.

Notice what you are thinking, feeling, and experiencing in your body."

_____

_____

Again, here is the opportunity to catch any disturbance that may have been missed.

Say, *"Are there any blocks, anxieties, or fears that arise as you think about this future scene?"*

_____

_____

If yes, say the following:

Say, *"Then focus on these blocks and follow my fingers* (or any other BLS).*"*

_____

_____

Say, *"What do you get now?"*

_____

_____

If the blocks do not resolve quickly, evaluate if the client needs any new information, resources, or skills to be able to comfortably visualize the future coping scene. Introduce needed information or skills.

Say, *"What would you need to feel confident in handling the situation?"*

_____

_____

Or say, *"What is missing from your handling of this situation?"*

_____

_____

If the block still does not resolve and the client is unable to visualize the future scene with confidence and clarity, use direct questions, the Affect Scan, or the Float-Back Technique to identify old targets related to blocks, anxieties, or fears. Remember, the point of the 3-Prong Protocol is not only to reinforce positive feelings and behavior in the future but again to catch any unresolved material that may be getting in the way of an adaptive resolution of the issue(s). Use the Standard EMDR Protocol to address these targets before proceeding with the template (see Worksheets in Appendix A).

If there are no apparent blocks and the client is able to visualize the future scene with confidence and clarity, say the following:

Say, *"Please focus on the image, the positive belief, and the sensations associated with this future scene and follow my fingers (or any other BLS)."*

_____

_____

Process and reinforce the positive associations with BLS. Do several sets until the future template is sufficiently strengthened.

Say, *"Go with that."*

_____

_____

Then say, *"Close your eyes and keep in mind the image of the future and the positive cognition. Then bring your attention to the different parts of your body, starting with your head and working downward. Any place you find any tension, tightness, or unusual sensation, tell me."*

_____

_____

If any sensation is reported, do BLS.

Say, *"Go with that."*

_____

_____

If it is a positive or comfortable sensation, do BLS to strengthen the positive feelings.

Say, *"Go with that."*

_____

_____

If a sensation of discomfort is reported, reprocess until the discomfort subsides.

Say, *"Go with that."*

_____

_____

When the discomfort subsides, check the VoC.

Say, *"When you think of the incident* (or picture) *how true do those words* _____ (clinician repeats the positive cognition) *feel to you now on a scale of 1 to 7, where 1 feels completely false and 7 feels completely true?"*

1   2   3   4   5   6   7
(completely false)   (completely true)

Continue to use BLS until reaching the VoC = 7 or there is an ecological resolution. When the image as future template is clear and the PC true, move on to the Movie as Future Template.

Movie as Future Template or Imaginal Rehearsing

During this next level of Future Template, clients are asked to move from imagining this one scene or snapshot to imagining a movie about coping in the future, with a beginning, middle, and end. Encourage clients to imagine themselves coping effectively in the face of specific challenges, triggers, or snafus. Therapists can make some suggestions in order to help inoculate them with future problems. It is helpful to use this type of Future Template after clients have received needed education concerning social skills and customs, assertiveness, and any other newly learned skills.

> Say, *"This time, I'd like you to close your eyes and play a movie, imagining yourself coping effectively with or in* _____ (state where client will be) *in the future. With the new positive belief* _____ (state positive belief) *and your new sense of* _____ (strength, clarity, confidence, calm), *imagine stepping into the future. Imagine yourself coping with any challenges that come your way. Make sure that this movie has a beginning, middle, and end. Notice what you are seeing, thinking, feeling, and experiencing in your body. Let me know if you hit any blocks. If you do, just open your eyes and let me know. If you don't hit any blocks, let me know when you have viewed the whole movie."*

_____

_____

If the client hits blocks, address as above with BLS until the disturbance dissipates.

> Say, *"Go with that."*

_____

_____

If the material does not shift, use interweaves, new skills, information, resources, direct questions, and any other way to help clients access information that will allow them to move on. If these options are not successful, usually it means that there is earlier material still unprocessed; the Float-Back and Affect Scan are helpful in these cases to access the material that keeps the client stuck.

If clients are able to play the movie from start to finish with a sense of confidence and satisfaction, ask them to play the movie one more time from beginning to end and introduce BLS.

> Say, *"Okay, play the movie one more time from beginning to end. Go with that."*

_____

_____

Use BLS.

In a sense, you are installing this movie as a Future Template.

After clients have fully processed their issue(s), they might want to work on other positive templates for the future in other areas of their lives using the above Future Templates.

Appendix B: Expanding the 11-Step Procedure: Unconsolidated Sensory Triggers and Desensitization—Running the Tape

Gene Schwartz

Running the Tape to Identify and Process Sensory Triggers Notes

Clinical Example 1

Based on clinical observation over many years, this author has found that processing an event using the Standard EMDR Protocol may leave affect laden sensory material associated with the event unprocessed. The initial observation came from the treatment of a Vietnam veteran who reported being triggered by a noise following the completed processing of a combat trauma. Initial work developed into two different uses of running a tape to look for arousal.

The veteran reported being triggered back to the original event after what was thought to have been the successful resolution of the event. He reported the noise from a door banging took him back to the event with the same high level of affect. He said, "You know a shell doesn't go boom it goes crack." The veteran processed the sound by replaying it in his mind while the therapist used bilateral stimulation (BLS) until he reported no further disturbance.

On a hunch, the man was asked to run a tape of the event starting at the beginning and looking for any other sounds that caused disturbance. If he found one, he was to stop the tape and tell this author. He eventually identified several other sounds such as men yelling, guns going off, helicopters coming in, and so forth. Each time he stopped at a sound, he was asked to hear it and BLS was used until the disturbance went to 0 on a subjective units of disturbance (SUD) scale.

He was then asked to back the tape up past where the work had been done and start running the tape again. This checked the trigger sound again as the tape went forward. He was asked to do this until he could run the whole tape listening for sound without noticing a disturbance.

Again, on a hunch, he was asked to start the tape running looking for pictures that caused any disturbance. The work was continued as above with pictures until the tape of pictures was clear. Smell, taste, and physical sensations were also done in the same way. Several sessions were needed until he could watch a tape of the event in living color with pictures, sound, taste, smells, and physical sensations without disturbance. At that point, he was asked to watch the tape thinking of the positive cognition (PC).

Since then as the last step of Phase 4 the Desensitization Phase, this author asks clients to run a tape of the event and look for disturbance. Clinical judgment determines how fully clients are asked to review the tape. When working on an event of negative learning without extreme affect the client is just asked to watch the tape. For events of heavily affect-laden clients, they are asked to review the tape for each sensory mode individually.

Clinical Example 2

Another clinical case led to a second use of running the tape. An adult client completed the processing of a sexual assault he experienced as a 10-year-old. Weeks later he reported experiencing a lot of arousal while attending a social event. Focusing on the arousal and negative cognition (NC), went back to the assault again but at a different age. He had processed the original event and run the tape looking at each sensory mode separately. The event should have been completed. The current affect was being driven by a triggered memory of friends calling each other names when he was about 14 years old. A friend called him queer. This type of teasing is not unfamiliar to young men, but in this case the teasing had particular impact. He had participated, although unwillingly, in the behavior his brain associated with the teasing. This second event was processed using the Standard EMDR Protocol. On a hunch he was asked to run a tape. He was to take the original assault, run a tape quickly through his life, and see if anything came up that connected. He stopped the tape at the point in his life when he was a married father of three children. His wife wanted to send the kids to a camp. The Standard EMDR Protocol was used here to process this until the SUDs were 0 and then he was asked to back the tape up and start again finding several other triggers before finishing the work.

This use of running the tape is particularly useful in many situations where an event has lasting impact on a person's life.

Clinical Example 3

A man was in an accident while driving a truck pulling a trailer. His wife, daughter, and his daughter's friend were in the truck with him. A car crossed the median and hit him head-on. Both vehicles burst into flame. He and the occupants of his truck were pulled out by witnesses and they were taken to shock trauma.

The event was processed starting at the worst part, the impact with a negative cognition of "We are going to burn to death." The event as represented by the worst part resolved to SUDs of 0. The client was then asked to run the tape using each sensory mode separately. Three sessions were needed to complete the work. He was triggered for example by: sounds of the crash, yelling, sirens, smells of burning, spilled fuel, bandages, taste of blood, dirt, pictures of flames, his family on the ground, his daughter not moving, physical sensations of being thrown against the steering wheel, pain, heat, and so forth.

After the accident processing was finished, he was asked to run a tape up to the time he was seen for treatment. He was triggered by memories of multiple trips back to shock trauma for infections, sounds of a doctor telling him he could lose a foot, fighting with an insurance company about the value of his loss, and worry if the other driver burned to death. As much work was completed as possible at the time. He was told the therapist would finish the work when the legal fight with the insurance company was completed. He returned several months later after the settlement and the affect surrounding the legal case was resolved. At that time he brought in a death certificate for the other driver showing death was due to a heart attack most likely the cause of his crossing the medium. A year later he returned for another issue. He reported no affect associated with memories of the accident.

Script for Running the Tape to Identify and Process Unconsolidated Sensory Triggers

This is a step that is added at the end of Phase 4 Desensitization to assure the processing of any affect-laden sensory material associated with the event that was left unprocessed.

The therapist needs to use clinical judgment here for events of less emotional impact as a last step in Phase 4. The therapist asks the client to run a tape of the event being sure to check all sensory modes (smell, taste, etc.). If a disturbance comes up, use BLS until the disturbance goes down and the SUD is 0. Then back the tape up past that stop and run the tape again until the tape is clear and then go on to the Installation Phase.

For events that have higher arousal or are more traumatic, the therapist can start with whatever modality seems most salient for the client, for example, it is possible to start with taste if that is the modality that seems most relevant, and so forth.

Sensory Triggers: Images, Sounds, Taste, Touch, Smells, Balance

Say, *"I would like to ask you to review the tape of the original event and see if there are any _____ (state the modality that you are using) that cause any disturbance. Please start at the beginning of the event and run a tape forward checking only for _____ (state the modality that you are using) and stopping the tape if the _____ (state the modality that you are using) causes you any distress."* (Pause)

_____

_____

If the patient stops the tape, say the following:

Say, *"What did you notice?"*

_____

_____

Say, *"Okay, now focus on the _____ (focus on whatever stopped the tape) while I _____ (state the BLS that you use) until the disturbance becomes neutral. Let me know when that happens."*

_____

_____

Say, *"Now, back the tape up and run it forward looking for any distress that you might still have. Go ahead and do that now."*

_____

_____

Wait for the client to let you know that they have found another disturbance, or if the tape is clean go to the next sensory modality.

Say, *"What do you notice? Is the _____ (state the modality that you are using) that you talked about still a cause for distress?"*

_____

_____

If a disturbance comes up, say the following:

Say, *"Let's go through it and sit with it until the distress level is down to 0 on our scale. Let me know when the distress is down."* (Pause)

_____

_____

Wait until the client is finished.

Say, *"What is your experience now?"*

_____

_____

When all of the affect-laden sensory data has been reprocessed with running the tape, the client is asked to run the tape of the event in living color with all of the sensory data that had been reprocessed until there is no disturbance.

Say, *"Okay, now I would like you to run the tape of this event in living color with all of the sensory data that we have reprocessed _____ (state the modalities used) until there is no disturbance. Go ahead and do this now and let me know when you are finished."*

_____

_____

When the tape is clean and there is no distress, running the tape is completed. If there is more material that comes up, continue to work with the material until there is no distress. If there is any new material that arises such as a blocking belief, it can be processed using the Standard EMDR Protocol.

The next step is to check the original positive cognition to make sure that it is still accurate or if it needs to be replaced. Then, install the positive cognition while running the tape again.

Say, *"Does your original positive cognition _____ (state the original positive cognition from the EMDR Standard Protocol) still fit or is there one that fits better?"*

_____

_____

Run the tape again with the new or original positive cognition.

Say, *"Let's run the tape again while you think about the positive cognition _____ (state the positive cognition). Let me know when you have completed it."* (Pause)

_____

_____

Wait until the client has completed the tape.

Say, *"What did you notice?"*

_____

_____

After installation of the positive cognition is completed, move on to Phase 6: Body Scan. This phase moves much quicker after using running the tape.

New Triggers

Catching sensory triggers so that the Standard EMDR Protocol is complete can be helpful in other scenarios as well. When there is an incident that is processed, it is often advantageous to run the tape taking the original target and negative cognition and then running the tape quickly through the time line of the client's life to see if anything comes up that is connected. If there is new material, the Standard EMDR Protocol can be used on the target. After this, back the tape up and find any other triggers that are left.

Say, *"Okay, now take the target about* _____ (state the target worked on) *and* _____ (state the negative cognition) *and run the tape quickly through your life to see if there is anything that comes up that is connected. Go ahead and do that."*

_____

_____

Allow ample time for the client to do this.

If the client comes up with anything, process it using the Standard EMDR Protocol until the SUD is 0. Then say the following:

Say, *"Now back the tape up to the beginning of the work about* _____ (state original work) *and look for any other triggers that might be left. Let me know when you have completed this."*

_____

_____

If there are more triggers, again use the EMDR Standard EMDR Protocol to reprocess the material. If not, continue with the installation of the PC, Body Scan, and closure phases of the target.

Appendix C: EMDR Worldwide Associations and Other Resources

In the Beginning

The EMDR Institute

Web site: (http://www.emdr.com/)
Contact Person: Robbie Dunton (rdunton@emdr.com)

EMDR Worldwide Associations Contact Information

Africa

Kenya

Contact Person: Alice Blanshard (alice@swiftkenya.com)
Gisela Roth (dr.roth.ac@aimint.net)

South Africa

Association: EMDR South Africa/Africa
Contact Person: Reyhana Seedat-Ravat (rravat@iafrica.com)

Asia

Bangladesh

Contact Person: Shamim Karim (shamim.karim@gmail.com)

Cambodia

Contact Person: Jane Lopacka (jane@ppcounselling.org)

China—Mainland

Contact Persons: WeiLi (Wu-lilywu22@yahoo.com)
Yuchuan Yang (yuchuany@yahoo.com.cn)
Li Fang (hxfangli@hotmail.com)

Hong Kong

Association: The EMDR Association of Hong Kong (http://hkemdr.org)
Contact Person: Atara Sivan (email@hkemdr.org)

India

Contact Person: Sushma Mehrotra (mehrotrasushma@gmail.com)

Indonesia

Association: EMDR Indonesia (http://www.emdrindonesia.org)

Japan

Association: Japan EMDR Association (http://www.emdr.jp/)

Korea

Association: Korean EMDR Association [KEMDRA] (http://emdrkorea.com/fine/)

Pakistan

Association: EMDR Pakistan (www.emdrpakistan.com)

Singapore

Association: EMDR Singapore Coordinating Committee
Contact Person: Matthew Woo (matthewwoo@imh.com.sq)

Sri Lanka

Association: EMDR Sri Lanka
Contact Person: George Fernando (geo-fern@eureka.lk)

Thailand

Association: EMDR Thailand Coordinating Committee
Contact Person: Dr. Nanthaphan Chinlumprasert (nanthaphanchn@au.edu)

Vietnam

Contact Person: Dr. Carl Sternberg (pv.carl@gmail.com)
International SOS Clinic Hanoi

Australia

Association: EMDR Association of Australia (http://emdraa.org/)

Europe

EMDR Europe Association: An association of European National EMDR Associations (www.emdr-europe.org)

Austria

Association: EMDR-Netzwerk Osterreich (http://www.emdr-institut.at/)

Belgium

Association: EMDR Belgium (Web site under construction)
Contact Information: emdr-belgium@telenet.be

Denmark

Association: EMDR Denmark (http://www.emdr.dk/)

Finland

Association: Suomen EMDR-vhdistys (http://www.emdr.fi)

France

Association: Association EMDR France (http://www.emdr-france.org/)

Germany

EMDRIA Deutschland (http://www.emdria.de)

Greece

Association: EMDR Greece (http://www.emdr.gr)

Israel

Association: The EMDR Israel Association (http://www.emdr.org.il)

Italy

Association: EMDR Italie (http://www.emdritalia.it)

Netherlands

Association: Vereniging EMDR Nederland (http://www.emdr.nl)

Norway

Association: EMDR Norge (http://www.emdrnorge.com/)

Serbia

Association: EMDR Serbia (http://www.emdr-se-europe.org)

Spain

Association: Asociacion E.M.D.R. Espana (http://emdr-es.org)

Sweden

Association: EMDR Sverige (http://www.emdr.se/)

Switzerland

Association: EMDR Schweiz-Suisse-Svizzera-Switzerland (http://www.emdr-ch.org/)

Turkey

Association: EMDR Turkiye (http://www.emdr-tr.org)

United Kingdom and Ireland

Association: EMDR Association United Kingdom and Ireland (http://www.emdr association.org.uk)

Ibero-America

(Includes Mexico South and Central Americas, Spanish Caribbean, and the Iberian Peninsula)
Association: EMDR-Iberoamerica (http://emdriberoamerica.org/)
Another EMDR Latin America association is as follows: Association: EMDR Latino-america (http://www.emdr.org.ar)

Argentina

Association: EMDR Iberoamerica Argentina (http://www.emdribargentina.org)

Brazil

Association: EMDR Brasil (http://www.emdrbrasil.com.br)

Columbia

Association: EMDR Colombia (http://emdrcolombia.org/)

Ecuador

Association: EMDR Ecuador (http://emdrecuador.org/)

Guatemala

Association: EMDR Ibero-America Guatemala
Contact: Ligia Barascout (ligiabps@yahoo.com)

Mexico

Association: EMDR Mexico (http://www.emdrmexico.org)

Portugal

Association: EMDR Portugal (http://www.emdrportugal.com)

Uruguay

Association: EMDR Uruguay (http://emdruruguay.org.uy)

North America

Canada

Association: EMDR Canada (http://www.emdrcanada.org)

United States

Association: EMDR International Association (http://emdria.org)

Related EMDR Humanitarian Associations

Europe

France

Association: HAP-France (http://www.hap-france.org)

Germany

Association: Trauma Aid (http://www.trauma-aid.org)

HAP-Europe

Association: HAP-Europe (Web site under construction)

Ibero-America

Argentina

Association: EMDR-Programa de Programa de Ayuda Humanitaria–Argentina
Email: emdrasistenciahumanitaria@fibertel.com.ar
(Web site under construction at same address)

Iberoamerica

EMDR Iberoamerica (http://emdriberoamerica.org/progamaayudahumanitaria.html/)

Mexico

Asociacion Mexicana para Ayuda Mental en Crisis A.C. (http://www.amamecrisis.com.mx)

North America

United States

EMDR Humanitarian Assistance Program [EMDR-HAP] (http://www.emdrhap.org)

The Francine Shapiro Library

Francine Shapiro Library's EMDR Bibliography (http://library.nku.edu/emdr/emdr_data.php)

EMDR Journals and E-Journals

The Journal of EMDR Practice and Research—The official publication of the EMDR International Association (http://www.springerpub.com/emdr)
The EMDR Practitioner—The official journal of the European EMDR Association (http://www.emdr-practitioner.net/)
EMDR-IS Electronic Journal (http://www.emdr.org.il)

Related EMDR Information

EMDR Network (http://www.emdrnetwork.org)

Related Traumatology Information

The Australian Trauma Web (http://welcome.to/ptsd)
David Baldwin's Trauma Pages (http://www.trauma-pages.com)

Children and War (http://www.childrenandwar.org)

European Federation of Psychologists Associations Task Force on Disaster Psychology [EFPA] (http://www.disaster.efpa.eu)

European Society for Traumatic Stress Studies (http://www.estss.org)

International Society for the Study of Trauma and Dissociation (http://www.isst-d.org)

The International Critical Incident Stress Foundation (http://www.icisf.org)

United States National Center for Posttraumatic Stress Disorder (http://www.ncptsd.va.gov/ncmain/index.jsp)

References

Abruzzese, M. (1994). *Use of Tourette's disorder with EMDR*. Paper presented at the 3rd EMDR Annual Conference, San Jose, CA.

Abruzzese, M. (1995). *Disruptive behaviors*. All day workshop presented at the International EMDR Annual Conference sponsored by the EMDR Institute, Inc. and the EMDR International Association, Santa Monica, CA.

Adler-Tapia, R., & Settle, C. (2008a). *EMDR and the art of psychotherapy with children*. New York: Springer Publishing.

Adler-Tapia, R., & Settle, C. (2008b). *EMDR and the art of psychotherapy with children treatment manual*. New York: Springer Publishing.

American Psychiatric Association (2000). *Diagnostic and statistical manual of mental disorders, (DSM-IV-TR)*. Washington, DC: Jaypee.

Antony, M. M., Orsillo, S. M., & Roemer, L. (Eds.). (2001). *Practioner's guide to empirically-based measures of anxiety*. New York: Kluwer Academic/Plenum.

Artigas, L., Jarero, I., Alcalá, N., & López, T. (2009). The EMDR integrative group treatment protocol (IGTP). In M. Luber (Ed.), *Eye movement desensitization and reprocessing (EMDR): Basics and Special Situations*. New York: Springer Publishing.

Artigas, L., Jarero, I., Mauer, M., López Cano, T., & Alcalá, N. (2000, September). *EMDR and traumatic stress after natural disasters: Integrative treatment protocol and the butterfly hug*. Poster presented at the EMDRIA Conference, Toronto, Ontario, Canada.

Austin, J. (1998). *Zen and the brain*. Cambridge, MA: MIT Press.

Beck, A. T., Steer, R. A. & Brown, G. K. (1996). *Beck depression inventory®-II (BDI®-II)*. San Antonio, TX: Pearson Education, Inc.

Beere, D. B. (1995). Loss of "background": A perceptual theory of dissociation. *Dissociation, 8*, 166–174.

Beere, D. B. (1996a). Switching: Part I—An investigation using experimental phenomenology. *Dissociation, 9*, 49–60.

Beere, D. B. (1996b). Switching: Part II—Theoretical implications of an investigation using experimental phenomenology. *Dissociation, 9*, 61–68.

Beere, D. B. (2003). *The dissociative disorders: Update, current research, and applications of EMDR*. Preconference workshop presented at the EMDR International Conference, Denver, CO.

Beere, D. B. (2009a). The self-system as 'mechanism' for the dissociative disorders: An extension of the perceptual theory of dissociation. In P. Dell and J. O'Neil (Eds.), *Dissociation and the dissociative disorders: DSM-V and beyond*. New York: Routledge.

Beere, D. B. (2009b). Dissociative perceptual reactions: The perceptual theory of dissociation. In P. Dell & J. O'neil (Eds.), *Dissociation and the dissociative disorders: DSM-V and beyond*. New York: Routledge.

Beere, D. B. (n.p.) *The effectiveness of EMDR with the dissociative disorders: A research study leading to the development of an EMDR protocol for DID*. Manuscript in preparation.

Beere, D. B., Simon, M. J., & Welch, K. (2001). Recommendations and illustrations for combining hypnosis and EMDR in the treatment of psychological trauma. *American Journal of Clinical Hypnosis, 43*, 217–231.

Benson, H. (with Klipper, M. Z.). (1975). *The relaxation response*. New York: HarperCollins.

Bergmann, U. (2000, October). *EMDR and ego state therapy: Treating the spectrum of personality disorders*. Paper presented at the EMDRIA Conference, Toronto, ON.

Bergmann, U. (2002, November). *Personality disorders as variants of dissociative phenomena: Treatment with an integration of ego-state therapy and EMDR*. Paper presented at the International Society for the Study of Dissociation Fall Conference, Baltimore, MD.

Bergmann, U. (2003, September). *Personality disorders as variants of dissociative phenomena: Treatment with an integration of EMDR and ego state work.* EMDRIA Conference, Denver, CO.

Bergmann, U. (2004, June). *Personality disorders as variants of dissociative phenomena: Treatment with an integration of the EMDR and ego state treatment.* EMDREA Conference, Stockholm, Sweden.

Bergmann, U. (2006, November). *Treating dissociation in the spectrum of personality disorders: Integrating EMDR and ego-state treatment.* International Society for the Study of Dissociation Fall Conference, Los Angeles, CA.

Bergmann, U. (2007, September). *Treating dissociation in the spectrum of personality disorders: Integrating EMDR and ego state treatment.* EMDR International Association Conference, Seattle, WA.

Bergmann, U. (2008a, September). *The neurobiology of EMDR: Current findings & insights.* Paper presented at the EMDR International Association Annual Conference. Phoenix, AZ.

Bergmann, U. (2008b). *She's come undone: A neurobiological exploration of dissociative disorders.* In F. Forgash & M. Copeley (Eds.), *Healing the heart of trauma and dissociation with EMDR and ego state therapy.* New York: Springer Publishing.

Bergmann, U. (2008c, September). *Treating dissociation in the spectrum of personality disorders: Integrating EMDR and ego state treatment.* Paper presented at the EMDR International Association Annual Conference. Phoenix, AZ.

Blanford, R., & Blanford, C. (1991, December). EMDR used as a treatment in chronic pain. *EMDR Network Newsletter, 1*(2), 8.

Boening, J. A. (2001). Neurobiology of an addiction memory. *Journal of Neural Transmission 108*(6), 755–765.

Boszormenyi-Nagy, I., & Krasner, B. (1986). *Between give and take: A clinical guide to contextual therapy.* New York: Brunner-Mazel.

Braun, B. G. (1988). The BASK model of dissociation. *Dissociation, 1*(1), 4–23.

Brewin, C. R., Dalgleish, T., & Joseph, S. (1996). A dual representation theory of posttraumatic stress disorder. *Psychological Review, 103,* 670–686.

Brown, D. P., & Fromm, E. (1986). *Hypnotherapy and hypnoanalysis.* Hillsdale, NJ: Erlbaum.

Brown, S., Gilman, S. G., & Kelso, T. (2008, September). Integrated trauma treatment program: A novel EMDR approach for PTSD and substance abuse. EMDRIA Conference, Phoenix, AZ.

Calof, D. (1993, March). *Managing self harm.* Paper presented at EMDR Annual Conference, San Jose, CA.

Calof, D. (1995, June). *The self of the therapist: An experiential clinic for clinicians working with abuse recovery issues.* Paper presented at the International EMDR Annual Conference sponsored by the EMDR Institute, Inc. and the EMDR International Association, Santa Monica, CA.

Calof, D. L. (with Mary Leloo). (1993). *Multiple personality and dissociation: Understanding incest, abuse, and MPD.* Center City, MN: Hazeldon Publishers.

Calof, D., Maltz, W., Shapiro, F., & Young, W. (1995, June). What can we learn from the "false/delayed memory" controversy? Evening Symposium and Town Meeting, EMDRIA Conference, Santa Monica, CA.

Capps, F. (2005). *Rebuilding trust: Healing for couples using EMDRl.* Paper presented at the EMDR International Association Conference, Seattle, WA.

Carlson, E. B., & Putnam, F. W. (1992). *Manual for the dissociative experiences scale.* Beloit, WI: Sidran Foundation.

Cheek, D. B., & LeCron, L. M. (1968). *Clinical hypnotherapy.* New York: Grune and Stratton.

Child and Adolescent Special Interest Group (2007). *EMDR & children: A guide for parents, professionals, and others who care about children.* Austin, TX: EMDR International Association.

Cloitre, M. (2008, June). *Treating adult complex trauma survivors.* Paper presented at a joint conference of the EMDR International Association Conference, ESTSS and ISTSS, London, England.

Cocco, N. (1995, June). *Applications of EMDR to children: EMDR in the treatment of darkness phobia in children.* Paper presented at the International EMDR annual conference sponsored by the EMDR Institute, Inc. and the EMDR International Association, Santa Monica, CA.

Cooper, A. (1995, June). *EMDR with victims of trauma: Protecting your client, protecting yourself.* Workshop presented at the International EMDR Annual Conference sponsored by the EMDR Institute, Inc. and the EMDR International Association, Santa Monica, CA.

Cox, R. P., & Howard, M. D., (2007). Utilization of EMDR in the treatment of sexual addiction: A case study. *Sexual addiction & compulsivity, 14*(1), pp. 1-20.

Damasio, A. (1999). *The feeling of what happens.* New York: Harcourt, Brace.

Damasio, A., Grabowski, T. J., Bechera, A., Damasio, H., Ponto, L., & Parvizi, J. (2000). Subcortical and cortical brain activity during the feeling of self-generated emotions. *Nature Neuroscience, 3,* 1049–1056.

D'Antonio, M. J. (1994). Jim and Sandy: Rebalancing relational responsibility. In G. R. Weeks & L. Hof (Eds.), *The marital-relationship therapy casebook: Theory and application of the intersystem model.* New York: Brunner-Mazel.

D'Antonio, M. (1997). *Shapiro meets Bowen & Satir: The uses of EMDR in couples therapy.* Paper presented at the EMDR International Association Conference, San Francisco, CA.

Dean, G. L., Fenstermaker, D., & Anderson, K. J. (1991a, November). Clinical use of eye movement desensitization/reprocessing (EMD/R) in recall and reprocessing of traumatic material in MPD patients PTSD treatments grow in evidence, effectiveness. International Society for the Study of Dissociation Fall Conference, Chicago, IL. Rush University, 79 and *Monitor on Psychology, 39*(1), 40–45.

Dean, G. L., Fenstermaker, D., & Anderson, K. J. (1991b, November). *PTSD treatments grow in evidence and effectiveness.* International Society for the Study of Dissociation Fall Conference, Chicago, IL.

De Charms, R. C., Maeda, F., Glover, G. H., Ludlow, D., Pauly, J. M., Soneji, D., et al. (2005). Control over brain activation and pain learned by using real-time functional MRI. *Proceedings of the National Academy of Science, USA, 102*(51), 18626–18631.

De Jongh, A. (1998, February 1). *Specific phobias.* EMDR Institute Listserv.

De Jongh, A. (1999, June). *The application of EMDR in the treatment of specific phobias.* EMDRIA Conference, Las Vegas, NV.

De Jongh, A. (2002). Gedragstherapie is niet effectiever dan EMDR. *DTH—Kwartaalschrift voor Directieve Therapie en Hypnose, 22*(2), 219–223.

De Jongh, A. (2003, June). *Anxiety disorders—Treatment of phobias with EMDR.* EMDREA Conference, Rome, Italy.

De Jongh, A. (2006, June). *Treatment of anxiety and phobias with EMDR: Rapid conceptualization: Effective procedures and proposals for changes of the protocol.* EMDREA Conference, Istanbul, Turkey.

De Jongh, A. (2008, September). *EMDR and phobias: Treatment of fears and phobias with eye movement desensitization and reprocessing (EMDR).* Pre-Congress on EMDR at the European Congress of Hypnosis, Vienna, Austria.

De Jongh, A., & ten Broeke, E. (1993). Een nieuwe behandelingsmethode voor angst entrauma's: Eye Movement Desensitization and Reprocessing. *Tijdschrift voor Directieve Therapie en Hypnose, 13,* 161–170.

De Jongh, A., & ten Broeke, E. (1994, June). Opmerkelijke veranderingen na één zitting met eye movement desensitization and reprocessing: Een geval van angst voor misselijkheid en braken—[Noteworthy changes after one session with eye movement desensitization and reprocessing: A case of fear of nausea and vomiting]. *Tijdschrift voor Directieve Therapie en Hypnose, 14*(2), 90–102.

De Jongh, A. & ten Broeke, E. (1998). Treatment of choking phobia by targeting traumatic memories with EMDR: A case study. *Clinical Psychology and Psychotherapy, 5,* 264–269.

De Jongh, A., & ten Broeke, E. (2000a). Why and how to use "in vivo exposure" in EMDR. *EMDRIA Newsletter, 5*(3), 18.

De Jongh, A., & ten Broeke, E. (2000b). The use of "exposure" in EMDR. *EMDRIA Newsletter, 5*(4), 4–8.

De Jongh, A., & ten Broeke, E. (2002a). Verwerking van schokkende gebeurtenissen met eye movement desensitization and reprocessing (EMDR). *Psychopraxis, 4*(1), 21–27.

De Jongh, A., & ten Broeke, E. (2002b). Eye movement desensitization and reprocessing (EMDR): Geprotocolleerde behandelmethode voor traumatische belevingen. *Tijdschrift van de Kinder en Jeugdpsychotherapie, 29*(3), 46–60.

De Jongh, A., & ten Broeke, E. (2003). *Handboek EMDR: Een geprotocolleerde behandelmethode voor de gevolgen van psychotrauma.* Lisse: Swets & Zeitlinger.

De Jongh, A., & ten Broeke, E. (2007). Treatment of specific phobias with EMDR: Conceptualization and strategies for the selection of appropriate memories. *Journal of EMDR Practice and Research, 1*(1), 46–57.

De Jongh, A., ten Broeke, E., & Renssen, M. R. (1999). Treatment of specific phobias with eye movement desensitization and reprocessing (EMDR): Protocol, empirical status, and conceptual issues. *Journal of Anxiety Disorders, 13,* 69–85.

De Jongh, A., ten Broeke, E., & Van der Meer, K. (1995). Eine neue entwicklung in der behandlung von angst und traumata: Eye movement desensitization and reprocessing (EMDR)—[A new development in the treatment of anxiety and trauma: Eye movement desensitization and reprocessing (EMDR)]. *Zeitschrift für Klinische Psychologie, Psychopathologie und Psychotherapie, 43*(3), 226–233.

De Jongh, A., Van den Oord, H., & ten Broeke, E. (2002, December). Efficacy of eye movement desensitization and reprocessing in the treatment of specific phobias: Four single-case studies on dental phobia. *Journal of Clinical Psychology, 58*(12), 1489–1503.

De Jongh, A., & Whisman, M. (2001, June). *Panic and phobias: Diagnosis, treatment, and incorporation of EMDR.* EMDRIA Conference, Austin, TX.

De Roos, C., & De Jongh, A. (2008). EMDR treatment of children and adolescents with a choking phobia. (2007). *EMDR and phantom limb pain: Theoretical implications, case study, and treatment guidelines. Journal of EMDR Practice and Research, 2,* 3, 201–211.

De Roos, C., Veenstra, A. C., Jongh de, A., Hollander-Gijsman den, M. E., Wee van der, N.J.A., Zitman F. G., et al. (0000). *Treatment of chronic phantom limb pain (PLP) with eye movement desensitization and reprocessing (EMDR): Ten cases.* Manuscript submitted for publication.

De Roos, C., Veenstra, S., & Van Rood, Y. (2005, June). *The use of EMDR in the treatment of phantom limb pain and post whiplash complaints.* EMDREA Conference, Brussels, Belgium.

DiNardo, P. A., Barlow, D. H., Cerny, J. A., Vermilyea, B. B., Vermilyea, J. A., Himadi, W. G., et al. (1985). *Anxiety disorders interview schedule-revised (ADIS-R).* Albany, NY: Center for Stress and Anxiety Disorders.

Dunton, R. (1992). *Treatment of Learning Disabilities.* Paper presented at the EMDR Symposium at the 4th World Congress of Behavior Therapy, Australia.

Dunton, R. (1993). *Using EMDR with children: School behavior and learning issues.* Paper presented at the International EMDR annual conference, Sunnyvale, CA.

Dworkin, M. (2001, June). *Counter transference and the intersubjective: Directions for treating traumatized clients with EMDR.* Paper presented at the annual conference of the EMDR International Association, Austin, TX.

Dworkin, M. (2002). *Relational strategies in EMDR.* Paper presented at the annual conference of the EMDR International Association, San Diego, CA.

Dworkin, M. (2003a). Integrative approaches to EMDR: Empathy, the intersubjective, and the cognitive interweave. *Journal of Psychotherapy Integration, 13*(2), 171–187.

Dworkin, M. (2003b, September). *EMDR from the heart: A relational view of healing traumatic memories.* Paper presented at the annual conference of the EMDR International Association, Denver, CO.

Dworkin, M. (2005a). *EMDR and the relational imperative: The therapeutic relationship in EMDR treatment.* New York: Routledge.

Dworkin, M. (2005b, June). *Clinical strategies for dealing with challenging EMDR clients.* Paper presented at the annual conference of the EMDR European Association, Brussels, Belgium.

Dworkin, M. (2005c, September). *Clinical strategies for dealing with challenging EMDR clients.* Paper presented at the annual conference of the EMDR International Association, Seattle, WA.

Dworkin, M. (2006, September). *The EMDR clinician and the challenging client: How to improve relational responsiveness.* Paper presented at the annual conference of the EMDR International Association, Philadelphia, PA.

Dworkin, M. (2008a, June). *Using the therapeutic relationship in EMDR with patients with complex PTSD.* Paper presented at the annual conference of the EMDR European Association, London, England.

Dworkin, M. (2008b, September). *Advanced clinical strategies for clients with complex PTSD and dissociation.* Paper presented at the annual conference of the EMDR International Association, Phoenix, AZ.

Dworkin, M., & Bender, S. (2000, October). *The role of transference and counter transference in EMDR.* Paper presented at the EMDR International Association Conference, Toronto, ON.

Earley, P. H. (2007). *Addiction memory in addiction recovery.* Atlanta, GA: Earley Associates, P.C., Addiction Recovery and Wellness Medicine.

Edmond, T., Sloan, L., & McCarty, D. (2004). Sexual abuse survivors' perceptions of the effectiveness of EMDR and eclectic therapy. *Research on Social Work Practice, 14*(4), 259–272.

Eimer, B. (1993a, Winter). EMDR for chronic pain. *EMDR Network Newsletter, 2*(2), 4–7.

Eimer, B. (1993b, Spring). Desensitization and reprocessing of chronic pain with EMDR. *EMDR Network Newsletter, 2*(2), 13–17.

Eimer, B. (1994). *Chronic pain.* EMDR Conference, San Jose, CA.

Eimer, B. (1995, June). *EMDR applications for pain management.* EMDRIA Conference, Santa Monica, CA.

Elofsson, U. O., Von Schèele, B., Theorell, T., & Sondergaard, H. P. (2008, May). Physiological correlates of eye movement desensitization and reprocessing. *Journal of Anxiety Disorders, 22*(4), 622–634.

EMDR Dissociation Task Force. (1994). *EMDR dissociation task force position paper*. EMDR Institute, Pacific Grove, CA.

Errebo, N., & Sommers-Flanagan, R. (2007). EMDR and emotionally focused couple therapy for war veteran couples. In F. Shapiro, F. Kaslow, & L. Maxfield (Eds.), *Handbook of EMDR and family therapy processes*. New York: Wiley.

Farrell, D. (1997, July). *Working with survivors of clergy sexual abuse & the utilization of EMDR as a treatment modality*. Paper presented at the EMDR International Association annual conference, Austin, TX.

Fenstermaker, D. (1991a, August). EMDR and MPD. *EMDR Network Newsletter, 1*(1), 3.

Fenstermaker, D. (1991b). *An innovative abreactive process for dissociative disorders: Eye movement desensitization and reprocessing (EMDR)*. California Psychological Association Annual Conference, San Diego, CA.

Fenstermaker, D. (1993, March). *Multiple personality disorder*. Paper presented at EMDR Annual Conference, Sunnyvale, CA.

Fine, C. G. (1990).The cognitive sequellae of incest. In R. P. Kluft (Ed.), *Incest-related syndromes of adult psychopathology*. Washington, DC: American Psychiatric Press.

Fine, C. G. (1991). Treatment stabilization and crisis prevention: Pacing the therapy of the multiple personality disorder patient. *Psychiatric Clinics North America, 14,* 661–676.

Fine, C. G. (1992). Multiple personality disorder. In A. Freeman & F. M. Dattilio (Eds.), *Comprehensive casebook of cognitive therapy*. New York: Plenum Press.

Fine, C. G. (1993a). A tactical integrationist perspective on multiple personality disorder. In R. P. Kluft & C. G. Fine (Eds.), *Clinical perspectives on multiple personality disorder*. Washington, DC: American Psychiatric Press.

Fine, C. (1993b, March). *EMDR and structured therapy for MPD*. Paper presented at EMDR Annual Conference, San Jose, CA.

Fine, C., & Berkowitz, A. (2001). The wreathing protocol: The imbrication of hypnosis and EMDR in the treatment of dissociative identity disorder and other dissociative responses. *American Journal of Clinical Hypnosis, 43,* 275–290.

Fine, C., & Comstock, C. (1989, November). *The completion of cognitive schemata and affective realms through the temporary blending of personalities*. Presented at the Fifth International Conference on Multiple Personality/Dissociative States, Chicago, IL.

Fine, C., Luber, M., Paulsen, Puk, G., Rouanzoin, C., & Young, W. (1995). A general guide to the use of EMDR in the dissociative disorders: A task force report. In F. Shapiro, *EMDR: Basic principles, practices and procedures*. New York: Guilford Press.

Fine, C., Luber, M., Paulsen, Puk, G., Rouanzoin, C., & Young, W. (2001). A general guide to the use of EMDR in the dissociative disorders: A task force report. In F. Shapiro (Ed.), *EMDR: Basic principles, practices and procedures* (2nd ed.). New York: Guilford Press.

Forgash, C. A. (2000, October). *EMDR and ego state therapy: Theoretical overview, diagnostic approach, and client preparation for EMDR*. EMDRIA Conference, Toronto, ON.

Forgash, C. A. (2002, November). *Addressing dissociation and its negative impact on the physical health of the adult sexual abuse survivor: An integrated EMDR and ego state treatment approach*. International Society for the Study of Dissociation Fall Conference, Baltimore, MD.

Forgash, C. A. (2003, June). *Attachment and complex trauma—Improving child sexual abuse survivor's health with integrated EMDR & ego state treatment*. EMDREA Conference, Rome, Italy.

Forgash, C. A. (2004). *Treating complex posttraumatic stress disorder with EMDR and ego state therapy*. EMDREA Conference, Frankfurt, Germany.

Forgash, C. A. (2005, June). *Healing complex trauma through EMDR, ego state therapy and somasensory work: Healing the heart of complex trauma*. EMDREA Conference, Brussels, Belgium.

Forgash, C. A. (2006, June). *The integration of EMDR and ego state*. EMDREA Conference, Istanbul, Turkey.

Forgash, C. (2007, September). *The negative impact of complex PTSD on health: An EMDR/ego state treatment plan*. EMDRIA Conference, Dallas, TX.

Forgash, C., & Copeley (Eds.). (2008). *Healing the heart of trauma and dissociation with EMDR and ego state therapy*. New York: Springer Publishing.

Forgash, C. A., & Knipe, J. (2001, June). *Safety-focused EMDR/ego state treatment of severe ego state disorders*. EMDRIA Conference, Austin, TX.

Forrest, M. S. (1995, June). *Self-soothing and the multiple trauma survivor*. Session 25 of the EMDRIA Conference, Santa Monica, CA.

Foster, S., Lendl, J., & Paulsen-Inobe, S. (2000). *EMDR for executive performance enhancement and strategic visioning*. Paper presented at the EMDR International Association Annual Conference, Toronto, Ontario, Canada.

Fowler, N. A. (2006). Aromatherapy, used as an integrative tool for crisis management by adolescents in a residential treatment center. *Journal of Child and Adolescent Psychiatric Nursing, 19*(2), 69–76.

Fraser, G. A. (1991). The dissociative table technique: A strategy for working with ego states in dissociative disorders and ego state therapy. *Dissociation, 4*(4), 204–213.

Fraser, G. A. (2003). Fraser's "dissociative table technique" revisited, revised: A strategy for working with ego states in dissociative disorders and ego state therapy. *Journal of Trauma and Dissociation, 4*(4), 5–28.

Gazzaniga, M.S., Holtzman, J.D., & Smylie, C.S. (1987). Speech without conscious awareness. *Neurology, 37*, 682–685.

Gelinas, D. (2003). Integrating EMDR into phase-oriented treatment for trauma. *Journal of Trauma & Dissociation, 4*(3), 91–135.

Gelinas, D. (2006, September). *Treating complex PTSD using EMDR.* Paper presented at EMDR International Annual Conference, Philadelphia, PA.

Gelinas, D. (2007, September). *Treating complex PTSD using EMDR.* Paper presented at EMDR International Annual Conference, Dallas, TX.

Gelinas, D. (2008, September). *Treating complex PTSD using EMDR.* Paper presented at the EMDR International Association Annual Conference, Dallas, TX.

Glang, C., & Penner, C. (1996). *Integrating EMDR with marital and family systems therapy.* Paper presented at the EMDR International Association Conference, Denver, CO.

Gold, S. (2000). *Not trauma alone.* Philadelphia: Brunner-Routledge.

Gould, E. (1993, Winter). Using the SUDs and VoC to map the memory network. *EMDR Network Newsletter, 3*(3), 10–11.

Gould, E., & Belton, R. (1993, March). *Incest trauma survivors.* Paper presented at EMDR Conference Annual Conference, San Jose, CA.

Gould, E., Korn, D., Nelson, S., & Forrest, M. S. (1993). *Sexual abuse.* EMDR Conference, Sunnyvale, CA.

Gould, E., Korn, D., Nelson, S., & Forrest, M. S. (1994). *Sexual abuse.* EMDR Conference, San Jose, CA.

Grant, M. (1997, June). *EMDR in a multi-modal approach to chronic pain.* EMDRIA Conference, San Francisco, CA.

Grant, M. (1999). EMDR in the treatment of pain. *EMDRIA Newsletter, 4*(2), 8–9, 15, 25–27.

Grant, M. (2000, May). EMDR: A new treatment for trauma and chronic pain. *Complementary Therapies in Nursing and Midwifery, 6*(2), 91–94.

Grant, M. (2001). *Pain control with EMDR.* Oakland, CA: New Harbinger Publications, Inc.

Grant, M. (2008). *Pain and stress; Why you hurt more than you should and how you can feel better.* Manuscript submitted for publication.

Grant, M. (2009). *Change your brain, change your pain, based on EMDR.* Sydney, Australia. Retrieved from www.overcomingpain.com

Grant, M., & Just, A. (2000). EMDR and compassionate psychotherapy: A new treatment for chronic pain. *EMDRIA Newsletter, 5*(3), 4.

Grant, M., & Threlfo, C. (2002). EMDR in the treatment of chronic pain. *Journal of Clinical Psychology, 58*, 1505–1520.

Greenwald, R. (1993a). *Using EMDR with children: Children and critical incidents.* Paper presented at the International EMDR Annual Conference, Sunnyvale, CA.

Greenwald, R. (1993b). Treating children's nightmares with EMDR. *EMDRIA Newsletter, 3*(1), 7–9.

Greenwald, R. (1999a). *Eye movement desensitization and reprocessing (EMDR) in child and adolescent psychotherapy.* Northvale, NJ: Jason Aronson Press.

Greenwald, R. (1999b). EMDR with children: The first ten years. *EMDRIA Newsletter, Special Edition, 4,* (4), p. 3.

Greenwald, R. (1999c). After zero, Further processing with teens. *EMDRIA Newsletter, Special Edition, 4,* (4), p. 14.

Greenwald, R. (1999d). A crisis response approach for suicidal teens. *EMDRIA Newsletter, Special Edition, 4,* (4), p. 23-25.

Hammond, D. C. (1990). *Handbook of hypnotic suggestions and metaphors.* New York: W. W. Norton.

Hase, M. (2005, June). *EMDR: Reprocessing of an addiction memory.* EMDREA Conference, Brussels, Belgium.

Hase, M. (2006, September). *EMDR applied to reprocess the addiction memory in alcohol addicted in-patients: Outcome and follow-up data of a clinical study.* EMDRIA Conference, Philadelphia, PA.

Hase, M., Schallmayer, S., & Sack, M. (2008). EMDR reprocessing of the addiction memory: Pretreatment, posttreatment, and 1-month follow-up. *Journal of EMDR Practice and Research, 2*(3), 170–179.

Hassard, A. (1993). Eye movement desensitization of body image. *Behavioural Psychotherapy, 21,* 157–160.

Hassard, A. (1995). Investigation of eye movement desensitization in pain clinic clients. *Behavioral & Cognitive Psychotherapy, 23*(2), 177–185.

Hoffman, B. M., Papas, R. K., Chatkoff, D. K., & Kerns, R. D. (2007). Meta-analysis of psychological interventions for chronic back pain. *Health Psychology, 26*(1), 1–9.

Hofmann, A. (1999). *EMDR in der therapie psychotraumatischer belastungs-syndrome.* Stuttgart, Germany: Thieme Verlag.

Hofmann, A. (2003). *Absorptionstechnik.* Germany: EMDR-Institut Deutschland.

Hofmann, A. (2004a). *EMDR-Arbeitsbogen: Anamnese.* Cologne, Germany: EMDR-Institut Deutschland.

Hofmann, A. (2004b, June). *The treatment of complex post-traumatic stress disorder with EMDR.* Paper Presented at the EMDREA Conference, Stockholm, Sweden.

Hofmann, A. (2004c, September). *EMDR in the treatment of complex PTSD patients.* Paper Presented at the EMDRIA Conference, Montreal, QC.

Hofmann, A. (2005, June). *EMDR in the treatment of complex PTSD patients.* Paper Presented at the EMDREA Conference, Brussels, Belgium.

Hofmann, A. (2006, September). *EMDR Master Series—I.* EMDR International Annual Conference, Philadelphia, PA.

Hofmann, A., & Luber, M. (2009). History taking: The time line. In M. Luber (Ed.), *Eye movement desensitization and reprocessing (EMDR) scripted protocols.* New York: Springer Publishing.

Hofmann, A., & Sack, M. (2006). EMDR in der Behandlung von Patienten mit chronisch komplexer PTBS und schweren dissoziativen Störungen. In F. Lamprecht (Ed.), *Praxisbuch EMDR—Modifizierungen für spezielle Anwendungsgebiete* (pp. 172–194). Stuttgart, Germany: Klett-Cotta.

International Society for the Study of Trauma & Dissociation (formerly International Society for the Study of Dissociation). (2005). Guidelines for treating dissociative identity disorder in adults. *Journal of Trauma and Dissociation, 6*(4), 69–149.

Jarero, I., Artigas, L., Mauer, M., Lopez Cano, T., & Alcala, N. (1999, November). *Children's post traumatic stress after natural disasters: Integrative treatment protocols.* Poster presented at the annual meeting of the International Society for Traumatic Stress Studies, Miami, FL.

Jarero, I., Artigas, L., & Montero, M. (2008). The EMDR integrative group treatment protocol: Application with child victims of mass disaster. *Journal of EMDR Practice & Research, 2*(2), 97–105.

Karpel, M. (2005). *Targeting the repetition compulsion in couples therapy.* Paper presented at the EMDR International Association Conference, Seattle, WA.

Kiessling, R. (2005). Integrating resource development into your EMDR practice. In R. Shapiro (Ed.), *EMDR solutions: Pathways to healing* (pp. 57–86). New York: W. W. Norton.

Kiessling, R. (2009). The wedging technique. In M. Luber (Ed.), *Eye movement desensitization and reprocessing (EMDR) scripted protocols: Basics and special situations.* New York: Springer Publishing.

Kitchur, M. (2000). The strategic developmental model for EMDR. *The EMDRIA Newsletter, Special Edition, 5*(5), 4–10.

Kitchur, M. (2005). The strategic developmental model for EMDR. In R. Shapiro (Ed.), *EMDR solutions: Pathways to healing* (pp. 8–56). New York: W. W. Norton.

Klaff, F. (1995). *Treatment of children's fears with EMDR.* Paper presented at the International EMDR Annual Conference sponsored by the EMDR Institute, Inc. and the EMDR International Association, Santa Monica, CA.

Kleinknecht, R. (1993, September). Rapid treatment of blood and injection phobias with eye movement desensitization. *Journal of Behavior Therapy and Experimental Psychiatry, 24*(3), 211–217.

Kluft, R. P. (1982). Varieties of hypnotic interventions in the treatment of multiple personality. *American Journal of Clinical Hypnosis, 24,* 230–240.

Kluft, R. P. (1984). Aspects of treatment of multiple personality disorder. *Psychiatric Annals, 14,* 51–55.

Kluft, R. P. (1988). On treating the older patient with multiple personality disorder: Race against time or make haste slowly? *American Journal Clinical Hypnosis, 30,* 257–266.

Kluft, R. P. (1989). Playing for time, temporizing techniques in the treatment of multiple personality disorder. *American Journal of Clinical Hypnosis, 32,* 90–98.

Kluft, R. (1993a). Basic principles in conducting the psychotherapy of multiple personality disorder. In R. Kluft & C. Fine (Eds.), *Clinical perspectives on multiple personality disorder* (pp. 19–50). Washington, DC: American Psychiatric Publishing.

Kluft, R. P. (1993b). The initial stages of psychotherapy in the treatment of multiple personality disorder patients. *Dissociation, 6,*145–161.

Kluft, R. P. (1994). Applications of hypnotic interventions. *Hypnos, 21,* 205–223.

Kluft, R. P. (2006). *When good trances go bad: The importance of de-hypnosis or alerting in protecting hypnotic subjects against adverse outcomes.* Presented at the American Society of Clinical Hypnosis Annual Meeting, Orlando, FL.

Knipe, J. (1995). Targeting defensive avoidance and dissociated numbing. *EMDR Network Newsletter, 5*(2), 6–7.

Knipe, J. (1998). It was a golden time . . . : Treating narcissistic vulnerability. In P. Manfield (Ed.), *Extending EMDR: A casebook of innovative applications* (pp. 232–255). New York: W. W. Norton.

Knipe, J. (1999). Strengthening affect tolerance and adult perspective through construction of imagined dissociative avoidance. *EMDRIA Newsletter, 4*(2), 10, 25.

Knipe, J. (2002). A tool for working with dissociative clients. *EMDRIA Newsletter, 7*(2), 14–16.

Knipe, J. (2005). Targeting positive affect to clear the pain of unrequited love, codependence, avoidance, and procrastination. In R. Shapiro (Ed.), *EMDR solutions: Pathways to healing* (pp. 189–212). New York: W. W. Norton.

Knipe, J. (2006, June). *EMDR toolbox: Video examples of methods of targeting avoidance, procrastination, affect dysregulation, the pain of being "dumped" by a lover, and a shame-based ego state in a client with an identity disorder.* Invited presentation at the EMDR European Conference, Istanbul.

Knipe, J. (2007, February). *EMDR toolbox: Video examples of methods of targeting avoidance, procrastination, affect dysregulation, the pain of being "dumped" by a lover, and a shame-based ego state in a client with an identity disorder.* Invited presentation at the EMDR Denmark Conference, Copenhagen.

Knipe, J. (2007, April). *EMDR toolbox: Video examples of methods of targeting avoidance, procrastination, affect dysregulation, the pain of being "dumped" by a lover, and a shame-based ego state in a client with an identity disorder.* Invited presentation at the Japan EMDR Association Annual Conference, Kyoto.

Knipe, J. (2007). *Loving eyes: Procedures to therapeutically reverse dissociative processes while preserving emotional safety.* In C. Forgash & M. Copeley (Eds.), *Healing heart of trauma and dissociation.* New York: Springer Publishing.

Knipe, J. (2008, April). *EMDR toolbox: Video examples of methods of targeting avoidance, procrastination, affect dysregulation, the pain of being "dumped" by a lover, and a shame-based ego state in a client with an identity disorder.* Invited presentation at the EMDR Netherlands Annual Conference, Amsterdam.

Knipe, J. (2008, June). *EMDR toolbox: Video examples of methods of targeting avoidance, procrastination, affect dysregulation, the pain of being "dumped" by a lover, and a shame-based ego state in a client with an identity disorder.* Invited presentation at the EMDREA Conference, London, England.

Knipe, J. (2008, June). *The CIPOS method—Procedures to therapeutically reduce dissociative processes while preserving emotional safety.* EMDREA Conference, London, England.

Koedam, W. S. (2007). Sexual trauma in dysfunctional marriages: Integrating structural therapy and EMDR. In F. Shapiro, F. W. Kaslow, & L. Maxfield (Eds.), *Handbook of EMDR and family therapy processes* (pp. 223–242). New Jersey: John Wiley & Sons.

Korn, D. (1995, June). *Integrative and strategic utilization of EMDR in treating survivors of sexual abuse.* Workshop D at the EMDRIA Conference, Santa Monica, CA.

Korn, D. (1996, June). *Clinical applications of EMDR in treating survivors of sexual abuse.* EMDRIA Conference, Denver, CO.

Korn, D. (1997, June). *Clinical applications of EMDR in treating survivors of sexual abuse.* EMDRIA Conference, San Francisco, CA.

Korn, D. (2001, June). *Clinical applications of EMDR in treating survivors of childhood abuse and neglect.* Paper presented at the annual meeting of the EMDR International Association, Austin, TX.

Korn, D. (2003, September). *EMDR master series—I.* EMDRIA Conference, Denver, CO.

Korn, D. (2006, September). *Complex PTSD.* EMDRIA Conference, Philadelphia, PA.

Korn, D. L. (2008a, May). *Utilisation d'EMDR dans le traitement des survivants d'abus ou négligence chroniques: Réparer les déficits développementaux et les sois éclatés* [EMDR treatment with survivors of chronic abuse and neglect: Repairing developmental deficits and shattered selves]. Paper presented at the EMDR Canada Conference, Montréal, Quebec.

Korn, D. (2008b, September). *EMDR Master Series—I.* EMDRIA Conference, Phoenix, AZ.

Korn, D. (2009, June). *EMDR and the treatment of adult survivors of childhood abuse.* Keynote presented at the annual meeting of the EMDR Europe Association, Amsterdam.

Korn, D. L., & Leeds, A. M. (2002). Preliminary evidence of efficacy for EMDR resource development and installation in the stabilization phase of treatment of complex posttraumatic stress disorder. *Journal of Clinical Psychology, 58*(12), 1465–1487.

Korn, D., Rozelle D., & Weir F. (2005a, June). *Bringing EMDR research into practice.* EMDREA Conference, Brussels, Belgium.

Korn, D., Weir, J., & Rozelle, D. (2005b, June). *Beyond the data: Clinical lessons learned from a four-year treatment outcome study comparing EMDR to prozac.* Paper presented at the EMDREA Conference, Brussels, Belgium.

Lanius, R. A., Bluhm, R., & Lanius, U. F. (2007). PTSD symptom provocation and neuroimaging: Heterogeneity of response. In E. Vermetten, M. Dorahy, & D. Spiegel (Eds.), *Traumatic dissociation: Neurobiology and treatment.* Washington, DC: American Psychiatric Press.

Lanius, R. A., Bluhm, R., Lanius, U. F. & Pain, C. (2006). A review of neuroimaging studies in PTSD: Heterogeneity of response to symptom provocation. *Journal of Psychiatric Research 40*(8), 709–729.

Lanius, R. A., Lanius, U. F., Fisher, J., & Ogden, P. (2006). Psychological trauma and the brain: Towards a neurobiological treatment model. In P. Ogden, K. Minton, & C. Pain (Eds.), *Trauma and the body: A sensorimotor approach to psychotherapy.* New York: W. W. Norton.

Lanius, R. A., Williamson, P. C., Densmore, M., Boksman, K., Neufeld, W., Gati, J. S., et al. (2004). The nature of traumatic memories: A 4–7 fMRI functional connectivity analysis. *American Journal of Psychiatry, 161,* 36–44.

Lanius, U. F. (2000, April). *Dissociative processes and EMDR—Staying connected.* Presentation at the North West Regional EMDR Conference, Vancouver, British Columbia.

Lanius, U. F. (2001, September). *Dissociation processes and EMDR: Staying connected.* Paper presented at the annual meeting of the EMDR International Association, Austin, TX.

Lanius, U. (2003). *EMDR and dissociative states: Enhancing therapeutic outcome.* Paper presented at the annual meeting of the EMDR International Association, San Francisco, CA.

Lanius, U. F. (2004a, September). *Dissociative processes and EMDR—Staying connected.* Paper presented at the EMDRIA Conference, Montreal, Ontario.

Lanius, U. F. (2004b, September). *Attachment and dissociation: The role of endogenous opioids.* Paper presented at the EMDRIA Conference, Montreal, Ontario.

Lanius, U. (2005). EMDR processing with dissociative clients: Adjunctive use of opioid antagonists. In R. Shapiro (Ed.), *EMDR solutions: Pathways to healing* (pp. 121–146). New York: W. W. Norton.

Lanius, U. F. (2006, September) *Thalamocortical dialogue.* Paper presented at the EMDR International Association Annual Conference, Philadelphia, PA.

Lanius, U. F. (2008, September). *The neurobiology of dissociation: Current findings.* Paper presented at the EMDR International Association Annual Conference, Phoenix, AZ.

Laub, B. (2001). The healing power of resource connection in the EMDR protocol. *EMDRIA Newsletter,* (special edition), 21–28.

Lazarus, A. A., & Lazarus, C. N. (1991). *Mutimodal life history inventory.* Champaign, IL: Research Press.

Leeds, A. M. (1998). Lifting the burden of shame: Using EMDR resource installation to resolve a therapeutic impasse. In P. Manfield (Ed.), *Extending EMDR: A casebook of innovative applications* (1st ed., pp. 256–281). New York: W. W. Norton.

Leeds, A. M. (2006). *Criteria for assuring appropriate clinical use and avoiding misuse of resource development and installation when treating complex posttraumatic stress syndromes.* Paper presented at the EMDR International Association Conference, Philadelphia, PA.

Leeds, A. M., & Korn, D. L. (1997, June). *In the eyes of the beholder: Reflections on shame, dissociation, and transference in complex post-traumatic stress and attachment disorders.* Paper presented at the EMDR International Association Conference, San Francisco, CA.

Leeds, A. M., & Korn, D. L. (1998). *Clinical applications of EMDR in the treatment of adult survivors of childhood abuse and neglect.* Topeka, KS: The Menninger Clinic.

Lendl, J., & Foster, S. (1997). *EMDR performance enhancement for the workplace: A practitioners manual.* Hamden, CT: EMDR HAP.

Levin, C. (1992, December). The heart of EMDR. *EMDR Network Newsletter, 2*(2),18.

Levine, L. (1998, June). *EMDR and sex therapy.* Paper presented at the EMDR International Association Annual Conference, Baltimore, MD.

Liotti, G. (2006). A model of dissociation based on attachment theory. *Journal of Trauma and Dissociation, 7*(4), 55–74.

Litt, B. (1998). *Trust, intimacy and sex: An integrated approach.* Paper presented at the EMDR International Association Conference, Baltimore, MD.

Litt, B. K. (2003, September). *The marriage of EMDR and ego state therapy in couples therapy.* Paper presented at the EMDR International Association Conference, Denver, CO.

Litt, B. K. (2004, September). *The marriage of EMDR and ego state theory in couples therapy.* Paper presented at the EMDR International Association Conference, Montreal, Ontario.

Litt, B. K. (2005, September). *The marriage of EMDR and ego state theory in couples therapy.* Paper presented at the EMDR International Association Conference, Seattle, WA.

Litt, B. K. (2006, September). *The marriage of EMDR and ego state theory in couples therapy.* Paper presented at the EMDR International Association Conference, Philadelphia, PA.

Litt, B. (2007a, September). *The marriage of EMDR and ego state theory in couples therapy.* Paper presented at the EMDR International Association Conference, Dallas, TX.

Litt, B. (2007b). EMDR in couples therapy: An ego state approach. In C. Forgash & M. Copeley (Eds.), *Healing the heart of trauma and dissociation with EMDR and ego state therapy.* New York: Springer Publishing.

Litt, B. (2008). *The marriage of EMDR and ego state theory in couples therapy.* Paper presented at the EMDR International Association Conference, Phoenix, AZ.

Litt, B. K., Forgash, C., & Twombly, J. (2002, November). *Integrating ego state therapy and EMDR in the assessment and treatment of dissociative disorders.* Paper presented at the International Society for the Study of Dissociation Fall Conference, Baltimore, MD.

Loewenstein, R. J. (1991). An office mental status examination for complex chronic dissociative symptoms and multiple personality disorder. *Psychiatric Clinics of North America: Multiple Personality Disorder, 14*(3), 567–604.

Loewenstein, R. J. (1993). Posttraumatic and dissociative aspects of transference and counter-transference in the treatment of multiple personality disorder. In R. P. Kluft & C. G. Fine (Eds.), *Clinical perspectives on multiple personality disorder* (pp. 51–85). Washington, DC: American Psychiatric Press.

Loewenstein, R. J. (2006). DID 101: A hands-on clinical guide to the stabilization phase of dissociative identity disorder treatment. *Psychiatric Clinics of North America: Dissociative Disorders: An Expanding Window into the Psychobiology of the Mind, 29*(1), 305–332.

Lohr, J. M., Tolin, D. F., & Kleinknecht, R. A. (1996). An intensive design investigation of eye movement desensitization and reprocessing of claustrophobia. *Journal of Anxiety Disorders, 10,* 73–88.

Lombardo, M. (2005, Fall). Knowing when to shift gears. *Conceive Magazine,* 25.

Lombardo, M., & Parker, L. J. (2007). *I am more than my infertility: 7 proven tools for turning a life crisis into a personal breakthrough.* Orlando, FL: Seeds of Growth Press.

Lovett, J. (1994). Case report: Treating a toddler with EMDR. *EMDRIA Newsletter 3,* 10.

Lovett, J. (1995). *EMDR with toddlers.* Paper presented at the International EMDR Annual Conference sponsored by the EMDR Institute, Inc. and the EMDR International Association, Santa Monica, CA.

Lovett, J. (1998). "Am I real?": Mobilizing inner strength to develop a mature identity. In P. Manfield (Ed.), *Extending EMDR: A casebook of innovative applications* (pp. 191–216). New York: W. W. Norton.

Lovett, J. (1999). *Small wonders: Healing childhood trauma with EMDR.* New York: The Free Press.

Luber, M. (1993, April). *EMDR for therapists' personal use.* Lecture at the EMDR Regional Network Meeting, Philadelphia, PA

Luber, M. (2006). In celebration of Neal Daniels: A life well-lived. *EMDRIA Newsletter, 11*(3), 18–19, 28–29.

Luber, M. (2007). In the spotlight: Robbie Dunton. *EMDRIA Newsletter, 12*(2), 16–22.

Lyons-Ruth, K., Dutra, L., Schuder, M., & Bianchi, I. (2006). From infant attachment disorganization to adult dissociation: Relational adaptations or traumatic experiences? *Psychiatric Clinic of North America, 29,* 63–86.

MacLean, P. (1990). *The triune brain in evolution.* New York: Plenum Press.

Maltz, W. (1995, June). *Healing the sexual problems caused by sexual abuse.* Workshop presented at the International EMDR Annual Conference sponsored by the EMDR Institute, Inc. and the EMDR International Association, Santa Monica, CA.

Manfield, D. (1998). Treating a highly defended client: Reworking traditional approaches. In P. Manfield (Ed.), *Extending EMDR: A casebook of innovative applications* (pp. 217–231). New York: W. W. Norton.

Manfield, P. (2005). *Effective targeting with couples.* Paper presented at the EMDR International Association Conference, Seattle, WA.

Manfield, P., Knipe, J., & Snyker, E. (1998, July). *Using EMDR with narcissistic personalities.* Paper presented at the EMDR International Association Annual Conference, Baltimore, MD.

Mann, K., & Ackermann, K. (2000). Die OCDS-G: Psychometrische kennwerte der deutschen version der obsessive compulsive drinking scale. *Sucht, 46*(2), 90–100.

Marich, J. (2009). Using EMDR to overcome roadblock in Addiction recovery: Insights from Phenomenological Inquiry. Paper presented at the EMDRIA Conference in Atlanta, GA.

Marquis, J. N. (1991). A report on seventy-eight cases treated by eye movement desensitization. *Journal of Behavior Therapy and Experimental Psychiatry, 22*, 187–192.

Marquis, J. N., & Puk, G. (1994, November). *Dissociative identity disorder: A common sense and cognitive-behavioral view.* Paper presented at the annual meeting of the Association for Advancement of Behavior Therapy, San Diego, CA.

Martinez, R. (1992, December). EMDR: Innovative uses. *EMDR Network Newsletter, 2*(2), 9.

Matthess, H. (2007, June). *Benefits from the theory of structural dissociation as applied to EMDR for patients with complex trauma.* EMDR European Association Conference, Paris, France.

McCann, D. L. (1992). Post-traumatic stress disorder due to devastating burns overcome by a single session of eye movement desensitization. *Journal of Behavior Therapy and Experimental Psychiatry, 23*, 319–323.

Meignant-Ordoux, I. (2008, June). *EMDR within systemic couple therapy.* Paper presented at the EMDR European Association Conference, London, England.

Melzack, R. (2005). The McGill Pain Questionnaire. From description to measurement. *Anesthesiology, 103*, 199–202.

Mendoza-Weitman, L. (1992). Case study. *EMDRIA Newsletter, 2*(1), 11–12.

Morrow, R. (2008). EMDR target tracking. *Journal of EMDR Practice and Research, 2*(1), 69–72.

Moses, M. D. (2003). Protocol for EMDR & conjoint couples therapy. *EMDRIA Newsletter, 8*(1), 4–13.

Moses, M. (2004). *Enhancing couple's therapy with EMDR: A protocol.* Paper presented at the EMDR International Association Conference, Montreal, Canada.

Moses, M. D. (2007). Enhancing attachments: Conjoint couple therapy. In F. Shapiro, F. W. Kaslow, & L. Maxfield (Eds.), *Handbook of EMDR and family therapy processes* (pp. 146–166). New Jersey: John Wiley & Sons.

Nathanson, D. (1992). *Shame and pride. Affect, sex and the birth of the self.* New York: W. W. Norton.

Nutting, R. E. (1996). *Working with couples: The use of EMDR in relationship counseling.* Paper presented at the EMDR International Association Conference, Denver, CO.

Ogden, P., & Minton, K. (2000). Sensorimotor psychotherapy: One method for processing traumatic memory. *Traumatology, 6*(3), 149–173.

O'Hanlon, W. H., & Weiner-Davis, M. (1989). *In search of solutions: A new direction in psychotherapy.* New York: W. W. Norton.

Onofri, A., & Hummel, H. (2003, June). *Attachment and complex trauma.* Paper presented at the EMDREA Conference, Rome, Italy.

Öst, L-G., & Sterner, U. (1987). Applied tension: A specific behavioral method for treatment of blood phobia. *Behaviour Research and Therapy, 25*, 25–29.

Panksepp, J. (2001). The neuro-evolutionary cusp between emotions and cognitions: Implications for understanding consciousness and the emergence of a unified mind. *Science, Evolution and Cognition, 7*, 141–163.

Parnell, L. (1995, June). *The use of imaginal and cognitive interweaves with sexual abuse survivors.* Paper presented at the International EMDR Annual Conference sponsored by the EMDR Institute, Inc. and the EMDR International Association, Santa Monica, CA.

Parnell, L. (1999). *EMDR in the treatment of adults abused as children.* New York: W. W. Norton.

Paulsen, S. L. (1992). *Ego state therapy: When the patient is dissociative but not multiple.* Advanced specialty presentation, Level II EMDR Workshop, Honolulu, HI.

Paulsen, S. (1993, October). *Ego state disorders (dissociative but not MPD).* 10th Annual Conference of the International Society for the Study of Multiple Personality Disorder, Chicago, IL.

Paulsen, S. (1995). Eye movement desensitization and reprocessing: Its use in the dissociative disorders. *Dissociation, 8*, 32–44.

Paulsen, S. L. (2003, September). *EMDR and ego state therapy: Energizing disowned aspects of self with dissociative table technique interwoven with EMDR.* Paper presented at the EMDRIA Conference, Denver, CO.

Paulsen, S. L. (2004a). *Softening the perpetrator introject.* Paper presented at the International Society for the Study of Trauma and Dissociation International Conference, New Orleans, LA.

Paulsen, S. L. (2004b, September). *Ego state therapy and EMDR: Activating, modifying and containing dissociated neural nets.* Invited Masters Series Lecture, EMDRIA International Conference, Montreal, Canada.

Paulsen, S. L. (2006, November). *ACT-AS-IF and ARCHITECTS approach to utilizing ego state therapy, somatic psychotherapy and EMDR with highly dissociative clients.* Paper presented at the 23rd annual conference for the International Society for the Study of Trauma & Dissociation, Los Angeles, CA.

Paulsen, S. L. (2008a). Treating dissociative identity disorder with EMDR, ego state therapy, and adjunct approaches. In C. Forgash, & M. Copeley (Eds.), *Healing the heart of trauma with EMDR and ego state therapy.* New York: Springer Publishing.

Paulsen, S. L. (2008b, November). *Conversion seizures manifesting as infant alters: EMDR, somatic and ego state therapy.* Paper presented at the International Society for the Study of Trauma and Dissociation, Chicago, IL.

Paulsen, S. L. (2009). *Looking through the eyes of trauma & dissociation: An illustrated guide for EMDR therapists and clients.* Charleston, SC: Booksurge.

Paulsen, S. L., & Golston, J. C. (2005). *Taming the storm: 43 secrets of successful stabilization.* EMDRIA Conference, Seattle, WA.

Paulsen, S. L., Vogelmann-Sine, S., Lazrove, S., & Young, W. (1993, October). *Eye movement desensitization and reprocessing: Its role in the treatment of dissociative disorders.* Symposium presented at the 10th annual meeting of the International Society for the Study of Multiple Personality Disorder, Chicago, IL.

Paulsen, S. L., & Watkins, J. G. (2003a, November). *Ego state therapy: EMDR & hypnoanalytic techniques.* Workshop at the Society for Clinical & Experimental Hypnosis, Chicago, IL.

Paulsen, S. L., & Watkins, J. G. (2003b, November). *Comparing ego state therapy and EMDR techniques.* Workshop at the 20th Annual Conference for the International Society for Study of Dissociation, Chicago, IL.

Paulsen, S. L., & Watkins, J. G. (2003c, November). *Ego state therapy: EMDR & psychodynamic techniques.* International Society for the Study of Dissociation Fall Conference, Chicago, IL.

Paulsen, S. L., & Watkins, J. G. (2005). *Best techniques from the armamentarium of hypnoanalytic, EMDR, somatic psychotherapy and cognitive behavioral methods.* Workshop presented at the International Society for the Study of Dissociation, Fall Conference, Toronto, Canada.

Paulsen-Inobe, S. (2000, October). *EMDR and ego state therapy: Practical implications for the desensitization and reprocessing of EMDR.* Paper presented at the EMDRIA Conference, Toronto, Ontario.

Paulsen-Inobe, S. (2001, December). *Integrating EMDR, ego state therapy, and dissociative table: A cartooning psychologist's glimpse into the mind's eye.* International Society for the Study of Dissociation Fall Conference, New Orleans, LA.

Paulsen-Payne, N. (1997). *The whole person fertility program: A revolutionary mind-body process to help you conceive.* New York: Three Rivers Press.

Pellicer, X. (1993). Eye movement desensitization treatment of a child's nightmares: A case report. *Journal of Behavior Therapy and Experimental Psychiatry, 24,* 73–75.

Phillips, M., & Frederick, C. (1995). *Healing the divided self: Clinical and Ericksonian hypnotherapy for post traumatic and dissociative conditions.* New York: W. W. Norton.

Popky, A. J. (1993). *Smoking protocol.* Paper presented at the EMDR Institute Annual Conference, Sunnyvale, CA.

Popky, A. J. (1994, February). *EMDR protocol for smoking and other addictions.* Paper presented at the EMDR Networker, Sunnyvale, CA.

Popky, A. J. (1995a, February). *Addiction protocol.* Paper presented at the EMDR Networker, Sunnyvale, CA.

Popky, A. J. (1995b). *Addiction protocol.* Specialty training at the EMDR Institute Level II specialty training, EMDR Institute, Pacific Grove, CA.

Popky, A. J. (1995c). Addictions research project. *EMDR Network Newsletter, 5*(3), 12.

Popky, A. J. (1999). *DeTUR (desensitization of triggers and urge reprocessing): A new approach to working with addictions.* EMDR Institute. Los Gatos, CA.

Popky, A. J. (2002). *DeTUR a new way to address addictions and dysfunctional behaviors.* Paper presented at the EMDR International Association Annual Conference, San Diego, CA.

Popky, A. J. (2003, June). *DeTUR (Desensitization of triggers and urge reprocessing).* Paper presented at the EMDR European Association Annual Conference, Rome, Italy.

Popky, A. J. (2005). DeTUR, an urge reduction protocol for addictions and dysfunctional behaviors. In R. Shapiro (Ed.), *EMDR solutions: Pathways to healing* (pp. 167–188). New York: W. W. Norton.

Popky, A. J., Vogelmann-Sine, S., Carlson, J. G., & Sine, L. F. (1996, June). *Addictions: An integrative approach and research design.* Paper presented at the EMDR International Association Annual Conference, Denver, CO.

Porges., S. W. (1995). Orienting in a defensive world: Mammalian modification of our evolutionary heritage: A polyvagal theory. *Psychophysiology, 32,* 301–318.

Protinsky, J., Sparks, J., & Lemke, K. (2001). Using eye movement desensitization and reprocessing to enhance treatment of couples. *Journal of Marital and Family Therapy, 27,* 157–164.

Puk, G. (1991a, June). *Applications of EMDR in treating dissociative disorders.* Pacific Grove, CA: EMDR Institute, Inc.

Puk, G. (1991b, November). *Eye movement desensitization and reprocessing: Treatment of a more complex case, borderline personality disorder.* Paper presented at the annual meeting of the Association for the Advancement of Behavior Therapy, New York, NY.

Puk, G. (1991c, June). Treating traumatic memories: A case report on the eye movement desensitization procedure. *Journal of Behavior Therapy and Experimental Psychiatry, 22*(2), 149–151.

Ray, A. R., & Zbik, A. (2001). Cognitive behavioral therapies and beyond. In C. D. Tollison, J. R. Satterhwaite, & J. W. Tollison (Eds.), *Practical pain management* (3rd ed., pp. 189–208). Philadelphia: Lippincott.

Rost, C. (2003). EMDR in derbehandlung von chronischem schmerz [EMDR in the treatment of chronic pain]. *Zeitschrift für Psychotraumatologie und Psychologische Medizin, ZPPM, 1*(3), 7–15.

Rost, C. (2005, June). *Using EMDR during the stabilization phase for patients with complex trauma.* EMDREA Conference, Brussels, Belgium.

Rost, C. (2008). *Ressourcenarbeit mit EMDR bewährte Techniken im Uberblick.* Paderborn, Germany.

Rouanzoin, C. C. (1993, Winter). Dissociative disorders and the "spatial map." *EMDR Network Newsletter, 3*(3), 10–11.

Rougemont-Buecking, A. (2007, May). *Addiction memory—Current concepts and perspectives for treatment and research.* Paper presented at the Swiss Addiction Research Day II, Lausanne, Switzerland.

Russell, M. (2008). Treating traumatic amputation-related phantom limb pain: A case study utilizing eye movement desensitization and reprocessing (EMDR) within the armed services. *Clinical Case Studies, 7*(2), 136–153.

Sack, M., & Matthess, H. (2005, November). *Psychobiological studies and practical implications of the use of EMDR with dissociative clients.* International Society for the Study of Dissociation Fall Conference, Toronto, Ontario.

Sanderson, A., & Carpenter, R. (1992, December). Eye movement desensitization versus image confrontation: A single-session crossover study of 58 phobic subjects. *Journal of Behavior Therapy and Experimental Psychiatry, 23*(4), 269–275.

Scharf, C., Berliner, K., Meyers, M., Schwartberg, N., & Weinshel, M. (2006, September). *Enhancing couples therapy with EMDR.* Paper presented at the EMDR International Association Conference, Philadelphia, PA.

Schmidt, S. J. (1998). Internal conference room ego-state therapy and the resolution of double binds: Preparing clients for EMDR trauma processing. *EMDRIA Newsletter, 3*(2), 10–14.

Schmidt, S. J. (1999). Resource-focused EMDR: Integration of ego state therapy, alternating bilateral stimulation, and art therapy. *EMDRIA Newsletter, 4*(1), 8, 10–13, 25–28.

Schmidt, S. J. (2000, October). *EMDR and ego state therapy: A resource-focused protocol using client art.* EMDRIA Conference, Toronto, Ontario.

Schneider, J., Hofmann, A., Rost, C., & Shapiro, F. (2007). EMDR and phantom limb pain: Theoretical implications, case study, and treatment guidelines. *Journal of EMDR Practice and Research, 1*(1), 31–45.

Schneider, J., Hofmann, A., Rost, C., & Shapiro, F. (2008). EMDR in the treatment of chronic phantom limb pain. *Pain Medicine, 9*(1), 76–82.

Schore, A. (1994). *Affect regulation and the origins of the self: The neurobiology of emotional development.* Hillsdale: Erlbaum.

Shapiro, F. (1995). *Eye movement desensitization and reprocessing: Basic principles, protocols and procedures.* New York: Guilford Press.

Shapiro, F. (2001). *Eye movement desensitization and reprocessing: Basic principles, protocols and procedures* (2nd ed.). New York: Guilford Press.

Shapiro, F. (2006). *EMDR: New notes on adaptive information processing with case formulation principles, forms, scripts and worksheets.* Watsonville, CA: EMDR Institute.

Shapiro, F., Kaslow, F., & Maxfield, L. (Eds.). (2007). *Handbook of EMDR and family therapy processes.* New York: Wiley.

Shapiro, F., Solomon, R., Kaufman, T., & Fenstermaker, D. (1991). *Origins and update; Origins of EMDR with critical incidents; Preliminary research and results; Clinical use of EMDR with dissociative patients.* International Society for Traumatic Stress Studies Fall Conference, Washington, DC.

Shapiro, R. (2005). Using EMDR in couples therapy. In R. Shapiro (Ed.), *EMDR solutions: Pathways to healing* (pp. 283–292). New York: W. W. Norton.

Sherman, R., & Friedman, N. (1986). *Handbook of structured techniques in marriage and family therapy.* New York: Brunner-Mazel.

Smyth, N. (1998). *Eye movement desensitization and reprocessing: Research and clinical applications: Linking theory with practice.* Paper presented at the Arbour Health Conference, Buffalo, NY.

Smyth, N., Vogelmann-Sine, S., & Sine, L. (1998, June). *Integrative treatment for chemical dependency.* Paper presented at the EMDR International Association Annual Conference, Baltimore, MD.

Sutton, J. (1993). *EMDR and a sexually abused child.* Paper presented at the International EMDR Annual Conference, Sunnyvale, CA.

Sutton, J. (1994). *EMDR and a sexually abused child.* Paper presented at the International EMDR Annual Conference, San Jose, CA.

Talan, B. S. (2007). Integrating EMDR and imago relationship therapy in treatment of couples. In F. Shapiro, F. W. Kaslow, & L. Maxfield (Eds.), *Handbook of EMDR and family therapy processes* (pp. 187–201). Hoboken, NJ: Wiley.

Ten Broeke, E., & De Jongh, A. (1995, November). Eye movement desensitization and reprocessing (EMDR): "Gewoon" imaginaire exposure? [Eye movement desensitization and reprocessing: Just imaginal exposure?]. *De Psycholoog, 30*(11), 459–464.

Ten Broeke, E., & De Jongh, A. (2008). *Praktijkboek EMDR: Casusconceptualisatie en specifieke patiëntengroepen.* Amsterdam: Harcourt.

Ten Broeke, E., Korrelboom, K., & De Jongh, A. (1998, December). Over de noodzaak van herhaalde en langdurige blootstelling aan traumatische herinneringen bij de behandeling van posttraumatische stress stoornis (PTSS)? [Is prolonged exposure to traumatic memories necessary in PTSD?]. *Gedragstherapie, 31*(4), 273–290.

Thompson, P. (1995). *Using EMDR with adolescents.* All day workshop presented at the International EMDR Annual Conference sponsored by the EMDR Institute, Inc. and the EMDR International Association, Santa Monica, CA.

Tinker, R. (1994). *Children and ADHD.* Paper presented at the International EMDR Annual Conference, San Jose, CA.

Tinker, R. (1995). *Using EMDR to treat children.* All day workshop presented at the International EMDR Annual Conference sponsored by the EMDR Institute, Inc. and the EMDR International Association, Santa Monica, CA.

Tinker, R. H., & Wilson, S. A. (1999). *Through the eyes of a child: EMDR with children.* New York: W. W. Norton.

Tinker, R. H., & Wilson, S. A. (2005). The phantom limb pain protocol. In R. Shapiro (Ed.), *EMDR solutions: Pathways to healing* (pp. 147–159). New York: W. W. Norton.

Tinker, R., Wilson, S., & Becker, L. (1997, July). *Treatment of phantom limb pain with EMDR: Two videotaped case studies with pre and post measures.* Paper presented at the annual meeting of the EMDR International Association, San Francisco, CA.

Tomkins, S. (1963). *Affect/imagery/consciousness: The negative affects* (Vol. 2). New York: Springer Publishing.

Treadway, D. (2008a). *Intimacy and healing: Utilizing EMDR in couples therapy.* Plenary paper presented at the EMDR International Association Conference, Phoenix, AZ.

Treadway, D. (2008b, September). *The heart of loving: A new model of couples therapy.* Full day seminar presented at the EMDR International Association Conference, Phoenix, AZ.

Twombly, J. (2000a, October). *Advance EMDR adaptations in the treatment of dissociative disorders.* Paper presented at the EMDRIA Conference, Toronto, Ontario.

Twombly, J. H. (2000b). Incorporating EMDR and EMDR adaptations into the treatment of clients with dissociative identity disorder. *Journal of Trauma and Dissociation, 1*(2), 61–81.

Twombly, J. (2001a, June). *Advanced adaptations in the treatment of dissociative disorders.* Paper presented at the annual meeting of the EMDR International Association, Austin, TX.

Twombly, J. H. (2001b, December). *Incorporating EMDR and EMDR adaptations into the treatment of dissociative disorders.* International Society for the Study of Dissociation Fall Conference, New Orleans, LA.

Twombly, J. H. (2001c, December). Safe place imagery: Handling intrusive thoughts and feelings. *EMDRIA Newsletter,* (Special Edition), 35–38.

Twombly, J. (2004, September). *Incorporating EMDR and EMDR adaptations into the treatment of dissociative disorders.* EMDRIA Conference, Montreal, Quebec.

Twombly, J. H. (2005). EMDR for clients with dissociative identity disorder, DDNOS, and ego states. In R. Shapiro (Ed.), *EMDR solutions: Pathways to healing* (pp. 88–120). New York: W. W. Norton.

U.S. Department of Health and Human Services. (1994, March). Clinical Practice Guideline, number 9. Management of cancer pain. *AHCPR Publication,* No. 94-0592, p. 25.

Van der Hart, O., Van der Kolk, B. A., & Boon, S. (1998). Treatment of dissociative disorders. In J. D. Bremner & C. R. Marmar (Eds.), *Trauma, memory, and dissociation* (pp. 253–283). Washington, DC: American Psychiatric Press.

Van der Kolk, B. A. (1996). Trauma and memory. In B. A. van der Kolk, A. C. MacFarlane, & L. Weisaeth (Eds.), *Traumatic Stress: The effects of overwhelming experience on mind, body, and society* (pp. 279–302). New York: Guilford Press.

Van der Kolk, B. A. (2002). Beyond the talking cure: Somatic experience and subcortical imprints in the treatment of trauma. In F. Shapiro (Ed.), *EMDR as an integrative psychotherapy approach: Experts of diverse orientations explore the paradigm prism* (1st ed., pp. 57–83). Washington, DC: American Psychological Association Books.

Van der Kolk, B. A., Burbridge, J. A., & Suzuki, J. (1997, June). The psychobiology of traumatic memory: Clinical implications of neuro imaging studies. *Annals of the New York Academy of Sciences, 821,* 99–113.

Van der Kolk, B. A., & Fisler, R. (1995). Dissociation and the fragmentary nature of traumatic memories: Overview and exploratory study. *Journal of Traumatic Stress, 8,* 505–525.

Van der Kolk, B., Korn, D., Weir, J., & Rozelle, D. (2004, September). *Looking beyond the data: Clinical lessons learned from an EMDR treatment outcome study.* EMDRIA Conference, Montreal, Quebec.

Van der Kolk, B. A., Spinazzola, J., Blaustein, M. E., Hopper, J. W., Hopper, E. K., Korn, D. L., et al. (2007, January). A randomized clinical trial of eye movement desensitization and reprocessing (EMDR), fluoxetine, and pill placebo in the treatment of posttraumatic stress disorder: Treatment effects and long-term maintenance. *Journal of Clinical Psychiatry, 68*(1), 37–46.

Vanderlaan, L. L. (2000, December). The resolution of phantom limb pain in a 15-year old girl using eye movement desensitization and reprocessing. *EMDRIA Newsletter,* (Special Edition), 31–34.

Vogelmann-Sine, S. (1998). Healing hidden pain: Resolving the effects of childhood abuse and neglect. In P. Manfield (Ed.), *Extending EMDR: A casebook of innovative applications* (pp. 167–190). New York: W. W. Norton.

Vogelmann-Sine, S., Popky, A. J., Lazrove, S., Sine, L., Speare, J., Wade, D., et al. (1995, June). *Symposium: Advanced clinical applications of EMDR to addictive behaviors.* EMDRIA Conference, Santa Monica, CA.

Vogelmann-Sine, S., & Sine, L. F. (1993a). EMDR with clients in recovery from chemical dependency. *EMDR Network Newsletter, 3*(3), 12–15.

Vogelmann-Sine, S., & Sine, L. (1993b). *Substance abuse.* Paper presented at the EMDR Institute Annual Conference, Sunnyvale, CA.

Vogelmann-Sine, S., & Sine, L. (1994). *Substance abuse.* Paper presented at the EMDR Institute Annual Conference, San Jose, CA.

Vogelmann-Sine, S., Sine, L. F., & Popky, A. J. (1997, June). *EMDR treatment for chemical dependency: Training for participation in a multisite study.* Paper presented at the EMDR Institute Annual Conference, San Francisco, CA.

Vogelmann-Sine, S., Sine, L. F., Smyth, N. J., & Popky, A. J. (1998). *EMDR chemical dependency treatment manual.* New Hope, PA: EMDR Humanitarian Assistance Program.

Wade, T., & Wade, D. (1996, June). *Integrative psychotherapy: Combining ego-state therapy, clinical hypnosis, and EMDR in a psychosocial developmental context.* Paper presented at the EMDRIA Conference, Denver, CO.

Wanders, F., Serra, M., & De Jongh, A. (2008). EMDR versus CBT in children with self-esteem and behavioral problems: A randomised controlled trial. *Journal of EMDR Practice and Research, 2,* 180–189.

Watkins, J. G., & Paulsen, S. L. (2003). *Ego state therapy: EMDR and hypnoanalytic techniques.* Workshop presented at the Society for Clinical and Experimental Hypnosis, Chicago, IL.

Watkins, J. G., & Watkins, H. H. (1997). *Ego states: Theory and therapy.* New York: W. W. Norton.

Welch, K. L., & Beere, D. B. (2002). Eye movement desensitization and reprocessing: A treatment efficacy model. *Clinical Psychology and Psychotherapy, 9*(3), 165–176.

Wesselman, D. (2007). Treating attachment issues through EMDR and a family systems approach. In F. Shapiro, F.W. Kaslow, & L. Maxfield (Eds.). *Handbook of EMDR and Family Therapy Processes* (pp 113–130). Hoboken, NJ. John Wiley: SMS Inc.

Wildwind, L. (1992, May). EMDR and MPD. *EMDR Network Newsletter, 2*(1), 11.

Wile, D. (1981). *Couples therapy: A nontraditional approach.* New York: Wiley.

Wilensky, M. (2000). Phantom limb pain. *EMDRAC Newsletter, 4*(2), 2.

Wilensky, M. (2006). Eye movement desensitization and reprocessing (EMDR) as a treatment for phantom limb pain. *Journal of Brief Therapy, 5,* 31–44.

Wilson, S. A., Tinker, R., Becker, L. A., Hofmann, A., & Cole, J. W. (2000, September). *EMDR treatment of phantom limb pain with brain imaging (MEG).* Paper presented at the annual meeting of the EMDR International Association, Toronto, Canada.

Wolffgramm, J., Galli, G., Timm, F., & Heyene, A. (2000). Animal models of addiction: Models for therapeutic strategies? *Journal of Neural Transmission, 107*(6), 649–668.

Wolffgramm, J., & Heyne, A. (1995). From controlled drug intake to loss of control: The irreversible development of drug addiction in the rat. *Behavioural Brain Research, 70*(1), 77–94.

Wolitzky-Taylor, K. B., Horowitz, J. D., Powers, M. B., & Telch, M. J. (2008). Psychological approaches in the treatment of specific phobias: A meta-analysis. *Clinical Psychology Review, 28,* 1021–1037.

Wolpe, J. (1958). *Psychotherapy by reciprocal inhibition.* Stanford, CA: Stanford University Press.

York, C. (1995). *Treating severely traumatized children: Assessment and treatment strategies for using EMDR.* All day workshop presented at the International EMDR Annual Conference sponsored by the EMDR Institute, Inc. and the EMDR International Association, Santa Monica, CA.

Young, W. (1992, May). Observations on using EMDR with patient's with a history of sadistic and ritual abuse. *EMDR Network Newsletter, 2*(1), 14–15.

Young, W., Puk, G., & Rouanzoin, C. C. (1993, June). *Dissociative disorders.* Workshop at the EMDRIA Conference, Sunnyvale, CA.

Young, W., Puk, G., & Rouanzoin, C. C. (1995, June). *Current trends using EMDR in dissociative disorders.* Workshop C at the EMDRIA Conference, Santa Monica, CA.

Zahorsky, R. (1995, June). *Using dream work and EMDR with survivors of sexual abuse.* Workshop presented at the EMDR Annual Conference sponsored by the EMDR Institute, Inc. and the EMDR International Association, Santa Monica, CA.

Zangwill, W. (2000). *Integrating with sexual & relationship therapy.* Paper presented at the EMDR International Association Conference, Toronto, Canada.

Zilbergeld, B. (1995). *Using EMDR in the treatment of sexual problems.* Workshop presented at the International EMDR Annual Conference sponsored by the EMDR Institute, Inc. and the EMDR International Association, Santa Monica, CA.

Zweben, J., & Yeary, J. (2006). EMDR in the treatment of addiction. *Journal of Chemical Dependency Treatment, 8,* 115–127.

Adler-Tapia, R. L., & Settle, C. S. (2008). *Establishing EMDR with children as evidence based practice: A Review of the literature*. Manuscript submitted for publication.

Australian Centre for Posttraumatic Mental Health. (2007). *Australian guidelines for the treatment of adults with acute stress disorder and post traumatic stress disorder*. Melbourne: Author.

Bacon, J. (2001, June). *Kids with severe learning disabilities: Coping, acceptance, and EMDR*. Paper presented at the annual meeting of the EMDR International Association, Austin, TX.

Bader, M. J. (2002). *Arousal: The secret logic of sexual fantasies*. New York: Thomas Dunn.

Bender, S. S. (2006, September). *Wash your hands: Healthy and practical EMDR practices*. Paper presented at EMDR International Association annual meeting, Philadelphia, PA.

Bender, S. S., & Britt, V. (2000, April). *Present in the past: Genograms, family themes & EMDR*. Paper presented at the New Jersey Regional EMDR International Association Semiannual meeting, Piscataway, NJ.

Bender, S. S., & Britt, V. (2003). *Real world EMDR: Integrating EMDR into everyday clinical practice*. Workshop presented Bender/Britt Seminars, Iselin, NJ.

Bender, S. S., Hollander, H. E., & Accaria, P. (2001). *EMDR and hypnosis*. Paper presented at the EMDR International Association Conference, Austin, TX.

Bender, S. S., & Sise, M. T. (2007). *The energy of belief: Psychology's power tools to focus intention and release blocking beliefs*. Fulton, CA: Energy Psychology Press.

Blore, D. C. (1993). Treating a miner with underground phobia. *British Journal of Nursing, 2*(20), pp. 1017, 1020–1021.

Blore, D. C. (1997). Reflections on "A day when the whole world seemed to be darkened" changes. *International Journal of Psychology and Psychotherapy, 15*(2), 89–95.

Blore, D. C. (2000). EMDR for mining and related trauma: The underground trauma protocol. *The EMDR Practitioner—Articles Archived* (an Internet journal), www.emdr-practitioner.net.

Blore, D. C., & Holmshaw, E. M. (2006). *The railway experience: "Being in control" the non-disclosure of traumatic memory content and EMDR*. Presented at the 4th Annual Conference of EMDR UK & Ireland, Royal Institute of British Architects, London, England.

Boël, J. (1999). The butterfly hug: Some history and updates on its use with children. *EMDRIA Newsletter, Special Edition, 4*(4), 11–13.

Boszormenyi-Nagy, I., & Spark, G. M. (1984). *Invisible loyalties*. New York: Brunner-Mazel.

Briere, J. A., & Scott, C. (2006). *Principles of trauma therapy: A guide to symptoms, evaluation, and treatment*. Thousand Oaks, CA: Sage Publications, Inc.

Brown, K. W., McGoldrick, T., & Buchanan, R. (1997). Body dysmorphic disorder: Seven cases treated with eye movement desensitization and reprocessing. *Behavioural and Cognitive Psychotherapy, 25*, 203–207.

Bryant, R. A., & Harvey, A. G. (2000). *Acute stress disorder: A handbook of theory, assessment, and treatment*. Washington, DC: American Psychological Association.

Carver, C. S., & Scheier, M. F. (1999). Stress, coping, and self-regulatory processes. In O. P. John & L. A. Pervin (Eds.), *Handbook of personality: Theory and research* (pp. 553–575). New York: Guilford Press.

Classen, C., Koopman, C., Hales, R., & Spiegel, D. (1998). Acute stress disorder as a predictor of posttraumatic stress symptoms. *American Journal of Psychiatry, 155*, 620–624.

Cohn, L., & Chapman, L. (2002). *Innovations in child trauma treatment: Combining EMDR and drawings*. Paper presented at the annual meeting of the EMDR International Association, San Diego, CA.

Daly, E., & Wulff, J. (1987). Treatment of a post-traumatic headache. *British Journal of Medical Psychology, 60*, 85–88.

D'Antonio, M. (2004–2006). *Using EMDR to treat sexual dysfunction*. EMDR supervision group at Council for Relationships, Philadelphia, PA.

De Jongh, A., & van der Oord, H.J.M. (2002a, March). *Efficacy of eye movement desensitization and reprocessing (EMDR) in the treatment of specific phobias*. 80th General Session of the International Association for Dental Research, San Diego, CA.

De Jongh, A., & van der Oord, H.J.M. (2002b, March). Efficacy of eye movement desensitization and reprocessing (EMDR) in the treatment of specific phobias. *Journal of Dental Research, 81*, 31.

Donovan, L. (2005, September). *Using EMDR in processing grief with children and families*. Paper presented at the annual meeting of the EMDR International Association, WA.

Dutton, P. (1999). Book reviews: Three EMDR books about children and adolescents. *EMDRIA Newsletter, Special Edition, 4*(4), 15–19.

Eckers, D. (2006). EMDR in der Praxis bei Kindern und Jugendlichen. In F. Lamprecht (Ed.), *Praxisbuch EMDR*. Stuttgart, Germany: Klett-Cotta.

Eckers, D. (2008). Ressourcenaktivierung und EMDR bei Kindern und Jugendlichen. In C. Rost (Ed.), *Ressourcenarbeit mit EMDR*. Paderborn, Germany: Junfermann.

Eichelman, B. (1985). Hypnotic change in combat dreams of two veterans with posttraumatic stress disorder. *American Journal of Psychiatry, 143*(1), 112–114.

Etzel, C. (2000). Hypnosis in the treatment of trauma: A promising, but not fully supported, efficacious intervention. *International Journal of Clinical and Experimental Hypnosis, 48*(2), 225–238.

Felz, D. L., & Landers, D. M. (1983). The effects of mental practice on motor skill learning and performance: A meta-analysis. *Journal of Sport Psychology, 5*, 25–57.

Foa, E. B., Davidson, J. R. T., & Frances, A. (1999). The expert consensus guideline series: Treatment of PTSD. *Journal of Clinical Psychology, 60*(Suppl. 16), 4–76.

Forgash, C. & Knipe, J. (2007). Integrating EMDR and ego state treatment for clients with trauma disorders. In C. Forgash & M. Copeley (Eds.), *Healing the heart of trauma and dissociation*. New York: Springer Publishing.

Forte, K. (1999). Group EMDR therapy in young children. *EMDRIA Newsletter, Special Edition, 4*(4), 20–22.

Freiha, T. (1998). *Sakkadische Augenbewegungen und Lidschläge bei cortikalen Läsionen*. Reihe: Psychophysiologie in Labor und Feld Band 6. Dissertation Universität zu Köln. Frankfurt, Germany: Peter Lang Verlag.

Freiha, T. (2005) Behandlung einer PTBS mit EMDR: Kasuistik II. In F. Resch & M. Schulte-Markwort (Hrsg.), *Kursbuch für Integrative Kinder- und Jugendpsychotherapie Schwerpunkt: Dissoziation und Trauma*. Weinheim, Germany: Beltz Verlag.

Gates, D. P. (2002). *Using EMDR with juvenile sex offenders and sexually reactive children*. Paper presented at the EMDRIA Conference, San Diego, CA.

Geller, P. A. (1999). Developmental considerations in using EMDR with adolescents. *EMDRIA Newsletter, Special Edition, 4*(4), 4–8.

Goldstein, A., & Feske, U. (1994). Eye movement desensitization and reprocessing for panic disorder: A case series. *Journal of Anxiety Disorders, 8*, 351–362.

Gomez, A. (2007, September). *Creative ways of administering the EMDR protocol with children*. Paper presented at the EMDR International Association Annual Conference, Dallas, TX.

Gomez, A. (2007). *Dark, bad...day go away*. A book for children about trauma and EMDR. Retrieved from AnaGomezTherapy.com

Gomez, A. (2008, September). *Beyond PTSD: Treating depression in children and adolescents using EMDR*. Paper presented at the EMDR International Association Annual Conference, Phoenix, AZ.

Graham, L. (2004). Traumatic swimming events reprocessed with EMDR. *The Sport Journal, 7*(1), 1–5. Retrieved from www.thesportjournal.org

Hofmann, A. (1995). Beginnings—the start of an in-client program for DID—clients in a German hospital. *Dissociation, 8*, 125–126.

Hofmann, A. (2006). *EMDR in der Therapie psychotraumatischer Belastungssyndrome* (2nd ed.). Stuttgart, Germany: Georg Thieme Verlag.

Hofmann, A. & Freiha, T. (2002). Neuere forschungen zur posttarumatischen belastungsstörung und therapieverläufe bei schwersttraumatisierten kindern. In *Kinder auf der Flucht* (pp. 4–14). Köln, Germany: Caritas Therapiezentrum für Folteropfer.

Hollander, H. E., & Bender, S. S. (2001). ECEM (eye closure eye movements): Integrating aspects of EMDR with hypnosis for treatment of trauma. *American Journal of Clinical Hypnosis, 43*, 187–202.

Jiranek, D. (1993). Use of hypnosis in pain management in post-traumatic stress disorder. *Australian Journal of Clinical and Experimental Hypnosis, 21*(1), 75–84.

Kahr, B. (2008). *Who's been sleeping in your head? The secret logic of sexual fantasies*. New York: Basic Books.

Kaplan, H. S. (1983). *The evaluation of sexual dysfunction*. New York: Brunner-Mazel.

Kellogg-Spadt, S., & Pillai-Friedman, S. (2005, May). Women, sexuality, and aging. *The American Journal for Nurse Practitioners, 9*(5), 27–28.

Kiessling, R. (1998, July). *Implementing present & future templates (utilizing the 3 stages of EMDR protocol)*. Paper presented at the EMDR International Association Conference, Baltimore, MD.

Kiessling, R. (2000a, August). *Integrating the EMDR approach into your clinical practice*. Paper presented at the EMDR International Association Conference, Toronto, Canada.

Kiessling, R. (2000b, August). *Using a conference room of resources to process, past, present, and future issues*. Paper presented at the EMDR International Association Conference, Toronto, Canada.

Kiessling, R. (2001). *A resource focused model of EMDR (getting beyond pathology)*. Paper presented at the EMDR International Association Conference, Austin, TX.

Kiessling, R. (2003, April). *Using resources as cognitive interweaves*. Paper presented at the EMDR International Association Conference, Denver, CO.

Kiessling, R. (2005, June). *Extending safe place/resource development protocols to increase client stability*. Paper presented at the EMDR International Association Conference, Seattle, WA.

Kiessling, R. (2006, September). *From BLS to EMDR: Treating survivors of trauma, natural disaster, and combat along a time and stability continuum*. Paper presented at the EMDR International Association Conference, Philadelphia, PA.

Kiessling, R., & Kacsur, R. (2002). *Being brief with EMDR*. Paper presented at the EMDR International Association Conference, San Diego, CA.

Kingsbury, S. J. (1993). Brief hypnotic treatment of repetitive nightmares. *American Journal of Clinical Hypnosis, 35*(3), 161–169.

Klaff, F. (2002). *Portrait of a family: Fitting EMDR to the family and child*. EMDRIA Conference, San Diego, CA.

Knipe, J. (2006, September). *Know the why and how to choose your what: Some essentials of EMDR model and methodology: Personality*. Paper presented at the EMDR International Association Conference, Philadelphia, PA.

Knipe, J. (2007, September). *Master Clinician Series*. Invited Presentation at the EMDR International Association Annual Conference, Dallas, Texas.

Knipe, J., & Forgash, C. (2001). *Using EMDR with narcissistic personalities*. Paper presented at the EMDR International Association Conference, Austin, Texas.

Kohl, R. M., & Fisicaro, S. A. (1995). Imaging goal-directed movement. *Research Quarterly for Exercise and Sport, 66*, 17–31.

Korn, D. L., Weir, J., & Rozelle, D. (2004, September). *Looking beyond the data: Clinical lessons learned from an EMDR treatment outcome study*. Paper presented at the EMDR International Association Conference, Montreal, Canada.

Krakauer, S. (2001). *Treating dissociative identity disorder: The power of the collective heart*. Philadelphia: Brunner-Routledge.

Krawchuk, L., Conill, A. M., & Pillai-Friedman, S. (2004, Fall). Rediscovering intimacy. *The Motivator* by Multiple Sclerosis Association of America, 8–19.

Kutz, I. (2005). Psychological first aid, acute and long-term treatment following terrorist attacks: Mental health interventions in a general hospital following terrorist attacks: The Israeli experience. *Journal of Aggression, Maltreatment & Trauma, 10*(1/2), 425–437.

L'Abate, L. (2004). *A guide to self-help mental health workbooks for clinicians and researchers*. Binghamton, NY: Haworth.

Laub, B. (2000, August). *The healing power of resource connection in the EMDR protocol*. Paper presented at the EMDR Europe Association Conference, London, England.

Laub, B. (2002). *The healing power of resource connection in the EMDR protocol*. Paper presented at the EMDR Association Canada Conference, Vancouver, British Columbia, Canada.

Laub, B. (2003, April). *Various uses of connections to resources within and without the standard EMDR protocol*. Paper presented at the EMDR International Association Conference, Denver, CO.

Laub, B. (2006, June). *Resource connection envelope (RCE)*. Paper presented at the EMDR Europe Association Conference, Istanbul, Turkey.

Laub, B., & Bar Sade, E. (2009). The Imma Group Protocol. In M. Luber (Ed.), *Eye movement desensitization and reprocessing (EMDR): Basics and special situations* (pp. 289–296). New York: Springer Publishing.

Lee, T. D., Chamberlin, C. J., & Hodges, N. (2001). Practice. In R. Singer, H. Hausen Blas, & C. Janelle (Eds.), *Handbook of Sport Psychology* (pp. 115–143). New York: John Wiley & Sons, Inc.

Litt, B. K. (1999, June). *Trust, intimacy and sex: An integrated approach*. Paper presented at the EMDR International Association Conference, Las Vegas, NV.

Litt, B. K. (2000, August). *Trust, intimacy and sex: An integrated approach*. Paper presented at the EMDR International Association Conference, Toronto, Ontario, Canada.

Litt, B. K. (2002, Fall). *Integrating ego state theory and EMDR into the assessment and treatment of dissociative disorders.* Paper presented at the ISSD National Conference, Baltimore, MD.

Litt, B. K. (2003a). *The interior life of the couple.* Paper presented at the ISSD Conference, Chicago, IL.

Litt, B. K. (2003b). *The interior life of the couple.* Paper presented at the ISSD Conference, Toronto, Ontario, Canada.

Litt, B. K. (2004, November). *The interior life of the couple.* Paper presented at the ISSD Conference, New Orleans, LA.

Litt, B. (2007). The child as identified patient: Integrating contextual therapy and EMDR. In F. Shapiro, F. Kaslow, & L. Maxfield (Eds.), *Handbook of EMDR and family therapy processes.* New York: Wiley.

Lovett, J. M. (2002). *Hospital trauma in children: When hurting is actually helping.* EMDRIA Conference, San Diego, CA.

Maltz, W. (2001). *The sexual healing journey: A guide for survivors of sexual abuse.* New York: Harper Collins, Inc.

Maxfield, L., Greenwald, R., de Roos, C., Satin, M., Azubuike, A., Borgen, R., et al. (2004, September). A review of PTSD treatment studies with children. In L. Maxfield (Chair), *New data on EMDR for children.* Symposium at the annual meeting of EMDR International Association, Montreal, Quebec Canada.

McCarthy, B., & McCarthy, E. (2003). *Rekindling desire: A step-by-step program to help low-sex and no-sex marriages.* New York: Brunner-Routledge.

Morris-Smith, J. (2003, June). *Restore joy to childhood: Healing our children with EMDR.* EMDREA Conference, Rome, Italy.

Naparstek, B. (1994). *Staying well with guided imagery: How to harness the power of imagination for health and healing.* New York: Warner Books.

Nofal, S. (2008). Protocolo de EMDR, para niños y adolescentes aplicado a traumas y fobias dentales. Dos casos clínicos. Parte 2 [Protocol of EMDR for children and adolescents applied to dental traumas and phobias]. In P. Solvey & R. C. Ferrazzano de Solvey (Eds.), *Terapias de avanzada [Series on advanced therapies].* Buenos Aires: Terapias de avanzada.

Ogelsby, C. (1999, September). *Report of a study of EMDR with college athletes.* Symposium presented at the Annual Conference of the Association for the Advancement of Applied Sport Psychology, Banff, Canada.

Orlick, T. (1986). *Psyching for sport: Mental training for athletes.* Champaign, IL: Human Kinetics.

Parnell, L. (1997). *Transforming trauma: EMDR.* New York: W. W. Norton

Quinn, G. (2005). *Eye movement desensitization and reprocessing with victims of traffic accidents, suicide bus bombings, and terrorist attacks in Israel.* Paper presented at the American Psychiatric Association Annual Conference, Atlanta, GA.

Quinn, G. (2007, March). *Emergency EMDR—treating victims from man made to natural disasters.* Paper presented at the EMDR England Ireland Conference, Glasgow, Scotland.

Quinn, G. (2007a, April). *Emergency EMDR—treating victims from man made to natural disasters.* Paper presented at the World Psychiatric Association Meeting, Seoul, Korea.

Quinn, G. (2007b, June). *Emergency EMDR—treating victims from man made to natural disasters.* Paper presented at the EMDR Europe Conference, Paris, France.

Quinn, G. (2008a, June). *Emergency EMDR & emergency response procedure (ERP).* Paper presented at the EMDR European Conference, London, England.

Quinn, G. (2008b, July). *Acute stress reaction: To treat or not to treat...* Keynote address presented at the Singapore International Conference—Traumatic Incidents: Early Intervention, Singapore.

Quinn, G. (2008c, September). *PTSD and EMDR.* Paper presented at Grand Rounds Ohio State University, Columbus, OH.

Rothbaum, B. O. (2001). Virtual reality exposure therapy for Vietnam veterans with posttraumatic stress disorder. *Journal of Clinical Psychiatry, 62*(8), 617–622.

Russell, M. C., & Silver, S. M. (2007). Training needs for the treatment of combat-related posttraumatic stress disorder. *Traumatology, 13*, 4–10.

Sartory, G., Rachman, S., & Grey, S. J. (1982). Return of fear: The role of rehearsal. *Behavior Research and Therapy, 20*, 123–133.

Shapiro, F. (Ed.). (2002). *EMDR as an integrative psychotherapy approach: Experts of diverse orientations explore the paradigm prism.* Washington, DC: American Psychological Association Books.

Shapiro, F. (2004). *Military and post-disaster field manual.* Hamden, CT: EMDR Humanitarian Assistance Program.

Shapiro, F. (2007). *EMDR: Part 1 training manual.* Watsonville, CA: EMDR Institute, Inc.

Shapiro, R. (2005). The two-hand interweave. In R. Shapiro (Ed.), *EMDR solutions: Pathways to healing.* New York: W. W. Norton.

Snyder, M. (1996). Intimate partners: A context for the intensification and healing of emotional pain. *Women and Therapy, 19,* 79–92.

Spindler-ranta, D. (1999). Slaying the monsters. *EMDRIA Newsletter, Special Edition, 4*(4), 9–10.

Stayton, W., & Pillai-Friedman, S. (2009). Religion and sexuality. In E. Schroeder & J. Kuriansky (Eds.), *Sexuality education: Past, present, and future issues* (Vols. 1–4). Westport, CT: Greenwood Publishing Group.

Terr, L. C. (1983). Chowchilla revisited: The effects of psychic trauma four years after a school-bus kidnapping. *American Journal of Psychiatry, 140,* 1543–1550.

Terr, L. (1990). *Too scared to cry: Psychic trauma in childhood.* New York: Harper and Row.

Tinker, R. H., & Wilson, S. A. (2006). The phantom limb pain protocol. In R. Shapiro (Ed.), *EMDR solutions: Pathways to healing* (pp. 147–159). New York: W. W. Norton.

Van, M. L., & Taylor, S. (1998). Comparative efficacy of treatments for post-traumatic stress disorder: A meta-analysis. *Clinical Psychology & Psychotherapy, 5*(3), 126–144.

Van Winkle, V. (1999). Breaking the cycle of violence: EMDR treatment of a traumatized violent teen girl. *EMDRIA Newsletter, Special Edition, 4*(4), 26–31.

Weiss, D. S., & Marmar, C. R. (1995). The impact of event scale-revised. In J. P. Wilson & T. M. Keane (Eds.), *Assessing psychological trauma and PTSD: A practitioner's handbook.* New York: Guilford.

Wernik, U. (1993). The role of the traumatic component in the etiology of sexual dysfunctions and its treatment with eye movement desensitization procedure. *Journal of Sex Education and Therapy, 19,* 212–222.

Wilson, S. A., Tinker, R., Hofmann, A., Becker, L., & Marshall, S. (2000, November). *A field study of EMDR with Kosovar-Albanian refugee children using a group treatment protocol.* Paper presented at the annual meeting of the International Society for the Study of Traumatic Stress, San Antonio, TX.

Wincze, J. P., & Carey, M. (2001). *Sexual dysfunction: A guide for assessment and treatment* (2nd ed.). New York: Guilford.

Wizansky, B. (2004). *Finding and connecting to resources in work with children.* Paper presented at the EMDR Europe Conference, Rome, Italy.

Wizansky, B. (2006, September). Footsteps through the maze. *The EMDRIA Newsletter,* 6–11, 17.

Wizansky, B. (2007). A clinical vignette: Resource connection in EMDR work with children. *Journal of EMDR Practice and Research, 1*(1), 57–61.

Wizansky, B. (2007, September). Trauma informed therapy. *Counseling Children and Young People,* 10–15.

Zilbergeld, B. (1999). *The new male sexuality: The truth about men, sex and pleasure.* New York: Bantam.

CPSIA information can be obtained
at www.ICGtesting.com
Printed in the USA
BVHW012145070322
630825BV00009B/109